BOTTOM LINE YEAR BOOK 2019

BY THE EDITORS OF

Bottom Line PERSONAL

BottomLineInc.com

Bottom Line Yearbook 2019

10 9 8 7 6 5 4 3 2 1

ISBN 0-88723-807-6

Bottom Line Books® publishes the advice of expert authorities in many fields. These opinions may at times conflict as there are often different approaches to solving problems. The use of a book is not a substitute for legal, accounting, investment, health or any other professional services. Consult competent professionals for answers to your specific questions.

Offers, prices, rates, addresses, telephone numbers and websites listed in this book are accurate at the time of publication, but they are subject to frequent change.

Bottom Line Books® is a registered trademark of Bottom Line Inc.
3 Landmark Square, Suite 201, Stamford, CT 06901

BottomLineInc.com

Bottom Line Books® is an imprint of Bottom Line Inc., publisher of print periodicals, e-letters and books. We are dedicated to bringing you the best information from the most knowledgeable sources in the world. Our goal is to help you gain greater wealth, better health, more wisdom, extra time and increased happiness.

Printed in the United States of America

Contents

3 • COMMON CONDITIONS & SOLUTIONS

4 • EASY FITNESS & WEIGHT LOSS

5 • THE NATURAL WAY

6 • VERY PERSONAL

PART TWO: YOUR MONEY

7 • MONEYWISE

8 • INSURANCE ADVISER

9 • TAX NEWS & MORE

10 • INVESTMENTS NOW

11 • CONSUMER GUIDE

PART THREE: YOUR FUTURE

12 • RETIREMENT REPORT

PART FOUR: YOUR LEISURE

13 • TRAVEL HACKS

14 • FUN & GAMES

PART FIVE: YOUR LIFE

15 • CAR CARE

Preface

We are happy to bring you our *2019 Bottom Line Yearbook*. Here you will discover numerous helpful and practical ideas for yourself and for everyone in your family.

At Bottom Line Books, it is our mission to provide all of our readers with the best information to help them gain better health, greater wealth, more wisdom, extra time and increased happiness.

The *2019 Yearbook* represents the very best and the most useful Bottom Line articles from the past year. Whether you are looking for ways to get the most from your money or ensure the retirement of your dreams...reduce your risk for cancer or lose those last 10 pounds...get your marriage back on track or handle those awkward situations in your life, you'll find it all in this book...and a whole lot more.

Over the past 38 years, we have built a network of thousands of expert sources.

When you consult the *2019 Yearbook*, you are accessing a stellar group of authorities in fields that range from natural and conventional medicine...to shopping, investing, taxes and insurance...to cars, travel, security and self-improvement. Our advisers are affiliated with the premier universities, financial institutions, law firms and hospitals. These experts are truly among the most knowledgeable people in the country.

As a reader of a Bottom Line book, you can be assured that you are receiving reliable, well-researched and up-to-date information from a trusted source.

We are very confident that the *2019 Bottom Line Yearbook* can help you and your family have a healthier, wealthier, wiser life. Enjoy!

The Editors, *Bottom Line Personal*
Stamford, CT

1

Health Watch

5 "Healthy" Habits That Might Not Be So Healthy

You ordered the egg-white omelet, skipped the toast and switched from coffee to tea. You're making healthier choices, right? Think again.

Dietitians have changed their stances on certain health topics based on recent research and evolving dietary guidelines. *Learn the truth behind these five "healthy" habits that actually aren't...*

1. Going gluten-free. Millions of people have cut out gluten to lose weight, gain energy and/or reduce gastrointestinal distress after eating. Contrary to popular belief, however, gluten-free does not equal healthy.

Only 1% of the population has celiac disease, a condition in which gluten damages the lining of the small intestine. Treatment of this disease requires a strict gluten-free diet. Some other people experience nonceliac gluten sensitivity in which they test negative for celiac disease but still experience gastrointestinal distress or other inflammatory reactions after eating gluten. This also is relatively rare. Everyone else has fallen into the fad-diet trap.

While a gluten-free diet may help people lose weight, it's not because they've said goodbye to gluten. It's because they're eating more whole, unprocessed foods and reducing simple carbohydrates such as chips, cookies and white grains.

Foods made from the three common gluten-containing grains—wheat, barley and rye—are nutritious as long as they aren't highly processed, and they won't cause stomach distress for most people. They can be good sources of dietary fiber and other vitamins and minerals

---

Torey Armul, MS, RD, CSSD, LD, a spokesperson for the Academy of Nutrition and Dietetics. She counsels clients on weight management, sports nutrition and pregnancy and family nutrition through her private practice in Columbus, Ohio. eatrightPRO.org

such as B vitamins, iron and zinc. People on a gluten-free diet run the risk of falling short in these nutrients when they cut out whole grains.

Unless you have celiac disease or gluten sensitivity, instead of eliminating gluten, replace your simple carbohydrates with complex carbs from vegetables, beans, legumes and whole grains. Choose brown or wild rice instead of white rice. Buy 100% whole-grain breads and cereals instead of white breads, dinner rolls, partially whole-grain breads and sugary cereals. When dining out, ditch the white bun and ask for a whole-wheat bun. Instead of fries or chips, choose a side salad, fresh fruit or steamed vegetables.

2. Choosing low-fat. Supermarkets are filled with low-fat and fat-free foods. But food fats can provide satiety, or fullness, after a meal and are important for heart health. The key is to differentiate between the different types of fats.

Monounsaturated and polyunsaturated fats are beneficial types of fat that can help reduce cholesterol levels and lower your risk for heart disease. The best sources of healthy fats are salmon and other fatty fish such as mackerel, herring, trout and sardines, olive oil and other vegetable oils, nuts, seeds, avocado and eggs.

While saturated fat—found in donuts, baked goods, fried foods, red meats and butter—may not be as bad as previously thought, it is not actually beneficial. When saturated fat is replaced with unsaturated fats, rates of heart disease drop significantly. It's OK to have some saturated fat in your diet as long as you also are eating plenty of unsaturated fats, vegetables, whole grains and legumes. As for full-fat dairy products, there is a growing amount of research showing that these have health benefits, such as a lower risk for diabetes, over fat-free dairy. For my clients, I generally recommend reduced-fat (not fat-free) dairy. Based on what we know now, I believe it's the best of both worlds for fewer calories and less saturated fat but with the health benefits and satiety provided by some fat.

3. Avoiding coffee. A whopping 83% of American adults drink coffee, yet many still view it as a bad habit. *Here's the good news:* Research indicates that coffee actually is quite good for you. People who drink coffee regularly are less likely to be obese or have high blood pressure or diabetes, according to various studies. Coffee may protect against DNA damage, and multiple studies link coffee to lower rates of stomach and skin cancers and reduced risk for heart failure. The compounds found in coffee also have been linked to reduced risk for Parkinson's and Alzheimer's diseases.

The caffeine in coffee may be beneficial, too. It works as a mild stimulant to the nervous system and can increase alertness, concentration and focus. Research has linked drinking caffeinated coffee to reduced risk for depression.

Coffee also may have a positive impact on your workout. According to multiple studies, drinking coffee can enhance performance and make your workouts feel easier by reducing perceived exertion. Most studies show beneficial effects when coffee is consumed about an hour before a workout.

Coffee's health benefits do have their caveats. Caffeinated coffee can disrupt sleep and make people feel jittery. Sticking to no more than three to four cups of coffee per day and avoiding caffeinated coffee within four to six hours of bedtime can help manage these effects.

4. Choosing egg whites. Egg whites may be lower in calories than whole eggs, but they're also lower in nutrition. That's because the yolk contains most of the egg's nutritional value. Eating eggs for protein? The yolk contains more than 40% of an egg's protein. Research has linked protein at breakfast with reduced appetite and fewer cravings later in the day.

The yolk also contains most of the vitamins, minerals and heart-healthy monounsaturated fats. Interestingly, these fats boost your body's absorption of antioxidants from vegetables. A study published in *American Journal of Clinical Nutrition* found that adding three whole eggs to a mixed-vegetable salad increased the antioxidant absorption of vegetables by three to eight times. You might not want to add three eggs to your salad, but even one hard-boiled egg (you can slice it or chop it up) can boost antioxidant absorption. Another study found that adding just three to five grams of fat to a meal improved absorption of the antioxidant beta-carotene. One large whole egg contains five grams of fat, almost all of which is found in the yolk.

5. Replacing dairy with soy. Some people have soured on cow's milk due to concerns over the use of hormones and antibiotics. These fears are unfounded, however, as dairy farmers rarely use hormones and must follow strict rules to dispose of milk that contains any trace of antibiotics. Nutritionally, cow's milk is an excellent source of calcium and vitamin D, nutrients that most Americans lack. It also is a good source of protein—eight grams per cup—which helps with satiety and appetite control.

Almond milk and other nut milks and soy milk may have the "cool" factor, but they're often less nutritious choices.

Almond and cashew milks are very low in protein and calcium, although store-bought options often are fortified with calcium. Soy milk has the same amount of protein as cow's milk, and the calories in unsweetened soy milk are equivalent to the calories in 2% milk. Soy milk also lacks calcium and vitamin D, although some manufacturers now add both nutrients during processing.

BEWARE...

Gluten-Free Warning

A gluten-free diet may be high in arsenic and mercury. Gluten-free foods often contain rice—not only rice itself but also rice flour, brown rice syrup and puffed rice. Elevated rice consumption can lead to higher intake of the toxic metals arsenic and mercury—rice is known to retain those metals after taking them in from fertilizers, soil and water.

Recent finding: People who ate gluten-free diets had nearly twice as much arsenic in their urine and 70% higher levels of mercury than people who did not eat gluten-free.

Self-defense: Look for non-rice–based substitutes to diversify your diet.

Maria Argos, PhD, assistant professor of epidemiology at Chicago School of Public Health, University of Illinois.

There's no need to cut out cow's milk unless you are lactose intolerant, lactose sensitive or have cultural or moral objections. If you do opt for alternative milk, be aware of potential nutritional gaps and look for fortified versions.

Is Salt Harmful for Everyone? Why *You* May Not Need to Cut Back

James J. DiNicolantonio, PharmD, a cardiovascular research scientist and doctor of pharmacy at Saint Luke's Mid America Heart Institute in Kansas City, Missouri. Dr. DiNicolantonio is also an associate editor of BMJ Open Heart, on the editorial advisory board of *Progress in Cardiovascular Diseases* and other journals and author of *The Salt Fix*, TheSaltFix.com.

We've all been told that a high-salt diet is a leading cause of high blood pressure (hypertension), heart attack, stroke and heart failure. What doctors don't tell patients—what many doctors don't know themselves—is that salt doesn't have the same effect on everyone's blood pressure.

A surprising fact: Many people do better when they consume more than the USDA's recommended daily sodium limit of 2,300 mg (roughly the amount in one teaspoon of salt). *Additional common misconceptions regarding sodium...*

***MYTH #1*: Salt raises blood pressure in everyone.** It's true that doctors have a right to worry about salt consumption for some patients. *Salt sensitivity*—generally defined as an increase of 5% or more in blood pressure when sodium is consumed—is most common in older adults, black people and people of Chinese descent.

Important: If you're sensitive to salt, exceeding the recommended daily limit of 2,300 mg of sodium can cause sharp rises in blood pressure.

But what's harmful for this subset of the population is not harmful for everyone. Research shows that salt sensitivity affects about half of people with high blood pressure and about 20% of people who have normal blood pressure.

MYTH #2: **Salt always increases heart disease.** If a high-salt diet increased blood pressure, it would obviously increase the risk for cardiovascular disease—but, as discussed earlier, this occurs only in some people. When researchers study whether eating highly salted foods increases the rates of high blood pressure and heart disease, the findings are mixed. Meanwhile, the correlation between high-salt diets and improved health is compelling.

Example: People consume staggering amounts of sodium in Japan, France and South Korea. The average South Korean, for example, consumes more than 4,000 mg of sodium a day. In France and other Mediterranean countries, very salty foods, such as prepared sardines, anchovies and many aged cheeses, are eaten with most meals. Yet these countries are among those with the lowest death rates from coronary heart disease in the world, and Japan and South Korea boast among the highest longevity.

Most people don't realize that a low-salt diet can sometimes raise blood pressure by stimulating the body's "rescue" system (the *renin-angiotensin aldosterone system*) that's designed to help the body retain salt and water. When this occurs, low salt intake can increase heart rate, blood clotting and the constriction of blood vessels. It's also been linked to insulin resistance and diabetes.

MYTH #3: **No one needs more salt.** The ubiquitous advice to reduce sodium intake might be justified if it helped some people and didn't hurt the rest. But this isn't always the case.

To remain in *homeostasis,* the physiological state that puts the least stress on the body, most people who are not salt sensitive need about 3,000 mg to 5,000 mg of sodium a day.

What's more, many of our food choices (sugar and caffeinated beverages, for example) deplete salt from the body. So do commonly prescribed medications such as some antidepressants, diuretics and diabetes drugs. In addition, the average nonathletic adult sweats out 600 mg of sodium a day.

MYTH #4: **Healthy diets are naturally low in salt.** The diets that experts recommend for disease prevention, such as the Mediterranean diet, do exclude many of the processed foods that happen to be high in salt (and other unhealthful ingredients)—but they're not low-salt diets overall. If anything, as mentioned above with such countries as Japan and South Korea, they contain more salt than Americans typically eat. Think seafood (clams, lobster, crab), olives, kimchi, etc.

Why do these countries have less cardiovascular disease than the US? While there is no definitive research that a high-salt diet is the reason, it's been my observation that people who indulge their salt cravings tend to eat more heart-healthy vegetables (particularly the bitter ones, such as bitter greens)...nuts... and seeds—most likely because these healthy foods taste better with salt.

What's more, there is often a lot of potassium in naturally salty foods—for example, spinach, Swiss chard and artichokes. When it comes to improving blood pressure and heart health, *more* potassium is probably more important than *less* sodium.

MYTH #5: **Everyone should check the sodium content on food labels.** Unless you eat a lot of pretzels, chips and other super-salty foods, you are unlikely to eat more salt than your body can handle—unless you're salt-sensitive (see below).

I do advise people to avoid processed foods—mainly because these foods tend to be high in sugar, which can increase the risk for high blood pressure, diabetes and obesity. Most processed foods also lack fiber, and a lack of fiber can cause sugar spikes. It's much better to indulge your salt cravings with foods that are naturally salty—for example, sea vegetables (kelp, seaweed and algae), seafood, cheese and olives.

ARE YOU SALT-SENSITIVE?

There are no readily available tests to determine whether a person is salt-sensitive. So how do you know whether a low-salt diet would help you or hurt you?

Try this: With your doctor's OK, for two weeks, reduce your sodium intake to less than

2,300 mg of sodium per day. If your blood pressure drops by 5% or more, chances are you are salt-sensitive. If your blood pressure does drop, be alert for dizziness, fatigue, nausea, muscle spasms/cramps and blurred vision—signs that your blood pressure may be too low. In these cases, you may be better off listening to your body's salt cravings and eating the salt that it demands rather than adhering to a strict low-sodium diet.

Important: Discuss this with your doctor, and monitor your blood pressure closely.

TAKE NOTE...

Why You Should Know Your "Type"

You may not realize it, but your blood type can provide valuable clues about your risk for disease. *Examples...*

• **Heart disease.** In a Harvard study, people with type AB blood were found to be 23% more likely to develop heart disease than those with type O blood, the most common blood type. People with types A and B faced higher risks of 5% and 11% respectively.

• **DVT.** When compared with those with type O, people with A, B or AB blood types were up to 40% more likely to develop deep vein thrombosis (DVT), a 30-year Danish study found.

• **Cancer.** Stomach cancer is 20% more common in those with type A blood than in people with type O.

Some doctors now believe that knowing your blood type is just as important as knowing your weight, blood pressure or cholesterol numbers. You can't change your blood type, but knowing the risks associated with certain blood types could encourage you to take other steps—a healthier diet, more exercise, etc.—to stay healthy.

Helpful: The next time your doctor orders a blood test, ask to have the sample tested to learn your blood type. Knowing this small piece of information can have a big payoff.

Rebecca Shannonhouse, editor, *Bottom Line Health,* BottomLineInc.com.

Don't Let the New Blood Pressure Guidelines Fool You

H. Gilbert Welch, MD, MPH, professor of medicine at The Dartmouth Institute for Health Policy and Clinical Practice, Lebanon, New Hampshire, and author of *Less Medicine, More Health: 7 Assumptions That Drive Too Much Health Care* and *Overdiagnosed: Making People Sick in the Pursuit of Health.* TDI.Dartmouth.edu

The definition of high blood pressure has reached a new low—130 is the new 140. According to guidelines set by the American Heart Association and the American College of Cardiology in late 2017, if your systolic (upper) number is 130 mm Hg or higher...and/or your diastolic (lower) number is 80 mm Hg or higher...you have high blood pressure, aka *hypertension.* The previous threshold was 140 mm Hg. (Diastolic, the lower number, is less important at predicting cardiovascular risk.)

Overnight, more than 30 million Americans "got" high blood pressure. Combined with those who met the earlier threshold, that's a total of about 103 million people. As an advocate for using less medicine whenever possible, I'm worried by these new guidelines. That's why I wrote an article in *The New York Times* titled, "Don't Let New Blood Pressure Guidelines Raise Yours." And it's why I enthusiastically agreed to do this article. It's not that controlling very high blood pressure isn't important. It's *critical.* Treating very high blood pressure with medication is one of the most important preventive interventions doctors do.

But doctors also can do too much prescribing. Aggressive medical management to reach the new goals for people at the margin may have only modest benefits that don't outweigh the risks for side effects. In a blow to wide acceptance, the American Academy of Family Physicians (AAFP) declined to endorse the new guidelines because they don't meet that organization's standards for medical evidence. It's sticking with the previous guidelines.

When doctors disagree, it can be confusing for patients. *Some facts to help you...*

MODEST NEW BENEFITS

While the new guidelines emphasize lifestyle changes such as getting more exercise, losing weight if you need to and eating a healthful diet as the first line of defense—good advice for all of us—the likely practical effect will be to push many more people into drug treatment. So let's examine the benefits.

The new guidelines stem from a federally funded study called the Systolic Blood Pressure Intervention Trial (SPRINT). It covered people over age 50 at high risk for cardiovascular disease. Half were treated to bring their systolic blood pressure down to less than 140 and half to bring it down to less than 120.

Result: Compared with those treated to less than 140, those treated to less than 120 had 25% lower risk for heart attack, stroke, heart failure and death from cardiovascular causes. Sounds impressive, right? But in reality, over the course of the three-year study, about 6% of participants who aimed for 120 had cardiovascular "events" such as heart attacks—compared with 8% of those who aimed for 140. That's only a two-percentage-point difference.

The truth is, while reducing very high blood pressure—say, from 160 or 180 to 140—has enormous benefits, going from 140 to 130 doesn't. According to a review that included 74 trials and more than 300,000 patients that was published in *JAMA Internal Medicine*, bringing blood pressure levels below 140 did not help prevent a first heart attack or stroke, reduce the rate of cardiovascular disease or help prevent death overall.

RISKS OF AGGRESSIVE TREATMENT

In the SPRINT trial, getting to a blood pressure goal of less than 120 required an average of three different drugs per patient—compared with two drugs for a 140 goal. While that extra drug didn't substantially increase side effects in that trial, it's still true that 38% of patients in the 120-target group had adverse events, including abnormally low blood pressure, loss of consciousness and acute kidney injury. I'm concerned about adding even one extra prescription medication, especially for many elderly patients who already may take eight or even 10 medications a day.

Blood pressure drugs, like all drugs, have side effects. The type called beta-blockers can cause dizziness, weakness and fatigue, as can ACE inhibitors, angiotensin II receptor blockers and alpha blockers. Dizziness and lightheadedness can result in more falls, which is particularly dangerous for older people, making them more prone to fractures—including hip fractures, which can have devastating consequences for health and independence.

These concerns are among the reasons that the AAFP and the American College of Physicians came out with blood pressure treatment guidelines specifically for people age 60 and older in 2017. *Recommendations:* Doctors should prescribe drugs for healthy patients only when systolic levels are 150 or higher. For patients at high cardiovascular risk, especially stroke patients, doctors are advised to start treatment at 140.

OVERDIAGNOSIS RISK

There's a bigger problem in extrapolating the results of the SPRINT trial to the real world. Blood pressure is an extremely volatile variable, and it can change within minutes in reaction to stress, activity or just the anxiety of sitting in a doctor's waiting room. To remove those stressors, the SPRINT researchers had patients measure their own blood pressure (using an automated cuff) after five minutes of quiet rest without staff in the room.

This may be an ideal way to measure blood pressure, but it's not what happens. You might have had a blood pressure reading of 130 in a situation such as the SPRINT trial, while it might be 140 or even higher when measured in your doctor's office. In practice, that may lead to many people being overmedicated.

WHAT TO DO NOW

Have the new guidelines pushed you into the official "high blood pressure" range? It's not a medical emergency if they have—but it is an opportunity to talk to your doctor about what blood pressure goal is right for you, given your age and risk factors.

Even if you wind up needing medication, a lifestyle plan is enormously important. Limit alcoholic drinks to no more than one a day if you're a woman or two a day if you're a man.

Revamp your diet to include plenty of fruits and vegetables and whole grains. Reduce your salt intake. Exercise regularly. If you smoke, quit. Lose weight if you need to. Find healthy ways to manage stress.

Ironically, the recent dramatic increase in the number of people with "high" blood pressure can distract patients and doctors from focusing on these important lifestyle changes. Doing those things is good for blood sugar, for better sleep and for overall well-being, regardless of blood pressure.

MEASURING BLOOD PRESSURE AT HOME

If you're concerned about your blood pressure, and especially if you've started to take medication to bring it down, consider measuring your blood pressure yourself at home. Many physicians advise this because it can help you become more aware of the things that move your blood pressure up or down.

Buy a monitor with an inflatable upper-arm cuff—more reliable than those with wrist cuffs or fingertip monitors. *Other tips...*

- **Relax.** Don't exercise or drink caffeinated drinks or alcohol for at least 30 minutes before measuring. Make sure your bladder is empty... sit quietly for five minutes before you take a measurement...sit still while you measure.
- **Watch your posture.** Sit with your back against a straight-back chair...feet flat on the floor, legs uncrossed. Support your arm on a flat surface with your upper arm at heart level. The middle of the blood pressure cuff should be placed just above where the elbow bends.
- **Place the cuff directly on your bare arm,** not over clothing.
- **Take your pressure at the same time every day.** Either morning or evening is fine. It doesn't matter whether you do it before or after taking medication—just be consistent.
- **Take two or three readings one minute apart.** Print out or write down the results or store them in your device's built-in memory.
- **Ask your doctor's office if you can do a practice run there.** That way you can be sure that you are using the monitor correctly.

Caution: Don't rely solely on your at-home readings. Compare them with the readings you get in your doctor's office as a backup.

Being a Sports Fan Can Kill You...and Other Surprising Heart Attack Triggers

Gregory S. Thomas, MD, MPH, medical director for the MemorialCare Heart & Vascular Institute at MemorialCare Long Beach Medical Center in California and clinical professor at University of California, Irvine. He is author or coauthor of more than 200 scientific papers that have appeared in leading medical journals including *JAMA*, *The Lancet*, *Journal of the American College of Cardiology*, *International Journal of Cardiology* and *Atherosclerosis*.

When health experts calculate the likelihood of someone having a heart attack, they typically look at *well-known* risk factors, including high blood pressure, smoking, a sedentary lifestyle and a family history of early heart disease.

What most people don't realize: There are "secret" or little-known risk factors for heart attack that most people (including most doctors) ignore. Many of these factors are as risky as the well-known ones above. *Here are the secret risk factors for a heart attack...*

AN INTENSE SPORTS LOSS

Researchers in Los Angeles tracked causes of death in the counties or states of teams playing in the "high drama" 2008 and 2009 Super Bowls—the New York Giants beating the New England Patriots (Massachusetts) in 2008...and the Pittsburgh Steelers beating the Arizona Cardinals in 2009. The researchers found that in the eight days starting on the day of New England's loss, the number of deaths from heart disease in Massachusetts was 24% *higher* than it had been after previous Super Bowls...and in the eight days starting on the day of Pittsburgh's win, the number of deaths from heart disease in the Pittsburgh area was 31% *lower* than it had been after previous Super Bowls. Meanwhile, in Arizona, where researchers had established that fan fervor for the home-state team was significantly lower than in Massachusetts and Pittsburgh, there was little difference in the rate of heart disease deaths after the team's loss. (Data could not be obtained from New York City.)

The disappointment of a losing game after fervently rooting for a team is a form of emotional stress, which can trigger heart attacks—possibly because stress hormones increase heart rate and blood pressure and make blood more likely to clot. (The researchers didn't theorize about what caused the decrease in the death rate in Pittsburgh after its win.)

But forlorn fans aren't the only folks whose hearts are harmed by emotional stress. Research shows that other events that cause emotional stress—holidays such as Christmas and New Year's...a nearby natural disaster...daily problems at work...or the recent death of a spouse—increase the risk for heart attacks. So does the emotional stress of acute anger, chronic hostility and pessimism.

Smart strategy: The risk from emotional stress can be dramatically reduced by regular exercise (see below).

AIR POLLUTION

Tiny particles of air pollution—congealed specks of floating carbon, metals and other "particulate" substances that emanate from exhaust pipes, industrial smokestacks and coal-fired power plants—cause heart attacks. In fact, in a scientific statement released in 2010, the American Heart Association said that just hours of exposure to these particulates can trigger heart attacks and that long-term exposure increases risk even more.

The people most at risk for heart attacks from air pollution have other risk factors for heart disease—they are over age 60, overweight, have diabetes and/or have had a previous heart attack or stroke. But years of exposure to air pollution can increase the risk for heart attack for any senior.

Scientific evidence: A recent study published in *Environmental Research* shows that even a few years of low exposure to air pollution in a city increased the risk of developing heart disease in older people by more than 20%.

Bottom line: Make air pollution less risky to your heart by working with your doctor to reduce other risk factors such as being overweight or having high blood pressure, high LDL cholesterol and high blood sugar.

Also, know when the air is unhealthy, and stay indoors at those times. *Resource:* AirNow.gov, which displays daily air-quality levels across the US.

Eat fatty fish two to three times a week or take a daily fish oil supplement for the omega-3 fatty acids. *Recent research:* Harvard Medical School scientists found that boosting blood levels of omega-3s can prevent the artery-damaging inflammation caused by air pollution.

MARIJUANA

In a study of nearly 4,000 people published in *Circulation*, researchers found that smoking marijuana caused a five-fold increased risk for heart attack during the first hour after smoking. In a similar study of nearly 2,000 people published in *American Heart Journal*, those who used marijuana weekly or more often had four times the risk for heart attack and nearly double the risk of dying from heart disease, versus people who didn't use marijuana at all.

Reason: The autonomic nervous system controls your heart's activity, and marijuana delivers a one-two punch to both parts of the autonomic nervous system. It *stimulates* the sympathetic nervous system, speeding up heart rate and raising blood pressure (making a heart attack more likely)...while *suppressing*

BETTER WAY...

Best Time for Heart Surgery?

Afternoon heart surgery may be safer than morning surgery. Patients who had open-heart surgery for aortic valve replacement in the afternoon had fewer heart attacks during surgery—and, over the next 500 days, fewer major adverse cardiac events, such as heart attack or heart failure. In a separate study, those operated on in the afternoon had much lower levels of *troponin,* a measure of heart-muscle damage.

Possible reason: Natural circadian variations in the genetic mechanisms that protect tissue under stress.

Bart Staels, PhD, professor of pharmacology, University of Lille, France, and senior author of two studies, one of 596 patients and one of 88, published in *The Lancet*.

the heart- and artery-relaxing parasympathetic nervous system (also putting you at greater risk for a heart attack).

Bottom line: Avoid using recreational marijuana if you have risk factors for heart disease. If you're using it medicinally, discuss the risk with your doctor.

ERECTILE DYSFUNCTION

Heart attacks occur when people develop *atherosclerosis*—a blockage of one or more coronary arteries by cholesterol-ridden arterial plaque. And one common sign that an older man has such blockage is erectile dysfunction (ED)—a problem often caused by a blockage of blood flow to blood vessels in the penis.

Compelling scientific evidence: Research shows that ED precedes the symptoms of heart disease (such as chest pain) in seven out of 10 men with heart disease—with ED usually showing up about three years earlier. And a study published in *International Journal of Impotence Research* shows that severe ED nearly triples the risk for heart disease.

Bottom line: The scientific consensus is that a diagnosis of ED is a warning of heart disease. If you're diagnosed with having ED, you need to get a cardiovascular workup—as soon as possible.

THE EXERCISE ELIXIR

The human cardiovascular system is designed for daily physical activity. Physical activity helps keep blood pressure normal... blood sugar stabilized...cholesterol low...the heart muscle strong...and the risk for heart attack minimized—including the risk from little-known risk factors. In my view, exercise is the best habit for your heart.

Compelling scientific research: In an eight-year study of more than 400,000 people published in *The Lancet*, researchers found that even 15 minutes of daily exercise reduced the risk of dying by 14%—and that includes the risk of dying from cardiovascular disease. And those 15 minutes don't even have to be continuous. To get the benefit, you can exercise for five minutes, three times a day.

My advice: Brisk walking is an ideal exercise. You can do it easily with others, which further reduces your risk for a heart attack. (Social isolation and loneliness increase the risk for heart disease by 29%, according to a recent study published in *Heart.*) And you can build walking into your other daily activities—such as parking five to 10 minutes away from your destination and walking the rest of the way.

Healthy Gums = Lower Stroke Risk

It's long been recognized that gum disease can increase risk for stroke caused by blood clots.

Now: In a recent study, risk for stroke was found to increase with the severity of gum disease. Those with severe gum disease had a stroke risk more than double that of someone with healthy gums. Inflammation caused by gum disease is thought to be the cause.

Self-defense: Be vigilant about brushing and flossing every day. See your dentist regularly—especially if your gums are red, swollen and/or tender.

Souvik Sen, MD, professor and chair, neurology, University of South Carolina School of Medicine, Columbia.

Recover *Faster* from a Stroke

Steven R. Zeiler, MD, PhD, head of stroke research at Johns Hopkins Bayview Medical Center in Baltimore.

You already know that the most important thing you can do if you are having a stroke (or suspect that you are) is to get to an emergency room as fast as possible. Every second that you save may stop precious brain tissue from dying.

But what you and your care team do in the days *immediately* after a stroke also is critical—especially for recovering from motor deficit and regaining control of your muscles.

Two important recent findings...

First finding: In animal studies in a lab, waiting just one week to start rehab led to significantly worse outcomes.

Second finding: A certain medication can prevent that stroke recovery window from closing so quickly.

The overall window for stroke recovery in people continues well past the first week, of course. Many people who have had strokes can continue to improve for months, even years. So never give up! *But here's what to do immediately after the emergency phase...*

• **Start rehab quickly.** Take advantage of that early recovery period—the sooner you begin, the greater your recovery. If your doctors don't start your rehab in the hospital a day or two after the stroke, ask about it and push for it—even if there are medical issues that make it difficult.

• **Ask about the medication *fluoxetine.*** Other recent research has shown that this antidepressant, aka Prozac, started within one day after a stroke, not only improves recovery but also extends the length of the recovery window. An earlier randomized clinical trial showed that patients with moderate-to-severe motor deficits after ischemic stroke (the most common kind, caused by a blood clot) who took fluoxetine every day for three months, starting five to 10 days after a stroke, had significantly greater improvement than patients who received a placebo. Other drugs in the same class also seem to improve stroke recovery, but the most data exist for fluoxetine—and the recent research adds to the urgency of that prescription. While more and more physicians are prescribing fluoxetine, it is not yet a standard of care—so ask.

• **Engage your brain right away.** What you do matters, too—so don't rely solely on rehab services. Do your best to stimulate your brain by playing games on a tablet or working on a puzzle. When people visit you in the hospital, rather than just watching TV together or exchanging pleasantries, have a real conversation about current events or a book you recently have read. In animal studies, mice kept in enriched and stimulating environments after stroke had greater recovery than those kept in simple cages. You want as much of your brain back as possible...so use it as soon as possible!

Why Even Normal-Weight People Can Be "Overfat"

Beware of being "overfat." Unlike the terms "overweight" or "obese," "overfat" simply means that you have just enough excess body fat to negatively affect health.

Surprisingly: Even normal-weight people can be overfat, with excess weight around the abdomen posing the most risk. Up to 90% of men and almost as many women in developed countries are overfat, a condition that raises the risk for high blood pressure, heart disease, stroke, cancer, type 2 diabetes, arthritis, sleep apnea and other conditions.

What to do: Measure your waist at the belly button...if it's more than half your height, you're overfat.

Philip B. Maffetone, DC, independent researcher, Oracle, Arizona.

Diabetes from Your Mouthwash?

Marvin Fier, DDS, Pomona, New York, about a study titled, "Over-the-counter mouthwash use and risk of pre-diabetes/diabetes," published in *Nitric Oxide.* SmileRockland.com

Using mouthwash twice or more a day may keep your breath "minty fresh," but it also may increase your risk of developing type 2 diabetes.

A recent study observed 945 adults for three years. The people studied, ages 40 to 65, were overweight or obese, so they already were at increased risk for diabetes—but the results may be important even for people who are not overweight.

Findings: Participants who used a mouthwash twice or more a day typically had 55% *higher* risk for prediabetes or diabetes than those who used mouthwash less frequently or not at all.

This kind of study can't show cause and effect, and it leaves many questions open—especially about the kind of mouthwash people used. But there are reasons to avoid excessive use. Most mouthwashes contain alcohol or other ingredients, either synthetic or essential oils, that kill microbes indiscriminately—including beneficial ones that help the body make nitric oxide. But you need nitric oxide—it's a remarkable compound that is important for everyone's health, protecting against not only obesity and insulin resistance but also high blood pressure.

The truth is, you don't *need* to use mouthwash at all. It's not particularly effective at improving oral health anyway. For example, brushing and flossing are much better at disrupting *plaque*, the biofilm that sticks to teeth and causes cavities, gum disease and, often, bad breath.

Tip: Thin, unwaxed floss is best at physically dislodging plaque. (If you still love the mouthwash habit, choose alcohol-free products to avoid drying the delicate mucous membranes of the mouth.)

Finally, don't ignore persistent bad breath. It could point to a health problem. If you are using mouthwash several times each day to get rid of bad breath or a bad taste, speak with your dentist or other health-care provider.

Buddy Up Against Diabetes

When Dutch researchers asked 3,000 study participants age 40 and older to count the people, including family and friends, in their social networks, those with type 2 diabetes reported having seven or eight people in their networks—two to four members fewer than their peers without diabetes.

Theory: A larger network may encourage more healthful eating as well as more physical activity.

Miranda T. Schram, PhD, associate professor, department of medicine, Maastricht University Medical Centre, the Netherlands.

Unusual Signs of Brain Cancer...and New Hope

Keith Black, MD, chair and professor of the department of neurosurgery at Cedars-Sinai Medical Center and director of the Maxine Dunitz Neurosurgical Institute and the Johnnie L. Cochran, Jr. Brain Tumor Center, both in Los Angeles. Dr. Black has operated on more than 6,000 patients with brain tumors. He is author of *Brain Surgeon: A Doctor's Inspiring Encounters with Mortality and Miracles.*

Senator John McCain made headlines after being diagnosed with a *glioblastoma*, the deadliest of all brain tumors. That grim description makes it sound like it's over for those who are afflicted.

But survival rates vary widely. Some of these tumors respond better than others to treatment, so it's important to recognize easy-to-miss symptoms of this disease. Early diagnosis means treatment can start sooner. And while it can't be cured, there are advances that may improve the odds of living longer.

WHAT IS A GLIOBLASTOMA?

This cancer is a *primary* brain tumor—it originates in the brain in contrast to cancers such as lung cancer, skin cancer or breast cancer that start somewhere else and may *spread* to the brain.

About half of primary brain tumors are benign (not cancerous)—and these have a high cure rate. The rest are malignant and tend to be aggressive and life-threatening. A glioblastoma is both the most common and the most aggressive kind of malignant primary brain tumor. It is a tumor that grows from cells that make up the gluelike supportive tissue of the brain, and tumor cells migrate throughout the brain, so it's hard for a surgeon to remove it entirely. Average survival after diagnosis is only 18 to 24 months, with 25% of patients alive after two years and 10% alive after five years.

Glioblastomas strike both men and women, often in their 40s, 50s or 60s. Few causes are known—exposure to high levels of radiation to treat a childhood cancer is one, and cell-phone use is a suspected cause (see below). There is rarely an identifiable genetic predisposition. The frustrating reality is that most cases, like Senator McCain's, are seemingly spontaneous—no one knows what brings them on.

SIGNS AND SYMPTOMS

With a glioblastoma, as the malignant cells spread, they increase pressure in the cranium, which leads to headaches in about half of patients. Blurry vision and/or seeing double can also occur. So can mood changes such as sudden-onset depression or anger. Muscle weakness or numbness in the arms and/or legs, which can lead to trouble walking, is another possible symptom. *More symptoms...*

• **Seizures.** Brain tumors can interfere with communication between nerve cells, causing abnormal electrical activity that manifests as seizures. Nearly one-third of brain tumor patients will experience at least one seizure. A seizure can range in intensity from a subtle twitching on one side of the body to a loss of consciousness. It may be preceded by an *aura*, an abnormal change in sensation such as tingling, sensing flickering lights or smelling an unpleasant odor.

• **Trouble reading.** While memory loss and confusion can be glioblastoma symptoms, some are more specific. Other commonly affected areas of the brain are the frontal, temporal or *parietal lobes*, which are responsible for language comprehension, math or spatial orientation. If a tumor grows in the left frontal or temporal lobes, a person may have difficulty speaking or understanding others or comprehending sentences containing cross-references or comparisons. With tumors in the parietal lobe, math may become unusually challenging and so may interpreting material shown in formats such as columns or charts—the parietal lobe also governs recognition of left-right or up-down positioning.

Just having one of these symptoms, or even more than one, does not mean that you have brain cancer, of course. One clue is how quickly symptoms come on. With a glioblastoma, several serious symptoms often arise in a matter of weeks or at most a few months.

NEW TREATMENTS

The first option after discovery of a glioblastoma is often surgery, followed by radiation and chemotherapy. A glioblastoma can't be cured, but it can be managed to extend life. *Some promising newer treatment options now being studied in humans...*

• **Immunotherapy.** A cutting-edge class of drugs known as checkpoint inhibitors ignite the immune system by blocking certain signals released by tumors. That allows tumors to be "seen" and attacked by the immune system. Several clinical trials are now under way to test immunotherapies for glioblastomas.

• **Drugs that cross the blood-brain barrier.** There is a dense lining of cells that surrounds and protects the brain. Most drugs can't cross it, including many chemotherapy drugs. But the budding field of nanomedicine—including the use of drugs as tiny as molecules—is

GOOD TO KNOW...

The Cell-Phone/Brain Cancer Connection

Wireless devices including cell phones emit radiation, which we know can penetrate into the brain and, over time, may cause normal cells to become cancerous. Some studies have found a link between cell-phone use and brain cancer, including glioblastomas. But others have failed to do so. *It makes sense to err on the side of caution...*

• **When speaking on a cell phone,** minimize radiation exposure by using wired earphones (not a wireless version) or use the speakerphone function.

• **Limit use to areas with good reception,** which enables your phone to function at reduced power and therefore with reduced radiation.

Keith Black, MD, chair, department of neurosurgery at Cedars-Sinai Medical Center, Los Angeles.

leading to investigational agents that breach the barrier, enter tumor cells and block key proteins.

• **Brain tumor vaccine.** Vaccines containing a patient's own immune cells—specifically, *dendritic cells* (cells that identify foreign invaders in the body)—may be able to activate a patient's immune system to attack the tumor. In a small 2017 study published in *Clinical Cancer Research,* of the 16 glioblastoma patients who received such a vaccine plus chemotherapy, four were still alive after five years. More trials are under way.

On the horizon...

• **Blood test before any symptoms arise.** Changes in tumor protein activity indicative of a future brain tumor may one day be detectable via a blood test.

• **Could Zika help?** Scientists are exploring whether the Zika virus, which can cross the blood-brain barrier, might in a deactivated form destroy brain tumor cells.

B Vitamins Linked to Lung Cancer in These Men

The lung cancer risk for male smokers taking the highest daily doses of B-6 (20 milligrams a day for years) was three times that of men who did not take the vitamin. The lung cancer risk for those taking high doses of B-12 (more than 55 micrograms a day) almost quadrupled.

Possible reason: The vitamins may hasten the development of lung cancer in male smokers who already have the disease at a subclinical level. There was no sign of increased risk in women taking high doses of the vitamins.

Theodore M. Brasky, PhD, research assistant professor in the department of internal medicine at The Ohio State University Comprehensive Cancer Center, Columbus.

Liver Cancer Has the Fastest-Rising Death Rate...but It's Very Preventable

Pankaj Vashi, MD, AGAF, FASPEN, chair of the department of medicine and chief of the department of gastroenterology/nutrition at Cancer Treatment Centers of America at Midwestern Regional Medical Center, Zion, Illinois. He is a member of the Society of Integrative Oncology, and his scientific papers have appeared in *The American Journal of Clinical Nutrition, BMC Cancer, European Journal of Clinical Nutrition, Nutrition Journal* and many other leading medical journals.

In June 2017, a team of scientific experts from the American Cancer Society issued a special report about liver cancer. *Sobering statistics:* Death rates from liver cancer (hepatocellular carcinoma) are rising faster than those of any other cancer—with rates doubling since the mid-1980s, said the report, published in *CA: A Cancer Journal for Clinicians.* This year, about 41,000 Americans will be diagnosed with the disease. The report also grimly notes that only one in five people with liver cancer is alive five years after diagnosis.

That is the bad news. *Here's the good...*

"A substantial proportion of liver cancer deaths could be averted" by prevention and early detection and treatment of the leading causes of liver cancer, the experts wrote. *More good news:* The main risk factors behind the rise in deadly liver cancer have been identified, and medical care and lifestyle changes usually can keep them under control.

Here's how to protect yourself from this deadly disease...

CRITICAL RISK FACTORS

The three-pound liver is the largest internal organ and for good reason—it performs a wide array of indispensable functions.

It filters and detoxifies your blood and makes proteins that help the blood clot. Food would be unusable without the liver—it's a must for the digestion of carbohydrates, protein and fat. The liver also stores *glycogen,* a type of carbohydrate called a polysaccharide that is used for fuel when blood sugar (glucose) is low. And the liver helps produce several crucial hormones such as *angiotensin*, which regulates blood pressure.

Because the liver is involved in such a broad range of metabolic activities, it is exposed to many factors that can weaken and damage it, increasing the likelihood of liver cancer. The two main factors are blood-borne viruses such as hepatitis C...and excess dietary fat.

• **Hepatitis C virus.** Half of all cases of liver cancer are caused by hepatitis C, which infects liver cells. Over the decades, a chronic case of hepatitis C can first cause liver inflammation and damage and then lead to cirrhosis (liver scarring, or fibrosis) and liver cancer.

About 3.5 million Americans are infected with hepatitis C, and 81% of them are baby boomers, people born from 1945 to 1965. Not surprisingly, baby boomers have the highest death rates from liver cancer, but older and younger people get it, too.

In the case of baby boomers, most with hepatitis C were probably infected in the 1960s, '70s and '80s by blood transfusions and organ transplants...contaminated medical equipment or procedures that exposed them to other people's blood...sharing needles in recreational drug use...or having sex with someone who was infected. This virus was discovered in 1989 and eliminated from America's medical blood supply in 1992.

Hidden time bomb: Most people (of any age) who have a chronic hepatitis C infection don't know that they're infected—because the infection rarely creates symptoms until the disease has reached an advanced state.

What to do: If you're a baby boomer, you must be tested for hepatitis C—it's that simple. (It also is the recommendation of the Centers for Disease Control and Prevention.)

If you're not a baby boomer, you still should be tested for the hepatitis C virus if you had a blood transfusion before 1989 or if you have a history of intravenous drug use.

The test detects antibodies to the virus. Some people infected with hepatitis C "clear" the virus and are no longer infected—but they still will test positive for antibodies that were formed at the time of the infection. That's why positive antibody tests are followed up with liver scans that can detect cirrhosis, and if you have cirrhosis, you definitely have an active infection. A liver biopsy is the medical "gold standard" for confirming hepatitis C.

If you find out that you're infected, be happy you found out—and don't despair. A few years ago, it was next to impossible to stop chronic hepatitis C from damaging the liver. But in the past few years, the FDA has approved daily drug regimens that can cure hepatitis C, eradicating the virus from the body in more than 90% of cases. The risk of developing liver cancer depends on the damage already done by the virus. But after successful treatment of hepatitis C, the risk decreases with time. If you're diagnosed with hepatitis C, talk to your doctor about the drug regimen that is best for you.

• **Hepatitis B virus.** Infection with hepatitis B is the main cause of liver cancer worldwide, but it is less common in the US, where it causes about 15% of cases.

What to do: As with hepatitis C, most people who are infected with hepatitis B don't know it. You should be tested for hepatitis B if you were born in Asia or Africa, where it is more common...you were never vaccinated for hepatitis B (a standard vaccination in the US)...you had sex with a person known to be infected with hepatitis B...you have an HIV infection...you're on hemodialysis for kidney failure...you are on chemotherapy or another immunosuppressive treatment...or you have ever used recreational drugs intravenously.

If you are infected with hepatitis B, treatment will depend on whether the infection is acute or chronic and the degree of liver damage. Talk to your doctor about the liver-protecting regimen that's right for you.

TAKE NOTE...

Hepatitis/Parkinson's Link

Hepatitis may raise Parkinson's risk. Hospitalized patients who had hepatitis B had a 76% higher risk for Parkinson's than patients who did not have hepatitis. And those who had hepatitis C had a 51% higher risk.

Analysis of the hospital records of 100,390 people by researchers at University of Oxford, UK, published in *Neurology.*

• **Obesity and diabetes.** The twin US epidemics of obesity and diabetes have led to a third epidemic—nonalcoholic fatty liver disease (NAFLD)—and NAFLD can lead to liver cancer. Obesity, of course, includes excess fat...and in diabetes, excess blood sugar eventually gets stored as excess fat. Fatty liver afflicts an estimated 20% to 30% of American adults, including more than 60% of those who are obese. *What happens:* Between 10% and 20% of people with NAFLD develop an even more serious form of fatty liver disease called *nonalcoholic steatohepatitis* (NASH). In NASH, liver cells are inflamed and swollen, and there often is cirrhosis. *Warning:* NASH puts you at the same risk for liver cancer as someone with hepatitis C.

What to do: There are no long-term medical therapies that successfully control NASH. But lifestyle changes have proved to both prevent and reverse the condition.

HEALTHY LIVER LIFESTYLE

If you're obese or have diabetes, you probably have NAFLD, and it's possible that you have NASH. Either way, your risk for liver cancer is elevated. Make the following lifestyle changes—starting today.

Note: The same lifestyle changes also are effective for strengthening the liver in people diagnosed with hepatitis C or hepatitis B.

• **Eat a Mediterranean diet.** It's the best dietary approach for managing NAFLD and NASH. *Latest development:* A scientific paper in the July 2017 issue of the medical journal *Liver International* declared the Mediterranean diet "the diet of choice" for NAFLD. The paper's authors point out that the diet can reduce fat in the liver even without weight loss...reduces liver inflammation and liver scarring (cirrhosis)...can prevent or treat diabetes...and is better than a low-fat diet for weight loss. (Losing as little as 7% to 10% of your total body weight can reverse NASH.)

Bottom line: Eat more fruits, vegetables, beans, whole grains, olive oil, nuts and seeds, and fish. Eat less saturated fat from red meat and dairy products, less sugar and less processed food, and drink fewer or no sodas, including diet sodas (which, research shows, increases the craving for sugar).

• **Don't fail to exercise.** The more physically active you are, the less likely it is that you will develop NAFLD. *My recommendation:* Go for a brisk walk of 30 minutes at least five days a week—a study shows that this regimen reduces liver fat by up to 43%.

• **If you drink coffee, don't stop.** Many studies link coffee intake to a healthier liver.

The standout scientific research: Coffee drinkers have a 40% lower risk for liver cancer than people who don't drink coffee, according to a study published in *Clinical Gastroenterology and Hepatology.* Those who drank the most coffee—three or more cups a day—had a 56% lower risk. The beverage is proved to reduce liver enzymes (a sign of inflammation) and to slow the progression of fibrosis.

• **Consider taking liver-supporting nutritional and herbal supplements.** Scientific studies show that certain nutritional and herbal supplements can decrease liver fat and fibrosis and improve liver function. *Check with your doctor about taking these top three supplements...*

• Omega-3 fatty acids. *Typical dose:* 500 milligrams (mg) to 2,000 mg daily.

• Vitamin E. *Typical dose:* 400 IU, twice daily.

• Silymarin (active ingredient in milk thistle). *Typical dose:* 250 mg, three times daily.

New Clue for Melanoma

Rebecca Shannonhouse, editor, *Bottom Line Health,* BottomLineInc.com.

You probably know the ABCDEs of detecting skin cancer. The early letters of the alphabet—Asymmetrical...irregular Borders...dark or multiple Colors...a Diameter of more than 6 mm (about the size of a pencil eraser)...and Evolving in size, shape or color—signal that a mole may no longer be just a harmless skin spot.

What's new: Researchers have now discovered that melanoma, the deadliest form of skin cancer, is more likely to be found in new spots on the skin instead of existing moles.

After reviewing 38 previous studies that looked at a total of more than 20,000 melanomas, researchers found that 29% arose from existing moles. However, a whopping 71% occurred as new skin spots, according to the research, which was published in the *Journal of the American Academy of Dermatology*.

Takeaway: People who are conscientious about performing regular skin checks should pay close attention to spots and growths that weren't there before. These growths—as well as any spots that fit the ABCDEs described above—should be examined by a dermatologist.

Very helpful: Go to the website of the American Academy of Dermatology (AAD.org) and search for "Body Mole Map." You can download a printable chart that allows you to note the location of new skin spots and growths and track any changes in old ones. If you notice a mole that's markedly different from the others—or one that changes, itches or bleeds—be sure to see a dermatologist right away.

What Your Skin Says About Your Health: Signs of Hidden Disease

Jeffrey P. Callen, MD, a professor of medicine and chief of the division of dermatology at the University of Louisville School of Medicine in Kentucky. He is the coeditor of *Dermatological Signs of Systemic Disease*, the author or coauthor of more than 400 scientific papers and the recipient of the 2017 Master Dermatologist Award from the *American Academy of Dermatology*.

A red, itchy rash...little yellow bumps...extremely dry skin. The list of skin problems can go on and on. But did you know that a skin issue isn't always just about your skin? It might be alerting you to an internal problem your doctor needs to know about and treat.

Plus, some skin conditions may mean that you have an increased risk for other health problems (for example, psoriasis has been shown to increase risk for cardiovascular disease), and you will want to take measures to reduce these risks.

EXTERNAL SIGNS, INTERNAL DISEASE

The following diseases are often accompanied by skin problems. If you notice any of the skin issues listed here, make an appointment with your primary care physician or dermatologist for an evaluation.

- **Cardiovascular disease (CVD).** CVD is characterized by narrowed or blocked blood vessels that can cause heart attack or stroke. In many cases, chest pain, heart attack or stroke is the first recognizable sign of CVD. *But several skin changes may indicate that you're at increased risk for CVD...*

Yellow plaques on the eyelids. These waxy growths (known as *xanthelasma*) are found mostly on the upper eyelids. They may be a sign of elevated cholesterol levels, a risk factor for CVD. In some cases, use of cholesterol-lowering drugs will resolve these growths.

Swollen and itchy legs and feet. Excess accumulation of fluid in patients with congestive heart failure can result in leg swelling (edema). If left untreated, *stasis dermatitis*, a condition characterized by itchy, red skin, may occur. Treatments that improve heart function, along with compression stockings and topical corticosteroids, help to alleviate symptoms and prevent recurrence.

- **Diabetes.** Chronically high levels of blood sugar (glucose) dramatically increase the risk for heart disease, stroke, Alzheimer's disease and many other problems, such as kidney failure, blindness and amputation. But millions of people are undiagnosed or have prediabetes (a precursor to full-blown diabetes). *Be alert for these skin changes that might signal problems with blood sugar control...*

Yellow-red bumps on the arms and legs. Known as eruptive xanthomas, these bumps can pop up anywhere on the body but are especially common on the buttocks, shoulders, arms and legs. They're caused by very high levels of triglycerides, a type of fat in the bloodstream that is common with insulin resistance, a condition that causes excess blood sugar and can result in prediabetes and diabetes. Once diabetes is treated, triglyceride levels often normalize and skin lesions resolve.

- **Hepatitis C.** This liver infection, caused by the blood-borne hepatitis C virus, increases the risk for cirrhosis and liver cancer. New medications can cure the disease, but it's symptomless in three out of four cases. *However, the skin can sometimes provide an early clue...*

Blistered, fragile skin on the backs of the hands. This condition can be a sign of hepatitis C. Called *porphyria cutanea tarda*, it's characterized by sensitivity to sunlight and is also seen in alcoholics and can occur as a drug side effect, particularly with nonsteroidal anti-inflammatory drugs (NSAIDs) such as aspirin and *ibuprofen* (Motrin, Advil). When the hepatitis C is effectively treated, the skin issue goes away.

Red, tender spots on the lower legs. This can be caused by inflammation of blood vessels, which occurs in some people who have hepatitis C. Like porphyria, it resolves when hepatitis C is treated.

• **Thyroid disease (Hashimoto's thyroiditis).** This autoimmune disease is one of the most common causes of *hypothyroidism*, a condition in which the thyroid gland doesn't produce enough thyroid hormone. An estimated 14 million Americans may have the disease—and most don't know it. *But your skin may sound the alarm...*

Dry skin. Hypothyroidism can cause a wide range of symptoms, including fatigue, muscle and joint pain, depression, mental sluggishness, low libido, weight gain, constipation, cold hands and feet, dry, coarse hair—and dry skin, one of the most common red flags.

Loss of eyebrow hair. People with hypothyroidism sometimes lose the outer third of their eyebrows.

When standard treatment for hypothyroidism (a thyroid replacement hormone) is given, skin problems typically resolve.

RISKS FROM SKIN CONDITIONS

If you have one of the following skin problems, you and your doctor need to be aware of the possible health risks that are linked to the condition...

• **Psoriasis.** This inflammatory autoimmune disease attacks skin cells, producing scales of silvery, thick skin and raised red patches that can be painful as well as itchy. The inflammation associated with psoriasis can increase risk for high blood pressure, heart attack, stroke, peripheral artery disease (poor circulation in the legs) and diabetes.

What to do: Standard treatments for psoriasis include medications, such as steroids, light therapy and stress management. While there's some evidence that treatments may lower CVD risk, it is best to work with your doctor to assess your CVD risk factors. You can then lower your risk by losing weight, exercising regularly, not smoking and, when necessary, using medication to control CVD risk factors such as high blood pressure and elevated cholesterol.

• **Lupus.** *Systemic lupus erythematosus* (SLE) is an autoimmune disease in which the immune system attacks various tissues and organs, including the skin. Patients with SLE often develop a "butterfly rash"—a red rash that spreads across both cheeks in the shape of a butterfly's wings. Other skin symptoms can include lesions that worsen when exposed to the sun.

People with lupus are at higher risk for many other health problems, including heart disease, stroke, cancer, kidney disease, bone disease and infections.

What to do: If you have lupus, you and your physician need to create a plan to minimize your risks of developing these other diseases. Elements of the plan should include controlling blood pressure and high cholesterol with lifestyle measures (such as regular exercise) and possibly medications...getting regular cancer screenings...and having regular checkups for kidney function and bone density.

The Cataract Fix: What Are You Waiting For?

David F. Chang, MD, clinical professor of ophthalmology at University of California, San Francisco, and past president of the American Society of Cataract and Refractive Surgery. He is an international authority on cataract surgery who frequently lectures surgeons about advanced cataract techniques and the newest lens implants. He is coauthor of *Cataracts: A Patient's Guide to Treatment*.

No one wants to have surgery—any surgery. But once you have had cataract surgery, you'll probably wonder why you waited so long.

Recent developments: Cataract surgery now takes about 20 minutes for most people. You'll go home soon after the procedure...serious, vision-threatening complications, such as infection, are extremely rare...and it's successful in about 99% of cases, making it one of the most effective of *all* surgeries.

The benefits are undeniable. Within days, you'll see better—with sharper vision, better nighttime eyesight and fewer bright-light "halos." But that's not all.

The procedure, which usually is done on one eye at a time, is performed while you're awake and while your eye is numbed with eye-drop anesthesia, so it's not even painful. Most health insurance plans pick up the tab.

To learn more about the latest advances in cataract surgery, we spoke with David F. Chang, MD, a noted authority on cataract techniques.

IS IT YOUR TIME?

Most people are familiar with the telltale signs of cataracts—the normally clear lens within your eye becomes cloudy and/or discolored. Because the lens focuses incoming visual images and transmits them to the retina, these changes, though generally gradual (occurring over a period of years), can cause significant vision loss if untreated.

Important: The lens sits behind the iris and pupil, so you can't self-diagnose cataracts by looking in a mirror. Only an eye doctor using a special microscope can actually see cataracts.

That's why it's important to see an eye doctor (in addition to having routine eye exams) if you're experiencing vision problems, including blurred vision, difficulty seeing details (such as small print or road signs) and glare or poor night-driving vision.

Age is the main risk factor for cataracts. When you're young, the proteins that form the lenses of your eyes are arranged in a way that makes the structures crystal-clear. Over time, these proteins eventually start to clump together and reduce the amount of light that passes through.

By your 60s and 70s, these changes will have gradually begun to occur. Most people, if they live long enough, will develop cataracts that are advanced enough for them to consider surgery.

Earlier-onset of cataracts has been associated with such risk factors as smoking, diabetes, prior retinal surgery, severe nearsightedness, excessive sun exposure and prolonged use of certain medications such as steroids.

WHAT ARE YOU WAITING FOR?

Cataracts can affect one or both eyes, either simultaneously or at different times. In the past, doctors advised patients to delay surgery until a cataract was "ripe"—meaning that it was so advanced that the benefits justified the lengthy recovery and the potential for complications due to the large incision that was used at that time. Unfortunately, many people are still operating under this misconception.

Newer thinking: You don't need to wait so long. If the cataract is impairing your daily activities, such as reading and/or driving, it makes sense to have cataract surgery sooner rather than later because of the procedure's exceptionally high success rate.

Now the lens is broken up into many small pieces using ultrasonic vibrations within the eye, then suctioned out. The incisions are so small that stitches aren't required—and cataracts can be safely removed at an earlier stage. The replacement artificial lens lasts a lifetime and is folded so that it can pass through the tiny (about one-eighth inch) incision.

The timing is important because cataracts can get so bad that they increase a person's risk for falls and auto/pedestrian accidents, as well as contribute to depression.

These factors may have something to do with the recent research regarding cataract surgery that was published online in the journal *JAMA Ophthalmology*.

Key findings: This study of more than 74,000 women ages 65 and older found that those who had undergone cataract surgery had a 60% lower risk of dying over the 20-year study period than those who did not get treated.

BETTER VISION WITHOUT GLASSES

You'll obviously see better once a cataract is removed. What some people don't realize is that they might see better than they ever did.

The surgeon will remove the cloudy lens and replace it with a clear, artificial lens that comes in more than 50 different powers.

Suppose that you have always worn glasses to see well in the distance. When you have cataract surgery, a replacement lens can be chosen to correct your particular type/degree of optical error. For example, some lenses correct for *astigmatism* (blurred vision that is caused by incorrect corneal curvature). Certain artificial lenses function like bifocals and reduce how frequently people must rely on reading glasses.

In most cases, having cataract surgery won't completely eliminate the need for glasses. Most people will have excellent distance vision without glasses following cataract surgery. However, most will need reading glasses—but can perhaps use them less often and/or get by with a lower-power prescription.

WHAT ELSE CAN YOU DO?

Surgery is the only treatment for cataracts, and it is a permanent solution—the new lens will remain transparent forever. Unfortunately, there is no medication that can halt or reverse cataract formation. What can one do to prevent cataracts?

- **Wear sunglasses outdoors.** The UV radiation in sunlight damages eye proteins and can lead to cloudiness. A large study that reviewed data from more than a half million people found a strong association between cataracts and skin cancer—more evidence that UV exposure is a major risk factor.

What to do: Wear sunglasses with UV protection whenever you plan to spend prolonged periods of time outdoors. Virtually all sunglasses today are UV-protected.

- **Wear a broad-brimmed hat to block UV radiation.** It will reduce your risk for eyelid skin cancer as well as cataracts.

- **Eat a nutritious diet.** Many studies have found an association between a healthy diet and fewer cataracts—but that's not the same as proof.

For example, several studies have suggested that particular nutrients—alone or in combination—can help prevent cataracts. The large Age-Related Eye Disease Study (AREDS) reported that people with cataracts who got the most lutein and zeaxanthin (antioxidants that are found in leafy greens and other fruits/vegetables) were 32% less likely to need cataract surgery.

Other research has looked at the effects of fish oil supplements (or regular meals including fatty fish)...vitamin C...vitamin E...and other nutrients.

It's common sense to eat a nutritious diet. If you want to take one of the AREDS formulations, check with your doctor first if you are a current or former smoker. Certain versions of these supplements (with lutein and zeaxanthin) also contain beta-carotene, which has been linked to increased risk for lung cancer in current and former smokers.

Stop Neglecting Your Eyesight: 4 Eye-Health Secrets Can Save Your Vision

Jeffrey D. Henderer, MD, professor of ophthalmology and the Dr. Edward Hagop Bedrossian Chair of Ophthalmology at the Lewis Katz School of Medicine at Temple University in Philadelphia. Dr. Henderer is the Secretary for Knowledge Base Development for the American Academy of Ophthalmology and has authored numerous articles and text-book chapters on glaucoma and genetics.

When it comes to staying on top of our health, far too many people take their eyesight for granted. It's obvious that we should get regular eye exams (see below), but there are other steps that often slip under the radar. *Here are the strategies that ensure you're doing all you can to protect your vision...*

Eye-health secret #1: **Use the right eyedrops.** Older adults and those of any age who are heavy users of computers and/or electronics know that they're more likely to suffer from dry eye. Lubricating drops, sometimes called artificial tears, are effective for this condition. But when you're in the store, it's easy to mistakenly pick up redness-reducing eyedrops, which temporarily constrict the blood vessels. These drops do not help with dry eye.

In fact, daily use of redness-reducing drops can cause rebound redness and set off an unhealthy cycle of using more eyedrops. For this reason, redness-reducing drops should be used only occasionally—and if the redness persists, see your eye doctor to find out why.

Best for dry eye are lubricating drops such as Refresh, Systane, GenTeal, Bion Tears and even pharmacy brands. *Caution:* If the preservatives they contain irritate your eyes, look for preservative-free brands.

Lubricating drops come in three viscosities—liquid, thicker gel-like formulas and ointments. The thicker drops and ointments last longer but can temporarily blur vision.

Eye-health secret #2: **Watch your medication.** Steroids—taken orally, inhaled or in eyedrop form—can cause cataracts and glaucoma. Cataracts can start to develop within months of regular steroid use, while glaucoma is slower and subtler. If you must take a steroid, ask your doctor for the lowest dose possible, schedule an eye exam one to two months after starting any form of the drug, then return every six to 12 months for monitoring. *Other drugs that can affect the eyes...*

- ***Tamoxifen*** **(Nolvadex),** which is used to treat and prevent recurrences of breast cancer, can cause eye irritation and dryness...lead to cataracts (usually after five years of use)...and accumulate in the retina, weakening color vision and central vision. Fortunately, as oncologists have started prescribing lower doses of tamoxifen, these side effects happen less often. *Self-defense:* Have an annual dilated eye exam with a retina specialist while you are taking tamoxifen and have him/her examine your retinas to be sure there is no accumulation in the retina.
- ***Tamsulosin*** **(Flomax),** used to treat an enlarged prostate, can make the iris, which is normally fairly rigid, turn floppy. Ordinarily, this shouldn't lead to vision complications, but if the patient undergoes cataract surgery, it can cause a condition called *intraoperative floppy iris syndrome* (IFIS), possibly complicating the procedure by preventing the pupil from dilating well and causing the iris to herniate out of the incision. *Self-defense:* If you plan to undergo cataract surgery, let your eye surgeon know if you are taking tamsulosin or have in the past.
- **Erectile dysfunction medicines** such as *sildenafil* (Viagra) and *tadalafil* (Cialis) can, in rare instances, cause irreversible damage called *nonarteritic anterior ischemic optic neuropathy* (NAION), which is like a stroke of the optic nerve. Incidences are not dose-related and can happen after a single use of the drug. *Self-defense:* Avoid erectile dysfunction medications if you have hypertension or diabetes (which put you at greater risk for NAION), and/or if you take nitrates to lower blood pressure—erectile dysfunction drugs can lower blood pressure even more.

Eye-health secret #3: **Keep diabetes well-controlled.** People with diabetes tend to develop cataracts at an earlier age than people without diabetes. They also have an elevated risk for visual impairment and blindness due to diabetic retinopathy, when high blood sugar levels damage blood vessels in the retina.

What to do: Get a dilated eye exam annually or more often if recommended by your doctor, particularly if you struggle to keep your sugar under control. Early treatment can prevent an astonishing 95% of diabetes-related vision loss!

Also important: The better you are able to control your blood sugar with diet, lifestyle changes and medication, the better your chances of delaying the onset of cataracts and diabetic retinopathy.

Eye-health secret #4: **Take this eye supplement.** If you're at high risk for advanced age-related macular degeneration (AMD)—that is, you have intermediate AMD or advanced AMD in one eye only—taking high levels of certain antioxidants plus zinc can reduce the risk of developing an advanced form of AMD by about 25%, according to a major National Eye Institute clinical trial called the Age-Related Eye Disease Study (AREDS). A leading cause of blindness among Americans age 50 and older, AMD causes damage to the retina that may lead to central vision loss.

What to do: Look for a supplement labeled "AREDS formula" (such as Bausch & Lomb PreserVision AREDS 2 Formula). It's not an AMD cure, but it may help preserve vision in susceptible individuals. Ask your ophthalmologist if it's right for you.

WHEN WAS YOUR LAST EYE EXAM?

Adults between the ages of 55 and 64 who are risk-free and have no eye symptoms should have eye exams *every one to three years*, but nearly half of those recently surveyed have not.

People who are over age 65 or of any age with a risk factor, such as high blood pressure, diabetes or a family history of eye disease, should have an eye exam at least every one or two years, according to the American Academy of Ophthalmology.

Because your eyes offer an unobstructed view of your blood vessels, nerves and connecting tissue, any abnormalities that show up in an eye exam may indicate similar changes elsewhere in the body. This means your optometrist or ophthalmologist can give you crucial information about your risk for serious conditions such as stroke, high blood pressure, diabetes and autoimmune disease, such as Graves' disease, a thyroid disorder. Insurance should cover these exams.

You Could Have a Spinal Fracture and Not Know It...

Vinil Shah, MD, assistant professor of clinical radiology and associate program director of the neuroradiology fellowship program at University of California, San Francisco. Dr. Shah's areas of academic interest include assessing clinical outcomes of spine intervention.

Did you know that you can get a spinal fracture from simply stepping off a curb, sneezing, lifting a small pet or even just getting out of bed?

Fractures due to osteoporosis are much more common than many people realize. In fact, after age 50, one in two women and one in five men will have an osteoporosis-related fracture in their lifetimes.

The most common type of fracture linked to osteoporosis is a vertebral compression fracture (VCF)—a break in a vertebra of the spine. VCFs are more common than hip or wrist fractures...often are painful...and can lead to loss of height and a stooped back. So why do a shocking two-thirds of VCFs go undiagnosed and untreated?

Osteoporosis can weaken the bones so much that even routine activities or seemingly innocuous movements can cause a spinal fracture. Sudden, nonradiating pain ranging from mild to severe is typically the first sign. But the pain is often mistaken for arthritis or a pinched nerve. And because many people with osteoporosis don't even know they have it, VCFs simply aren't on their radar.

QUICK ACTION IS VITAL

An undiagnosed VCF will often heal on its own, with the pain diminishing in six to eight weeks. But you *don't* want this fracture to go undiagnosed! One VCF increases the risk for a subsequent VCF fivefold. And multiple fractures result in a loss of height and stooped posture. With each additional untreated VCF, the spine can get a few millimeters shorter. If the vertebrae in the upper back fracture and become wedge-shaped, the spine curves abnormally causing *kyphosis*, a rounding of the back better known as a dowager's hump.

If you're a woman or man over age 50 or a postmenopausal woman under age 50 who is experiencing new, unexplained mild-to-severe midline back pain that doesn't go away in a day or two, you need to see a doctor. Your primary care physician will perform a physical exam to check for back tenderness and will likely order an X-ray to confirm the diagnosis, following up with a CT scan or MRI to evaluate the problem further. Your doctor will then advise you on the best treatment for your specific situation.

TREATING THE FRACTURE

If the pain and loss of function from a VCF are mild, conservative treatments are usually recommended...

• **A few days of bed rest.** VCF pain tends to worsen when sitting or standing and improves when lying down.

• **Pain relievers.** Over-the-counter pain relievers, such as *ibuprofen* (Advil) or *acetaminophen* (Tylenol), help reduce mild pain.

• **A hyperextension back brace.** Wearing a rigid hyperextension back brace for a few weeks can help relieve pain and improve function in some patients. Ask your doctor for guidance.

• **Physical therapy (PT).** PT helps strengthen back muscles and can improve posture and prevent the development of chronic pain. It also has a beneficial effect on bone mineral density in osteoporosis patients and may prevent future fractures. *Note:* PT can be started once the patient's pain is under control.

Conservative treatment of a VCF is not recommended for more than a few weeks or for those with more severe pain or limited function. Prolonged bed rest may lead to loss of bone mass (up to 1% loss each week) and muscle strength (10% to 15% loss each week). Bed rest can also increase risk for blood clots and bed sores, and painkillers should only be used short term.

OTHER TREATMENTS

Patients whose pain doesn't resolve in two to three weeks with the treatments above may be candidates for a minimally invasive procedure called *vertebroplasty.* Guided by computed tomography and/or fluoroscopy (a continuous X-ray "movie"), the doctor injects bone cement into the fracture. The outpatient procedure takes about 45 minutes while the patient is typically conscious but sedated. The cement not only stabilizes the fractured vertebra, it also prevents nearby nerve endings from causing pain.

Studies show that 75% to 100% of patients enjoy good-to-moderate pain relief and increased mobility quickly after vertebroplasty, often the next day. The procedure usually doesn't restore much height loss, but it can prevent further height loss and additional fractures.

With *kyphoplasty,* a modification of vertebroplasty, a balloon is inflated in the fractured vertebra to create a cavity that is then filled with cement. This procedure may offer a better chance of restoring height loss. However, kyphoplasty is more expensive than vertebroplasty, and there is mixed data on its benefit over vertebroplasty.

In general, vertebroplasty and kyphoplasty are safe when done by an experienced doctor. Interventional radiologists and neuroradiologists often do these procedures. Look for a doctor who has experience in using image guidance for spine procedures. Like all invasive medical procedures, these treatments do have risks—such as infection or bleeding. And in rare cases, the cement can leak into the spinal canal, causing nerve compression, or travel into adjacent veins, which can lead to blood clots in the lungs or heart.

The best candidates for these procedures are patients who have pain of at least moderate intensity (rated a five or greater out of 10) that impacts their mobility and daily quality of life. Additionally, those who have fractures that have occurred recently (within a few months prior to the procedure) tend to have more success with vertebroplasty and kyphoplasty than those who have older fractures. The age of a fracture can be determined by an MRI.

PREVENTING FUTURE FRACTURES

Treating the underlying osteoporosis to help prevent future fractures is crucial. Ask your doctor for a bone mineral density test called a DXA (or DEXA)—this low-dose X-ray measures bone density in the hip and spine and can guide your physician in choosing the best course of action for your case. Options include prescription medications such as bisphosphonates (patients should weigh the risks versus benefits of these drugs with their doctors)…calcium and vitamin D supplementation…and weight-bearing exercise to improve bone strength and other exercises to build core strength. Multiple clinical trials have shown that early treatment of osteoporosis can increase bone mineral density by 5% to 15%, reducing vertebral fracture rates by 40% to 70%.

Is Your Arthritis Really an Infection? How to Tell

David Lans, DO, FACP, a clinical assistant professor of medicine at New York Medical College in Valhalla, New York, chief of rheumatology at NewYork-Presbyterian/Lawrence Hospital in Bronxville, New York, and an internist and a rheumatologist in private practice at Integrative Rheumatology of Westchester in New Rochelle, New York. Dr. Lans is board-certified in rheumatology, internal medicine and allergy and immunology.

When you think of arthritis, what probably comes to mind is *osteoarthritis*, the wear-and-tear disease that affects more than 30 million Americans.

What you may not realize: Other types of arthritis can ravage joints, including arthritis caused by infection. For example, a recent study published in *Arthritis Care & Research* found that more than 16,000 people go to the emergency room every year with *septic arthritis*, an infection that can cause irreversible damage and deformity to joints.

Infections play a role in many cases of arthritis, both acute and chronic. Because these types of arthritis are less common than osteoarthritis, they are often misdiagnosed or overlooked. *What you need to know about...*

- **Septic arthritis.** Triggered by bacteria in the bloodstream that settle in a joint, this is the most serious form of infectious arthritis. Without prompt treatment, deep bone infections may occur and take months to resolve. One-third of people with septic arthritis suffer joint damage—and 10% die.

About half the time, the infection is in the knee, and pain and swelling are so severe that walking is difficult. The joint will also be red and hot. And you'll have a fever and chills and feel very sick. The knee is a common site for septic arthritis because of its large size and location.

People who have weakened immune systems, including adults over age 65 and children, are the most common victims of septic arthritis. You're also at higher risk if you already have a joint problem, such as osteoarthritis, gout or rheumatoid arthritis, which is an autoimmune disease...if you're taking medications for rheumatoid arthritis, which suppress the immune system...if you have an immune-weakening disease, such as diabetes or cancer...or if you have fragile skin that is easily injured and heals poorly (a fairly common problem among older adults and those with diabetes), allowing bacteria ready access into your bloodstream.

Many types of bacteria can cause septic arthritis. The most common bacterial culprits are *Staph* and *Streptococcal* species. If the infection isn't stopped, bacteria can destroy cartilage, causing permanent damage.

What to watch out for: Sudden, severe pain in a knee or other joint, and flulike symptoms, including fever and chills.

Treatment: Go to the emergency room or see a doctor—immediately. The joint will be drained with a needle or tube (arthroscopy), and the fluid will be cultured to identify the bacteria. It's likely you'll also get blood tests to help pinpoint the infection and X-rays to see if the joint has been damaged.

If you're diagnosed with septic arthritis, you'll receive IV antibiotics, followed by oral antibiotics. The usual antibiotic treatment duration is about six weeks. If antibiotics aren't effective, you may need surgery to drain the infection.

- **Reactive arthritis.** This type of arthritis can plague joints for weeks to years. Doctors aren't certain if reactive arthritis is an infection of the joint...or a joint-centered inflam-

INTERESTING FINDING...

Calcium/Vitamin D Myth?

Whether used separately or together, these two common supplements *do not* reduce the risk of breaking a hip compared with use of placebo or no treatment, according to recent analysis. Research shows that the best advice for people concerned with bone health is to eat a healthy diet and engage in weight-bearing activity.

Analysis by researchers at Tianjin Hospital, China, of 33 clinical trials involving 51,145 participants over age 50, published in *JAMA* and reported in *The Washington Post*.

mation triggered by an infection elsewhere in the body. Either way, the arthritis is typically caused by either a sexually transmitted bacterial infection, such as *chlamydia* or *gonorrhea*, or a gastrointestinal infection, such as *C. difficile* or *salmonella*. Food poisoning is a common trigger.

What to watch out for: Joint pain that develops a few weeks or months after a sexually transmitted or gastrointestinal infection.

Treatment: A blood test will be given to detect the bacteria. If it's positive, you'll take antibiotics that target the organism. Nonsteroidal anti-inflammatory drugs (NSAIDs), such as *ibuprofen* (Motrin)...corticosteroids...or antirheumatic drugs, such as *methotrexate* (Trexall), may also be prescribed.

• **Lyme arthritis.** Lyme disease, a bacterial infection from a tick bite, is found throughout the US, but mainly in the Northeast, from Maine to Virginia, and in Minnesota, Wisconsin, Michigan and northern California. Some people never overcome the infection and develop chronic Lyme disease. Among those, more than half develop Lyme arthritis—one or more swollen joints (usually a knee), with pain (typically mild) that is intermittent or constant.

What to watch out for: Lyme arthritis usually develops several months after the tick bite. As with all types of arthritis, joint swelling and pain can occur.

Treatment: Lyme arthritis often resembles reactive arthritis. To make a definitive diagnosis, your doctor will order a blood test to detect antibodies to *B. burgdorferi*, the bacterium transmitted from the tick bite. The doctor may also remove fluid from your joint for a *polymerase chain reaction* (PCR) test, which detects the presence of DNA from *B. burgdorferi*.

If one or both of these tests are positive, your doctor will probably prescribe oral or intravenous antibiotics for one to three months. In most cases, this treatment cures Lyme arthritis, especially if it's initiated early on.

However, in some patients, the treatment fails, and chronic arthritis, as well as other symptoms (such as fatigue, headache and difficulty concentrating), may persist. If the disease isn't controlled, a drug used for rheumatoid arthritis—a *disease modifying antirheumatic drug*, or DMARD—often helps control the Lyme arthritis. Some patients require long-term treatment, while others improve over a period of months.

• **Viral joint infections.** Many viruses can trigger acute arthritis, but the joint pain that results is usually mild and goes away on its own after a few weeks. *Viral infections that can cause arthritis include...*

Zika virus, from mosquitoes that carry it.

Epstein-Barr, the virus that causes mononucleosis.

Hepatitis A and B, the liver-infecting viruses that cause about one-third of virus-triggered arthritis.

Parvovirus, a respiratory infection common in adults who are routinely exposed to children, the primary carriers of this infection, which causes a distinctive face rash.

What to watch out for: Sudden, mild joint pain (viral arthritis can affect almost any joint).

Treatment: Your physician will order a blood test for antibodies to specific viruses that can cause acute arthritis. Pain control is the goal, typically with an over-the-counter NSAID, such as ibuprofen or *naproxen* (Aleve).

New Help for Knee Arthritis

Cooled radiofrequency ablation (CRFA) gives better pain reduction and functional improvement than steroid injections. The procedure uses radiofrequency energy to interrupt pain transmission from the genicular nerve in the knee. The procedure is done on an outpatient basis with local anesthesia and minimal sedation.

Recent study: After one month, patients in a clinical trial who gave their initial pain scores as seven on a 10-point scale gave a score of four if they had steroid shots and three if they had CRFA. After six months, 74% of CRFA patients had at least a one-half reduction in pain scores, compared with 16% of those who had steroid injections.

Further research is planned. Availability, cost and insurance coverage for CRFA vary.

Leonardo Kapural, MD, PhD, pain physician, Carolinas Pain Institute and Center for Clinical Research, Winston-Salem, North Carolina, and leader of a study of 151 patients, published in *Regional Anesthesia & Pain Medicine.*

Better Than Opioids

Topical treatments for chronic pain can be as effective as opioids and prescription nonsteroidal anti-inflammatory drugs (NSAIDs) for some patients. Prescription topical treatments, such as *diclofenac* and *ketoprofen*, may work for the pain of moderately severe arthritis, neuropathic conditions and musculoskeletal disorders. Treated patients for whom the topical approach worked said that they favored topical treatments for their convenience.

Jeffrey Gudin, MD, director of pain management and palliative care, Englewood Hospital and Medical Center, New Jersey, and leader of a study published in *Journal of Pain Research.*

Is It Normal... Alzheimer's...or Something Else?

Jason Brandt, PhD, professor of psychiatry and behavioral sciences, professor of neurology and director of the division of medical psychology, all at Johns Hopkins University School of Medicine, Baltimore. He also directs the Cortical Function Laboratory at Johns Hopkins Hospital and has developed several widely used neuropsychological tests. He is on the editorial advisory board of *Alzheimer's & Dementia* and is a senior editor of *Journal of Alzheimer's Disease.*

The pot you forgot boiling on the stove. The longtime neighbor whose name you suddenly can't recall. The car keys you think you've lost, only to discover they're...in your pocket.

Chances are you have had a momentary memory lapse like these, often called a "senior moment." Though they happen to everyone on occasion, there's a reason for the moniker—these slipups may reflect the gradual loss of one's mental sharpness with aging.

It's no wonder, then, that repeated lapses can be alarming, especially for those with a family history of Alzheimer's disease or some other form of dementia. The good news is that the minor memory misfires that tend to affect people over age 50 often are caused by *normal* age-related changes in the brain and nervous system.

But still, memory lapses can be an early marker of Alzheimer's or another type of dementia. So if you have been noticing more of those senior moments, it is perfectly reasonable to see your doctor about it and ask about undergoing a cognitive assessment. These tests can put your mind at ease...or help diagnose a potential problem at the earliest possible stage.

TESTING 1, 2, 3

To gauge cognitive function, your physician likely will observe your responses to standardized memory and thinking exercises. Many physicians give patients the Mini-Mental State Examination (MMSE). This exam starts with a set of simple questions that measure orientation—*What year is it? What season? What is today's date? What town are we in?* Next, the doctor will read a short list of words and ask the patient to repeat them back immediately and then five minutes later.

The doctor also will ask the patient to write a sentence and copy a geometric design. Finally, the doctor will ask the patient to perform a series of actions (such as "touch your left shoulder and then tap your head twice"), which gauges the ability to understand language and follow commands.

Helpful: A perfect MMSE score is 30, and a healthy adult should approach that number (anything above 27 is usually fine).

If your physician is concerned, he/she may refer you to a neuropsychologist for further diagnostic testing. Just as a neurologist and radiologist can decipher the images of a brain MRI scan, this kind of doctor examines patterns of scores on a variety of brain-function tests to try to identify specific disorders.

Among the more commonly used tests for assessing a patient with possible Alzheimer's is the Boston Naming Test. Here, the patient looks at drawings of objects and names them. It begins with common nouns (a dog, a tree) and advances to increasingly obscure ones (a padlock, a zebra) that require the test taker to retrieve rarely used words from memory. This is valuable information, as Alzheimer's patients tend to have trouble recalling the names of objects.

Alzheimer's also diminishes the ability to learn and remember new things. Doctors measure this by reading a brief story and asking the patient to repeat it right away, then 20 minutes later.

Finally, since people in the early stages of Alzheimer's tend to develop spatial confusion, we see whether they have difficulty copying, say, a geometric design or drawing common objects (for example, a daisy) upon request.

Important: Don't look up these tests or "prepare" for them in advance. They are useful only if you don't know exactly what to expect and haven't "practiced."

WHAT A DECLINE MEANS

Many patients who visit my clinic have parents or other relatives with Alzheimer's. They're acutely aware of their own periodic memory failures and are understandably worried about how well their minds are working.

Good news: As often as not, after running these tests, I end up telling them, "You're functioning like an average person your age. What you're experiencing looks like typical age-related decline."

That may not sound comforting, but face the facts. Your brain is affected by "wear and tear" as you age. You probably can't run as fast at age 55 as you could at age 35, and your mind isn't quite as efficient as it was two decades ago, either. But if you perform within the average range for your age, there's no cause for concern.

If your results fall below that level, you might be diagnosed with *mild cognitive impairment* (MCI). If so, your brain function is below the norm for your age even though you don't have dementia.

Keep in mind: MCI is a broad category and encompasses a variety of different things. A patient with MCI who finds it difficult to recall events or the right word to describe an object or who displays spatial confusion, may be in the very earliest stage of Alzheimer's.

In contrast, someone who possesses a solid memory but struggles with executive function (for example, he can't plan well or solve problems effectively) may be at greater risk of developing a frontotemporal dementia—a type of dementia in which personality and language changes are common.

Important: While 10% to 15% of people over age 65 who have MCI will progress to Alzheimer's each year, the diagnosis is not necessarily dire. Many published studies show that patients with cognitive impairment in only one area—*just* memory or *just* language or *just* spatial cognition—have a very strong chance (perhaps as high as 50%) of returning to normal within one year.

How? It could be that the patient who fell into the MCI category was feeling ill the day of assessment...or was sleep-deprived...or drank too much (or not enough) coffee...or even was just in a very bad mood.

Although many factors affect an individual's cognitive performance, these tests are ex-

TAKE NOTE...

New Dementia Link

People who feel dizzy upon standing are 40% more likely to develop dementia than those who don't, according to a 20-year study of nearly 12,000 adults.

Theory: That quick drop in blood pressure, which often leads to dizziness (a condition known as *orthostatic hypotension*), may cause lasting damage by reducing blood flow to the brain.

Temporary dizziness may indicate an underlying condition such as dehydration or anemia or may be caused by prescription medications.

Andreea Rawlings, PhD, postdoctoral researcher at Johns Hopkins Bloomberg School of Public Health in Baltimore.

tremely useful when they are interpreted by an expert neuropsychologist. Recent studies indicate that the brains of patients with Alzheimer's disease undergo changes (observable with special brain-imaging methods) many years before the diagnosis is typically made. So getting a baseline neuropsychological assessment in middle age or a little older may help identify people who should be targeted for more active Alzheimer's prevention.

YOUR NEXT STEPS

If you do well on the cognitive tests but remain worried about memory decline, work hard to keep what you have.

To achieve this (as well as maintain good overall health), follow these lifestyle choices: Eat a healthful diet...get regular exercise...participate in brain-stimulating activities you enjoy...keep your blood pressure under control...and moderate your alcohol intake.

For a patient who is newly diagnosed with early-stage Alzheimer's, I often recommend that he stop driving as a safety measure, advise him to keep written notes and calendars to aid recall and suggest that he talk with his doctor about whether a prescription Alzheimer's drug might help improve mental function. I also recommend beginning a discussion of future care needs and end-of-life plans with family.

As for people who fall in the middle and display some signs of MCI, I often explain that the "senior moments" they're experiencing might be the beginning of something more serious...or they might mean nothing at all.

Best way forward: Follow the blueprint for patients who tested well cognitively—live a healthful lifestyle, and try to avoid "stressing out." (I frequently recommend mindfulness-based stress reduction programs.) Then I will reevaluate a year later and take other measures if needed.

Diet Soda and Dementia

Adults who drank one or more artificially sweetened soft drinks daily were almost three times more likely to develop dementia or suffer a stroke, compared with those who did not consume diet drinks, according to a recent 17-year observational study.

Self-defense: Drink water instead of artificially sweetened drinks or sugary beverages, which have been linked in earlier studies to obesity and related chronic conditions.

Matthew P. Pase, PhD, researcher, department of neurology, Boston University School of Medicine.

When Other Treatments for Depression Fail...

The anesthetic *ketamine* may treat depression when other approaches don't work. Ketamine works quickly—especially important for treating suicidal depression since no rapid-onset antidepressants have been approved for such treatment. But ketamine can cause hallucinations, nightmares, confusion and agitation—for these reasons and because it must be given by intravenous or intramuscular administration, it is not a first-line treatment for depression.

Ruben Abagyan, PhD, professor, Skaggs School of Pharmacy and Pharmaceutical Sciences, University of California, San Diego.

No Shoes, Please!

Kelly Reynolds, PhD, environmental microbiologist and associate professor at University of Arizona.

Taking off your shoes when you come home not only keeps your home cleaner, it turns out that it might protect your health as well. A recent study found that 26.4% of shoe soles tested positive for a nasty bacterium called *C. difficile*. According to the Centers for Disease Control and Prevention, *C. difficile* is responsible for nearly 30,000 deaths in the US each year.

And *C. difficile* is just one of many health risks that could be hitching a ride into our homes on the soles of our shoes. The research shows that the bottoms of our shoes carry a variety of bacteria.

True, there's a good chance that our health will not suffer even if we do track bacteria or other toxins into our homes. Most of these unwanted houseguests pose substantial health risks only if they get into our digestive systems. And most people don't eat off the floor.

But we also could pick up contaminants if we put our feet up on a coffee table and later place food on that table...or if we fail to wash our hands thoroughly after touching the floor. Young children are at particular risk—they often take things off the floor and put them in their mouths. Add it up, and it certainly seems like it's worth a few seconds to remove our shoes when we get home and put them back on when leaving.

Your Cash Could Make You Sick

Philip M. Tierno, Jr., PhD, a microbiologist and director of clinical microbiology and diagnostic immunology at New York University Langone Medical Center, New York City. He is author of *The Secret Life of Germs*.

Your cold hard cash could give you a cold—or worse. Recent research conducted by New York University's Center for Genomics & System Biology identified roughly 3,000 types of bacteria on paper money, including germs that cause food poisoning, staph infections and pneumonia.

Touching a germy bill will not necessarily make you sick. Typically, a relatively large number of germs must enter the body to cause infection, and that usually does not occur when you handle money in normal ways—but there are exceptions. *Example*: A single norovirus virion (the infectious form of a virus) can cause infection.

The health risks from germ-covered money increase greatly when money is handled by someone who also handles food, such as a sandwich-shop worker or street-food vendor. This opens the door for germs to be transferred from money to the food we eat, allowing many more of the germs to enter the body.

Coins tend to harbor fewer germs than paper money because certain metals used in coins, including copper, nickel and zinc, naturally inhibit germ growth. Crisp, new bills tend to harbor fewer germs than old, worn ones because US paper money has antimicrobial properties that seem to diminish with time and usage.

What to do: Wash your hands or use a hand sanitizer as soon as possible after handling money. Choose a hand sanitizer with an alcohol percentage of 85% or higher—unlike most germs, the norovirus can survive 60% to 65% alcohol hand sanitizers.

Beware This Deadly Bacteria

The vibrio bacteria is not well-known but it is deadly. The bacterium can cause deadly skin infections or gastrointestinal problems, particularly in people who have a compromised immune system or liver disease. The death rate in these patients approaches 50%. Vibrio bacteria live in warm coastal waters and get into people's bodies through unhealed cuts or if someone swallows the bacteria—which can happen when eating raw or undercooked shellfish.

Aaron E. Glatt, MD, FACP, a spokesperson for the Infectious Diseases Society of America, is chairman, department of medicine, South Nassau Communities Hospital, Oceanside, New York.

2

Medical Insider

Online Doctor Reviews: Don't Get Fooled

Whenever I'm about to buy a new appliance or car or even when I'm deciding on the next book to read, I check out online customer reviews. For many reasons, online patient reviews of doctors are not as reliable. Yet according to studies, nearly 60% of patients say that online reviews are an important factor in choosing a health-care provider. So is there a smart way to use these reviews when looking for a new doctor, dentist, physical therapist, etc.—without falling victim to their shortcomings? Yes, there is. *Here's how...*

- **Recognize which information is most helpful.** If you are trying to determine just how competent a doctor is, patient reviews are not the best place to look. One patient may say a particular doctor is the best, while another says he/she is the worst. But that feedback is colored by the fact that you don't necessarily know the patient's medical condition or medical history. Nor do you know whether the person submitting the review even saw the doctor. Unlike some online retail shopping sites, privacy laws make it virtually impossible for a health-related website to verify that the review was written by a real patient.

Another problem: With more than 950,000 active licensed physicians in the US, most websites have only a handful—if any—patient reviews about a given doctor. Fewer than 20 reviews of a doctor is not a valid sample of patient experience. When can patient reviews be helpful? Even though the feedback is still somewhat subjective, reviews that discuss a doctor's "bedside" manner...time spent with

Charles B. Inlander, a consumer advocate and health-care consultant based in Fogelsville, Pennsylvania. He was founding president of the nonprofit People's Medical Society, a consumer advocacy organization credited with key improvements in the quality of US health care, and is author or coauthor of more than 20 consumer-health books.

the patient during a visit...ease of getting an appointment...and/or how well the office staff responds to questions or requests can provide useful information.

• **Put the review to good use.** To get the best use from a patient review, rely on it when you're formulating questions to ask a doctor you might be seeing for the first time. If a doctor's reviews complain that test results are not received in a timely manner, ask about that if you choose to see that doctor. Look for points that are important to you, such as taking time to answer questions or helping you set up appointments with other specialists.

• **Choose the right sites.** From my experience, three of the best websites for finding reviews of health providers are Healthgrades.com...Vitals.com...and RateMDs.com. Each provides a good deal of basic information about the provider, including his specialty, whether the provider is board-certified in that specialty (an indication that the doctor has done extra study and continuing education to meet the specialty's highest standards), along with contact information (including the doctor's office location, etc.).

Note: The reviews and details on the provider usually include a date on the web page, which gives you an idea of how recent the information is.

Insider tip: Many hospital websites now include patient reviews for doctors on their staff or those with admitting privileges. Often under a link titled "find a physician," many of these sites allow you to search for a doctor by specialty, look at his background—such as schools attended and academic degrees attained—and post patient reviews. Even though it's the hospital's website, not all the reviews are positive.

• **Don't forget!** You can help other patients by submitting reviews of your experience to the websites listed above. But be careful not to defame or otherwise attack a doctor. In recent years, doctors have been suing patients whom they feel have wrongly accused them of malpractice or poor treatment.

BEWARE...

Hackers Targeting Medical Records

Hackers are targeting your medical records. There were 233 major breaches in the first half of 2017 (latest data available), exposing more than 3 million patient records. Hackers use stolen records to commit identity fraud.

Self-defense: Don't put your Social Security number on forms. Check at OCRPortal.hhs.gov/ocr/breach to see whether a provider has had a breach. If so, keep a close eye on your financial accounts.

Bob Diachenko, chief communications officer, Kromtech, New Orleans, which develops cybersecurity solutions. Kromtech.com

8 Mistakes to Avoid If You Get Bad Medical News

Steven Z. Pantilat, MD, a palliative-care physician and the Kates-Burnard and Hellman Distinguished Professor in Palliative Care, University of California, San Francisco School of Medicine. His research has been published in journals including *JAMA Internal Medicine*, *Journal of Palliative Medicine* and others, and he is author of *Life After the Diagnosis: Expert Advice on Living Well with Serious Illness for Patients and Caregivers.*

Sooner or later, it happens to most of us—we find ourselves sitting in a doctor's office hearing some very bad news. The diagnosis is heart failure, cancer, dementia, kidney failure, Parkinson's disease or some other serious (and possibly terminal) illness. At that moment, we are scared and vulnerable. It's easy to make mistakes when we're in a frantic quest to beat back illness. *Here's how to avoid or overcome these common mistakes...*

MISTAKE #1: **Making rash decisions.** Even when a diagnosis is dire, jumping right into treatment can be a mistake. So slow down, and make sure you have all the information you need. That means asking how your illness and the treatments you are considering will affect your day-to-day life...how likely it is that treatments will work...and what "working" means. To truly understand the answers, you need to also (politely) insist that doctors cut the jargon—so you won't end up thinking, for example, that a "response rate" is the same as a "cure rate."

Cancer patients often are surprised to learn that they can wait a bit before starting chemotherapy or other treatments—it is almost always safe to wait two to three weeks, but the doctor can tell you if it's not. These days, this short pause will often include waiting for a genetic analysis of the tumor, which might point to a more effective, targeted treatment. Getting extra information like that can make a wait worthwhile.

MISTAKE #2: **Believing everything you read online.** By now, everyone knows that all online information is not created equal. But many people cannot resist reading everything they find—and, in the process, they stumble across a lot of information that is scary, wrong or not relevant to their personal situation.

Best approach: Ask your doctor for reputable information sources, and discuss what you find with him/her.

MISTAKE #3: **Not focusing on what you really want.** Let's say you might benefit from a cutting-edge treatment, but you learn that getting it will mean frequent trips or a long stay in another city.

Those trips might be worth the hassle if your goal is to explore every avenue for treating the illness and taking any chance, no matter how small, to find a cure or at least manage an illness—but not if your primary goal is to enjoy the comforts of home and family in what might be precious remaining weeks or months.

The right question to ask: Will this procedure or medicine help me to get back to my home and family? If it won't, what will?

MISTAKE #4: **Focusing on death instead of living.** It's important to think and talk about the end of life, but not at the expense of planning for the weeks, months or years that might still lie ahead. What will you need to do to keep up cherished hobbies and habits for as long as possible? Can you take a long-delayed trip, reconnect with long-lost friends or reach other personal goals?

To do that planning, you need to know the truth, so do not be afraid to ask your doctor how much time you have left, even if he has to estimate. You might have a lot more (or less) time than you assume.

Helpful: Regardless of your prognosis, ask about "palliative care"—care aimed at helping you function better, with less pain and stress and more emotional and spiritual support.

MISTAKE #5: **Keeping your illness a secret.** It might come as a surprise in this age of online over-sharing, but many people still keep serious illness a secret from family members, friends and others. That's a mistake. At the very least, you want a support person to go with you to important medical appointments to act as a second set of ears.

But you also may find a wider network of people eager to help with everything from meals to rides to lawn-mowing. Let them help. Share your hopes and fears with people you love and trust to help keep your stress levels in check.

Helpful: If you are wondering whether to tell someone close to you, try turning the table. What if you learned that this person had a serious illness and had not shared it so that you could help him? If you wish this person had told you, then you should think about sharing your news with this person.

MISTAKE #6: **Assuming that the most aggressive or newest treatments are best.** Even if your main goal is to live as long as possible, the most aggressive treatments are not always the best choices. You might sacrifice both quality and quantity of life by going ahead with a treatment that has little chance of helping you and a high probability of harming you.

For example, for some people with heart failure, a *left ventricular assist device* (LVAD), a pump surgically implanted into your heart to help pump the blood, might seem like a great idea. But there are serious complications, such as bleeding and stroke. Many people who have an LVAD implanted feel better, but some never get over the operation or have complications early and may feel that they are worse off with the LVAD than without it.

Helpful: Ask your doctor what is the best case, worst case and likely case with a particular treatment...and ask for the same assessments if you don't get that treatment.

***MISTAKE #7:* Limiting your health care to alternative treatments.** Complementary therapies—especially yoga, meditation, acupuncture and others that have been shown in research to have benefits—can be helpful when combined with standard treatments or when the benefits of standard treatments are exhausted. But patients who rely only on unproven approaches, including those pitched by pricey foreign clinics and online hucksters, sometimes wait too long to get evidence-based treatments that could have made a difference in how well and long they live.

***MISTAKE #8:* Beating yourself up.** Many people blame themselves for getting sick—a woman may have forgotten to get a mammogram, for example, and developed breast cancer. Give yourself a break. It's true that there are risk factors for serious diseases. But generally speaking, the development of illness is more complex than that.

Also, don't beat yourself up for not staying positive enough. While cultivating joy, hope, gratitude and love will help you face your illness, blocking off all sadness, worry and grief will not help. Find a balance.

Helpful: Talk about things that are real, meaningful and personal with those who care about you.

TAKE NOTE...

24/7 Checkups

Wearable monitoring devices—for checking heartbeat and other health indicators—soon may be incorporated into eyeglasses, shoes and other common items. The devices can be powered by body heat and movements.

Advanced Materials.

New Way to Predict Disease?

Researchers have developed an experimental method of measuring incredibly minute changes in the interactions among molecules in the body.

Implication: These changes could be used to predict the eventual impairment from Alzheimer's disease, diabetes, cancer, heart disease, depression and other serious conditions.

University of Virginia Health System.

Is That Medical Test Really Necessary?

Dennis Gottfried, MD, an associate professor of medicine at University of Connecticut School of Medicine, Farmington, and a general internist with a private practice in Torrington, Connecticut. He is author of *Too Much Medicine: A Doctor's Prescription for Better and More Affordable Health Care.*

Getting all the health screening tests possible sounds like a great idea. After all, frequent screening tests help detect diseases early and help you live longer, right? *Not always...*

DO YOU NEED THAT TEST?

People who are sick obviously need medical attention and appropriate tests. So do those at high risk for certain diseases. If you have a family history of melanoma, for example, I believe an annual skin check is wise. But many tests administered to millions of healthy people every year have *no* clear benefits. So why, then, do doctors order unnecessary tests? According to a 2014 physician survey, more than half admitted that they do it to protect themselves from malpractice lawsuits...36% said they recommend these tests "just to be safe"...and 28% said they do it because patients insist.

My advice: Before getting any medical test, ask your doctor why he/she is recommending it and what he will do with the information. Will the test reveal a problem that needs to be fixed? Is it likely that you will live longer if your doctor confirms a tiny thyroid nodule? If the answer is no, the test might be unnecessary—and needlessly risky.

Common tests you may not need...

LATE-LIFE COLONOSCOPY

Most people are advised to have a colonoscopy every 10 years, starting at age 50. The benefits seem obvious. Colonoscopy allows doctors to detect early-stage cancers and remove precancerous growths. Overall, the test has reduced the risk for death from colorectal cancer by about 40%.

Exception: For those who are age 75 or older, the risks of colonoscopies usually outweigh their benefits. A Harvard study looked at data from more than 1.3 million Medicare patients between the ages of 70 and 79. The researchers found that while colonoscopy *slightly* reduced cancer death rates in those who were under age 75, the test made little to no difference in those who were older.

Why: Between 30% and 50% of Americans will eventually develop polyps in the colon, but the vast majority of polyps will never turn into cancer. This is particularly true in the elderly because cancers take a long time to develop. Someone who's age 75 or older probably won't live long enough for the polyps to become cancerous.

Routine colonoscopies are generally safe but not totally risk-free. Bleeding and perforations can occur, and in rare cases, there have been deaths as a result of complications of colonoscopy. Plus, the test is expensive, and the "bowel prep" can be very unpleasant.

My advice: Get a colonoscopy every 10 years starting at age 50 (or as directed by your doctor), but if nothing serious is ever found, you can skip the test after age 75.

SKIN EXAMS

Millions of Americans ask their dermatologists to perform an annual head-to-toe skin exam. The early detection and removal of *melanoma* skin cancers is critical. More than 80,000 cases are diagnosed annually, and almost 10,000 people will die from melanoma. But only about 1% of all skin cancers are melanomas. The vast majority of skin cancers are basal and squamous cell carcinomas, which are slow-growing and present little health risk.

The US Preventive Services Task Force (USPSTF), an independent group of national experts that makes evidence-based recommendations about tests and other medical services, concludes that the evidence is insufficient to recommend for or against annual dermatological screening for melanomas. According to the group, the downsides of screening include overdiagnosis (the detection of diseases that are unlikely to ever be a threat) and the possibility of disfigurement caused by needless biopsies. There is also the expense of procedures and visits to the dermatologist. The USPSTF consciously did not address screening for basal and squamous cell carcinomas because of their relative medical insignificance.

My advice: An annual skin screening by a dermatologist doesn't make sense for everyone—particularly individuals who don't have a personal or family history of melanoma or those who are not severely immune impaired, such as people who have HIV. However, do be sure to see a dermatologist if you notice a mole, growth or "spot" that meets the ABCDE criteria—Asymmetrical...Border irregularity...Color that is not uniform (often with shades of black, brown or tan)...Diameter greater than 6 mm (which is about the size of a pencil eraser)... and Evolving size, shape or color, or new symptoms such as bleeding or itching. These are the changes most likely to signal melanoma.

PROSTATE-SPECIFIC ANTIGEN (PSA) TEST

Before this blood test was developed, about 70,000 men in the US were diagnosed with prostate cancer every year. With the advent of PSA testing in the 1990s, that number has increased to about 161,000 per year, and at the same time, the number of men dying from prostate cancer has decreased slightly. Is this due to early diagnosis using PSA testing? Many experts believe that the decline in prostate cancer death is from improved treatment of advanced prostate cancer, *not early detection*.

The vast majority of cancers that are discovered by routine PSA tests are *indolent*, meaning that they grow so slowly that they're unlikely to ever threaten a man's health. In fact, prostate cancer is typical in aging men. By age 80, about 60% of men have cancer in the prostate gland, but most never know it and go on to die from something else. Finding these cancers early is of no value and even may cause harm.

PSA test findings can lead to treatments that are not risk-free. For example, men who have elevated PSA levels will often be advised to undergo biopsies, which carry risks, such as bleeding and infection. Others will have radiation therapy, which can cause fatigue and frequent urination...or surgery, which can cause incontinence, impotence and, in rare cases, death. Plus many men will have to live with the scary knowledge that they have cancer, even though most of the cancers pose no risk at all.

The USPSTF recommends that men ages 55 to 69 discuss the benefits and harms of PSA screening with their doctors in order to make the best decisions for themselves based on their values and preferences. But for men age 70 and older, the group has concluded that the risks of routine testing outweigh the likely benefit and that PSA testing should not be done.

The USPSTF does not address PSA screening in men under age 55, but the American Cancer Society recommends that men at average risk for prostate cancer discuss screening with their doctors beginning at age 50 and that men at high risk consider screening at age 45. The American Urological Association recommends that men discuss PSA screening with their doctors before age 55 if they are at high risk for prostate cancer...between the ages of 55 and 69 if they are at average risk...and at age 70 or older if they have a greater than 10-year life expectancy.

Bottom line: Men should be sure to discuss the pros and cons of PSA testing with their doctors.

THYROID SCREENING

Ultrasound technology has made it easier to find and evaluate growths in the thyroid gland. As a result, there has been a threefold increase in the diagnosis of thyroid cancers, but there hasn't been any change in the thyroid cancer death rate.

A study from the Department of Veterans Affairs Medical Center and Dartmouth Geisel School of Medicine concluded that the apparent increase in thyroid cancer was mainly due to improved detection. About 87% of the cancers measured were just 2 cm or smaller and were unlikely to ever pose a threat. Yet patients were treated surgically with the risk for bleeding, vocal cord paralysis and disfigurement. They also had to deal with the psychological trauma of being told they had cancer. Radiation is also standard treatment for thyroid cancer and can cause side effects. Additionally, radiation exposure presents a cumulative lifetime risk of developing cancer.

My advice: Don't get routinely screened for thyroid cancer. However, if you have a neck mass or lump...you notice changes in your voice...or have a family history of medullary thyroid cancer, an ultrasound of your thyroid may be advised.

Remember: At the proper age and appropriate intervals, screening tests, such as colonoscopy, mammograms and Pap smears, *are* necessary. Also be sure to get a cholesterol test every five years and blood pressure checks annually...and regular dental and eye exams.

Genetic Testing Alert

People who learn that they have genetic health risks may be more likely to experience symptoms associated with those risks.

Recent study: People who were told that they had a higher genetic risk for depression remembered experiencing more depressive symptoms than people who were told that they did not have that risk—though the "test results" were made up.

Matthew Lebowitz, PhD, postdoctoral research fellow, Columbia University, New York City, and leader of the study.

GOOD TO KNOW...

What Did the Doctor Say?

Translate "medspeak" terms that doctors and nurses use such as *edema* and *non-nucleoside reverse transcriptase inhibitors* into plain English at a website from the Medical Library Association. At MLANet.org, click on "For Patients," then on "What Did My Doctor Say?"

New MRI Danger

Emanuel Kanal, MD, professor of radiology and neuroradiology and director of magnetic resonance services at University of Pittsburgh Medical Center. He serves as a consultant to the FDA on magnetic resonance safety issues and is lead author of the American College of Radiology's Guidance Document on Magnetic Resonance Safe Practices.

Actor Chuck Norris says that his wife, Gena, is enduring ongoing weakness and bouts of pain due to an injection she received as part of an MRI scan—is he right?

If you have an MRI, you might first be given an injection of *gadolinium*, a metal element that serves as a component of a "contrast agent" that makes tumors and inflammation easier to spot. But gadolinium can be toxic, and recent studies have found that traces of gadolinium can linger in patients' brains, bones or other tissues for years, rather than be flushed away by the kidneys in a few hours as previously believed.

Medical science cannot yet say even if gadolinium is responsible for Gena Norris's symptoms or whether it is dangerous in the small concentrations that linger after an MRI—research is ongoing. But it is reasonable to not want even a tiny amount of an unneeded and potentially harmful metal in your body.

What to do: If your physician recommends that you get an MRI, ask whether he/she requested that a contrast agent be used. If the answer is yes, ask your doctor to speak with the radiologist to confirm that using the contrast agent is necessary with your specific MRI. In many MRIs where the referring physician requests a contrast agent, it may not actually be needed. Only digital radiologists are trained in the complex subject.

If you do not have kidney disease and if the radiologist confirms that using a contrast agent is crucial to your MRI, the benefits of undergoing an MRI examination in which a contrast agent is used likely dwarfs any potential risk from the gadolinium itself.

Biopsy Breakthrough—A Simple Blood Draw May Be All That's Needed

Stanley R. Hamilton, MD, head of the division of pathology and laboratory medicine and the Frederick F. Becker Distinguished University Chair in Cancer Research at The University of Texas MD Anderson Cancer Center in Houston. He has served as the principal investigator of the Cancer Center Support Grant-Sponsored Tissue Biorepository and Pathology Resource core facility at MD Anderson since 1998.

In the near future, a vial of blood may be all that's needed to track cancers and make important decisions about chemotherapy and other treatments—without the need for risky and potentially uncomfortable biopsies.

Latest development: Blood tests known as "liquid biopsies" are already used routinely for certain lung cancer patients. The genetic information of other cancers, including melanoma and malignancies of the breast and pancreas, can also be found in a vial of blood.

What you need to know about this new type of biopsy...

AN EASIER TEST

Traditional biopsies, known as *tissue biopsies*, are a standard part of cancer care. They are done to confirm or rule out a cancer diagnosis...to identify and characterize different types of cancer...and to track cancer changes over time.

With tissue biopsies, small portions of tissue are surgically removed or extracted with a needle and sent to a laboratory for analysis. The procedure comes with the risk for tissue damage, infection or other complications. It's also highly stressful for patients who are already dealing with the challenges of having cancer.

Another drawback: Up to 20% of tumors can't be biopsied at all. They may be located in an inaccessible part of the body or too close to a vital structure (such as an important blood vessel). Or the procedure might be too risky for a patient who's already seriously ill.

With liquid biopsies, all the doctor needs is a blood sample. What information can be gleaned from a vial of blood? When tumor cells die, they cast off small amounts of DNA into the bloodstream. A blood test can analyze the DNA and map genetic abnormalities that may affect subsequent treatments. The tests can also detect whole tumor cells that malignancies sometimes shed. The cancer cells themselves can be analyzed for important abnormalities that may guide treatment decisions.

WEALTH OF INFORMATION

The genetic information provided by image-guided tissue biopsies and liquid biopsies can be used to tailor treatments for specific cancer patients. Genetic alterations that drive certain cancers can be detected before cancer treatment begins, or they can emerge during therapy or at some time in the future. *Examples of genes that could be detected with either a liquid or tissue biopsy and potentially affect cancer care for certain malignancies...*

- **Breast cancer.** About 20% of breast cancer patients have genetic factors that cause them to produce high levels of the HER2 protein. Standard chemotherapy drugs don't work well for these patients, but they often respond to targeted therapy drugs such as *trastuzumab* (Herceptin).
- **Melanoma.** For the 40% to 60% of melanoma patients with a specific mutation of the BRAF gene, targeted therapy drugs such as *vemurafenib* (Zelboraf) are a good choice.
- **Lung cancer.** About 5% of lung cancer patients have a mutation in the ALK gene and may not respond (or may stop responding) to standard chemotherapy. However, these patients often do respond when they are given targeted drugs such as *ceritinib* (Zykadia).

Promising research: Scientists recently used liquid biopsies to identify genetic mutations in patients with colorectal, biliary (related to the bile duct) and other gastrointestinal cancers. They found that nearly 80% of patients who had become resistant to drug therapy had a specific genetic alteration...and about half had multiple genetic mutations. With this information, oncologists will know what treatments to start—or when it's time to switch treatment strategies.

THE RESEARCH

Liquid biopsies are still so new that there's no definitive research on their reliability.

The largest study done so far: Research presented at the 2016 annual meeting of the American Society of Clinical Oncology looked at 15,000 blood samples taken from patients with a variety of cancers. For several hundred of the patients, tissue biopsies were also available. In a head-to-head comparison, the same genetic mutations that appeared in tissue biopsies were also found to be present in the liquid biopsies between 94% and 100% of the time.

More good news: In the same study, the genetic changes were detected in nearly two-thirds of patients and provided critical information for oncologists—when to choose certain drugs, for example, or when to encourage patients to enroll in a genetic abnormality directed clinical trial.

WHAT COMES NEXT?

It is too soon to conclude that liquid biopsies will become the new gold standard for identifying and tracking cancer-related gene abnormalities.

The current tests have inherent limitations. Some cancers, particularly those that are small and early stage, don't shed detectable levels of DNA into the blood. A blood test would miss these cancers, but an image-guided tissue biopsy may not.

Expense is another factor. A liquid biopsy can cost more than $5,000. It's covered by some, but not all, insurers. While the test isn't cheap, it might be a bargain compared with some traditional biopsies. A lung cancer tissue biopsy usually costs about $14,000 and has a known rate of complications, including pneumothorax (air in the chest cavity), bleeding and infection. A blood "stick" is much easier—and safer.

GETTING TESTED...

The Guardant360, one of the most widely used "liquid biopsies," looks at 73 different genes that could be tied to melanoma as well as lung, breast, colorectal and pancreatic cancers. Since the testing can be done with a routine blood sample, there are no additional risks—and you will be spared the discomfort of a traditional biopsy.

Your Biopsy Results Might Not Actually Be Yours

John D. Pfeifer, MD, PhD, professor and vice chair for clinical affairs in the pathology and immunology department at Washington University School of Medicine in St. Louis. WUSTL.edu

It's no secret that biopsies occasionally produce inaccurate results. But what if the biopsy result you get is accurate—but the tissue sample came *from someone else's body*?

Yes, it happens. A study of more than 13,000 prostate biopsies found that switched or contaminated samples caused the wrong patient to be told he had cancer approximately three times in 1,000. Additionally, three times in 1,000, a patient is told he doesn't have cancer when in fact he does. And there's no reason to assume that such mix-ups are limited to prostate biopsies.

Lab mix-ups such as these can have catastrophic consequences. A healthy person might be subjected to life-altering treatments, including surgery, chemotherapy and/or radiation, for someone else's medical problem. Meanwhile, the person who actually has this major medical problem might be told that he is fine, delaying potentially lifesaving treatments.

What to do: When the stakes of a biopsy are high, ask your doctor, "Does it make sense to do a DNA test to confirm that the tissue that was tested originated from me?" Some private labs that do DNA testing for criminal investigations also test to make sure that biopsied tissue samples truly came from the patients who received the results. This type of DNA test typically is covered by health insurance—contact your insurance provider for details. If not, expect it to cost several hundred dollars.

Example: Strand Diagnostics, a reputable DNA-testing lab that is accredited by the FBI and CLIA, charges $290 (KnowError.com).

5 Tests That Tell Your *Real* Risk for Heart Disease

James de Lemos, MD, a professor of internal medicine in the division of cardiology at UT Southwestern Medical Center, Dallas. He is the current medical director of the Dallas Heart Study.

Everyone's familiar with the traditional risk factors for heart disease. There is elevated cholesterol...high blood pressure...and diabetes.

What you might not realize is that these measures are not very effective at predicting *who* will have a heart attack. More than half of cardiovascular "events," including heart attacks, occur in patients who would not be considered at high risk based on the usual risk factors. Another shortcoming is that these factors address only one particular type of heart disease (from atherosclerosis, or plaque buildup in the arteries) even though there are other, equally serious heart threats.

A better approach: A simple, relatively inexpensive panel of tests that can identify your risk for a broader range of heart issues, including death from heart disease, as well as heart attack, stroke, heart failure (an inability of the heart to pump blood efficiently) and atrial fibrillation, or AF (an irregular heartbeat that increases risk not only for heart-related death but also for stroke). The panel of tests can even estimate future risks in patients with none of the usual risk factors.

Why it works: Each of the tests detects abnormal processes that affect the heart. But their real strength lies in their collective value. When the tests are combined, they provide an accurate assessment of your risk of developing heart disease within the next 10 years.

These tests improve upon the performance of the Heart Disease Risk Calculator, CVRiskCalculator.com, created by the American College of Cardiology and the American Heart Association. (If you know your blood pressure and cholesterol numbers, you can do this online test yourself.)

WHAT'S BEEN MISSED

If you worry about heart disease (or already have it), you've probably been told to keep your cholesterol down, stop smoking, manage your blood pressure, etc. It's good advice for everyone, but the benefits mainly involve atherosclerotic cardiovascular disease.

Many people have taken this advice, which is why the prevalence of clot-related heart attacks (as well as stroke) has declined in recent years. But there's been an *increase* in the rates of heart failure and AF, conditions that are time-consuming and expensive to treat—and are often fatal. The traditional cardiovascular risk factors don't affect your odds of getting AF or heart failure.

The five-test panel can give a better view of cardiovascular risks than the currently used methods. It's particularly useful for people who appear to be in good health and don't have any of the usual risk factors—but who want to ensure that their hearts stay as healthy as possible.

A BROADER VIEW

Each of the five tests below reflects a different aspect of heart health. Used individually, the tests are only modestly useful. Their real predictive strength is additive. You might want to do a baseline battery of these tests in your mid-40s and then again on a schedule your doctor suggests. *The five heart tests to have...*

• **A 12-lead EKG.** An electrocardiogram (EKG) measures voltage (the electrical activity created by each heartbeat) using electrodes placed on the chest. Someone with an abnormally enlarged heart will show high voltage. An enlarged heart isn't always dangerous—it often occurs in highly trained athletes in excellent health. But in average adults, an enlarged heart can increase the risk for heart failure, blood clots and cardiac arrest. It can also indicate if someone has had a silent heart attack (one that happens without noticeable symptoms).

• **Coronary calcium scan.** This low-radiation CT scan looks for calcium deposits in the arteries—a sign of cholesterol plaque buildup and future heart risk.

• **C-reactive protein (CRP) blood test.** Elevated CRP (above 3 mg/L) indicates inflammation in your body and can be a marker for increased risk for coronary artery disease.

• **NT-proBNP blood test.** BNP (B-type natriuretic peptide) is a hormone produced by the heart. It's a protective hormone, so levels rise when the heart is under stress. Levels higher than 100 pg/mL indicate that there might be stress or strain within the chambers of the heart—a sign that heart failure is developing or getting worse.

• **High-sensitivity troponin T blood test.** Troponin T is a protein that's released when the heart muscle is damaged. Hospitals test for it to diagnose heart attacks. The newer, higher-sensitivity test can detect the smallest amounts of damage to the heart muscle caused by high blood pressure, infection or even a heart attack that's so minor that a patient never experiences symptoms.

WHAT THE RESEARCH SHOWS

With the exception of the high-sensitivity troponin T test (which only recently received FDA approval), none of these tests are new. Cardiologists have used them individually for years. But they've only recently been tested *together* as a tool for predicting cardiovascular risks.

Important recent finding: Researchers looked at nearly 9,000 participants from the Dallas Heart Study and the Multi-Ethnic Study of Atherosclerosis for a study that appeared earlier this year in the journal *Circulation*. The participants, who were followed for more than 10 years, were screened to be sure they had no cardiovascular disease, and all were given the five-test panel at the beginning of the study.

Results: Patients with one abnormal test result (approximately 30%) were about three to four times more likely to be diagnosed with one of the heart conditions described earlier. The risk was sixfold higher in those with two abnormal tests...12 times higher in those with three abnormal tests...and more than 20 times higher in the 5% with four or five abnormal tests. Even after accounting for traditional risk factors such as high blood pressure and weight, people with high scores had five to six times the risk for future heart incidents than those with scores of zero.

SHOULD YOU GET TESTED?

One out of every four deaths in the US is caused by heart disease. Coronary artery disease, commonly linked to smoking, high cholesterol and genetics, is the most prevalent form, but heart failure, AF and other cardiovascular diseases affect millions of Americans.

The five-test panel is the first approach that permits a global view of risk. Previously, there have not been good predictive strategies. Patients who are given the five tests—which will be used along with the traditional tests for cholesterol, blood pressure, etc.—will have the clearest sense of their future risks. Identifying the risk for heart failure is particularly important because this condition will eventually affect about 25% of Americans…it carries the highest cardiovascular mortality rate…and it isn't predicted by the "standard" risk factors.

For now, we mainly recommend the panel for individuals without obvious risk factors who want to do everything possible to protect their hearts…those with a family history of heart disease…or those interested in the most accurate information about future risk, for example. If you already know you're at risk, the extra information may not be as useful, since your doctor would recommend the same healthful strategies—weight loss, a healthier diet, lower blood pressure and cholesterol, etc.—in either case.

In the future: The panel could be used to target existing treatments and to encourage at-risk patients to make lifestyle changes.

Example: The diabetes medicine *empagliflozin* (Jardiance) can reduce heart failure by 35%, but it's expensive. The cost could be justified for diabetics who learn that their heart-failure risk is high. Similarly, heart patients with abnormal test results might be more motivated to get serious about weight loss, fitness, healthy eating and other lifestyle changes.

The panel isn't expensive. You can expect to pay about $50 to $100 for the calcium scan…$25 to $50 for each blood test…and $50 to $100 for an EKG. The entire panel might be offered for about $400. Insurance companies may cover the costs—but check first.

Drugs That Can Turn Deadly: Is Your Med Making You Suicidal?

Jack E. Fincham, PhD, RPh, professor of pharmaceutical and administrative sciences, Presbyterian College School of Pharmacy, Clinton, South Carolina. Dr. Fincham has been a teacher and researcher for more than 30 years and has served as an adviser to the FDA and other federal agencies. He is the regional editor for North America for *International Journal of Pharmacy Practice.*

Americans use a lot of medications, filling prescriptions and buying over-the-counter (OTC) drugs several *billion times* each year. All these medications come with potential benefits *and* risks. But in the ubiquitous TV and print ads targeted to consumers, the benefits get much more attention than the risks.

Surprising danger you should know about: The use of certain medications is linked to suicidal thinking. That's right—a medication that you take to feel better might twist your thoughts, suddenly and powerfully, so that you feel bad enough to consider ending your life.

My analysis: When I recently completed a search of Clinical Pharmacology powered by ClinicalKey, a trusted database of drug information, this potential side effect is listed for 188 different drugs, including both prescription and OTC medications that are taken by several million Americans. Use of certain drugs with this possible side effect has also been linked to increased risk for suicide attempts and completed suicides.

To be fair, just because this possible side effect is listed does not mean that a drug always causes suicidal thinking…nor that the drug is to blame if this frightening problem does occur. But it does mean that cases have shown up—either in clinical trials conducted before the drug was approved or in reports sent to FDA regulators after it hit the market.

Unfortunately, it is impossible to say with any certainty how often people experience this (or any other) side effect in real-world use. That's because not everyone having a problem reports it, nor do regulators hear from people who have no problems with the drug.

Still, if suicidal thinking is a possible side effect of a drug you're taking for, say, depression, asthma, allergies or acne, it's something you want to know so that you, your doctor and the people close to you can be on the alert—and fully consider all the risks and benefits of that medication or alternatives.

Important: Do not stop taking a medication your doctor has prescribed without checking with the doctor or pharmacist. Some drugs may have additional side effects if stopped abruptly.

DRUGS ON THE DANGER LIST

Among the medications that have been linked to suicidal thinking...

• ***Montelukast* (Singulair).** Singulair is the best known of a group of medicines known as *leukotriene inhibitors*. Usually taken in pill form, it is used to treat asthma and, in some cases, nasal allergies. Other drugs in this class include *zafirlukast* (Accolate) and *zileuton* (Zyflo).

Since 2009, the FDA has required these drugs to carry labels saying that suicidal thinking and actions (and mental health problems such as anxiety and depression) have been reported in some patients.

My advice: Assuming you've talked with your doctor about the risks and potential benefits and have decided to use a leukotriene inhibitor, stay alert for any changes in your typical feelings and thoughts. If any occur, it may be that you could safely use another drug, such as a beta-agonist, or switch to something else entirely, such as an inhaled corticosteroid. These medications have not been linked to suicidal thinking.

• **Antidepressants.** While studies in older adults have not found a definitive link between antidepressant use and suicidal thinking, studies in children, teens and adults under age 25 have been concerning enough to lead the FDA to put so-called black-box warnings (the strongest kind) about the possible risks for young people on all antidepressants.

It's unclear why young people might be especially vulnerable to such a drug side effect. Perhaps medical providers and parents are more vigilant and more likely to report known suicidal thoughts or attempts when the patient is young. Or perhaps young brains react differently to the drugs. Whatever the reason, the FDA says the risk appears greatest in the early weeks of treatment or right after a dose is increased or decreased.

My advice: When anyone you know—but particularly a young person—is taking an antidepressant, be alert for warning signs, including worsening depression...talk of suicide...sleeplessness...agitation...and social withdrawal.

• ***Varenicline* (Chantix).** This prescription pill can help some people quit smoking. But for years, the FDA has required this medication to be labeled with a black-box warning alerting users that the drug has been linked with serious mental health problems, including suicidal thinking and behavior.

In 2016, citing new information, the FDA removed the strong warning, saying that the benefits of using Chantix to quit smoking outweighed the possible mental health risks and that those risks appear to be lower than previously suspected.

However, the risk for suicidal thinking continues to be mentioned on the manufacturer's website.

What may not be brought to your attention: Some of the best smoking-cessation tools, including nicotine-replacement products such as gums and patches, are available without a prescription and have not been linked to suicidal thinking. In-person and telephone counseling (call 800-QUIT-NOW) also can help some smokers.

My advice: If you're uneasy about taking Chantix, try one of the other approaches mentioned above. But do stay resolved to quit smoking!

OTHER DRUGS

The list of widely used medications linked to suicidal thoughts or actions also includes the OTC allergy drugs *cetirizine* (Zyrtec) and *levocetirizine* (Xyzal)...the acne drug *isotretinoin* (Accutane)...the nerve pain drug *pregabalin* (Lyrica)...and a variety of medications, including *carbamazepine* (Tegretol), that are used to treat seizures. Studies differ on which seizure medications are associated with the risk, so the FDA requires warnings on all of them.

Good rule of thumb: If you just don't feel "right" when starting any new medication or a new dose of a medication, talk to your pharmacist, physician or other health-care provider. You also can read about the possible side effects of any medication at FDA.gov—search "Index to Drug-Specific Information."

Critically important: If you or someone you know is having suicidal thoughts, immediately call your doctor...go to a hospital emergency room...or call the confidential and toll-free National Suicide Prevention Lifeline at 800-273-TALK (8255). Help is available!

If You Take This Drug, Don't Eat This Food!

Torey Armul, MS, RD, CSSD, LD, a spokesperson for the Academy of Nutrition and Dietetics. She counsels clients on sports nutrition, weight management and pregnancy and family nutrition through her private practice in Columbus, Ohio. eatrightPRO.org

If you're one of the nearly 70% of Americans taking prescription drugs, you may need to carefully watch what you eat. That's because the nutrients in food can interact with drugs—often in harmful ways. Certain nutrients make certain drugs less effective than they should be...while conversely, some nutrients can make certain drugs too powerful. Also, because some drugs can deplete your nutrient stores, there are some foods that you should probably eat more of to avoid nutritional deficiencies.

If you're taking any of the following prescription drugs, watch what you eat as described. As always, if you are on medication, check with your doctor before making any changes to your medications or supplements.

IF YOU TAKE AN ANTIBIOTIC

Watch out for dairy and salads. Two types of antibiotics—quinolones, which include *ciprofloxacin* (Cipro), *norfloxacin* (Noroxin) and *ofloxacin* (Ocuflox), and tetracyclines (*doxycycline, minocycline* and *tetracycline*)—may be poorly absorbed, and therefore not work as well, when combined with calcium. To prevent this interaction, wait two to four hours between taking an antibiotic and consuming a calcium supplement or calcium-rich foods such as milk, yogurt and other dairy products.

The absorption of antibiotics also can be decreased by large amounts of magnesium. Avoid taking a magnesium supplement or eating large amounts of magnesium-rich foods, such as leafy greens, one hour before and two hours after taking an antibiotic. Use of antibiotics also may lead to magnesium deficiency, characterized by weakness and muscle spasms. A healthy diet with plenty of fruits and vegetables, spaced two hours apart from your antibiotic medications, can help prevent magnesium deficiency.

IF YOU TAKE AN ANTIDEPRESSANT

Watch out for cheese, cured meat and alcohol. Certain antidepressants can be harmful when paired with foods such as chocolate, aged cheeses, cured meats and alcoholic drinks, which all contain *tyramine*, which helps to regulate blood pressure. Tyramine levels are controlled by an enzyme called *monoamine oxidase* that is blocked by antidepressants

EASY TO DO...

To Swallow Pills Easily...

Place the capsule on your tongue, take a sip of water without swallowing...then tilt your chin down toward your chest and swallow. This method helps about 90% of people who try it.

Harvard Health Blog, Health.Harvard.edu/blog.

called monoamine oxidase inhibitors (MAO-Is). When high-tyramine foods are consumed by people taking MAOIs, tyramine can build up in the body and cause dangerously high blood pressure.

Many antidepressants don't affect tyramine levels, so check with your physician or pharmacist before making significant changes to your diet.

Folate has been shown to improve patients' response to some antidepressants. Talk to your doctor about whether increasing your folate intake could enhance your treatment. Folate-rich foods include leafy greens, asparagus, brussels sprouts, citrus fruits, beans, legumes and folic acid–fortified cereals.

Omega-3 fatty acids also may improve the response to antidepressant medications. *Example:* The combination of an antidepressant and *eicosapentaenoic acid* (EPA) was shown to improve symptoms of depression in some people better than an antidepressant alone. The best food sources of EPA are fatty fish such as mackerel, salmon, herring, anchovies and white tuna. Fish oil supplements also are excellent sources of EPA.

IF YOU TAKE ESTROGEN

You're at risk for vitamin depletion. Estrogen frequently is used as part of hormone replacement therapy for women after menopause. However, it can reduce the body's folate, magnesium, vitamin B-6 and vitamin B-12 levels. A woman who follows a healthful, balanced diet is unlikely to be deficient in these nutrients even with estrogen therapy. However, someone with an unhealthy diet or limited access to fruits and vegetables and who is on estrogen therapy may benefit from supplementation with these nutrients.

IF YOU TAKE BLOOD PRESSURE MEDICATION

Watch out for bananas, tomatoes and leafy greens. ACE-inhibitor drugs are commonly used to treat high blood pressure. Numerous studies have found that these drugs, which include Capoten, Vasotec, Zestril, Monopril and others, cause zinc depletion. They bind to zinc and make it unavailable for use in the body, limiting its valuable role in wound healing, new cell growth and immune function.

Someone taking an ACE inhibitor over the long term may benefit from zinc supplementation. Eating foods that contain zinc, such as oysters, beef, poultry, beans, yogurt and zinc-fortified cereal, also will protect against deficiency.

ACE inhibitors can interfere with the body's potassium levels, causing a buildup of potassium over time. Get frequent blood work to make sure that your potassium levels are in check. If your potassium is high, adjust your diet as needed to minimize the intake of high-potassium foods such as bananas, tomatoes, potatoes and leafy greens.

IF YOU TAKE CHOLESTEROL MEDICATION

Watch out for grapefruit—and check your vitamin D level. Statin drugs are widely used to reduce cholesterol levels in the blood. However, cholesterol is required for the production of vitamin D, which helps with immune function, building strong bones and the absorption of calcium.

Research is mixed on statins and vitamin D. Some data show that statins decrease the level of vitamin D in the body, while other data show just the opposite. There is some evidence that statins affect levels of the other fat-soluble vitamins A, E and K, but more research is needed to understand this relationship. If you take a statin, your best bet is to eat a variety of nutrient-rich foods, including plenty of fruits and vegetables, and talk to your doctor about any supplements you may want to take.

Better understood is the interaction between statins and grapefruit. The juice in grapefruit, in particular, amplifies the amount of certain statins in the blood, which increases the risk for statin side effects such as muscle pain and liver and kidney damage. If you're taking *simvastatin* (Zocor) or *atorvastatin* (Lipitor), avoid grapefruit or ask your doctor about changing to a statin that is less affected by the fruit.

IF YOU USE BIRTH-CONTROL DRUGS

You're at risk for vitamin depletion. Several studies have found that birth-control drugs are associated with lower folate levels. Folate is critical for the prevention of some neural tube defects in early pregnancy, and hormone-based birth control doesn't provide perfect protection against getting pregnant, so adequate levels of folate are important for all women of childbearing age who are sexually active. Heartburn medications, such as Tagamet and Pepcid, and nonsteroidal anti-inflammatory drugs (NSAIDs), such as Advil and Aleve, also can reduce levels of folate in the body.

The use of birth-control drugs has similarly been linked to depleted levels of B vitamins, vitamin C, magnesium and zinc. Choose fruits and vegetables, whole grains, fish, poultry, beans, nuts and healthy fats, along with a multivitamin, for optimal health.

Ibuprofen Warning

Taking unsafe doses of *ibuprofen* is very common. About 15% of adults who use the medication—primarily over-the-counter—take too much, either at one time or over 24 hours on a weekly basis. That can lead to stomach bleeding and kidney problems.

Mistakes: Taking two pills when a single pill delivers the standard 200-mg dose or taking several medications that all contain ibuprofen—or believing it is safe to choose your own dose. It's not.

Daniel W. Kaufman, ScD, an epidemiologist at Slone Epidemiology Center of Boston University, Massachusetts, and lead author of a study of 1,326 ibuprofen users, published in *Pharmacoepidemiology & Drug Safety.*

Digital Pills Help Compliance

A new digital version of the antipsychotic Abilify, used for schizophrenia, has an embedded sensor to tell doctors whether patients have taken their medicine and when they did so. The digital enhancement is designed to reduce noncompliance, which costs an estimated $100 billion a year because patients who do not take medicine get sicker and need more treatment or hospitalization. Patients must sign consent forms before being given the new form of the pill. Some doctors and privacy-rights advocates are concerned that the system may seem coercive to patients. Advocates say the pill is designed for patients who want to take their medicine but tend to forget.

Roundup of experts on the recent Food and Drug Administration approval of the digital pill, reported at MSN.com.

Best Time to Get Your Flu Shot

Get your flu shot early in the morning. In a recent finding, senior citizens who received their flu shots between 9 am and 11 am had a higher antibody response to the flu one month later compared with those who had their shots between 3 pm and 5 pm.

Study of 276 senior citizens by researchers at the University of Birmingham, UK, published in *Vaccine.*

ON THE HORIZON...

Drug Delivery Breakthrough

New microparticles can deliver, and store, multiple drugs at the same time.

Implication: A onetime injection could allow for the release of vaccines or other drugs at specific times, possibly over years.

Science.

Smart Bandage Coming

A preloaded "smart" bandage could contain antibiotics, painkillers and other medications to treat chronic wounds and battlefield injuries. A signal from a wireless device would trigger the release of one or more of the required drugs.

Advanced Functional Materials.

A Better Shingles Vaccine

Adults age 50 and up should be vaccinated against shingles with the new vaccine Shingrix. (The original vaccine, Zostavax, was given starting at age 60.) Shingrix is more effective—97% versus 51%—at preventing shingles, caused by the chicken pox virus. Get it even if you don't remember having chicken pox or have received Zostavax. You'll need two shots, two to six months apart. Side effects include muscle aches, fatigue and soreness at the injection site.

Kathleen Dooling, MD, MPH, a medical officer at Centers for Disease Control and Prevention, Atlanta.

Is Your Surgeon Double-Booked?

"Double-booked" surgeries are more likely to lead to complications. When a surgeon oversees two operations at the same time, rates of serious complications, including infections, rise.

Results: Complication rates are 80% to 90% higher if a surgeon oversees two operations for as little as 30 minutes.

Self-defense: Before consenting to surgery, make sure yours is not double-booked.

Bheeshma Ravi, MD, PhD, a hip surgeon at Sunnybrook Health Sciences Centre, Toronto, and leader of a study of 91,000 hip operations, published in *JAMA Internal Medicine*.

Music Eases Postsurgical Pain

In a recent study, 60 postsurgical spinal-fusion patients got standard medical care, including pain medications. One group also received a 30-minute patient-preferred, live music therapy session within about 72 hours of surgery. The medication-only group saw a slight increase in pain, while the music group reported a significant decrease.

Theory: Music reduces tension associated with pain.

If you're facing surgery: Consider music therapy, or listen to your favorite tunes during recovery.

John Mondanaro, MA, clinical director at Louis Armstrong department of music therapy, Mount Sinai Beth Israel Hospital, New York City.

Acupuncture in the ER

A large study conducted in Australia found that acupuncture rivaled drugs for the long-term relief of pain (back pain, ankle sprains, etc.) in ER patients—without the risk for addiction.

Medical Journal of Australia.

Beware of Dirty Gloves

When certified nursing assistants (CNAs) working in long-term-care facilities, such as nursing homes, were studied, they failed to change gloves at 66% of "glove change points"—for example, after handling body fluids or between patients. *Bottom line:* Don't be afraid to remind the CNA, nurse or doctor to don new gloves when caring for you or a loved one.

Deborah Patterson Burdsall, PhD, RN-BC, CIC, adjunct assistant professor, University of Iowa College of Nursing, Iowa City.

Warm Weather Increases Infection Risk

According to a recent study, as the weather becomes warmer, the risk of developing an infection at the site of a surgical wound increases. Researchers found that there were 26.5% more cases of surgical-site infection (SSI) in August, compared with January, and that for every five-degree Fahrenheit increase in average monthly temperature, the risk for hospital readmission for an SSI increased by 2.1%.

Philip M. Polgreen, MD, associate professor of internal medicine and epidemiology, University of Iowa, Iowa City, and senior author of a study of more than 55 million hospitalizations in more than 2,500 hospitals over 13 years, published in *Infection Control & Hospital Epidemiology*.

Hospice Helps You *Live* Better

John Mastrojohn III, RN, MSN, MBA, executive vice president and chief operating officer of the National Hospice and Palliative Care Organization, NHPCO.org, the largest nonprofit membership organization representing hospice and palliative care programs and professionals in the US. His scientific papers have appeared in *Journal of Pain Symptom Management*. To learn more about hospice, consult CaringInfo.org.

Everyone's life ends. But not everyone has the same quality of life at the end of life. Many are in pain or not comforted physically, emotionally or spiritually. Others die in a hospital when they would have wanted to die at home, surrounded by loved ones in a beloved place.

Yet sadly, countless individuals who could receive hospice care don't get it. Many don't even know it's an option. And among those who do use hospice, many take advantage of it only in the last week or two of life. But research shows that hospice can provide important benefits—and for a much longer period of time than just the final few days.

Scientific evidence: In a study published in *Journal of Clinical Oncology*, researchers from Harvard Medical School and two cancer centers talked with 2,307 family members of individuals who had died.

Results: When hospice was used, patients had more appropriate relief from pain, better symptom relief and higher-quality end-of-life care...they received care that was more in accordance with their wishes...and they were more likely to have died in a preferred place (usually at home, rather than in the hospital).

What you and your loved ones need to know about hospice care...

THE FACETS OF HOSPICE CARE

Even though most people assume that they know what hospice is, few can explain exactly when it's used in the course of an illness or how it works. Medicare, the main payer of hospice care, defines hospice as a system of care for people who have approximately six months or less to live if the disease runs its normal course. In order for a patient to elect hospice care, he/she must be certified as meeting the criteria described above by an attending physician and the hospice medical director. Over 90% of people in hospice receive care at home or in the place they reside.

Hospice care is delivered by a team of doctors, nurses, home-health aides, social workers, therapists, chaplains, counselors and trained volunteers. The care plan varies according to the patient's needs, but it is not around-the-clock care (except for in the rare cases when continuous home care is needed for a brief period of crisis, such as uncontrolled pain). For that reason, family caregivers are an integral part of the care team.

Managing the patient's pain and/or controlling symptoms is a priority, and hospice provides medication and medical equipment and supplies (such as a hospital bed and/or oxygen) for these purposes. During hospice care, curative treatment for the illness itself is discontinued. *In addition, hospice care...*

- **Provides emotional support to address the myriad of feelings and issues affecting hospice patients and their families.** Spiritual support is also offered for those patients who choose it and can be delivered by the hospice and/or the patient's clergy or other faith leader.

- **Offers the surviving family bereavement care and counseling,** typically for 13 months following the death of a patient. These services include written materials, phone calls, visitation and support groups.

Important: Though the Medicare hospice benefit is the predominate payer of hospice services, managed care and private insurers will often cover hospice services.

DEBUNKING MYTHS

Common myths about hospice stop many people from getting the end-of-life care they need. *For example…*

MYTH #1: **Hospice mainly serves terminal cancer patients.** Only 37% of hospice patients have cancer. Other terminal diagnoses include dementia, heart disease, lung disease, stroke, kidney disease, liver disease, HIV/AIDS and others.

MYTH #2: **The doctor must bring up hospice.** Anybody can inquire about and refer to hospice—the patient, a family member, a counselor or the doctor. But only a physician can certify that a patient is eligible for hospice care.

MYTH #3: **The hospice patient can't keep his/her own doctor.** Hospice encourages a patient to keep his primary physician. The primary physician typically knows the patient best and can consult with the hospice medical director and other hospice team members to provide the best care. Patients may still visit their primary care physician if they choose.

MYTH #4: **Hospice care hastens death.** Hospice neither hastens nor postpones dying. Just as doctors and midwives lend support and expertise during the time of childbirth, hospice provides specialized knowledge and skill for patients and families at the end of life.

MYTH #5: **Hospice means giving up.** Hospice is not about hopelessness or giving up. For example, if a patient decides to seek curative care for any disease, he can revoke the hospice benefit at any time and return to curative therapy or even try a new therapy.

FINDING HOSPICE CARE

All hospices are licensed by the state in which they operate and certified by Medicare. But not all hospices are alike. In the US, 60% are independent…20% are part of a hospital system…16% are part of a home-health agency…and 4% are part of a nursing home. Hospices are both large and small, rural and urban, and range from for-profit national chains to local nonprofits.

To find a hospice program anywhere in the US: Use the National Hospice and Palliative Care Organization's "Find a Provider Tool" at Moments.nhpco.org/find-a-hospice. Once you (or the certifying doctor) contact the hospice, enrollment should happen quickly. *Helpful:* Look for a hospice that is accredited by an independent accrediting organization, such as the Accreditation Commission for Health Care…the Community Health Accreditation Program…or The Joint Commission.

My advice: Have the conversation about end-of-life care with your loved ones early so you understand their wishes. If you decide that you want hospice care, once you've chosen the program, you'll have an initial consultation to develop a plan of care, typically with a hospice nurse.

If the patient is comfortable with the idea, I encourage not only the family caregiver (such as a spouse) but other family members (such as adult children) to attend the initial consultation. In that way, all those involved with the patient's care will hear the same information regarding hospice care and will have the opportunity to get their questions answered. This approach also helps the hospice nurse understand the patient's needs and develop a personalized plan of care.

Get Acute Care at Home

Some acute care that once required hospitalization for conditions such as serious infections or asthma can now be provided at home just as effectively and at half the cost. Adults who have home-based care also are more active and receive fewer tests. While acute home hospital care is not common in the US, some Medicare Advantage plans now offer it.

David M. Levine, MD, a clinician-investigator at Brigham and Women's Hospital and Harvard Medical School, both in Boston, and lead author of a study of 20 patients, published in *Journal of General Internal Medicine.*

3

Common Conditions & Solutions

5 Embarrassing Health Problems with *Very Easy* Solutions

Do you have an embarrassing health problem? Unfortunately, embarrassment often prevents people from seeking solutions to their problems. And that's a shame because there are simple, fast, natural solutions for most embarrassing health problems.

Caution: If nondrug remedies don't work after a week or two, see your doctor—your health problem may have a serious cause that requires medical attention.

BAD BREATH

Sulfur-generating bacteria in the mouth cause most cases of bad breath. And those bacteria usually are on your tongue.

Solution: Use a tongue scraper.

Scientific evidence: A study in *Journal of Periodontology* showed that tongue scraping reduced "volatile sulfur compounds" by 75%, while cleaning with a toothbrush reduced them by 45%.

What to do: First, buy a tongue scraper, available for less than $10 online and in drugstores.

Your goal is to remove the creamy-looking white, brown or orange layer of gunk on your tongue with the scraper. Gently but firmly scrape both the top and the sides of your tongue (but not the underside) from back to front. Start scraping as far back on the tongue as you can without gagging. If the gunk isn't completely gone, go over the same area until it is removed. After you are done, rinse the scraper.

Bill Gottlieb, CHC, a health coach certified by the American Association of Drugless Practitioners and former editor in chief of Rodale Books and Prevention Magazine Health Books. He is author of 16 health books including *Bottom Line's Speed Healing*. His website is BillGottliebHealth.com.

Also helpful: In a scientific study published in *The Journal of Clinical Dentistry*, chewing gum with cinnamon essential oils reduced sulfur compounds in the mouth by more than 50%. And in a recent study on bad breath, published in *Archives of Oral Biology*, scientists tested 10 essential oils and found that cinnamon oil was the most effective in reducing sulfur in the mouth.

Good product: Cinnamon-flavored, sugarless Spry gum, which contains bacteria-reducing *xylitol*. Chew it after every meal.

PASSING GAS

You *need* to pass gas—it's a natural part of digestion, and the average person does it anywhere from six to 21 times a day. But passing it excessively is uncomfortable and embarrassing.

Most excessive passing of gas is caused by *dysbiosis*—an imbalance in intestinal bacteria, with "bad" bacteria such as *Clostridium difficile* outnumbering "friendly" bacteria such as *Lactobacillus acidophilus*.

Solution: Take a daily probiotic, a supplement containing friendly bacteria.

Scientific evidence: Researchers from the Mayo Clinic and other institutions analyzed the results of six studies on probiotics involving more than 560 people—and found that the supplement "significantly improved" flatulence.

Also helpful: If you're about to be in a social situation where gas is a no-no, take a preventive dose of activated charcoal, which works by binding with toxins (including unhealthful bacteria) and ushering them out of the body. Follow the dosage recommendations on the label.

ANAL ITCHING

There are many possible causes of anal itching including diarrhea, incontinence, psoriasis, genital warts or a yeast infection. But one common cause is *hemorrhoids*, the swollen and inflamed anal veins that affect half of Americans over age 50. (If you have pain and bleeding with the itching, a hemorrhoid is the likely cause. But confirm the cause of anal itching with your doctor.)

Solution: To ease itching from hemorrhoids, one vein-strengthening food factor works particularly well—hesperidin, a flavonoid (plant pigment) found in citrus fruits.

Scientific evidence: A study in *British Journal of Surgery* analyzed 14 other studies on flavonoids and hemorrhoids, involving more than 1,500 people. The scientists found that consuming flavonoids cut the risk of itching from hemorrhoids by 35%—and also significantly reduced bleeding and pain.

What to do: Look for a supplement containing diosmin, a specially processed form of hesperidin. Take 500 milligrams (mg), twice daily. Diosmin is very safe, but a few people may experience intestinal discomfort—if that happens, stop taking the supplement.

Also helpful: Other ways to help prevent and heal hemorrhoids include drinking more water (60 ounces a day is a good goal)...increasing your intake of fiber-rich foods such as fruits, vegetables and whole grains...and regular exercise, such as brisk walking.

LEAKING AFTER YOU PEE

A few drops of urine leak out after you think you're done using the bathroom, leaving a wet spot. That embarrassing scenario is called *post-micturition dribble*, and it affects an estimated 12% of American men and 9% of American women. The cause usually is weakness and loss of tone in the bulbocavernosus muscle, which squeezes to force urine out.

Solution: Strengthen the muscles of the *pelvic floor*, the area between the genitals and the pelvis, where the bulbocavernosus is located.

You might be familiar with Kegel exercises to strengthen the pelvic wall—but most people do them wrong. *Here's how to do them right...*

- **First, locate the muscles of your pelvic floor** by slowing or stopping the stream of urine the next time you go to the bathroom. When you're doing Kegels correctly, you will feel the same sensation you feel when stopping your stream of urine—a pulling sensation in your rectum or (for women) a lifting sensation in your vagina.
- **Several times a day**—standing, sitting or lying down—squeeze the muscles and hold the contraction for 10 seconds. (If you can't hold

the contraction that long, start with a count of three and build up to a count of 10.) Breathe normally, and check to see that your abdomen is relaxed. (Holding your breath or squeezing the muscles in your abdomen or buttocks—neither of which isolates the muscles of your pelvic floor—are common errors.)

• **Do 45 Kegels a day—**15 Kegels in a row, three times a day. You can do them during other activities, such as taking a shower, brushing your teeth or eating.

DANDRUFF

The flaking and itchiness of dandruff are caused by overproduction of a substance that's called *sebum* from glands in the scalp. These glands typically are hyperactive when the scalp is excessively dry. While dandruff shampoos control symptoms, they don't address the underlying problem. In fact, they often contain harsh cleansers that destroy the scalp's delicate balance of water and oil, further irritating the scalp and perpetuating the problem.

Solution: I often recommend a simple, natural, homemade antidandruff lotion, developed by aromatherapist Roberta Wilson. It normalizes the water- and oil-secreting glands of the scalp, helping to eliminate dandruff.

How to make it: To eight ounces of unscented, mild shampoo, add 10 drops of tea tree oil, eight drops of cedarwood oil, six drops of pine oil, six drops of rosemary oil, four drops of clary sage oil and four drops of lemon oil. Use the shampoo two or three times weekly, leaving it on for a minute or two each time. You should see results within a week or two.

Caution: If you have very sensitive skin, test each essential oil first. Put a dab on the inside of your wrist. If there is any redness or irritation after a few minutes, don't use it.

TAKE NOTE...

Leak When You Cough? Try This...

When 500 women received 18 real or sham electroacupuncture treatments (acupuncture with electrical stimulation) with the needles placed on the lower back over a six-week period, two-thirds of those receiving the actual treatments had a decrease of 50% or more in the amount of leakage. For longer-lasting effects, an additional round of electroacupuncture is recommended.

Theory: Acupuncture may strengthen the muscles in the pelvic floor that help control the bladder.

To find an acupuncturist: Consult the National Certification Commission for Acupuncture and Oriental Medicine, NCCAOM.org.

Baoyan Liu, MD, researcher, China Academy of Chinese Medical Sciences, Beijing.

Natural Cough Remedies That Work Better Than OTC Drugs

Gustavo Ferrer, MD, a pulmonologist in private practice in Weston, Florida. He is author of *Cough Cures: The Complete Guide to the Best Natural Remedies and Over-the-Counter Drugs for Acute and Chronic Coughs.* Dr. Ferrer grew up in Cuba, a culture that effectively utilizes herbal teas and folk remedies for coughs and colds.

It's enough to make you dizzy—hundreds of boxes and bottles lining the drugstore shelves, all promising to eradicate your cough...and perhaps also chest congestion, postnasal drip, sneezing and other related symptoms. Americans spend billions a year on over-the-counter (OTC) respiratory medications—including cough suppressants, decongestants and antihistamines. Coughs are also one of the top reasons why we see a doctor.

Here's a surprise...most of the time, it's all unnecessary. Why? Most acute coughs brought on by a cold or the flu go away on their own within a few days and don't require a doctor's care. Sometimes, though, a cough can linger as long as two or three weeks, so you want to take something for relief.

Here's the real bombshell: Most OTC cough remedies just don't work! Back in 2006, the American College of Chest Physicians concluded that there's no strong evidence of effectiveness for the vast majority of drugstore cough medications. In 2014, a Cochrane review of 29 clinical trials involving nearly 5,000 people reached the same conclusion. But they are heavily advertised, so people still buy them.

But don't despair. There is real help out there. Some OTC remedies really do relieve coughs—though not in the way you'd expect. Even better are natural cough remedies, using readily found ingredients, which are both effective and safe.

THESE OTC PRODUCTS MAY HELP

Nine times out of 10, acute cough symptoms are triggered by post-nasal drip—that annoying mucus trickling down the back of your throat. *These OTCs decrease secretions to ease postnasal drip...*

• **Antihistamines.** *Loratadine* (Claritin), *fexofenadine* (Allegra), *cetirizine* (Zyrtec) and *diphenhydramine* (Benadryl) block histamine, a naturally occurring chemical that provokes mucus production. They dry up mucus and decrease nasal secretions—even if you don't have an allergy.

Caution: They can cause water retention as a side effect. Avoid if you have glaucoma or prostate enlargement or are taking diuretics. Also, because these old-fashioned antihistamines can make you drowsy, you can become dependent on them to fall asleep.

My advice: Take half the recommended dose, for no more than a week.

• **Saline nasal spray.** Salt plus water—it doesn't get much more natural than that! The simple act of spraying this combination into nasal passages usually alleviates the stuffiness that can trigger constant hacking. Try versions that contain only these two active ingredients, such as Ocean Nasal Spray, Ayr Saline Nasal Mist or Little Remedies Saline Spray/Drops.

Caution: Avoid sprays containing *oxymetazoline* (Afrin), *phenylephrine* (Sudafed PE) or *xylometazoline* (Triaminic), which lead to "rebound congestion" when they wear off.

NATURAL REMEDIES FOR THE WIN

These natural cough relief remedies are your best bet for cough relief. They calm throat irritations, dry up mucus and boost the immune system—safely. *My top picks...*

• **Warm lemon and manukah honey "tea."** Everyone knows about the lemon/honey combo, which calms a cough while cutting mucus. But you can make it even more effective with *manukah* honey, a special kind from New Zealand that has strong antimicrobial properties, so it protects against the underlying cold virus. Regular raw honey also has antimicrobial properties. Blend a tablespoonful of honey with the juice from half a lemon in a cup of just-boiled water. For optimal benefit, drink it just before bedtime, when coughs typically rev up...and again in the morning.

• **Dark chocolate.** Most people have no idea that one of their favorite treats is also a natural cough suppressant—thanks to *theobromine*, a chemical component in chocolate. The darker the chocolate, the more theobromine, so aim for versions containing more than 65% cocoa. Eat a small square—about one-half to one ounce—two or three times a day.

Caution: Chocolate has caffeine, so don't eat it in the evening.

• **Beet and/or pineapple juice.** Both beet and pineapple juices have long been standbys for coughs due to bronchitis. Both help open bronchial passages and make it easier for your body to bring up excess mucus. Whichever you choose, a half cup (four ounces) is enough. It's fine to drink it two or three times a day. (*Note:* If you've been told to limit nitrates, avoid beet juice.)

• **Elderberry syrup.** Elderberry syrup, readily available in health-food stores, is a traditional remedy for colds, coughs and the flu. It acts as an expectorant and also has antiviral and antiflu properties. Take as directed on the package, up to three times a day. Dilute in water if that makes it easier to take.

Important: If your cough lasts beyond three weeks—or includes symptoms such as coughing up blood, significant shortness of breath, chest pain or persistent fever—see a doctor.

AVOID THESE OTC COUGH PRODUCTS

• **Cough suppressants.** A common ingredient is *dextromethorphan* (DXM), which was first introduced 60 years ago. It's found in popular brands including NyQuil, Coricidin HBP Cough & Cold, Delsym and Dimetapp DM. Not only is there no evidence that it works, it can provoke a narcotic-like "high" when taken in large amounts, leading to potential for abuse.

• **Cough expectorants.** *Guaifenesin*, the active ingredient in Mucinex, Robitussin, Tussin and Guaifenesin LA, doesn't have the narcotic-like downside of DXM, but there's no evidence that it works, either.

• **Combination products.** Most OTC remedies combine ingredients in the same product to treat a variety of symptoms. *Example:* DXM, guaifenesin, an antihistamine, plus *acetaminophen*. This kitchen-sink approach is a bad idea—you're treating symptoms you don't have with drugs you don't need. The biggest pitfall? You might be taking acetaminophen for a headache or fever and don't realize that it's also in your combo cough remedy...so you may exceed the safe daily limit, which increases the risk for liver damage.

3 Natural Sore Throat Fixes

Jamison Starbuck, ND, a naturopathic physician in family practice and writer/producer of *Dr. Starbuck's Health Tips for Kids*, a weekly program on Montana Public Radio, MTPR.org, both in Missoula. She is a past president of the American Association of Naturopathic Physicians and a contributing editor to *The Alternative Advisor: The Complete Guide to Natural Therapies and Alternative Treatments*. DrJamisonStarbuck.com

When a dry, achy feeling envelops the back of your throat, do you reach for a box of lozenges? Plenty of people do, but they're missing out on some highly effective natural cures. A sore throat can have lots of causes. Allergies, dehydration or exposure to polluted air could be to blame. A sore throat may, of course, also herald the beginning of a flu virus or a strep bacterial infection. Whatever the cause, you can try all three remedies below or one of the contrast hydrotherapies plus the honey and herb mix at the first sign of sore throat pain.

The first two of my favorite sore throat remedies rely on contrast hydrotherapy, a naturopathic technique that stimulates the immune system by using hot and cold water to move the blood. Hot water brings blood to the area where heat is applied. Cold water drives blood away from the area. When blood moves, new cells are brought to areas of the body that need attention. Fresh blood cells fight infection, reduce inflammation and revitalize the body.

CURE #1: **Throat wrap.**

What to do: Get a thin piece of cotton cloth, such as a dish towel, soak it in cold water, wring it out well and keep it nearby. Then soak a second cotton cloth in hot water, wring it out and wrap the hot towel around your neck in a wide band. *Caution:* Be sure the towel is not so hot that you burn yourself.

Cover the cloth with a dry wool scarf (for maximum warmth). Leave it on for two minutes, then quickly replace the hot towel with the cold towel, cover it with the wool scarf and leave it in place for 15 minutes. Remove the cold towel, then briskly rub your neck downward from jaw to shoulder. This stimulates the movement of lymphatic fluids to help rid the body of toxins. Cover your neck with dry, warm clothing, such as a turtleneck sweater or another dry scarf. Do the throat wrap one to three times daily.

CURE #2: **Footbaths.** Bet you're surprised, right? There is a reason why footbaths help a sore throat. This therapy stimulates a big movement of blood throughout the body, which speeds healing.

What to do: Fill a washbasin with hot water (enough to cover your ankles), and fill another with cold water. Start with hot water, and soak both feet for three minutes. Then immediately move your feet to the cold water, and soak for one minute. Go back and forth, three times each, ending with cold. During a sore throat episode, do a footbath at least twice daily.

Caution: People who have peripheral vascular disease, diabetes or a loss of sensation in their feet should not do hot/cold footbaths.

CURE #3: **Honey.** While it's not a cure-all, honey is a mild antiseptic and an anti-inflammatory, so it eases sore throats.

What to do: Mix together equal parts slippery elm powdered bark and honey (I like raw, local honey). Stir it up really well, and put a spoonful of the mixture in your mouth. Let it melt down the back of your throat. It's soothing and tasty, and you can do this as often as you wish until your sore throat is better. In my experience, this therapy is more effective than gargling with salt water.

Caution: Do not take slippery elm within two hours of taking medication—it can interfere with absorption. If you are pregnant, consult your doctor before taking slippery elm.

Note: If you develop a fever (101°F or above), have significant sore throat pain and/or red, swollen tonsils, sometimes with white spots on them, see your physician. You may have a strep infection and need an antibiotic.

Don't Make These Allergy Mistakes...

Common seasonal-allergy mistakes and...what to do instead...

Mistake: Opening windows, which lets pollen in. *Better:* Run the air conditioner, and use high-efficiency filters to trap pollen.

Mistake: Not taking regular antipollen steps. *Better:* Wash hair at the end of every day, keep pets clean, avoid hanging laundry outdoors.

Mistake: Neglecting your eyes, through which pollen often enters the body. *Better:* Wear sunglasses and a brimmed hat when outdoors, and use eye rinses regularly.

Mistake: Waiting too long to start on allergy medicines. *Better:* Take them at the start of pollen season instead of waiting for symptoms to get worse.

Mistake: Overusing nasal sprays. *Better:* Use them for no more than five days in a row to avoid irritating sinuses and the lining of the nose.

Clifford Bassett, MD, founder and medical director, Allergy and Asthma Care of New York, quoted at LiveScience.com.

Troubled by Sniffling... Runny Eyes? Dust Mites Could Be the Culprit

Michael L. Lewin, MD, an allergist who has been practicing for 30 years. He has offices in New York City and Wilton, Connecticut, and is a faculty member of Weill Cornell Medical College in New York City. LewinAllergy.com

More than half of all Americans test positive for at least one kind of allergen. But there's one culprit that often gets overlooked by allergy sufferers.

What you may not realize: Dust mites, which thrive in warm, humid weather, are one of the most common household triggers for allergies and asthma. Dust mites are tiny, eight-legged creatures that are too small to be seen by the naked eye, but they can wreak havoc if you are allergic to them.

Dust mites lurk in beds, carpets, draperies and upholstered furniture and surfaces. Their primary food source is human skin cells that we shed naturally. In fact, each of us sheds enough cells each day to feed one million dust mites. And depending on its age, a mattress can harbor up to 10 million dust mites! *What you need to know to protect yourself...*

ARE DUST MITES TO BLAME?

Allergies to dust mites are caused not by the mites themselves, but rather by their waste particles and dead body parts. Since we are constantly exposed to dust mites, those of us who have a dust mite allergy are likely to experience year-round symptoms. These can include sneezing...runny nose...red, itchy or watery eyes...stuffy nose...postnasal drip...and cough. (Eczema and asthma symptoms can be triggered or exacerbated by contact with dust mites.) Because dust mite allergy symptoms are so similar to those caused by other common allergens, such as pollen, some patients fail to recognize when the ubiquitous little creatures are the cause of their allergy symptoms or worsening symptoms due to another allergy.

If you have a dust mite allergy: You may notice that your symptoms are worse when you're in bed or when you first wake up in the morning. That's because of the high concentration of dust mites in mattresses and bedding. Your symptoms may also flare up when you're dusting or vacuuming—droppings can easily become airborne...or when the temperature and humidity are higher than usual.

EASY TESTS

There are a few testing methods that can determine whether you are allergic to dust mites.

The easiest is a skin-prick test: A drop of dust mite antigen is placed on the skin...the doctor lightly scratches your skin through the drop...and then watches to see if you develop redness, swelling or itching within about 20 minutes.

If you cannot have a skin test (some skin conditions and medications make the test unreliable), your doctor might recommend a blood test that looks for antibodies that are produced in response to specific allergens.

AVOIDANCE FIRST

As a first step to treating a dust mite allergy, it's a good idea to follow the strategies below to reduce the load of dust mites in your home. You can't eliminate them entirely, but reducing their number may be enough to lessen or eliminate symptoms. *To start...*

- **Cover your bedding.** Your bed has more dust mites than any other area in the house.

What helps: Cover your mattress, box spring, pillows and comforters with dust mite encasings. These encasings work by creating a barrier between you and the dust mites. These products, which are available online, are made of microporous fabrics with a pore size that is too small to be permeated by dust mites.

- **Hot-water washes.** Once a week, be sure to wash your bedding (sheets, blankets, mattress covers, pillowcases, etc.) in water that's 130°F or hotter. It will kill mites as well as their eggs.

- **Vacuum frequently.** Avoid wall-to-wall carpeting since it provides a large area for dust mites to inhabit. Vacuum your rugs, carpeting, drapes and other upholstered or fabric-covered surfaces once a week. A vacuum fitted with a HEPA filter will help prevent allergy-causing particles from getting stirred up in the air you breathe.

- **Steam clean.** A steam cleaner that produces *superheated* steam will kill mites and deactivate the allergy-causing proteins in their droppings. Consider steam cleaning carpets, drapes, upholstery, etc., once or twice a year.

- **Keep humidity low.** Because dust mites thrive in warm, humid environments, keep your humidity levels below 50%. Use a dehumidifier if necessary during the more humid months of summer. You can place it in the room(s), including the bedroom, where you spend the most time. To keep an eye on the humidity levels in your home, you can purchase a hygrometer online for less than $10.

- **Use a HEPA filter air purifier.** House "dust" contains copious amounts of skin cells and mites and their droppings, but you can reduce allergy symptoms by using a filtering mechanism to remove airborne particles. Portable HEPA units filter all the air in a room, trapping particles as they pass through. You can also consider a full-house filter for your HVAC system.

GOOD NEWS...

Vitamin D and Asthma

In an analysis of 955 asthma patients, vitamin D (400 IU to 4,000 IU daily) taken with an asthma medicine, such as an inhaled bronchodilator, reduced the need for steroids by 30% and need for emergency or hospital care by 50%, compared with the use of asthma medication alone.

Why: Vitamin D boosts immune response to respiratory viruses and helps reduce airway inflammation.

Adrian Martineau, PhD, professor of respiratory infection and immunity, Queen Mary University of London, UK.

FOR ADDITIONAL HELP

If the steps above don't alleviate your symptoms, you may want to consider either over-the-counter or prescription medications such as antihistamines, nasal sprays or eye drops. If medication—plus environmental control—still doesn't give you adequate relief from your symptoms, you should consider trying allergen immunotherapy.

Allergen immunotherapy is the process by which the body builds immunity to allergens such as dust mites. This is accomplished by administering small, incremental doses of dust mite (or other antigens), prompting the immune system to respond by decreasing the body's reactivity to these substances.

Allergen immunotherapy can be administered by subcutaneous injections (commonly called allergy shots)—given in a doctor's office (usually weekly in the beginning, then once every few weeks for maintenance) for three to five years.

A newer method is sublingual immunotherapy—allergy drops. Allergy drops are made of the same antigens as allergy shots but are formulated into drops that are placed under the tongue.

Once you have been tested and your allergies have been identified, your doctor can prepare your allergy drops based on your test results. Allergy drops are an effective, safe and convenient way to treat allergy symptoms. Once your drops have been formulated, you take the first dose at your doctor's office and then continue treatment at home daily for three to five years.

Heartburn Drug Alert

Heartburn drugs are linked to gastrointestinal infections. Patients who use proton-pump inhibitors (PPIs), such as Nexium and Prevacid, or H2-receptor blockers, such as Pepcid and Zantac, are 52% more likely to have recurring *C. difficile* infections, which can cause diarrhea and life-threatening inflammation of the colon, than patients not taking the medicines.

Sahil Khanna, MBBS, assistant professor of medicine, division of gastroenterology and hepatology, Mayo Clinic, Rochester, Minnesota, and leader of an analysis of 16 studies including 7,703 patients with *C. difficile*, published in *JAMA Internal Medicine*.

Natural Help for Reflux

In a recent study, the combination of a Mediterranean diet and alkaline water was as effective as proton pump inhibitor (PPI) drugs in treating *laryngopharyngeal reflux* (LPR). The diet is low in meat and dairy and high in olive oil, fish, beans, fruits and vegetables. Alkaline water is less acidic than typical tap water and can be found in large grocery stores.

LPR is a disease in which stomach acid comes up into the throat. It's not the same as the far more common gastroesophageal reflux disease (GERD), in which stomach acid enters the lower esophagus.

Craig H. Zalvan, MD, chief of otolaryngology, Phelps Memorial Hospital Center, Sleepy Hollow, New York, and leader of a study published in *JAMA Otolaryngology—Head & Neck Surgery*.

INTERESTING FINDING...

Migraines and the Heart

Migraines are associated with greater heart disease risk.

Recent finding: Women who get migraines are 50% more likely to develop major cardiovascular disease than those who do not suffer from the headaches. Migraines probably do not cause heart disease—more likely, the underlying factors that lead to migraines also lead to increased cardiovascular risk. Migraine sufferers should be aware of the association and be especially attentive to signs of a possible heart attack or stroke.

Study of more than 115,000 women ages 25 to 42 over two decades, led by researchers at Harvard T.H. Chan School of Public Health, Boston, published in *The BMJ*.

Fracking and Common Conditions

Fracking is linked to sinusitis, fatigue and migraines. In fact, people living closest to hydraulic-fracturing sites were 49% more likely to have sinusitis and migraines...88% more likely to have sinusitis and fatigue...95% more likely to have migraines and fatigue...and 81% more likely to have all three symptoms, compared with those living far from fracking sites.

Study of 7,785 participants led by researchers at Johns Hopkins Bloomberg School of Public Health, Baltimore, published in *Environmental Health Perspectives.*

Quick Fixes for a Bellyache

Jamison Starbuck, ND, a naturopathic physician in family practice and writer/producer of *Dr. Starbuck's Health Tips for Kids*, a weekly program on Montana Public Radio, MTPR.org, both in Missoula. She is a past president of the American Association of Naturopathic Physicians and a contributing editor to *The Alternative Advisor: The Complete Guide to Natural Therapies and Alternative Treatments.* DrJamisonStarbuck.com

Have you ever woken up with a bellyache? Or had a queasy feeling in your stomach late in the day? If you get this type of bellyache—and who doesn't?—a few simple remedies can help you feel better in a day or so. *What may be causing the problem—and the easy fixes I recommend...*

- **Indigestion.** If you've overeaten or consumed a high-fat, high-protein meal, the food could be rotting in your gut rather than being properly broken down for digestion.

Red flags: You are gassy, bloated, burping and/or still feeling full hours after a meal.

What helps: Try drinking tea made from herbs in the mint family—peppermint, spearmint, lemon balm and/or catnip. You can use just one of these herbs, combine all of them or look for a "tummy ache" mixture. Make a strong tea using two teaspoons of dried herb or two tea bags per 12 ounces of water. Drink six ounces every 15 minutes for an hour.

- **Constipation.** Medical doctors define constipation as having a bowel movement less than three times a week, but I believe this should be a daily event to help clear toxins from your body.

Red flags: You suffer from lower abdominal cramping...and/or have an urge to move your bowels but nothing happens.

What helps: Smooth Move tea (made by Traditional Medicinals). It contains senna, a botanical laxative. It also contains the herbs licorice, ginger, fennel and cinnamon—all of which soothe the digestive tract. Usually one cup, taken on an empty stomach, is enough to relieve infrequent constipation. Bedtime is an ideal time for the tea if you usually have a morning bowel movement.

Caution: Don't use Smooth Move, or any senna product, if you know you have a bowel disease, such as Crohn's or ulcerative colitis. Senna works by irritating the gut wall, which can worsen bowel disease. To be on the safe side, check with your doctor if you have any question about using senna. And do not use Smooth Move for more than two or three days—as with any laxative, you may become dependent on it.

- **Stomach virus.** Even though a stomach virus can lead to diarrhea and vomiting, sometimes these symptoms are quite mild. The only signs could be a loose stool, lack of appetite and/or not feeling quite right for 24 hours.

Red flags: Someone in your household or workplace has had the same thing...or you've recently spent time with small children, who are common carriers of these nasty viruses.

What helps: Activated charcoal capsules appear to absorb viruses and move them out of your body. Take two charcoal capsules on an empty stomach four times a day for 24 or 48 hours. Check with your doctor first if you take any medications.

- **Worry or anxiety.** Anticipating an event—whether it's a happy occasion or something that has you feeling worried and anxious—makes digestion difficult.

Red flag: You've just gone through an emotionally charged time...or you are about to enter one.

What helps: Just ten minutes of purposeful walking will relax you—and promote improved digestion. While you're walking, breathe deeply so that air makes it all the way to your tight, tension-filled stomach. Listening to meditation or visualization podcasts can also be a big help!

Important: If your bellyache lasts longer than a day or two—or if it becomes a regular occurrence—see your doctor to rule out bowel disease such as diverticulitis, gastritis or irritable bowel syndrome.

Natural Ways to Beat Constipation

Christopher Vasey, ND, a naturopathic physician who specializes in detoxification and rejuvenation in Chamby-Montreux, Switzerland. He lectures regularly about natural health in Europe, Canada and the US, and is author of *Freedom from Constipation: Natural Remedies for Digestive Health*. ChristopherVasey.ch/anglais/home.html

---

Constipation is a topic that many people are too embarrassed to discuss with their doctors. But there's no need to suffer in silence.

It's widely known that infrequent and/or painful bowel movements often have relatively simple explanations—you're not getting enough water...you're skimping on fiber...and/or you're too sedentary. If you drink more fluids, add fiber to your diet and get some exercise, you're usually good to go, right? Unfortunately, that is not the case for everyone.

What you may not know: For approximately 15% of Americans, constipation is a chronic problem. This can occur if you're taking a certain medication, such as an antacid, antidepressant or narcotic painkiller...or have a medical problem, such as low thyroid (hypothyroidism), Parkinson's disease or multiple sclerosis, that can cause constipation.

Is a pharmaceutical laxative (pill or liquid) the next best bet? Not always. These products can cause side effects, such as bloating, cramping or gas, and may even interfere with the absorption of some medications and various nutrients.

A better way: Most people can beat constipation without using a pharmaceutical. *Here's how...*

START WITH THESE STRATEGIES

If you are troubled by constipation, make sure you give the strategies below a try...

- **Drink up!** A healthy bowel movement is about 75% water. Constipation can occur when the stool water content falls below 70%—this can cause the stool to become too hard for the body to evacuate easily.

To avoid constipation, most people need 2 to 2.5 quarts of fluids a day. You don't need that much if you eat a lot of vegetables, fruit and other plant foods—they have a high water content that counts toward the daily total.

But: If you exercise or sweat a lot, you will need more than the recommended 2 to 2.5 quarts of fluids a day.

My advice: Drink a big glass of water (or a mug of herbal tea) all at once, several times a day. Like many naturopaths, I advise against drinking fluids with meals to avoid diluting digestive juices.

- **Get your roughage.** Plant fibers take up space in the large intestine and cause the intestinal walls to stretch—the process that triggers intestinal *peristalsis* (contractions) and bowel movements.

Important: All plant fibers are good for constipation, but the water-soluble type—found, for example, in vegetables, fruits (raspberries, figs, dates and passion fruit are especially beneficial), flaxseed and beans—is particularly good because it absorbs water and can double or even quadruple in size in the intestine, which helps move things along.

My advice: Be sure to get enough fiber each day. For people over age 50, that's about 30 g daily for men and 21 g daily for women. Those who are constipated may need even more fiber.

- **Avoid constipating foods and beverages.** These include bananas, blueberries, fresh apricots, white rice and red wine. Generally, you would need to have these foods/drinks on

TAKE NOTE...

How Do Doctors Define Constipation?

Depending on what's being eaten, it can take about 30 to 40 hours for food to be transformed into stools and evacuated from the body. But sometimes the body doesn't work as intended.

Doctors define constipation as having fewer than three bowel movements a week...straining or having hard stools more than 25% of the time...and/or feeling that your bowel movements are often "incomplete."

Christopher Vasey, ND, a naturopathic physician located in Chamby-Montreux, Switzerland.

a regular basis to have a problem, but sometimes having the food/drink just once causes an issue.

• **Walk the right amount.** Walking is very effective for constipation because it stimulates nerves that trigger peristaltic activity.

My advice: To work for constipation, you need to walk for at least 40 minutes a day. If it's more convenient, you can break it up into two, 20-minute sessions.

Note: Other types of exercise can also help constipation, but walking is the easiest and most convenient for most people.

FOR MORE HELP

If the advice above does not give you relief within 15 days, then it's time to step up your game. *The following tips can help—you can try all of them...*

• **Heat the liver.** According to the principles of Eastern medicine, a loss of heat from the liver—often triggered by fatigue or stress—causes blood capillaries to shrink...reduces circulation...and lowers production of bile, which you need for healthy digestion.

What to do: Place an old-fashioned rubber hot-water bottle over the liver—halfway down the right side of the abdomen, on the ribs under the right breast. The heat will increase circulation and cause the liver to expand, which has a stimulating effect on bowel movements.

Keep the bottle in place for about 15 to 30 minutes. Repeat the treatment up to three times a day, preferably after meals. People who do this for a month in addition to the steps above often find that constipation is no longer a problem. Or you can use the hot-water bottle indefinitely if you feel that it is continuing to help.

• **Self-massage.** To stimulate the peristaltic muscles that push stools out of the intestine, it helps to stretch, knead and compress the intestines with self-massage.

What to do: Using your fist or fingertips, firmly rub your abdomen (the area surrounding the navel) in a clockwise direction. This mimics the clockwise direction of intestinal peristalsis and stimulates different parts of the intestine. Once a day, rub the area for five to 10 minutes, at least two hours after a meal. You will most likely start to notice an improvement in bowel movements within three or four days.

• **Improve your bacterial balance.** There's an ideal ratio of bacteria in the gut—about 85% of the organisms should be "good" bacteria involved in fermentation (the dividing of food particles)...and the rest of the organisms should be "bad" bacteria that cause putrefaction (the decomposition of the particles). People who eat a lot of animal foods tend to have an excess of the second type and not enough of the first.

To restore a healthier balance, be sure to cut back on animal foods and consume more high-fiber plant foods such as fruits, vegetables and whole grains. These foods have probiotic effects—they increase levels of the fermenting organisms.

Another option: A daily probiotic supplement that provides high doses (numbering in the billions) of beneficial bacteria, such as *bifidus* and/or *acidophilus* strains. Follow label instructions.*

• **Strengthen the "push" muscles.** Because of their sedentary lifestyles, many Americans don't have the strength in the abdominal and/or intestinal muscles to readily generate the

*Although probiotics are generally considered safe, anyone with a weakened immune system, including those who take corticosteroids, as well as pregnant women, should check with their doctors before taking them.

pressure needed for a bowel movement. This exercise can help.

What to do: Sit on the floor with your knees bent. Recline backward and rest your weight on your forearms. Extend one leg straight out in front of you...slowly bend it to bring it back to the starting position...then do the same with the other leg. Alternating legs, extend-and-bend each leg five times, then rest and repeat the cycle two more times. Do this daily. As you get stronger, increase the number of leg extensions to 10 or 20. You can extend-and-bend both legs at the same time, but it's more challenging.

• **A better position.** Our early ancestors squatted on their heels to evacuate. This position strongly facilitates evacuation of the bowels because it relaxes the muscles of the anal sphincter, encouraging it to open, and puts the colon in a vertical position. To achieve these benefits on a toilet, raise your feet four to eight inches with a stool.

Cut Risk for UTIs by 50%

Cut your risk for urinary tract infections (UTIs) in half by drinking an extra six cups of water a day. Young women who had frequent UTIs and drank six more cups of water daily were 48% less likely to have another UTI (the women had been drinking about four cups of fluid a day before the study). And the water drinkers were able to reduce their use of antibiotics by 47%. Fluid intake may reduce UTI risk by preventing bacteria from adhering to the bladder and reducing overall bacterial concentration.

Thomas Hooton, MD, clinical director, division of infectious diseases, University of Miami School of Medicine, and coauthor of a study of 140 healthy premenopausal women who had at least three UTIs in the previous year, presented at the IDWeek 2017 conference in San Diego.

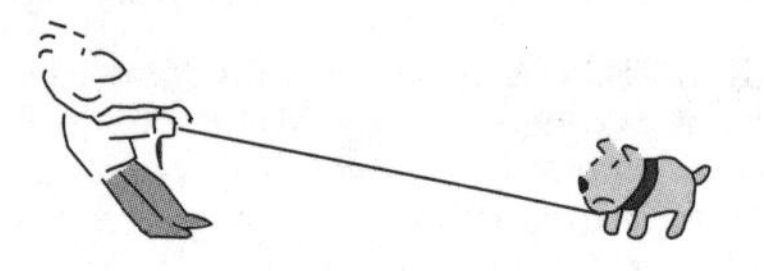

How to Prevent Food Poisoning

Jamison Starbuck, ND, a naturopathic physician in family practice in Missoula, Montana. She is a past president of the American Association of Naturopathic Physicians and a contributing editor to *The Alternative Advisor: The Complete Guide to Natural Therapies and Alternative Treatments.* DrJamisonStarbuck.com

Whether it's caused by eating food left out too long on your kitchen counter or from consuming underdone meat at a restaurant, we've all gotten a nasty case of garden-variety food poisoning at one time or another—the intense symptoms such as nausea, stomach pain, diarrhea and sometimes vomiting are unmistakable. Plus, from time to time there are news reports about particularly virulent food poisoning outbreaks that affect a large number of people.

Case in point: In summer 2017, more than 200 people were sickened (and one person died) after eating papaya from Mexico.

While we can't know for sure where the next food poisoning threat will come from, there are things we can do to help protect ourselves from getting this very uncomfortable condition—beyond just looking at the "sell by" dates of the food you buy and carefully monitoring the shelf life of foods in your home...

• **Boost the healthy bacteria in your gut.** Having plenty of beneficial bacteria, such as the probiotics *acidophilus* and *bifidus*, in your digestive tract is essential for good health. Research shows that people with an abundant supply of these beneficial bacteria are less vulnerable to food poisoning than people with inadequate good bacteria. These beneficial bacteria are found abundantly in foods like yogurt, kefir and sauerkraut. Be sure to eat such foods several times a week. You especially need probiotics if you've been on antibiotics recently. In that case, you may need to take an over-the-counter probiotic supplement* containing high amounts (five to 10 billion units daily) of *acidophilus* and *bifi-*

*Tell your health-care provider about any supplements you are taking. If you have a weakened immune system or a critical illness, do not take probiotics.

dus. Also, when traveling, you are at greater exposure to food poisoning from restaurants, public restrooms and potentially water, so it's best to supplement with probiotics the week before you leave, throughout your trip and for one week after you return.

• **Avoid acid-blocking medications,** such as *omeprazole* (Prilosec) and *esomeprazole* (Nexium), which are frequently used to relieve heartburn. Sufficient stomach acid is needed to kill harmful bacteria ingested from food. (Beneficial bacteria, on the other hand, thrive in an acidic environment.) If you've got heartburn, consider seeing a naturopathic physician to learn about nondrug treatments such as deglycerized licorice, which can soothe symptoms. Reducing your consumption of cheese, meat, fatty foods and alcohol can help reduce heartburn. Testing for food allergies is also a good idea, since food allergies create indigestion.

• **Take digestive bitters.** A botanical formula made from herbs such as gentian, anise and ginger, bitters help stimulate digestive enzyme production and protect the gut from harmful bacteria. Follow label instructions.

• **Don't forget to wash.** Wash produce thoroughly with water before eating...and wash refrigerator shelves twice a month with soap and water—even if they don't look dirty.

• **Defrost meat in the refrigerator, not on the counter, and refrigerate leftovers quickly.** And always cook meats, fish and other foods to the proper internal temperature. (Go to FoodSafety.gov and click on "Safe Minimum Cooking Temperatures" for guidelines.)

EASY TO DO...

Healthier Way to Start the Day

Add fresh lemon juice to a morning glass of water. This provides the body with hydrating electrolytes in the form of potassium, calcium and magnesium—we get dehydrated overnight. Lemon juice also may help your liver purge more toxins. And it increases your intake of vitamin C, strengthening your immune system.

Frank Lipman, MD, integrative medicine physician and founder and director of BeWell, BeWell.com.

6 Best Foods for Your Skin

Torey Armul, MS, RD, CSSD, LD, a spokesperson for the Academy of Nutrition and Dietetics. She counsels clients on weight management, sports nutrition and pregnancy and family nutrition through her private practice in Columbus, Ohio. eatrightPRO.org

Want healthier skin and fewer wrinkles? Men and women can look younger and lower their risk for skin cancer, psoriasis, eczema and more by eating certain foods. *The following foods have been scientifically proven to boost the health, strength and appearance of your skin...*

YELLOW BELL PEPPERS

Yellow bell peppers are one of the most abundant sources of vitamin C. The body depends on vitamin C to form *collagen,* a protein that provides strength, support and elasticity to skin, hair, muscles and other tissues. Collagen also assists with cell regrowth and repair. As we age, our bodies produce less collagen, which can lead to reduced elasticity of the skin and more wrinkles.

The relationship between vitamin C and skin appearance was studied in more than 4,000 women in a report published in *The American Journal of Clinical Nutrition.* Researchers found that higher dietary intake of vitamin C was associated with lower likelihood of skin dryness and fewer wrinkles, as assessed by dermatologists. These results were independent of age, race, sun exposure, body mass index and physical activity.

Why not eat oranges, famous for their vitamin C, instead? A typical large orange contains 163% of the recommended daily value (DV) of vitamin C. That's good—but just half a yellow bell pepper contains nearly 300% of the DV of vitamin C. (Red and green peppers have less vitamin C than yellow ones but still are excellent sources.)

Eat yellow peppers raw to maximize the nutrient content. Vitamin C is sensitive to cooking and, as a water-soluble vitamin, leaches into cooking water. If you prefer to cook yellow peppers, keep the heat as low as possible for your recipe. Use the cooking juices, too (whenever possible), so that the vitamin C in the water is not wasted.

SWEET POTATOES

Sweet potatoes are an excellent source of carotenoids, antioxidant pigments that give many foods their bright red, orange, yellow and green colors—and help keep skin cells healthy.

In a study published in *British Journal of Nutrition*, participants who ate more carotenoid-rich vegetables had significantly fewer facial wrinkles.

Eating carotenoids also can make you look healthier overall and more attractive to others. Carotenoid levels in skin contribute to healthy skin coloration. In fact, researchers from University of St. Andrews, Scotland, found that people whose faces were rated as healthy by others had consumed an average of 2.9 fruit and vegetable portions each day...and whose faces were rated separately as attractive had consumed 3.3 daily portions.

Carotenoids are fat-soluble, which means that they're better absorbed when paired with a fat-containing food—so sprinkle nuts or drizzle olive oil over your sweet potatoes for a delicious skin boost.

SALMON

Although protein in your food does not directly affect protein in your body's collagen, some research shows that amino acids (the building blocks of protein) are related to collagen synthesis in the skin.

Some amino acids are "essential," meaning that they're necessary for life but are not made in the body. They must be provided by food or supplements. Salmon contains all the essential amino acids—and essential amino acids play a unique role in skin health. In a study published in *Amino Acids*, researchers found that consuming a combination of essential amino acids significantly increased the rate of collagen synthesis in mice with UV-damaged skin.

Salmon also is a good source of monounsaturated fat, which was found to be positively associated with skin elasticity in older women in a study published in *British Journal of Nutrition*.

Don't love fish? Essential amino acids also are found in poultry, eggs, beans and whole grains.

WALNUTS

Walnuts are rich in omega-3 polyunsaturated fatty acids, which help the body make the collagen needed for healthy skin. Omega-3s help reduce inflammation and have been shown to reduce symptoms in inflammatory skin diseases such as psoriasis and acne.

The European Journal of Cancer published research comparing omega-3 fat intake to the development of malignant melanoma in more than 20,000 women. Data showed that higher intakes of omega-3s were associated with an 80% lower risk for skin cancer, leading researchers to conclude that these fats "have a substantial protective association" against melanoma.

Like essential amino acids, omega-3 fats are vitally important but are not made in the body. You must get them from your diet or supplements. Aside from walnuts (and salmon, discussed above), other excellent sources of omega-3s include flaxseed oil, ground flaxseed, chia seeds, canola oil and tofu.

RASPBERRIES AND POMEGRANATES

There is exciting research on collagen and how it is affected by *ellagic acid*, an antioxidant found in certain fruits and vegetables.

A study published in *Experimental Dermatology* found that mice who received ellagic acid had significantly reduced collagen breakdown from UV light, compared with mice who did not receive ellagic acid. The treatment group also developed fewer wrinkles. While most research focuses on the treatment of skin damage, this study was unique in its ability to show the role of nutrition in the prevention of collagen breakdown, wrinkles and skin damage.

Foods that are high in ellagic acid include raspberries and pomegranates (as well as blackberries, strawberries and cranberries).

CHICKPEAS

Zinc is an important ingredient for skin health because it supports the regeneration of new skin cells. The benefits are most apparent with skin repair and wound healing, but zinc also may be able to help with other skin problems such as rashes, eczema and acne.

A study published in *BioMed Research International* found a correlation between participants' zinc levels and the severity of their acne symptoms. Researchers believe that this is partly due to zinc's ability to inhibit the overgrowth of *Propionibacterium acnes*, a bacterium that contributes to acne.

Legumes were the focus of another study in *The Journal of the American College of Nutrition*. Researchers found that higher intakes of legumes, such as chickpeas, appeared to protect against sun-induced wrinkles in people with a variety of ethnic and geographic backgrounds.

Chickpeas are a good source of zinc, as are other beans, oysters, poultry, tofu, oatmeal and zinc-fortified cereals.

How to Nourish Your Skin

Kara Fitzgerald, ND, clinical director of the Sandy Hook Clinic, a practice devoted to functional medicine in Sandy Hook, Connecticut. DrKaraFitzgerald.com

Your skin is alive with visitors. Every square inch hosts *millions* of microbes... and that's a good thing. Like the "good bugs" in your gut, the skin's microbiome protects your health in many ways.

Consider skin bacteria. Some hold in water, helping to moisturize. Others protect you from ultraviolet light. But the most amazing benefit is the ability to help protect skin from infection by communicating with immune cells. A microbiome imbalance has been linked with eczema, psoriasis, rosacea, acne, poor wound healing, fungal infections—even plain old dandruff.

On the horizon: Topical live "probiotics" that treat eczema and other skin conditions.

But there's something we all can do now—protect this beautiful and elegant system. *A healthy diet (fruits and veggies, little sugar, few refined carbs) and staying hydrated are essential but only the start...*

- **Shower less often.** You're stripping your skin of natural moisturizers, literally washing away beneficial bacteria. If you now shower or bathe daily, try doing so every other day, even every third day.

Tip: If you're not particularly dirty or stinky, skip washing areas exposed to light and air such as your arms and neck.

- **Swear off antimicrobial soap.** The FDA has banned *triclosan*, an antimicrobial compound, from soaps and cleansers. It kills "good" bugs and may promote antibiotic-resistance in "bad" bugs. But now some soap manufacturers have switched to other antimicrobials, and there's no evidence that they are safer. *What to buy:* Soap that doesn't mention killing microbes/bacteria on the label.

- **Wash lightly.** Regular soap often is alkaline and can interfere with the natural acidity of skin, which is key to preventing the growth of harmful organisms. Even gentle soap can wash away beneficial bacteria if you use it too frequently. One product that won't disturb skin microflora is Face & Body Cleanser from MotherDirt, which costs $15 (*disclosure:* the company is a sponsor of my blog).

- **Do wash your hands.** Here's an exception to the "wash less" idea—to prevent the spread of infection, wash your hands with soap and water, especially if you're sick, you sneezed, you used the bathroom or you are going to handle food.

Tip: If you're not near soap and water, an alcohol-based hand sanitizer is a good idea. Still, don't overdo it—do you really need to squeeze that bottle 10 times a day?

- **Lotion up.** I like lotions that contain *ceramides,* fats that are a natural constituent of skin cells and help repair the skin's protective barrier. They help treat both eczema and psoriasis (ask your doctor if you have one of those conditions).

- **Work up a sweat.** Perspiration is good for your skin microflora. It is believed to act as a prebiotic—food that these critters feed on. Working up a sweat two or three times a week should help keep your skin happy.

Don't Get Bitten by Mosquito Myths

Jonathan F. Day, PhD, professor of medical entomology at the University of Florida in Vero Beach. He has published more than 100 peer-reviewed scientific articles about mosquitoes and the diseases they transmit.

While some people consider mosquitoes to be little more than a minor, itchy annoyance, these pesky insects can put you at risk for a number of mosquito-borne diseases.

One of the most common diseases transmitted by mosquitoes to humans in North America is West Nile Virus (WNV), which can cause flulike symptoms and, in rare cases, inflammation of the brain (*encephalitis*).

The most recent mosquito-borne disease to cause alarm in the US is Zika virus. If a pregnant woman is infected with Zika virus, her child may be born with a serious birth defect called *microcephaly*, which is associated with incomplete brain development. People who are bitten by a Zika-infected mosquito can transmit the virus to their sexual partners for months afterward...the virus can also be transmitted when an infected person is bitten by an *Aedes aegypti* mosquito and that insect successfully incubates the virus before biting another person.

Here's the truth behind some commonly held myths about what makes the little buzzers bite—and what we can do to stop them...

MYTH #1: **Mosquitoes bite only at dusk and dawn.** *Truth:* While most common types of mosquitoes feed mainly at dusk and dawn, some species feed during the day while other species feed at night. In fact, the Aedes aegypti mosquito that transmits Zika virus is most active during the day.

MYTH #2: **Mosquitoes are attracted to people who have type O blood.** *Truth:* You may have heard that mosquitoes prefer to bite people with type O blood. Not true. Aside from the fact that type O is the most common blood type in the US, mosquitoes do not choose a host based on blood type.

What does attract mosquitoes: Carbon dioxide. People with high metabolic rates produce more carbon dioxide than do people with low metabolisms—those producing high levels of CO2 (as may occur, for example, during vigorous exercise such as running or biking) attract more mosquitoes. Another mosquito draw is lactic acid, a compound found in sweat—you'll be more likely to get an armload of bites if you sit outside after a run.

MYTH #3: **You don't need to worry about mosquitoes if you live in a dry climate.** *Truth:* While mosquitoes are not as abundant in dry climates as they are in tropical rain forests, you will find them ready to bite in dry habitats, including the desert Southwest and the High Plains east of the Rocky Mountains.

Research shows that mosquito populations increase with higher spring soil moisture levels—heavy snowpack, snowmelt and spring rain all provide sufficient standing water to allow the development of immature mosquitoes, even in typically "dry" areas.

For up-to-date forecasts on mosquito activity: Go to the website AccuWeather.com. Add your location to the search box, then look for "mosquito" in the drop-down menu under "Personalized Forecasts."

For mosquito prevention, keep standing water away from your home. And don't just look for the obvious places like kiddie pools. Be sure to check for water that collects in rain gutters and buckets, too. Empty and refresh water in birdbaths and fountains at least once a week to keep mosquitoes from maturing. Small ponds can be treated with Bti Briquets, a sustained-release larvicide that floats on the water's surface. Vegetation around larger ponds should be controlled, especially cattails and water hyacinth.

MYTH #4: **DEET is toxic to humans.** *Truth:* Developed by the US Army in 1946, DEET (short for *N,N-diethyl-meta-toluamide*) is one of the few products that is effective against mosquitoes and biting flies. It was registered for human use in 1957 and has been found to be safe even for pregnant and nursing women when applied according to label instructions.

Concerns about DEET come primarily from the toxic effects seen when it is ingested, inhaled or used in other ways inconsistent with label instructions. Do not apply DEET products more often than recommended...and do not apply over cuts, wounds or irritated skin. For more information on DEET, check out the EPA website, EPA.gov/insect-repellents/deet.

***MYTH #5:* Non-DEET repellents don't work.** *Truth:* Research published by the Centers for Disease Control and Prevention (CDC) demonstrated that products containing oil of lemon eucalyptus, whose active ingredient *para-menthane-diol* is derived from the eucalyptus tree, can be as effective as low-concentration DEET. But most botanical formulations require frequent reapplication—usually every 10 to 20 minutes.

Another option is Avon Skin So Soft. Its current formula contains *picaridin* (a synthetic compound that resembles the natural compound found in the plants used to produce black pepper) and *IR3535* (structurally similar to the naturally occurring amino acid B-alanine). Both ingredients are registered with the EPA as effective and safe.

***MYTH #6:* Sprays are more effective than creams.** *Truth:* When it comes to efficacy, what really matters is the concentration of the active ingredient—for example, the CDC recommends DEET, oil of lemon eucalyptus and picaridin-based repellents. This means that a 3% DEET spray and a 3% DEET lotion are equally effective. The downside of an aerosol is the risk for inhalation.

But there are ways to apply a DEET spray without inhaling it. For instance, when using an aerosol, spray the product onto the palm of your hand and apply the liquid to areas you want to treat—your arms, neck and forehead.

Note: Sunscreen/repellent combinations are *not* recommended—the effectiveness is less than if you used two separate products. When both are needed, apply sunscreen first...then bug repellent.

Also: For unknown reasons, mosquitoes are attracted to dark colors, so wear tightly woven, *light-colored* apparel. And if you must wear sandals, apply a CDC-recommended insect repellent. Some mosquitoes reportedly love the smell of feet!

GOOD TO KNOW...

Sunscreen Savvy

Don't forget to apply sunscreen on your eyelids and the area surrounding your eye sockets. These spots are prone to skin cancer, yet people often miss them when applying sunscreen.

Tip: Sunscreens labeled "for sensitive skin" are less likely to sting if they get in your eyes.

Study by researchers at University of Liverpool, UK, published in *PLOS ONE.*

Sprained Ankles Are More Serious Than You Think

Phillip Gribble, PhD, ATC, FNATA, associate professor of athletic training at University of Kentucky, Lexington, and program director for the university's post-professional master's program in athletic training. He is codirector of the International Ankle Consortium, a nonprofit research organization.

A sprained ankle might seem like a temporary inconvenience, but there's growing evidence that the consequences can be serious and long lasting. Recent studies have found that people who suffer one ankle sprain are extremely likely to experience recurrences, with 40% to 70% of first-time sprainers developing "chronic ankle instability."

Self-defense: Whether or not you've had an ankle sprain, do ankle-strengthening exercises regularly. These can include hopping in place or hopping from place to place on one leg or standing on one foot and bending over to pick things up from the floor.

Consider wearing ankle braces when engaging in activities that often cause sprained ankles such as tennis, basketball or hiking on uneven ground, especially if you have sprained your ankle before. Lace-up braces or rigid braces can be equally effective or you can have your ankles taped by an athletic trainer. But avoid slip-on neoprene ankle sleeves, which provide very little support.

If you do sprain your ankle...

• **Resist the urge to "walk it off."** Instead, keep your weight off the ankle as much as possible for at least 24 to 48 hours to give the ligaments a chance to heal. Use crutches to get around. During these first few days, use ice and keep the ankle elevated as much as possible.

• **When the ankle starts to feel better, try balancing on that side.** If you can do this without pain for 30 seconds, try the balance training exercises such as the hopping and reaching exercises described above. If you can do those without pain, too, your ankle probably is ready to return to sports or hiking.

Note: It's always a good idea to seek a consultation from a medical professional. He/she can confirm the initial evaluation and determine what additional follow-up is needed.

Natural Fixes for 3 Foot Problems

Jamison Starbuck, ND, a naturopathic physician in family practice and writer/producer of *Dr. Starbuck's Health Tips for Kids*, a weekly program on Montana Public Radio, MTPR.org, both in Missoula. She is a past president of the American Association of Naturopathic Physicians and a contributing editor to *The Alternative Advisor: The Complete Guide to Natural Therapies and Alternative Treatments*. DrJamisonStarbuck.com

Foot problems are hard to ignore. When your tootsies are unwell, something as simple as shopping for groceries becomes a chore. *Fortunately, some well-chosen natural remedies can really help these common foot problems...*

• **Toenail fungus.** This is a stubborn problem, particularly for people with poor circulation or diabetes. You'll know you have a fungal infection if your nail is yellowed and/or raised or if there's white, flaky debris under the nail. Keeping your nails clipped, clean and dry can reduce the chances that the problem will spread to other toes. In mild cases, which usually involve just the top of the nail and/or skin around the nail, applying full-strength white vinegar two times daily to the site of the infection can reduce fungus. In more severe cases, an effective prescription topical drug regimen is *ketoconazole* (an antifungal) mixed with DMSO, a liquid substance made from wood pulp. DMSO enables the penetration of other liquids—such as ketoconazole—through skin and nails. This regimen is usually prepared by a compounding pharmacist and must be prescribed by a physician. (To find a compounding pharmacist, search online or ask your drugstore pharmacist.) Apply this mixture twice daily to nails and the surrounding skin for several months.

• **Cracked heels and soles.** If you have deep cracks in those thick, unsightly calluses on your feet, lotions, herbal salves and petroleum jelly offer little benefit because the problem is caused more from the inside than the outside. Deep cracks on the bottoms of your feet can indicate a deficiency in vitamin A. Vitamin A is not abundant in food (except in liver). Instead, the body makes vitamin A from beta-carotene, a nutrient that is plentiful in beets, carrots, cantaloupe, sweet potatoes and squash. You can also take a beta-carotene supplement. A typical dose for callus cracks is 50,000 international units (IU) daily, taken with food. You may need to do this for several months for lasting results. After your feet improve, consider taking 25,000 IU of beta-carotene daily as a maintenance dose.

Caution: If you have lung, liver or heart disease, are a smoker or heavy drinker or take prescription medication, check with your doctor before using a beta-carotene supplement. Do not use if you take a multivitamin that contains vitamin A.

• **Swollen feet.** Edema, a term used to mean puffy and swollen, can be caused by circulatory problems, heart and kidney disease, standing for long hours, pregnancy and air travel. Done properly, hydrotherapy can relieve edema by improving your circulation so that your blood vessels and lymph system move excess fluid out of your feet.

Do-it-yourself hydrotherapy: Put hot water (enough to cover your ankles) and one cup of Epsom salts into a basin. Place another basin filled with cold water next to the hot water basin. Soak your feet in the hot water for three minutes, then in the cold for one minute. Alternate between the basins three times, always beginning with hot and ending with cold. Thoroughly dry your feet, and then elevate them above your navel for five minutes. You can do this once or twice daily for as long as needed.

Important: If you have neuropathy and cannot feel hot or cold sensation in your feet, be sure to test the water temperature with your hand first.

Also helpful: Walk for at least 10 minutes two times daily...and elevate your feet while sitting.

The Sleep-Better Yoga Plan

Carol Krucoff, a yoga therapist at Duke Integrative Medicine in Durham, North Carolina. She is cofounder and codirector of the Yoga for Seniors trainings and network, Yoga4Seniors.com. Ms. Krucoff is also author of several books, including *Yoga Sparks: 108 Easy Practices for Stress Relief in a Minute or Less* and *Healing Yoga for Neck and Shoulder Pain.* HealingMoves.com

The day is waning, your warm bed beckons...and yet your mind continues to race, making peaceful slumber a far-off dream. What's the best way to bring on the z's?

Many Americans opt for a powerful sleeping pill or even a nightcap to help drift off at bedtime. Even though these so-called sleep "aids" may help you doze off, they leave you vulnerable to wee-hour awakenings...or pose dangerous side effects such as dizziness that make you prone to falls.

An under-recognized solution: Yoga is a safe approach that can easily be added to your sleep-hygiene toolbox. *Here's how...*

THE YOGA SOLUTION

Yoga is a perfect sleep inducer because it is designed to quiet the mind—targeting the racing thoughts that can keep us from drifting off. Yoga is also a proven pain-fighter, easing backaches, arthritis and other common sleep saboteurs.

When adults over age 60 who had insomnia took three months of twice-weekly classes incorporating yoga poses, meditation and daily home practice, they reported significant improvements in their sleep, according to a 2014 study in *Alternative Therapies in Health and Medicine.*

HOW TO BREATHE RIGHT

When we are drifting off to sleep, the pace of our breathing naturally slows. But when our racing mind keeps us awake, turning our attention to our breath and deliberately slowing and deepening the breath can trigger a cascade of relaxing physiological changes—the heart rate slows, blood pressure decreases, muscles relax, anxiety eases and the mind calms.

Surprisingly, many people do not know the basics of correct deep breathing.

What to do: Put yourself in a comfortable position—lying on your back, for example—and place one of your palms on your belly. Relax your abdomen, and invite your breath to completely fill your lungs. You might notice that when you inhale fully this way, your belly rounds and your hand rises. With the exhale, your belly gently drops inward and your hand falls.

To get the most from abdominal breathing: Go a step further by making the exhale a bit longer. This type of breathing sends a clear signal to your central nervous system that everything is fine...just let go.

THE SLEEP-INDUCING POSES

Once you have become comfortable with the relaxed breathing described above, here are some sleep-better yoga poses to do right before bed. For each pose below, start by lying on the floor (on a yoga mat or carpet for comfort) or on your bed with your knees bent and your arms at your sides. If your chin juts up, place a small pillow or folded towel under your head so that your chin is at the same level or slightly lower than your forehead.

- **Knees to chest.** *What to do:* Do the relaxed abdominal breathing described above for several minutes.

Once you're feeling relaxed, bring both knees toward your chest, holding onto your thighs or using a yoga strap (or a bathrobe tie) to catch your thighs and bring them toward your chest. Notice where you feel the sensation of stretch, and use your breath to help relax any tension. On the exhalation, draw your thighs in toward your body...on the inhalation, allow your thighs to drift away from your body. If it's uncomfortable to hug both legs, hug one leg at a time. Continue for six to 10 cycles of breath—each inhalation and exhalation is one breath cycle.

• **Neck release.** *What to do:* Take an easy, full breath in, then as you exhale, rotate your head to the right. Your eyes can be open or closed, whichever feels better.

Inhale as you bring your head back to center, then exhale as you turn your head to the left. Continue for six to 10 breaths, moving with your breath. Next, turn your head as far as it will comfortably go to the right and relax your left shoulder toward the ground. Linger here for three to five easy breaths, then bring your head back to the center and repeat to the left.

• **Arms overhead.** *What to do:* With your arms alongside your body and your palms facing down, tune in to your breath. As you inhale, extend your arms up and back so that the backs of your hands move toward the surface behind you. If your hands don't reach the surface behind you, that's fine. As you exhale, return your arms to their starting position along your sides. Repeat six to 10 times, moving with your breath—inhale your arms up and over...exhale them back down to your sides. Sleep tight...

SURPRISING FINDING...

A Sense of Purpose Improves Sleep

In a recent finding, people who reported a strong sense of purpose were 63% less likely to have sleep apnea and 52% less likely to have restless legs syndrome, compared with their peers who scored lower on the purpose scale.

Study of 825 people by researchers at Northwestern University Feinberg School of Medicine, Evanston, Illinois, published in *Sleep Science and Practice*.

Stop Getting Up at Night to Pee!

If you often get up at night to urinate, try cutting back on salt. When Japanese adults who consumed high levels of salt—11,000 milligrams (mg) a day, about five times what US authorities recommend—cut back to 8,000 mg a day, their number of nighttime bathroom trips dropped from 2.3 to 1.4, on average. Even 8,000 mg is three-and-a-half times the recommended level in the US—further cutbacks might give more benefit.

Reason: People who eat a lot of salt feel thirstier, so they may drink more, increasing the need for nighttime urination.

Matsuo Tomohiro, MD, researcher, department of urology, Nagasaki University Hospital, Nagasaki, Japan.

Help for Night Owls

Are you awake at night and sluggish in the morning? Many night owls have a gene mutation that causes delayed sleep phase disorder, an alteration of the body's biological clock.

For better sleep: Try bright-light exposure during the day.

Cell.

"Go Pink" for More Z's and Better Memory

Rebecca Shannonhouse, editor, *Bottom Line Health*, BottomLineInc.com.

Few things in life are more satisfying than a good night's sleep. But as we age, deep sleep often becomes increasingly elusive.

Good news: Researchers at Northwestern University may have a solution to enhance sleep quality—and memory—in older adults.

What's the secret? The soothing sound of "pink noise" may hold the key.

Most people are familiar with the static-y sound of white noise. Pink noise—a consistent mix of sound frequencies, like the gentle patter of falling rain—appears to have special benefits. Pink noise increases the amplitude and synchronization of brain waves during deep sleep—a process that appears to also help consolidate memories into long-term storage.

In the study, 13 adults age 60 and older wore headphones during the night and took memory tests before bed and again in the morning. They were exposed to pink noise on one night but not on the other. After listening to pink noise, they performed an average of *three times better* on a word-recall test than they did after the no-sound nights. Larger and longer studies are needed to prove that pink noise is an effective memory tool, but the initial results are promising.

In the meantime, you can buy pink-noise machines (such as SONEic, $19.99...or the Goldline PN2 Pink Noise Generator, $125) online. Pink noise phone apps are also available.

Caveat: For memory improvement, the sounds must be initiated at precise moments during slow-wave sleep. This requires tracking brain activity in real time, which the home devices obviously can't do—but they still may help you sleep better!

Need an Energy Boost? These 5 Foods Do the Trick

Lisa R. Young, PhD, RD, CDN, a nutritionist in private practice and an adjunct professor of nutrition at New York University in New York City. Dr. Young has taught and counseled for more than 20 years, regularly lecturing at corporations, schools and public health departments on a wide variety of topics. She is author of *The Portion Teller Plan.* PortionTeller.com

Hitting a wall at 3 pm—even though you had a full night's sleep? Your first instinct may be to reach for a cup o' joe or a sugary treat just to keep you going.

EASY TO DO...

Simple Memory-Boosting Trick

Boost your memory by shutting your eyes. In a recent study, researchers asked participants questions about a short film they had been shown. Participants who shut their eyes while being asked the questions gave 23% more correct answers than those who kept their eyes open.

Theory: Closing your eyes blocks out distractions and reduces your brain's cognitive load, which helps you remember more.

Study of 178 people by researchers at University of Surrey, UK, published in *Legal and Criminological Psychology*.

Why this is a mistake: It's common for our blood sugar levels to drop in the late afternoon, making us feel tired and hungry. But the mind-buzzing, heart-racing effects of so-called quick fixes soon lead to a crash-and-burn, putting us right back where we started.

WHAT WORKS BETTER

Once you accept that quick fixes are really nothing more than "fool's gold," you can embrace the true source of sustained vitality—energy-producing *real* foods.

What you need to know: Often it is not a single ingredient itself that invigorates but how that powerhouse is *combined* with flavorful and nutritionally satisfying add-ons.

Rule of thumb: The best foods for natural all-day vibrancy typically balance a complex carbohydrate with a healthy fat and a punch of protein—a combination that takes longer to digest and stabilizes blood sugar levels for hours.

For advice on the best foods to eat for all-day energy, we spoke with leading nutritionist Lisa Young, PhD, RD, CDN, to learn about her top choices for maintaining day-long vim and vigor...

AVOCADO

Avocado contains heart-healthy monounsaturated fat and provides nearly 20 vitamins and minerals.

My favorite way to eat avocado: *Sliced or smashed on whole-grain toast.* In addition to being a perfect base for creamy avocado, whole-grain toast boasts its own benefits and makes for a great energy-boosting combo—it fills you up with fiber and is low in saturated fat.

CANNED SALMON

What's easier than peeling back the lid on a ready-to-serve portion of this versatile, tasty fish? Especially when two ounces of canned salmon contain just 90 calories and only 1 g of saturated fat in a convenient protein source.

Note: To reduce possible toxins, I recommend wild salmon sold in a BPA-free can.

My favorite way to eat canned salmon: *On salad greens topped with heart-smart olive oil and a side of polenta.* Cornmeal-based polenta, which is loaded with complex carbs to keep blood sugar levels stable for hours, even comes in ready-made refrigerated tubes. You can cook up a slice or two in just minutes on the stove or in the oven!

FARMER'S CHEESE

Protein-packed foods such as farmer's cheese—born from farmers' efforts to use milk left over after cream is skimmed for butter—can help you stay on top of your game. Two tablespoons of farmer's cheese offer 4 g of protein with only 2.5 g of fat and 40 calories.

My favorite way to eat farmer's cheese: *On Ezekiel 4:9 bread with cinnamon and/or fresh walnuts on top.* You can spread farmer's cheese, with its ricotta-like texture, on Ezekiel bread—itself an efficient protein source as well as a unique blend of six grains and legumes. A dash of cinnamon not only adds the yin-yang of sweet and savory, but also helps control blood sugar levels. A few diced walnuts provide satisfying crunch and omega-3 fats that promote cardiovascular health.

QUINOA

Quinoa (pronounced "keen-wah") contains iron, B vitamins, magnesium, calcium, potassium and other nutrients, boasting zero saturated or trans fats. Even better, it takes only about 15 minutes to prepare.

My favorite way to eat quinoa: *With chopped veggies and garnished with chickpeas.* By topping with chickpeas, you'll boost the overall protein, vitamin and mineral content—and stay fuller longer. Or you can try a quinoa-based hot cereal.

SORGHUM

Sorghum, a substantial source of protein and dietary fiber, is a versatile, gluten-free grain that keeps your belly full and your energy levels high.

My favorite way to eat sorghum: *In a tomato and red pepper slaw.*

To prepare: After simmering and draining your desired amount of sorghum, add some color by folding in a julienned slaw of tomatoes and red peppers.

Tomatoes, with their energy-boosting carbs and fiber, are also a major source of the anticancer nutrient lycopene...while red peppers aid in the absorption of iron from food, which boosts energy by promoting optimal blood oxygen levels.

Nature's Stress Fighters

Maria Noël Groves, RH, a clinical herbalist and founder of Wintergreen Botanicals Herbal Clinic & Education Center in Allenstown, New Hampshire. She is registered with the American Herbalists Guild and is certified by the Southwest School of Botanical Medicine. She is author of *Body into Balance: An Herbal Guide to Holistic Self-Care.* WintergreenBotanicals.com

In today's always-on-the-go, connected-to-everyone world, many of us feel *constantly* stimulated. No wonder up to 90% of all doctor visits are prompted by stress-related complaints, such as fatigue, pain, high blood pressure and cardiovascular disease.

Of course, a doctor visit usually means another prescription. It's not surprising that sedatives, antidepressants and antianxiety drugs are among the best-selling drugs in the US. While these potent pharmaceuticals may *temporarily* improve mood and other stress-related symptoms, they're not a permanent fix and often come with side effects.

NATURE'S STRESS FIGHTERS

The best way to deal with stress is with some basic—but critical—lifestyle changes, such as getting regular exercise, eating a healthier diet and maintaining a stress-reducing practice, such as meditation.

To augment those healthy habits, you can often use herbal medicines to help your body (and brain) cope with stress-related symptoms.*

For stress-related disorders, so-called *adaptogenic* herbs work well. Also known as stress modulators, these herbs can create balance when your body's stress-related hormones are too high or too low. The herbs aren't always a substitute for prescription drugs but may help you avoid them.

The following herbs can be taken singly or in combination. If you're combining herbs, be sure to keep their individual properties in mind as they can lessen each other's effects or work in synergy. While you can safely combine most adaptogenic herbs, be aware of what you're eating and drinking. Coffee, for example, can negate the calming effects of many herbs.

Options for herbal therapy: You can take the herbs below as a tea, tincture or capsule. Follow the recommended doses listed on the product labels.

BEST STRESS-FIGHTING HERBS

1. Ashwagandha. This nutty-tasting herb gives a mild energy boost. Paradoxically, it can also improve sleepiness at bedtime.

A study in the *Indian Journal of Psychological Medicine* found that people who took ashwagandha for 60 days had levels of cortisol (one of the main stress hormones) that were nearly 28% lower than those who took a placebo. The herb also gives a mild boost to thyroid function.

Caution: Ashwagandha is in the nightshade family. Try a small amount at first if you react to nightshades such as tomatoes and potatoes. If you have hyperthyroid disease or are on thyroid medication, consult your physician before taking ashwagandha.

2. Schizandra. It's a "mid-range" adaptogen that both calms and energizes, depending on what your body needs. It can help people with stress-related insomnia. It's also good for boosting vitality, mood and libido, and is one of the best herbs for stimulating digestion and improving liver detoxification.

Caution: Schizandra occasionally aggravates an active ulcer or gastroesophageal reflux disease (GERD).

HERBS FOR ANXIETY

If you mainly suffer from anxiety or stress-related "nerves," try one of the calming adaptogens below...

3. Holy basil. This herb contains eugenol and other aromatic compounds that give it a pleasant odor—and that appear to reduce stress and improve mental clarity.

Studies suggest that holy basil reduces the stress hormone cortisol. In addition, it's often used for reducing anxiety and grief.

You can take this herb as needed or on a long-term basis. I particularly love it as tea and grow it in my garden.

How to try it: Steep one teaspoon to one tablespoon of dried holy basil (or a handful of the fresh herb) in eight ounces of water for 15 minutes. Drink one to three times daily.

4. Gotu kola. There is some evidence that this herb improves brain circulation and mental functions, while also reducing anxiety. The effects of gotu kola are subtle, making it ideal for long-term emotional balance.

You may not notice significant improvements for two to three months, and you can take it for a year or more. You can also safely combine it with other adaptogens, such as holy basil or ashwagandha, if you feel you need more potent (and faster) effects.

Note: Combination stress formulas are readily available on the market and can often be helpful. Take a look at the ingredients and consider each herb's individual benefits and potential side effects. Pick a formula that makes sense for your needs, and listen to your body.

Using these herbs: Most of the herbal adaptogens listed above will have some effect within one to three days, but with regular use, the effects tend to get more pronounced over the course of several weeks. If you don't notice improvement after two months, try one of

*Before trying herbal therapy, consult your pharmacist or seek a naturopathic doctor or clinical herbalist's assistance, especially if you take prescription medications or have a chronic medical condition.

the other herbs. Side effects, if any, will usually occur within the first day or two.

While you could take any of these herbs as needed—for example, a cup of holy basil tea on a stressful day—they work better when taken regularly for several months to a year. They're generally not dangerous to take on an ongoing basis, but most people find that they don't need them after a while.

SHOPPING FOR HERBS

You can find good-quality herbs at your local herb shop or natural-food store. Seek organic herbs whenever possible—they are grown without synthetic chemicals and more likely to be good quality. Some of my favorite brands for capsules and tinctures include Gaia Herbs, Herb Pharm, Oregon's Wild Harvest and MegaFood.

Good online sources for dried herbs include Zack Woods Herb Farm at ZackWoodsHerbs.com...and Mountain Rose Herbs at MountainRoseHerbs.com.

Boost Your Mood Naturally

Too-low levels of the powerful neurotransmitter *serotonin* have been linked to depression, anxiety, irritability as well as mental decline.

Natural ways to raise serotonin levels: Vigorous aerobic exercise...20 minutes a day of peaceful meditation...learning to replace negative thoughts and reactions with more positive ones...exposure to sunlight or lamps that mimic its effects...consuming probiotic foods such as pickles, sauerkraut, kefir and yogurt with active cultures...adding the spice turmeric to food...eating foods high in omega-3 fatty acids, such as cold-water fish including halibut, herring and salmon as well as flaxseed oil and walnuts.

Massachusetts General Hospital's publication *Mind, Mood & Memory.*

How to Breathe to Reduce Stress

Deep breathing, which uses the diaphragm rather than chest muscles, pulls oxygen in more effectively than shallower breathing.

To practice it, sit straight in a comfortable chair with feet flat on the floor or lie down flat...close your eyes, and place one hand on your stomach...breathe deeply through your nose, into the back of your throat and down to your belly, letting your chest expand...let your abdomen slowly deflate as you breathe out...repeat several times, increasing the amount of time for inhalation and exhalation...direct your breath into your upper back, letting your ribs spread and relax with each breath in and out...don't force it—let your breath flow naturally.

HealthLetter.MayoClinic.com

No More Emotional Eating...

Break emotional eating patterns by figuring out what triggers them and finding alternative responses to those stimuli...

Chew sugarless gum so you have the sensation of chewing. *Relax* whenever emotional cravings strike—try a hot shower, a soak in a tub or listening to music. *Become mindful* by learning meditation-based mindfulness, which helps you become more aware of eating triggers and behaviors. *Exercise* when emotions start to take over—go for a walk or jog, or do yoga or tai chi. *Distract yourself* by playing a game on your phone, doing a hobby or organizing a messy closet.

NutritionLetter.Tufts.edu

4

Easy Fitness & Weight Loss

9 New Ways to Lose the Last 10 Pounds

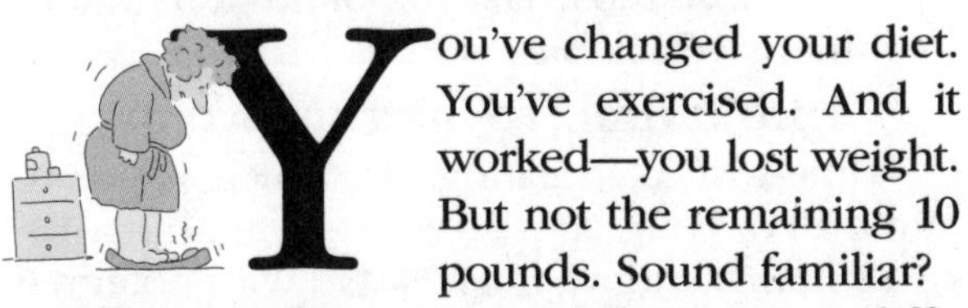

You've changed your diet. You've exercised. And it worked—you lost weight. But not the remaining 10 pounds. Sound familiar?

Those last few pounds really are more difficult to lose. One reason, ironically, is that you weigh less now—so you need fewer calories to maintain your weight. Your body also fights back, resisting further weight loss through hormonal and metabolic means. Your resting metabolic rate falls, so you burn fewer calories at rest. Hormones kick in to increase your appetite. The result may be a weight plateau—or even weight regain.

What to do? If you can't bear the thought of cutting more calories or spending more time exercising, here are some unconventional methods to get you over the finish line…

DRINK GREEN TEA

A green tea habit may help you lose weight.

One reason: Gut bacteria. A recent study showed that mice that received green and black tea extracts had fewer gut microbes linked to obesity and more linked to lean body mass. Green tea is particularly rich in gut-friendly polyphenols. In a study published in *Clinical Nutrition*, women who consumed green tea extract every day for 12 weeks lost an average of 2.5 pounds—without following a reduced-calorie diet.

GET OUTSIDE—AND GO HIGH

Do you exercise mostly indoors? Head out! Exercising outside burns more calories, due to harder terrain and wind resistance, and can improve your mood and increase your enjoyment of the workout.

Torey Armul, MS, RD, CSSD, LD, a spokesperson for the Academy of Nutrition and Dietetics. She counsels clients on weight management, sports nutrition and pregnancy and family nutrition through her private practice in Columbus, Ohio. eatrightPRO.org

Fun fact: Gardeners weigh less than nongardeners, according to research—11 pounds less for women, 16 for men.

To really jump-start your weight loss, though, book your next vacation in the mountains. Research published in *Obesity* found that spending one week at a high altitude (8,700 feet) led study participants to eat less than those at sea level and to lose an average of three pounds. Both metabolic rate and levels of *leptin* (the "satiety" hormone) were higher.

GO BEYOND CALORIES

Counting calories still is the primary way most people approach weight loss—but different foods with the same calorie counts can have very different effects on satiety levels and weight.

Case in point: Plant-based proteins—beans, legumes, nuts, seeds, soy and grains such as quinoa—help you feel more full than animal-based proteins. Fiber is one reason. In one study, participants who ate a plant-based rather than an animal-based breakfast spontaneously ate about 100 fewer calories at lunch.

SHARE A SELFIE

If you've kept your weight goals to yourself, it's time to share them aloud. Make a public commitment. It will increase accountability and help build a community of support. That comes in handy when you need motivation or experience a setback.

One study from Northwestern University found that people in an online weight-loss group who "friended" others in the group and posted photos of their progress lost more weight than those who were less active online. In another study, those who shared goals with friends were more likely than those who didn't to meet them (62% versus 43%). Social-media outlets such as Twitter and Facebook can help, too, studies show—just be sure to unfollow people who don't support you or who make fun of your goals.

ADD SOME WEIGHT ON PURPOSE—MUSCLE WEIGHT

Building strength may not have been your focus in the initial stages of your weight loss, but it's crucial now. As you lost weight, your metabolic rate decreased. Strength training helps bring it back up. In one study, for example, a 26-week strength-training program increased resting metabolic rate by 7%.

Muscles are not miracle calorie burners, though. Their ability to radically change metabolism often is hyped in the media. The average actually is about 50 calories a day, according to a research review—not much if you're seeking a big weight loss. But adding muscle is great if you want a little edge to lose those last few pounds, since 50 calories per day translates to losing five extra pounds a year.

DON'T LET ANOTHER NIGHT GO BY

You know that sleep is essential for health, but you might not realize how even a little sleep deprivation can drive cravings and slow metabolism.

Amazing statistic: After a single night of poor sleep, study subjects ate an average of 385 extra calories the next day, according to statistical analysis of multiple studies. In fact, just two consecutive sleep-deprived nights (four hours each night) may be enough to alter your metabolism, according to research published in *Endocrine Development*. It increases the body's level of the hunger-stimulating hormone *ghrelin* and decreased hunger-reducing *leptin*. To lose those last 10 pounds, commit to healthier sleep habits.

TIME-RESTRICTED DAYTIME EATING

"Time-restricted eating," in which you consume all of your calories each day within a 10- or 12-hour window, is a new fad with potential weight-loss benefits. But to make it work best, eat your calories relatively early in the day. One two-month study from the University of Pennsylvania's Perelman School of Medicine found that participants who ate all their calories between 8 am and 7 pm weighed less than those who did so between noon and 11 pm—and they all consumed the same number of calories. For the daytime eaters, ghrelin peaked earlier and leptin peaked later. That helps deter late-night cravings.

If you're truly hungry late in the evening, don't be a martyr! Instead, choose a snack with fiber and protein, such as a handful of nuts...or fruit with Greek yogurt.

REDEFINE YOURSELF

One of the greatest predictors of weight-loss success is in your own head. A study published in *International Journal of Obesity* found that regardless of actual weight status, people who perceived themselves as overweight were significantly more likely to gain weight. It may not be easy, but give yourself credit for the weight you have lost (even if you haven't hit your goal), and try to think positively about yourself and your weight. Love and respect yourself just as you are.

TAKE A BREAK

Dieting all the time is exhausting—and can be self-defeating. Research published in *International Journal for Obesity* found that men who took a two-week break from dieting lost more weight than those who dieted continuously. During their dieting break, the men ate simply to maintain their weight. So take a break when you feel you need it, be kind to yourself and envision yourself meeting your goals.

TAKE NOTE...

Get Sleep to Lose Weight

Not getting enough sleep puts you at a higher risk for obesity. Individuals who slept an average of six hours per night had waist measurements 1.2 inches greater than those who slept nine hours per night. Less sleep also was associated with reduced levels of HDL, or the "good" cholesterol that can help protect against heart disease.

Study of 1,615 adults by researchers at University of Leeds, UK, published in *PLOS ONE*.

Why Popular Weight-Loss Plans Fail

Gerard E. Mullin, MD, a gastroenterologist and associate professor of medicine at The Johns Hopkins University School of Medicine and director of Integrative GI Nutrition Services at The Johns Hopkins Hospital, both in Baltimore. Dr. Mullin's most recent book is *The Gut Balance Revolution: Boost Your Metabolism, Restore Your Inner Ecology, and Lose the Weight for Good!*

Many popular weight-loss approaches work at first but actually set you up for long-term weight gain. How? By creating an imbalance in your digestive tract microbes, aka your gut microbiome. *Common mistakes...*

- **Yo-yo dieting.** Dieters often lose a lot of weight and then regain it—sometimes more than they lost. One reason may be that yo-yo dieting harms the gut microbiome. In one recent study published in Nature, the microbiomes of animals that lost and regained weight changed in ways that quickened weight regain.

- **Eating too much or too little fat—or the wrong kinds.** While high-fat diets permit harmful gut bugs to thrive, going on a low-fat diet can backfire, too. You want healthful fats, which are anti-inflammatory and feed your good bugs. The best anti-inflammatory fats include olive oil and, for high-heat cooking, canola and coconut oils. Eat seafood for gut-friendly omega-3 fatty acids—flaxseeds and chia seeds are good sources, as well. On the other hand, minimize your consumption of conventionally raised red meat, which is chockful of inflammatory omega-6 fats. (If you really love meat, go for grass-fed cattle raised on pasture—the meat is lower in inflammatory fats.)

- **Too little fiber.** Too many diets, especially low-carb ones, skip high-fiber foods. But a healthy gut microbiome needs fiber to thrive. Aim for 25 grams to 35 grams a day.

Best sources: Beans, cruciferous vegetables (broccoli, cauliflower, kale, cabbage), fruits (especially berries) and oats. Eat a variety of fiber-rich foods to diversify your microbiome.

- **Artificial sweeteners.** Saccharin, sucralose and aspartame may have zero calories, but they change the gut biome and not in a good way. Animal and human studies link them to weight gain.

- **The wrong probiotic.** If you take a probiotic supplement and are trying to lose weight or keep weight off, look for a product containing *Lactobacillus gasseri*, *Lactobacillus plan-*

tarum and/or *Lactobacillus paracasei*. Even better—eat more probiotic-rich fermented foods such as yogurt, kefir, sauerkraut, kimchi, tempeh and miso.

After two months, the egg eaters had lost 65% more weight than the bagel eaters.

From *Bottom Line's Speed Healing* by Bill Gottlieb, CHC, available at BottomLineStore.com/speed.

Trick to Eat Less

Use Grandma's dishes to reduce portion size. Vintage dishes are smaller than the dishes we use today. Smaller plates make portions seem larger—you'll serve yourself less food!

Lisa R. Young, PhD, RD, CDN, nutritionist and adjunct professor, New York University, New York City, and author of *The Portion Teller Plan*. PortionTeller.com

Best Fruits for Weight Loss

People who ate the most fruits high in antioxidant flavonoids (especially those with anthocyanins, found in dark-colored fruits such as blueberries, red grapes and cherries) gained less weight than those who ate the least, according to a 25-year study of more than 124,000 adults.

Theory: Flavonoids may help boost metabolism and reduce fat absorption.

Note: Both fresh and frozen dark-colored fruits can be eaten.

Monica Bertoia, PhD, MPH, research associate, Harvard T.H. Chan School of Public Health, Boston.

Dieters: Eat Eggs

In a recent study, one group of dieters ate two eggs for breakfast, and another group ate bagels with the same number of calories.

Tasty Fixes for Food Cravings!

Janet Bond Brill, PhD, RDN, FAND, a registered dietitian nutritionist, a fellow of the Academy of Nutrition and Dietetics and a nationally recognized nutrition, health and fitness expert who specializes in cardiovascular disease prevention. Located in Allentown, Pennsylvania, Dr. Brill is author of *Blood Pressure DOWN, Cholesterol DOWN* and *Prevent a Second Heart Attack*. DrJanet.com

It's been a long, hectic day, when all of a sudden you pass your local bakery and simply *must* have that gooey fudge brownie. *Translation*: Lots of butter, sugar, chocolate...and calories. You gobble it down, lick the fudge off your fingers, then proceed to feel guilty about indulging in such a decadent treat and resolve to forgo sugar. Smart idea? Not really. A better approach would be to analyze when and where these cravings tend to occur. Once you determine your vulnerable times, you can plan ahead and have healthy treats at hand. *Simple substitutions to reach for the next time you have that insatiable urge to splurge on something that is...*

• **Sweet.** If you're in the mood for something sinfully delicious, chocolate may be your guilty pleasure. If so, have some emergency backups around such as a 60-calorie chocolate pudding cup, topped with fat-free whipped topping. Or how about a rich dark chocolate peppermint patty? It's got 70% less fat than candy bars and only 140 calories. Be sure to buy the single patties and not a huge bag of minis, or you may not be able to stop at just one! Maybe you're yearning for a slice of strawberry shortcake smothered in real whipped cream (to the tune of about 400 calories). Instead, you'd be much better off having a slice of low-calorie angel food cake, topped with thawed Lite Cool Whip, fresh strawberries and a fresh raspberry purée. This version offers all the deliciousness for half the calories, along with the nutrition from the fresh berries (fiber, antioxidants and many vitamins and minerals—especially vitamin C and potassium).

• **Salty and crunchy.** If you find yourself eating out and need some crunch with your sandwich, you don't have to give yourself a big hit of sodium by grabbing a bag of chips. Instead, head to the salad bar and have some thick carrot slices to satisfy that urge to crunch. If you feel you must have some chips during your favorite miniseries, you can make your own healthy version of potato chips by using extra-thin sliced potatoes (coat with olive oil, season and bake at 400°F for about 30 minutes). Dying for fatty, salty movie popcorn? Try buying popcorn kernels and popping them up in a microwave popper. Add your own seasoning and a spray oil, and you avoid the added calories, bad fat and sodium found in the commercial brands. Or you can munch on seaweed snacks, the latest nutrition trend that's *delicious,* not fishy at all, and truly addicting. Most seaweed snacks, available at many major supermarket chains such as Walmart, Whole Foods and Trader Joe's, house a cocktail of nutrients, including vitamins A and C, calcium, iodine, potassium, iron and magnesium. And all this for a measly 50 calories a pack!

• **Fast food.** If a juicy burger with the works is on your mind, make your own veggie burger or portobello mushroom burger at home and add on all the toppings (this satisfies your craving for a fraction of the fat and calories). It's not fast food, but definitely a tasty substitute. Or what if you just have to have that gooey, cheesy slice or two of pizza? Make your own by using a whole-wheat pita or tortilla topped with tomato sauce and lots of melted low-fat mozzarella cheese. In the mood for Chinese fried rice? Try making your own using cauliflower rice (chop florets in a blender to make the "rice," then fry in extra-virgin olive oil and season with a touch of low-sodium soy sauce and pepper).

The truth is, it's OK to splurge on unhealthy foods once in a while. It's when these indulgences become a daily habit that these less-than-nutritious choices can harm your health and lead to weight gain. If you try these healthy and satisfying swaps, you can (occasionally) have your cake and eat it, too!

BETTER WAY...

Have Your Pasta and Lose Weight, Too

Do as many Europeans do and eat a small portion of pasta as an appetizer...then have a big salad as your main course.

Lisa R. Young, PhD, RD, CDN, nutritionist and adjunct professor, New York University, New York City, and author of *The Portion Teller Plan*. PortionTeller.com

A Hot Bath Burns 140 Calories

A one-hour bath in 104°F water raises core body temperature by 1.8 degrees—as much as one hour of cycling. Although cycling burns more calories, this kind of bath burns as many calories as a 30-minute walk.

Steve Faulkner, PhD, research associate, Loughborough University, UK, and leader of a study published in *Temperature*.

The Ultimate Workout: 2 Exercises Keep You Fit!

Michael J. Joyner, MD, physician-researcher and leading expert on human performance and exercise physiology at the Mayo Clinic, Rochester, Minnesota. His research has focused on how humans respond to various forms of physical and mental stress. DrMichaelJoyner.com

If you're similar to most efficiency-minded Americans, you may be on the lookout for the exercise that's going to whip you into shape, keep you fit and slow down aging—

with the least amount of time and fuss. For those of us looking to streamline our workouts to just the essentials, two simple exercises can do the job. They are challenging but worth the effort...and can be easily modified to suit your individual fitness level.

THE DYNAMIC DUO

Burpees and jumping rope are the dynamic duo, in my opinion. Why burpees and jumping rope? Of all the exercise choices, these maintain high vigor while promoting strength, endurance, balance and coordination *all at once*—precisely the capabilities that tend to deteriorate as we age, increasing our risk for falls and other mishaps. *These exercises are also...*

- **Compact.** Both can be done almost anywhere—whether you're in a hotel room...in your family room...or in your backyard. *Note:* If you're indoors, you need adequate ceiling height to jump rope.
- **Quick.** The regimen can be compressed into a tidy five minutes if you're starting out and extended to a 10-, 20- or 30-minute workout when you're ready to up your game.

PERFECTING YOUR TECHNIQUE

To get the maximum benefits and reduce your risk for injuries, it's important to do both of these exercises properly...

- **Burpees.** Unless this exercise is already part of your workout, start slowly to make sure you've got the right technique. Ready?
    - Stand straight with your arms at your sides.
    - Squat down until you can put your hands on the ground in front of your feet.
    - Kick your legs back into the plank position, straight behind you.
    - Do a push-up on your toes or on your knees.
    - Pull your legs back into the squat position.
    - Jump up as high as you can with your arms overhead.

For a somewhat easier version: Do the same exercise without the push-up and jump. If the plank position is too difficult, modify it by kicking your legs back only halfway.

- **Jumping rope.** Maybe you haven't jumped rope since you were a kid, but it will come back to you. Keep the jump low to minimize the impact on your ankles and knees. When you feel ready, try using a weighted jump rope (which incorporates 1-, 3- or 5-pound weights) to rev up your heart rate and build upper-body strength. Skip the added weight if you have existing shoulder, arm or wrist problems. Use a jump rope that feels right to you—whether it has anti-slip handles or plastic beads strung on a nylon cord.

WARMING UP

Jumping jacks and running in place are great ways to warm up. These exercises are also good substitutes for burpees and jumping rope if you haven't been physically active in a while and/or want a gentler way to ease into your routine.

If jumping jacks and running in place don't appeal to you or you are concerned about your risk for falling or joint pain, there are other ways to modify the burpee–jump rope regimen while you increase your fitness.

Instead of burpees, try: *Knee bends* (also known as "squats"). If you're worried about your knees, skip the knee bends and simply stand with your back against a wall and lift up one leg with your knee bent as high as you feel comfortable. Repeat with the other leg.

Or try *push-ups,* either on the floor or against a counter.

Instead of jumping rope, try: *Brisk walking*—set a pace that puts you at the edge of being short of breath.

THE WORKOUT

To begin a burpee–jump rope regimen, do five burpees alternating with 30 seconds of jumping rope. Do each set three to five times (for a total of 15 burpees and a minute and a half of jumping rope...or 25 burpees and two and a half minutes of jumping rope). Then work up to sets of 10 burpees alternating with one minute of jumping rope. As your stamina builds, continue to alternate exercises until you work up to longer sets of up to two minutes of each. Try to do the burpee–jump rope workout two to three days a week with brisk walking or cycling on the other days.

Important: If you have any chronic medical conditions, consult your doctor before trying this workout. Stop immediately if either activity causes pain. It will take time to build up your stamina. Scale up according to your age and ability.

Intense Workout Lowers Libido

Men who classified themselves as athletes and did prolonged or intense workouts reported lower sex drives than men whose exercise routines were moderate or light in intensity. The study did not prove cause and effect, but previous studies of men who exercise intensely have found reductions in the sex hormone testosterone both immediately and over the long term.

Study of 1,077 physically active adult men by researchers at University of North Carolina at Chapel Hill, published in *Medicine & Science in Sports & Exercise.*

Lots of Exercise Needed to Keep Weight Off

In a study of former contestants on *The Biggest Loser* TV show, only those who did at least 80 minutes a day of moderate activity such as walking, or 35 minutes a day of vigorous exercise such as running, did not regain weight within six years. Significant weight loss causes the body's metabolism to slow down, so additional exercise is needed to compensate for the lower caloric needs. To keep weight off after losing it, it is necessary to increase physical activity well beyond what is recommended for people who are trying to maintain their weight without having lost a lot of it. Ask your doctor for details.

Jennifer C. Kerns, MD, hospitalist and codirector of bariatric surgery, Washington DC Veterans Affairs Medical Center, former contestant on *The Biggest Loser,* and lead author of a study of 14 contestants, published in *Obesity.*

EASY TO DO...

The Workout Work-Around

Do you find it difficult to keep up with the standard exercise recommendation of 150 minutes per week?

Recent study: When the activity levels of 6,000 women ages 63 to 99 were tracked for seven days, just 30 minutes of light housework per day (such as sweeping or doing the laundry) was linked to a 12% lower risk for death over the next three years. Those who added another half-hour of daily exercise slashed their risk by 39%.

Takeaway: As you age, don't get hung up on "working out"—just keep moving!

Michael LaMonte, PhD, research associate professor of epidemiology, University at Buffalo, New York.

How to Stick to an Exercise Routine

Two secrets for sticking to an exercise routine...

- **Work out at the same time on most days.** Pick a regular time for exercise, and stay with it as many days of the week as possible—workouts will become part of your regular day.
- **Use visual cues to get yourself going.** For example, lay out running clothes, shoes and headphones in a specific place so that you see them when you wake up. This also helps turn exercise into a routine that you do automatically without having to give it much thought.

Navin Kaushal, PhD, postdoctoral fellow in preventive medicine, Montreal Heart Institute, University of Montreal, and leader of a study published in *British Journal of Health Psychology.*

Even Weekend Warriors Live Longer

I-Min Lee, MD, ScD, professor of medicine at Harvard Medical School, Boston, reported by Bob Barnett, editor, *Bottom Line Personal*, BottomLineInc.com.

My wife swims three times a week, works out at the gym on other days... fits in yoga at home frequently...and walks our Labradoodle most mornings.

Me, I plan to exercise about twice as often as I do. I squeeze in workouts on weekdays, yes, but to be honest, there are weeks that I say hi to the gym only on Saturday.

So I was happy to learn the good news—*I might not die young*!

Fitness guidelines traditionally stress exercising at least three to five times per week. The goal is to accumulate 150 minutes of "moderate" intensity exercise such as brisk walking or 75 minutes of "intense" exercise such as running.

But it turns out that procrastinators, even fitness underachievers, live longer, too. In a recent study published in *JAMA Internal Medicine*, researchers tracked activity habits and longevity of more than 63,000 people, age 40 and older, over a period of nearly 20 years.

Findings: "Weekend warriors" who exercised only once or twice per week enjoyed virtually the same longevity advantages as several-times-a-week go-getters—even when they didn't quite make the 75/150 goal. They were 30% less likely to die over that period than inactive folks who almost never exercised.

Is a daily exercise habit good? Of course it is. But the point is, any regular exercise is a lot healthier than none. "We need to dispel the myth that you have to run marathons or do triathlons for health benefits," says study coauthor I-Min Lee, MD, ScD, professor of medicine at Harvard Medical School. "We don't even say 'exercise'—it's just 'physical activity.'"

As for me, I love bike rides on weekends. They might even be lifesavers.

If You Sit Too Much...

Exercise is not enough to combat the health risks of sitting too much. Adults age 60 and older spend an average of 8.5 to 9.6 hours a day sitting, and prolonged sedentary time could increase the risk for diabetes, heart disease and death from any cause.

Self-defense: Stand up or exercise while watching TV, walk around while talking on the phone, stand up or walk around at regular intervals.

Statement by the American Heart Association, published in *Circulation*.

Does Exercising in the Cold Burn More Calories?

While exercising in the cold weather can burn hundreds more calories per hour than exercising in warm weather, this effect primarily results from shivering. To burn extra calories, leave off a layer while keeping your hands, feet and head covered. If you have a heart or circulation issue, check with your doctor before exercising in the cold.

The downside of cold weather exercise is that your strength, power and endurance are all decreased, which often translates into shorter and less intense workouts.

Tom Holland, CPT, exercise physiologist, Darien, Connecticut. TeamHolland.com

Best Way to Track Your Steps

What's best for tracking steps—a pedometer, fitness band or app?

If your aim is simply to track your steps and you get frustrated with technology, buy a pedometer (under $20) and just clip it on your belt loop or waistband. Higher-end pedometers will track other metrics (such as calories burned) and will sync to your smartphone or tablet.

An electronic fitness band, worn like a watch, will count your steps, too. Most also measure your heart rate and track the hours you sleep and the calories you burn. Sync the device to your phone or computer to chart your workouts and goals on a graph. These range in price from under $100 to $200, and the battery must be recharged every few days.

Many fitness apps track the same things as an electronic fitness band but require a smartphone, smart-watch or tablet. Some apps are free, others require a fee.

Tom Holland, CPT, exercise physiologist, Darien, Connecticut. TeamHolland.com

Yoga Can Be Dangerous: Avoid These Common Mistakes

Timothy McCall, MD, a board-certified internist and medical editor at *Yoga Journal*...coeditor of the 2016 medical textbook *The Principles and Practice of Yoga in Health Care*...and author of the best-selling *Yoga as Medicine*. Dr. McCall, who lives in Burlington, Vermont, has practiced yoga and meditation for more than 20 years and has studied with many of the world's leading yoga teachers and yoga therapists. He lectures and teaches yoga therapy seminars throughout the world. DrMcCall.com

Yoga is good for you, right? Not always. *Troubling recent finding:* For one year, researchers tracked more than 350 people who took yoga classes. Nearly 11% of the participants developed a new pain problem, often lasting a few months. And 21% reported that yoga had aggravated existing injuries.

What I tell my patients and clients: As a medical doctor and yoga instructor for more than 20 years, I know that the risk for injury from practicing yoga can be much lower than from many other forms of exercise such as running or tennis—if you avoid making common mistakes. And by staying injury-free, you will enjoy the many benefits of regular yoga practice—relaxation and stress relief...pain relief...a stronger, more flexible body...and a more peaceful mind.

Here's how to bypass the injury-causing errors people often make when they practice yoga...

WRONG TYPE OF CLASS

There are many different styles and types of yoga—from the gentle and restorative to the intense and aerobic. Some of the styles investigated in the recent study were intense types in which participants move quickly from pose to pose without stopping. (*Examples*: Vinyasa Flow, Power Yoga and Ashtanga Yoga.)

In my experience, most yoga injuries happen to people doing more vigorous and acrobatic styles of yoga. Vigorous, flowing styles of yoga such as Vinyasa can be challenging and invigorating and therefore appealing. But it is not always a safe choice for anyone middle-aged or older because it's too fast and demanding, making injury more likely. Also, because the sequence of poses is quick, participants often do the poses incorrectly, with muscles and bones improperly aligned, increasing the risk for injury. The teacher may not notice these mistakes in alignment because students move so quickly from pose to pose.

My advice: If you are fit and under age 50, more athletically demanding yoga may be fine for you. If you are over age 50 and already practice flowing yoga without problems, you may be fine to continue, but the older you get, the riskier it becomes. If you are not fit or if you have a chronic health problem such as rheumatoid arthritis, poorly controlled high blood pressure or a degenerative disease of the nervous system such as Parkinson's, choose a gentler style of yoga. Examples may be called gentle yoga, restorative yoga or yoga for seniors. Other good choices include Yin Yoga and beginning Iyengar Yoga classes.

Helpful: If you want to practice a fast-paced Vinyasa-style yoga, first take a few classes in which you learn to do the poses slowly and correctly—and then speed up.

Red flag: Anyone who is pregnant, has multiple sclerosis or a chronic inflammatory condition such as lupus or inflammatory bowel disease should avoid hot yoga, including a type of hot yoga called Bikram Yoga—in which the room may be heated to 105°F. The intense heat can aggravate inflammatory conditions or harm a growing fetus.

UNDERTRAINED TEACHER

All the yoga teachers in the recent study had at least 200 hours of training—the amount required by the Yoga Alliance, a nonprofit association of yoga teachers and schools.

That might sound like a lot of training, but it's nowhere near enough to ensure quality instruction. In some instances, much of that training happens online without direct supervision by a qualified teacher.

Bottom line: You are more likely to be injured in a class conducted by a teacher who is undertrained.

My advice: If possible, find a teacher who has more training, say, 500 hours, or one who has many years of experience. To check the teacher's qualifications, you can call a yoga studio, check online or ask the teacher directly.

If you have a serious medical condition, consider consulting a yoga therapist, a yoga teacher trained to work with students with a wide variety of illnesses. To be certified in yoga therapy by the International Association of Yoga Therapists (IAYT), a teacher needs at least 1,000 hours of training. The IAYT website (IAYT.org) has a search function for finding IAYT members in a growing number of locations.

STRAINED BREATHING

In a good yoga class, you are taught to pay attention to your breath. And if you do that, the breath becomes an indicator of whether you are about to make a mistake and hurt yourself.

Often the first sign of an imminent mistake is strained breathing—gasping or holding your breath. If you maintain a discipline of breathing slowly and deeply, it's much less likely that you will hurt yourself. Added benefits of attending to your breathing include a greater sense of calm and mindfulness (steady focus in the present).

My advice: Tune into the breath throughout your yoga practice. If it becomes strained or uneven, make an adjustment that corrects the problem or come out of the pose.

TRYING TOO HARD

A common cause of injury in yoga is what I call "over-efforting"—trying to stretch more deeply into a pose when your breath and body are telling you that the extra stretch is not a good idea. Sharp pain and/or strained breathing are sure signs that the deeper stretch is a mistake. Over-efforting often happens because of peer pressure—almost everyone else in class is doing the pose in a certain way, so you want to keep up, too.

My advice: A yoga pose should be a balance of effort and ease. If the pose is more effort than ease—get out of it. If you get a sharp pain, particularly one in a joint such as the knee—get out of it. Even if the rest of the class is doing the pose...and even if the yoga teacher is telling the class to stay in the pose...if your body is telling you to get out of the pose, get out of it.

RISKIER POSES

There are several common yoga poses that are the most likely to cause injury, and they should be avoided by beginners and many people with chronic medical conditions. *These poses include...*

- **Headstands,** which can damage the neck. When I attend a general yoga class, it often is the case that about half the class should not be doing a headstand—ever. While doing the pose, their faces are red and strained, and they obviously can't wait for the teacher to tell them to come out of the pose. Upside-down poses also can be risky for those with eye problems caused by glaucoma, retinal disease or diabetes.

- **Shoulder stands and Plow pose.** These poses can overstretch the back of the neck. If your neck feels tight or uncomfortable, you probably should not be doing the pose.

My advice: It may help to put folded blankets under your shoulders (but not under your head and neck) to take the strain off your neck.

- **Lotus pose,** a sitting pose in which you put the right foot over the top of the left thigh and vice versa. This pose is only for people with flexible hips. If you use your hands to force your legs into this position, you create tremendous torque on your knee joint and you could rip or otherwise injure a knee ligament.

• **Chaturanga (yoga push-ups),** pictured here. In many athletic yoga classes, students cycle through a series of 12 poses known as a sun salutation. One element is Chaturanga, where you lower your body from Plank pose to a low push-up position. Doing this repeatedly can be murder on your shoulder—particularly if you allow the top of your upper-arm bones to jut forward in the shoulder joint.

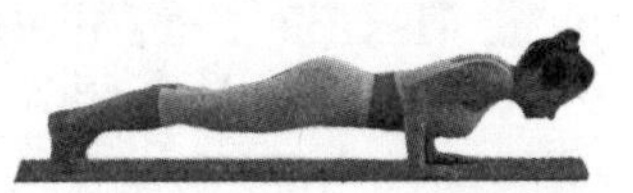

My advice: If you can't maintain good shoulder alignment, drop both knees to the ground in Plank pose, which takes some weight off, then descend the upper body to Chaturanga.

• **Deep back bends,** twists or forward bends. When in doubt, favor less extreme versions of these poses.

Surprising: Less demanding versions of poses confer most or all the health benefits of the deeper versions.

AGGRESSIVE ADJUSTMENT

Another potential cause of serious yoga injuries is when a teacher aggressively pushes on your body to take you more deeply into a pose (light touching to indicate how or where to move is fine).

My advice: Do not allow an instructor to manually force your body into any yoga position. Find a new instructor.

Photos of yoga poses: iStock.com/fizkes/londoneye/Clicknique

The Danger of Exercising Angry

Andrew Smyth, MD, PhD, postdoctoral researcher at Population Health Research Institute at McMaster University, Hamilton, Ontario, Canada, and the HRB Clinical Research Facility in Galway, Ireland.

You have a fight with your spouse or someone else, and you're red-hot angry. So you go for an intense run or to the gym. Healthy way to blow off steam, right?

BEWARE...

Pollution Negates Benefits of Exercise

Smog lowers the value of exercise. Walking in an area without traffic pollution produced better lung function and improved cardiovascular health. But the benefits were reduced or absent when people walked in a high-traffic area where they were exposed to pollution.

Kian Fan Chung, MD, DSc, professor of respiratory medicine, Imperial College London, UK, and corresponding author of a study of 119 people, published in *The Lancet*.

Not so fast. The truth is, you may be putting your heart at risk. Anger spikes adrenaline, constricts blood vessels and increases heart rate and blood pressure—and so does intense exercise. And the combination of exercising while angry is enough to trigger a heart attack in some people.

Surprising recent finding: In a study of 12,461 people in 52 countries who had a first heart attack, what happened in the hour before the attack mattered. Compared with controls who didn't have heart attacks, those who did were three times more likely to have been angry/upset and to have engaged in intense exercise beforehand—specifically, in the 60 minutes preceding the attack.

A new excuse to kick back on the couch? Not at all! Regular physical exercise plays a key role in preventing cardiovascular disease, including heart attacks. Nor should you avoid exercise when you're angry. If exercise is your go-to way to relieve stress, go ahead—just stick with your usual workout. That's true even if your regular exercise is intense—the key is not to increase the intensity or duration more than is normal for you.

Save those fitness ambitions for when your emotions are on an even keel. In the meantime, work on ways to have fewer episodes of anger—and better manage those that you do have. You might benefit from yoga, meditation, a walk in the woods, reading—or a combination.

Just remember: When you are feeling stressed, it's not the time to push your physical limits.

Why Exercise Can Cause Cavities

The more hours a week a person exercises, the higher the risk for tooth decay.

Probable reason: Exercise reduces production of saliva, which the body uses to shield tooth enamel from decay.

Self-defense: Before a workout, brush with a fluoride toothpaste.

Study done by researchers at University Hospital Heidelberg, Germany, published in *Scandinavian Journal of Medicine & Science in Sports.*

6 Common Stretching Mistakes That Can Hurt You

Karl Knopf, EdD, director of fitness therapy and senior fitness for the International Sports Sciences Association and retired director of adaptive fitness at Foothill College in Los Altos Hills, California. He is author of many fitness books including *Stretching for 50+* and a board member of Sit and Be Fit, a nonprofit organization dedicated to healthy aging.

We now know that stretching is key to staying limber and flexible. But did you know that it also could be dangerous?

Many people stretch improperly, overstressing muscles and even tendons in ways that lead to strains and sprains. An injury can come on gradually as a result of cumulative "insults" from performing a stretch a certain way over and over again. You don't know you're hurting yourself...until you're really hurt.

Other people don't stretch wrong—they just don't stretch at all or only once in a while. Many people focus more on cardiovascular exercise and weight training, yet often neglect stretching—until they get hurt. To benefit from a flexibility program, you need to practice it regularly, ideally every day.

As we age, stretching becomes even more important. Our bodies undergo changes that result in lack of elasticity. Women tend to be more flexible than men, but starting in their 50s, both genders start to lose flexibility and range of motion, especially in the shoulders and low back, which can lead to shoulder and back issues. The good news is that this age-related decline can be slowed through a regular stretching program.

By learning to stretch properly, you'll maximize your mobility...greatly reduce the risk for pain and injury...perform better at any sport you engage in...and look younger. (*One caution*: If you've had a recent fracture, sprain, injury or surgery, or if you suspect that you have osteoporosis, speak to your doctor/physical therapist first.)

Here are common stretching mistakes that can hurt you—and how to steer clear of them...

HOLDING YOUR BREATH

One common stretching mistake is holding your breath as you hold a stretch. Muscles need oxygen throughout a stretch—plus, holding your breath can elevate your blood pressure. Breathe slowly and consistently during each phase of a stretch—especially when you're holding one.

Simple stretches, such as shoulder rolls (see "Safe, Effective Stretches You Can Do Anywhere" below), don't require that you hold them. But most do. These stretches should be held for at least 20 seconds—and recent studies suggest that for older adults, 60 seconds is even better. Breathe throughout.

STRETCHING COLD

Not that long ago, we were instructed to stretch before playing sports when our muscles were "cold." Now we know that's a bad idea. Think of your muscles and tendons as taffy. Then imagine trying to stretch and bend cold taffy. It can snap. On a micro level, that's like stretching a cold, tight muscle. *Ouch*!

Much better: Warm up for five minutes or more first, before you do any stretch that you hold. Try light running...a few minutes in a steam room or sauna...or, if you're home, a warm bath.

GETTING INTENSE

Too many people follow the old paradigm that the more intense the exercise, the better. They overdo it with weights, aerobics—and stretching. In my opinion, no pain, no gain is...insane. If you feel sore a few hours after exercising, you overdid it.

Much better: When stretching, move slowly and gently, and stay within your comfort zone. You should feel mild tension in your muscles and joints. Don't push past it. Listen to your body, especially your neck, back, shoulders and knees. If you have tightness or joint pain, take some time off. If it continues, see your doctor or a physical therapist before it turns into a real issue.

GOING OLD SCHOOL—FAST AND BOUNCY

If you played a sport in high school, it's time to unlearn some things you learned, including bouncing toe touches. These moves weren't safe then, and they are even riskier now that you're older. Those neck circles you started every gym class with? Terrible! They strain supporting ligaments and can lead to pinched nerves.

That hurdler stretch where you sit with one leg out in front of you and the other bent behind you? It stresses the meniscus and the medial collateral ligament of your knee—an injury in the making. Windmill toe touches? No! Bending and rotating at the same time is a recipe for trouble.

Red flag: Avoid stretches such as the hurdler that make your knees twist or move in an unnatural position. Be careful about back bends that call for you to raise both hands over your head and lean back. That can pinch the facet joints of the spine.

Much better: Always keep knees "soft" (slightly bent) when stretching. When turning, move your body slowly, as a unit, and pivot your feet.

STRETCHING ONLY WHEN YOU EXERCISE

Chances are that if you stretch, you do so only before working out or playing a sport. Big mistake! To maintain flexibility, your muscles need to be worked just about every day.

Much better: Think of stretching as part of your daily routine, like brushing your teeth. You don't need a designated area or even to wear gym clothes. Spend a few minutes doing a body-flexibility session daily, especially in high-risk areas such as the hamstrings, shoulders and lower back.

NOT BEING WELL-BALANCED

The body is designed with opposing muscle groups, and each group needs to be worked equally. Weight training can unbalance muscles, so you need stretching to get you back into balance. *Example:* If you do a movement such as a bench press that rolls your shoulders forward, you should do a stretch that pulls them back. My golden rule is, *Do unto the front as you do unto the back, and do unto the left as you do unto the right.*

Conversely, being too flexible can be a problem, especially if you don't have muscles that are strong enough to support your joints. I once taught a dancer who kept dislocating her shoulder joints because her muscles weren't strong enough to keep her shoulders in place. It's all about balance.

One final tip—enjoy your stretching session. It's a great time to integrate the mind and the body.

SAFE, EFFECTIVE STRETCHES YOU CAN DO ANYWHERE

Here are two different kinds of stretches—no-hold stretches that you can do anywhere anytime and standard stretches for which you warm up for five minutes and then hold for at least 20 seconds, ideally 60.

Together, these stretches work on your upper and lower body. Repeat each one at least three times.

Upper-body no-hold stretches...

- **Elbow touches (for the chest).** Place your hands on your shoulders (left on left, right on right), elbows pointing forward as much as possible. Slowly move your elbows out to the side as far as is comfortable, pinching the shoulder blades together, and hold for just a few seconds. Bring your elbows back to the starting position and repeat.

• **Shoulder rolls (for the upper back).** With your arms hanging down naturally, shrug your shoulders up and squeeze them back, as if attempting to touch them together...then relax them.

• **Apple pickers (for the shoulders).** Place your hands on your shoulders (left hand on left, right on right). Then slowly raise your right hand as high up as is comfortable—reach for that apple! Return to the start position, and repeat with the left hand. Keep good posture throughout.

These are standard "hold 'em" stretches...

• **Chest stretch (for the chest and shoulders).** Stand facing a corner. Place one hand on each side wall, with your elbows in a push-up position. Lean gently into the corner until you feel a stretch across your upper chest. Hold for at least 20 seconds.

• **Seated knee to chest (for the lower back and gluteal muscles/butt).** Sit on a stable chair with your feet flat on the floor. Clasp your hands beneath your left leg. Pull your left knee toward your chest with your hands and hold for at least 20 seconds, feeling the stretch in the gluteal and low-back area. Return to start position, and repeat with other leg.

• **Rear calf stretch (for your calves).** Stand facing a wall, with both hands on the wall at shoulder height. Your knees should be slightly bent. Keeping the heel down, slide your right leg back until you feel the stretch in the calf area. Hold for at least 20 seconds. Switch sides and repeat.

Watch What You Think...

Unhealthy thoughts shorten life. In a 21-year study of more than 60,000 adults, those who believed that they were less active than other people were 71% more likely to die during the study period than those who thought they were more active—even when the activity levels were similar.

Health Psychology.

Muscle Weakness Is *Not* Inevitable: How to Fight Sarcopenia

John E. Morley, MD, director of the division of geriatric medicine and the Dammert Professor of Gerontology at Saint Louis University School of Medicine. He is coeditor of the textbook *Sarcopenia* and editor of the professional publication *Journal of the American Medical Directors Association*. Dr. Morley is also a recipient of the American Geriatrics Society's Lascher/Manning Award for Lifetime Achievement in Geriatrics.

If you're age 50 or older, you've probably noticed that your suitcases and grocery bags have gotten mysteriously heavier. It's hard to admit it, but your muscle power is not what it used to be.

Unfortunately, far too many people assume that this age-related condition known as *sarcopenia*, which literally means "loss of muscle or flesh," is an inevitable part of aging. But that's simply not true. New and better ways to prevent and diagnose this condition now are available—and there's more reason than ever to not ignore it.

The dangers of sarcopenia are more serious than experts once thought—and may involve other crucial elements of your health such as your risk for diabetes, dementia and other chronic conditions.

MORE THAN MUSCLE LOSS

With advancing age, our muscles shrink because the body loses some of its ability to convert protein into muscle tissue. By age 50, the average adult loses about 1% to 2% of muscle mass *every year*.

That's bad enough, but the real problem is what results from this muscle loss. Over time, it becomes more difficult to stand up from a chair...climb a flight of stairs...or even open a jar. People with sarcopenia are far more likely than stronger adults to suffer falls and/or bone fractures. They're also more likely to be hospitalized or admitted to a nursing home—and even die during a given period of time.

An increasing body of evidence shows that people with weak muscle strength have a higher risk of developing type 2 diabetes—a disease that can also double your risk for heart attack and stroke.

Recently discovered danger: People with sarcopenia are at increased risk for cognitive decline, including brain atrophy and dementia, according to research published in *Clinical Interventions in Aging*. In this study, people with sarcopenia were six times more likely to suffer from physical/cognitive impairments than those without this condition.

What this means to you: Collectively, the risks associated with sarcopenia are so great that clinicians from a variety of disciplines assess signs such as weight loss (from shrinking muscles)...fatigue...and a loss of strength to determine which patients are at highest risk for frailty and to work toward intervention.

THE 4-STEP PLAN

As scientists learn more about sarcopenia, the better your odds are of fighting it—if you take the appropriate steps. *What works best if you have sarcopenia...*

STEP 1: **Load up on protein.** Everyone needs protein to increase muscle size/strength. People with sarcopenia need a lot of protein. The recommended daily allowance (RDA) for protein is 0.8 g per kilogram of body weight. (That's about 54 g for a 150-pound woman.) If you've been diagnosed with sarcopenia, you need much more (about 1.2 g per kilogram of body weight).

My advice: Whenever possible, get most or all of your protein from natural foods rather than from protein-fortified foods—the nutrients in natural foods work synergistically to provide greater benefits than supplements. (For example, a small, 3.5-ounce serving of lean pork has about 26 g of protein...one-half cup of pinto beans, 7 g...and a large egg, about 6 g.)

Note: If you have kidney disease, you may have been told to limit your protein intake. Ask your nephrologist for advice on optimal protein levels for you.

Helpful: If you find it difficult to get enough protein from food alone, try whey protein supplements. You can buy these milk-based supplements in powder and liquid forms. Products such as Ensure typically provide 12 g to 20 g of protein per serving, while some protein powders deliver up to 60 g in two scoops mixed in a smoothie, for example. An advantage of whey protein supplements is that they contain *leucine*, an amino acid involved in muscle synthesis. If you can't have dairy, ask your doctor about taking an essential amino acid supplement enriched with leucine.

STEP 2: **Get enough vitamin D.** You need vitamin D for both muscle and bone strength. Depending upon the time of year and where you live, you can get all you need from 10 or so minutes of daily unprotected sun exposure. But many older adults don't spend that much time in the sun...and those who do are probably covering up or using sunscreen to protect against skin cancer.

My advice: Consume at least 1,000 international units (IU) of vitamin D daily. You can get some of this from D-fortified cereal, milk or juice. If you don't eat a lot of these foods, you may find it easier to take a 1,000-IU vitamin D supplement.

STEP 3: **Eat fish.** There's good evidence that two-to-four weekly meals of fatty fish (such as salmon, mackerel or sardines) will improve blood flow to all of the body's muscles, including the heart. In theory, this should help people with sarcopenia maintain or gain muscle mass, but the evidence that it helps isn't conclusive. Even so, I still recommend fish because it's a good protein source and has many other health benefits.

STEP 4: **Exercise the right way.** Exercise is the only way to build muscle, even if you consume plenty of protein. Aerobic exercise (such as brisk walking) is good—everyone should get some because it improves both muscle and cardiovascular health. But strength training is the real ticket for building muscle. As an added bonus, it also appears to promote brain health.

Important recent finding: When Australian researchers had 100 people age 55 or older with mild cognitive impairment (a condition that often precedes Alzheimer's) do weight-lifting exercises twice a week for six months, the stronger the study participants' muscles got, the greater their cognitive improvement, according to a study published in 2016 in *Journal of the American Geriatrics Society*.

Even if you are not able to use weight-lifting machines at a gym, there are plenty of ways to do strength training. The American College of Sports Medicine recommends lifting weights (hand weights are fine) or using elastic resistance bands two to three days a week. Unfortunately, that's too ambitious for many people.

My advice: Just do *some* exercise, whether it's 10 minutes every day or an hour once a week. If you feel too weak to start with "real" exercise, you can keep things simple.

Example: A chair-stand exercise, in which you sit in an armless chair...extend your arms in front of you...slowly stand up...then slowly lower yourself back down. Do this five to 10 times, twice daily.

For arm strength: Hold the ends of a large elastic resistance band in each hand, and stand with both feet on the middle of the band. Keeping your body straight and your elbows by your side, slowly curl your hands up toward your shoulders. You can raise both hands together or one at a time. Try to repeat the movement eight to 12 times, twice daily.

For leg strength: Sit on a chair. Keeping your back straight, slowly extend your right leg straight out in front of you and hold for several seconds before lowering it slowly back down. Repeat with the left leg. Do 10 repetitions on each leg. When this becomes easy, strap on an ankle weight that's heavy enough so that you cannot do more than 15 repetitions per leg.

IF YOU TEND TO GET BORED WITH EXERCISE...

Research shows that people who work with an exercise coach or personal trainer—at home or at a health club—are more likely to stick with regular exercise. In a program that my colleagues and I supervise, patients with sarcopenia first attend physical therapy to help restore flexibility, balance and endurance, then attend weekly sessions led by exercise coaches who are enthusiastic and keep people motivated.

My advice: Consider using an exercise coach. It may be one of the best things you do for your overall health! To find an exercise coach near you, consult the American Council on Exercise, ACEfitness.org.

ON THE HORIZON...

Skin Patch Shrinks Love Handles

An experimental patch releases medication that transforms inert white fat into calorie-burning brown fat. Mice treated with the patch had a 20% reduction in fat in four weeks.

Columbia University Medical Center and University of North Carolina.

Help for Jiggly Upper Arms

Age-related fat deposits, hormonal changes and thinning skin are to blame for "bat wings."

Injectable fillers can improve upper-arm appearance by stimulating collagen production to thicken "crepey" skin—but they do not remove flab. Ultrasound, lasers and cryolipolysis (CoolSculpting) have not proved to be effective at firming upper arms. Liposuction removes upper-arm fat but is not effective at tightening skin. Brachioplasty, the only permanent treatment for excess upper-arm skin, eliminates bat wings but leaves a scar from armpit to elbow. It is not covered by insurance and costs about $4,000.

Exercise won't tighten excess skin, but it does tone the underlying muscles.

Best: Weight-lifting exercises that target your biceps and triceps. Work up to 25 reps with 10-pound weights three times a week.

Anthony Youn, MD, a plastic surgeon in Troy, Michigan, and author of *The Age Fix*. DrYoun.com

5

The Natural Way

Studies Say Berries Are More Powerful Than Drugs!

If you were asked to make a list of "superfoods"—nutrient-loaded foods that effectively fight disease—you'd probably include items such as kale, beans, walnuts, broccoli, green tea, wild-caught salmon...and berries.

What very few people are aware of: As a superfood, berries—blueberries, strawberries, raspberries, blackberries, cranberries and the like—are in a class by themselves. They can be more health-giving than medications or supplements, according to experts at Harvard Medical School and Harvard T.H. Chan School of Public Health. The antioxidants in berries—*anthocyanins*, the compounds that give these fruits their lustrous colors—deliver a pure dose of prevention and healing to the brain, heart and every other system and cell in the body. And you don't have to eat a bushelful to get the benefits.

Here's what you need to know about the amazing power of berries...

BERRIES AND YOUR BRAIN

For more than a decade, scientists at the Jean Mayer USDA Human Nutrition Research Center on Aging at Tufts University have been studying the effect of berries on the brain—in cells and in laboratory animals. They have found that regular ingestion of blueberries, strawberries and/or blackberries can help improve "plasticity," the ability of brain cells to form new connections with one another...generate new brain cells...stop inflammation and oxidation from damaging brain cells...ease the destructive effect of stress on the brain...prevent and reverse age-related memory loss, particu-

Bill Gottlieb, CHC, a health coach certified by the American Association of Drugless Practitioners and former editor in chief of Rodale Books and Prevention Magazine Health Books. He is author of 16 health books including *Bottom Line's Speed Healing*. His website is BillGottliebHealth.com

larly short-term, or "working," memory...and protect against amyloid-beta, the plaques in the brain that cause Alzheimer's disease. *Now research has shown that blueberries can help rejuvenate the aging human brain...*

Startling recent findings: The researchers from Tufts studied 37 people, ages 60 to 75, dividing them into two groups—one group consumed one ounce of freeze-dried blueberries every day (the equivalent of one cup of fresh blueberries)...the other a blueberry placebo. At the beginning, middle and end of the three-month study, the participants took tests measuring learning and memory. By the end of the study, those in the blueberry group had a 20% improvement in their scores on a memory test compared with those in a placebo group.

Strawberries are good, too. The Tufts researchers gave participants either freeze-dried strawberry powder (the equivalent of two cups of fresh strawberries) or a placebo. After three months of daily intake, the strawberry group had much greater improvements in memory than the placebo group.

What to do: Eat one cup of blueberries or strawberries daily, either fresh or frozen. Choose organic. Every year, the Environmental Working Group announces its "Dirty Dozen," a list of the produce with the most pesticides. In 2017, strawberries topped the list and blueberries ranked number 17.

BERRIES AND YOUR HEART

Hundreds of studies show that anthocyanins battle oxidation and inflammation, the evil twins of chronic disease—including heart disease. *Berries can...*

• **Reduce high blood pressure**—the number-one risk factor for heart attack and stroke. Researchers from Florida State University studied 48 postmenopausal women with high blood pressure, giving them either one-third cup of freeze-dried blueberry powder daily or a placebo. After two months, the women getting the blueberry powder had a drop in systolic blood pressure (the upper number in a blood pressure reading) of 5.1% and a drop in diastolic blood pressure (the lower reading) of 6.3%—decreasing the risk for heart attack and stroke. Their arteries were also more flexible. There were no changes in the placebo group.

• **Decrease other risk factors for heart disease.** The cranberry is no slouch when it comes to guarding the heart. Scientists from the USDA's Human Nutrition Research Center studied 56 people, average age 50. Half of them drank two eight-ounce glasses of no-sugar-added cranberry juice daily...the other half made no changes to their diets. After two weeks, the scientists measured several risk factors for heart disease. Those drinking the juice had lower levels of *C-reactive protein* (CRP), a biomarker for heart-damaging inflammation... lower levels of triglycerides, a heart-hurting blood fat...and lower levels of blood sugar.

Bottom line: More berries, fewer heart attacks. In a study published in *Circulation,* researchers examined 18 years of health data from 93,600 women and found that those who ate three or more servings of blueberries and strawberries per week (one serving is one-half cup) had a 34% lower risk for heart attack, compared with women who ate them less than three times weekly.

What to do: If you have heart disease or any risk factors for heart disease (high blood pressure, high LDL cholesterol, high blood sugar, high CRP, a family history of heart disease), eat three cups of blueberries or strawberries per week.

BERRIES AND CANCER

Cellular research and animal research have shown that berries can fight just about every kind of cancer.

Example: A scientific paper recently published by researchers from the Medical College of Wisconsin in *Antioxidants* shows that cranberries can help fight 17 different types of cancer, including bladder, blood, brain, breast, colon, esophageal, oral, prostate and stomach cancers.

But the real test of berries' anticancer power is whether berries can help *people* with cancer. *Research published in 2016 shows that they can...*

• **Oral cancer.** Researchers at The Ohio State University Comprehensive Cancer Center gave lozenges of freeze-dried black raspberry powder (which contains very high levels of anthocyanins) to people with oral cancer for two weeks. Analyzing the tumors, they found that several genetic markers of cancer severity—prosurvival genes and proinflammatory genes—were significantly reduced by up to 21%.

In an earlier study, researchers at University of North Carolina and three other universities gave a "bioadhesive" black raspberry gel or a placebo to 40 people with premalignant oral lesions (*neoplasia*), which often progress to oral cancer. After four months, the lesions of those using black raspberry had shrunk in size and were less likely to advance to cancer.

• **Colon cancer.** In several studies on colon cancer at the National Cancer Institute and other institutions, daily intake of 60 grams of black raspberry powder (the equivalent of 15 servings of black raspberries) reversed dozens of biomarkers of the disease. These studies showed that the powder can kill cancer cells, block the growth of new blood vessels to tumors (*angiogenesis*), kill cancer cells (*apoptosis*) and stop cancer cells from dividing and growing (*proliferation*).

What to do: If you are at risk for oral or colon cancer...or are being treated for one of those diseases...or are a survivor of any of them—talk with your doctor about adding black raspberry powder to a daily smoothie. (You could never eat enough black raspberries to get the cancer-reversing effect.)

Good product: Freeze-dried black raspberry powder from BerriHealth (BerriHealth.com).

INTERESTING FINDING...

Blueberries Battle Cancer Cells

Chemicals in blueberries are radiosensitizers that make radiation therapy more effective.

Recent lab study: A radiation/blueberry extract combo decreased cervical cancer cells by 70%, compared with just 20% from radiation alone.

University of Missouri School of Medicine, Medicine.Missouri.edu.

For preventing cancer, eat five or more servings of fruits and vegetables every day—including berries.

"Forgotten" Disease-Fighting Greens

Michael T. Murray, ND, a licensed naturopathic physician based in Paradise Valley, Arizona. Dr. Murray has published more than 30 books, including *Bottom Line's Encyclopedia of Healing Foods*, with coauthor Joseph Pizzorno, ND. DoctorMurray.com

Leafy greens are the superstars of the vegetable brigade. Kale, widely considered the reigning king, is unusually high in calcium, magnesium and vitamin K...and, like other greens, is loaded with disease-fighting phytochemicals, such as lutein and vitamin C.

But let's be honest—kale's somewhat bitter taste isn't for everyone...and even if you love this veggie, you're probably not going to eat it every day. What other disease-fighting greens do you need in your diet?

TARGETED NUTRITION

Basic nutrition is just one reason that experts advise Americans to eat at least five servings of greens and other vegetables daily. But if you're concerned about specific medical conditions, research has shown that some leafy greens are particularly effective. *For example...*

• **Arugula and cancer.** Arugula is a peppery green with a sharp taste that adds a distinctive zip to otherwise bland salads. The pungent flavor has earned it the nickname "salad rocket."

The zesty flavor of arugula is largely due to its high concentration of sulfur-containing compounds. We think of arugula as a salad green, but it's actually a *crucifer*—in the same plant family as superfoods such as broccoli, cabbage and kale. Like other crucifers, it contains a group of anticancer compounds known as *glucosinolates*, which have detoxifying effects.

How arugula helps: Compounds in arugula, including *sulforaphane* and *indole-3-carbinol*, increase the body's excretion of a form of estrogen that has been linked to breast cancer. A Chinese study found that women who regularly ate a daily serving of cruciferous vegetables were 50% less likely to develop breast cancer. Another study found that just one weekly serving was enough to reduce cancer risk (including oral, colorectal and kidney malignancies).

Bonus: The sulforaphane in arugula has another benefit. It appears to help the body eliminate *H. pylori*, a bacterium that causes most peptic ulcers and greatly increases the risk for gastric cancer.

• **Spinach and macular degeneration.** As the US population ages, there's been a dramatic increase in age-related macular degeneration, a leading cause of blindness. Could a few weekly servings of spinach make a difference? There's good evidence that it might.

How spinach helps: Spinach is exceptionally high in lutein, a plant pigment that concentrates in the eyes and deflects damaging light from sunshine. Studies have found that people who consumed 6 mg of lutein daily—the amount in about one-half cup of cooked spinach—were 43% less likely to develop macular degeneration. Research published in *JAMA Ophthalmology* shows that people who consume generous amounts of lutein are also less likely to develop cataracts than those who eat less.

Important: Whether you prefer your spinach raw or cooked, be sure to have it with a little bit of oil or fat—a drizzle of olive oil is plenty—or a small amount of some other fat such as chopped nuts or avocado. Lutein is a fat-soluble nutrient, which means it is absorbed more efficiently when it's consumed with a little fat.

• **Parsley and UTIs.** Most people think of parsley as a colorful garnish—pretty to look at, but not much of a food. But around the world, parsley is found in tabbouleh, pesto (with or without basil) and other fragrant dishes...and it's a good green to eat if you get frequent urinary tract infections (UTIs).

About half of all women will eventually get a UTI...men get them, too, but less often. Patients with recurrent UTIs (defined as two separate infections within six months or three within one year) often depend on antibiotics—and resign themselves to the likely side effects of these drugs, such as diarrhea.

How parsley helps: It contains apigenin, a compound that acts as a diuretic and also has anti-inflammatory effects. According to a report in the journal *Case Reports in Medicine*, women who combined parsley with other herbal treatments (such as garlic) had an impressive decrease in urinary frequency and other symptoms—by 80%, in one case. Parsley's UTI-fighting effect is presumably because of apigenin's diuretic effect.

Another benefit: Reduced risk for cancer. Chlorophyll and other compounds in parsley have anticancer effects—including the ability to help inhibit the cancer-causing effects of fried foods.

Since parsley is so concentrated in nutrition and phytochemicals, just a few sprigs (or about one-quarter cup) consumed whenever possible provides exceptional health benefits. Chopped parsley can be added to salads, sauces, soups and grilled fish.

• **Kale and osteoporosis.** Kale's reputation as the king of veggies is based, in part, on its ability to promote bone health. People often think that milk is a great calcium source, but the absorption of calcium from kale and other leafy greens is actually higher—between 40% to 64%, compared with about 32% from milk.

And that's not all. In addition to being rich in calcium, kale also is an excellent source of vitamin K, a critical nutrient that helps anchor calcium into bone. One cup of raw kale supplies more than 600% of the recommended daily vitamin K intake. If you're concerned about bone health, you should definitely make an effort to eat more kale.

Another benefit: Improved heart health. Kale and other greens, as well as beets and celery, have been found to improve blood pressure and blood flow. While a high intake of fruit and vegetables is associated with healthy blood pressure and reduces risk for heart disease and stroke, kale and cruciferous vegetables are linked to even greater protection. *A good goal:* Three to four servings of kale and other greens a week.

Important caveat: In normal amounts, kale is among the healthiest foods you can eat. But some people go overboard. Too much kale, like other cruciferous vegetables, can cause flatulence (gas) for many people. Eating too much raw kale (for example, more than three servings a week) can also interfere with the production of thyroid hormone, leading to the formation of a goiter. And because kale is such a rich source of vitamin K, anyone taking *warfarin* (Coumadin), an important anticlotting drug that interacts with this vitamin, should consult a doctor before eating kale or any leafy greens.

Go "Green" for a Much Younger Brain

People who ate the most leafy greens daily (just over one serving, such as one cup of raw spinach or one-half cup cooked) over a 10-year period had brains that were roughly 11 years "younger" in terms of memory and cognition than people who reported rarely or never eating greens, according to a study of 960 adults ages 58 to 99 without dementia. Whether cooked or raw, spinach, kale and other leafy greens are rich in vitamins E and K, lutein and other substances that may slow cognitive decline.

Martha Clare Morris, ScD, director of nutritional epidemiology, Rush University Medical Center, Chicago.

It's Teatime for Your Brain!

A single cup of black, green or oolong tea daily was linked to a 50% reduction in the risk of developing dementia, according to a study involving 957 people over age 55. Why? These teas are made from the *Camellia sinensis* plant and are full of *catechins* and *theaflavins*—both of which have anti-inflammatory and antioxidant properties that appear to protect against vascular damage and neurodegeneration. While tea bags are OK, the tea should be freshly brewed.

Feng Lei, PhD, assistant professor, Yong Loo Lin School of Medicine, National University of Singapore.

TAKE NOTE...

Avocados for Your Eyes

The fruit offers the antioxidants *lutein* and *zeaxanthin* that filter harmful blue UV rays from the sun and help prevent macular degeneration and cataracts. Also, the high levels of monounsaturated fats found in avocados may help reduce risk for macular degeneration.

Marvin M. Lipman, MD, chief medical adviser for Consumer Reports.

Tea Staves Off Glaucoma

In a survey of 1,678 people, those who drank hot tea at least once daily were 74% less likely to develop glaucoma—a potentially blinding condition due to a buildup of pressure in the eyeball—than those who drank no hot tea.

Theory: Black and green teas contain polyphenols, antioxidants with anti-inflammatory properties that help fight glaucoma.

Anne L. Coleman, MD, PhD, professor of ophthalmology, David Geffen School of Medicine, UCLA, California.

Medicinal Mushrooms: They Fight Cancer, Heart Disease, Arthritis, More

Mark Stengler, ND, a naturopathic doctor in private practice at Stengler Center for Integrative Medicine in Encinitas, California. He is author of more than 30 books, including *The Health Benefits of Medicinal Mushrooms* and *The Natural Physician's Healing Therapies*, and coauthor of *Bottom Line's Prescription for Drug Alternatives* and *Prescription for Natural Cures*. He is also host of the PBS program *Supercharge Your Immune System*. MarkStengler.com

Mushrooms may not seem like a big health deal—most people think of them simply as earthy additions to meals and salads.

What most people don't realize: Dozens of varieties of mushrooms are medicinal. Rich in unique carbohydrates (polysaccharides) called *beta glucans*, they can energize the body's disease-fighting immune cells.

Here's what you need to know about three effective medicinal mushrooms...

Note: Mushroom supplements generally are safe, but because they activate the immune system, they should not be taken by organ-transplant recipients on immunosuppressive drugs. Also, look for a hot-water (or hot-water/ethanol) extract. This may be stated on the supplement label—if not, check the company's website. I typically recommend that patients take one mushroom supplement at a time, rather than two or three.

MAITAKE

I consider the maitake mushroom (*Grifola frondosa*)—native to northern Japan and called the "King of Mushrooms" throughout Asia—to be one of the most powerful allies in the battle against cancer. It can be used for immune enhancement in addition to conventional cancer treatment.

Compelling research: Chinese doctors studied more than 300 people with bladder cancer after they had surgery for the disease, tracking the effectiveness of five standard and natural therapies, including supplements of a maitake mushroom extract. After an average of seven years, those taking maitake had the lowest rate of cancer recurrence (35%). And in a study of 36 cancer patients published in *Alternative Medicine Review*, maitake supplements improved symptoms and decreased the size of tumors in 69% of breast cancer patients, 63% of lung cancer patients and 58% of liver cancer patients. The supplements also boosted the cancer-killing power of chemotherapy by up to 40%—doses ranged between 50 milligrams (mg) to 150 mg daily (some patients received chemotherapy and some did not).

Decades of research from Japan show that one "fraction" or extract of maitake—the D-fraction—is most effective in boosting the immune system and fighting cancer. Specifically, D-fraction boosts the number and power of *natural killer cells*, immune cells that can "recognize" and kill cancer cells and viruses.

Best product and dose: For my patients with cancer, I often prescribe the over-the-counter product MaitakeGold 404, used in many studies on cancer. I prescribe a daily dose of 0.5 mg to 1 mg per kilogram (2.2 pounds) of body weight. For everyday immune-strengthening, I often recommend 5 mg to 15 mg daily taken 20 minutes before meals or on an empty stomach.

You can find maitake mushrooms in your supermarket, farmers' market or gourmet market—and add them to your diet to help *prevent* cancer. The mature mushroom—also called "Hen of the Woods"—has large, fleshy grayish-brown caps. Cut off the tough white base, then slice and sauté the caps for 10 to 15 minutes with salt, pepper and garlic. They're great in pasta, risotto, eggs and other dishes. I recommend two to three servings of maitake mushrooms weekly.

TURKEY TAIL

The turkey tail mushroom (*Trametes versicolor*) grows around the world and has a fan-shaped, brown-and-tan cap that resembles turkey feathers. Used for centuries in folk and traditional medicines in China and Japan, this mushroom can treat lung infections, hepatitis (liver infection) and cancer. Modern medicine has focused on cancer.

Compelling research: More than 400 studies show that turkey tail can fight cancer. Nearly all the studies on people have been with PSK (*krestin*), a proprietary extract that has been used as a supportive therapy by thousands of cancer patients in Japan. In one study published in *Anticancer Research*, Stage 1 and 2 lung cancer patients taking the extract had a five-year survival rate of 39%, compared with 16% for patients taking a placebo. Other studies show higher survival rates in people taking PSK for colorectal, esophageal and stomach cancers.

Best product and dose: For those with cancer, I often recommend 1,000 mg to 1,500 mg, twice daily, taken in the morning and evening on an empty stomach. Look for a product that has 20% beta glucans. As for your diet—turkey tail is not an appetizing mushroom.

REISHI

Reishi (Ganoderma lucidum)—a shiny fan-shaped mushroom with colors ranging from reddish brown to black—has been used for thousands of years by traditional healers in Japan and China. (Chinese healers call this the "Mushroom of Immortality.") Among mushrooms, it's your best choice for an everyday tonic to boost the strength of your immune system. And it also strengthens the rest of the body. *Proven benefits include...*

• **Reversing fatty liver disease.** Fatty liver afflicts an estimated 25% of Americans and can lead to liver disease and liver cancer. In a new study published in *Pharmaceutical Biology*, the livers of people with fatty liver completely normalized after they took reishi for six months. And their levels of cell-damaging oxidants fell by 42%. The participants made no other changes in diet, exercise or anything else.

• **Improvement in fibromyalgia.** In a recent study by Spanish researchers published in *Nutrición Hospitalaria*, people with the pain, stiffness and poor fitness typical of fibromyalgia saw improvements in flexibility, strength and endurance after taking reishi for six weeks.

• **Eliminating oral HPV virus.** Oral infection with some strains of human papillomavirus (HPV) can cause throat cancer. In a study of 61 people with cancer-causing oral HPV, published in *International Journal of Medicinal Mushrooms*, 88% of people who took reishi for two months had complete clearance of the virus.

• **Easing rheumatoid arthritis pain.** In a study of people with rheumatoid arthritis published in *Arthritis & Rheumatism*, people who took reishi had less inflammation and pain compared with those taking a placebo.

• **Raising HDL "good" cholesterol in people with diabetes.** In a study published in *British Journal of Nutrition*, people with diabetes who took reishi had an increase in "good" HDL cholesterol.

• **Preventing altitude sickness.** Reishi is a favorite natural remedy of travelers and trekkers to prevent altitude sickness. Start taking the supplement 10 to 14 days before you travel to a higher altitude.

Best product and dose: Look for an extract product containing a minimum of 10% polysaccharides (beta glucans) and 4% triterpene (another active ingredient). Take 800 mg two to three times daily.

Reishi is bitter and woody-tasting and not ideal for culinary use.

Herbs and More for Leaky Gut

Jamison Starbuck, ND, a naturopathic physician in family practice and writer/producer of *Dr. Starbuck's Health Tips for Kids*, a weekly program on Montana Public Radio, MTPR.org, both in Missoula. She is a past president of the American Association of Naturopathic Physicians and a contributing editor to *The Alternative Advisor: The Complete Guide to Natural Therapies and Alternative Treatments.* DrJamisonStarbuck.com

If you've got celiac disease, food allergies or an autoimmune bowel disease, such as Crohn's disease or inflammatory bowel disease, you probably have leaky gut syndrome. Also known as gastrointestinal permeability, leaky gut syndrome is a condition in which microscopic "holes" develop in the lining of the digestive tract as a result of medications, allergies to foods, genetics and other causes. Your digestive tract, or gut, is designed to keep food particles in your intestines and out of your bloodstream. When food is properly digested and broken down, food nutrients pass through the filter of the intestinal wall and into the bloodstream. This is how your body gets the nutrition it needs to survive.

With leaky gut syndrome, your gut wall is like a torn window screen. Insects that are meant to stay outside enter your home. When leaky gut occurs, overly large food molecules pass through these microscopic holes into your bloodstream. To the body, these large molecules are an enemy. The immune system responds protectively and makes defenders known as antibodies. If you have a lot of food-related antibodies, you have food allergies (or a food sensitivity). You'll also have an inflamed bowel and leaky gut syndrome.

One way to heal the symptoms of leaky gut syndrome, which include indigestion, irregular stools, generalized fatigue and inflammation, skin rashes and migraines, is to avoid the foods to which you are allergic. That can help. However, if you don't repair the intestinal wall, you'll continue to suffer with many of the above symptoms and may even become allergic to other foods.

How, then, do you treat the gut wall? *What I recommend...*

• **Eat the right foods.** Sauerkraut is rich in probiotics, which help crowd out pathogens that damage the gut wall. Do not use canned sauerkraut—the probiotics are killed in the heating process that is required for canning. Plant-based oils, such as olive, sunflower and borage, are nourishing to the intestine. Fish, baked or cooked on a grill, can also help heal a leaky gut. It is easy to digest, anti-inflammatory and contains helpful proteins and oils. Just be sure to avoid fried fish and fried foods generally. You may also want to try a probiotic supplement. Follow label instructions.

Caution: People with weakened immune systems (such as those using chemotherapy) should consult their doctors before eating probiotic-rich food or taking a probiotic supplement.

• **Consider these herbs.** My favorite herbs for leaky gut are slippery elm...marshmallow root...and plantain (a medicinal plant not to be confused with the banana-like food). You can use one of these herbs or combine two or more.

To treat leaky gut: You need to take herbal medicine between meals—60 minutes or more after a meal or 30 minutes or more before a meal—to ensure that the herb comes into direct contact with the gut wall.* You can take these herbs in capsules, tea or bulk powders.

Typical daily dose: Three standard-sized capsules two times a day...three cups of tea... or two teaspoons of the bulk-powdered herb.

GOOD TO KNOW...

Nuts Fight Stomach Cancer

A study involving 566,000 older adults found that regularly eating nuts and peanut butter was associated with a 27% lower risk for *gastric noncardia adenocarcinoma* (cancer of the lower stomach), compared with people who reported consuming these foods infrequently.

Possible reason: The beneficial polyphenols, fiber, vitamins and minerals in nuts and peanuts (which are technically legumes).

Christian C. Abnet, PhD, MPH, senior investigator, division of cancer epidemiology and genetics, National Cancer Institute, Bethesda, Maryland.

For convenience and taste, put the powdered herb in a small amount (one-eighth cup or less) of applesauce or oatmeal.

With my patients, treatment usually takes about three months to heal leaky gut. Assuming that one's diet stays healthy, the regimen above can often be discontinued when symptoms subside.

*If you use any prescription medication, have a chronic medical condition (such as diabetes) or are pregnant or nursing, consult your doctor before taking any herbs.

Easy Way to Ease IBS

Vitamin D deficiency is common among people with irritable bowel syndrome (IBS), according to a recent review of seven studies.

Finding: Vitamin D supplements (3,000 IU daily in one study) appear to relieve the severity of symptoms, including abdominal pain, bloating, diarrhea and constipation.

If you have IBS: Ask your doctor about checking your vitamin D levels, and discuss whether supplements would be right for you.

Bernard M. Corfe, PhD, senior lecturer, department of oncology and metabolism, University of Sheffield, UK.

More Fish for Arthritis

Eating fish has many health benefits, including reducing inflammation.

New finding: In a study of the diets of 176 patients with rheumatoid arthritis, those who ate non-fried fish two or more times a week had less rheumatoid arthritis activity—as measured by a combination of swollen and tender joints and a blood marker for inflammation—than those who ate fish once a month or never.

Sara K. Tedeschi, MD, MPH, rheumatologist at Brigham and Women's Hospital, Boston.

Yogurt May Help Keep Bones Healthy

Older adults who ate yogurt daily had a 3% to 4% higher bone-mineral density measurement compared with those who did not eat yogurt. Daily yogurt consumption also was linked to lower risk for osteoporosis—39% lower in women and 52% lower in men. The study showed association but not cause and effect. Daily yogurt eaters may live a more healthful lifestyle. Other dairy products did not produce a similar effect on bone strength.

Eamon J. Laird, PhD, research fellow, Trinity College Dublin, Ireland, and leader of a study of 4,310 Irish adults, ages 60 and older, published in *Osteoporosis International.*

These Tasty "Bad" Foods Are Actually Good for You

Bill Gottlieb, CHC, a health coach certified by the American Association of Drugless Practitioners and former editor in chief of Rodale Books and Prevention Magazine Health Books. He is author of 16 health books including *Bottom Line's Speed Healing.* His website is BillGottliebHealth.com.

There are foods you probably don't eat because "everybody knows" they're bad for you—foods such as eggs (too high in cholesterol), white pasta ("empty" carbs) and soy (too high in natural estrogens, raising the risk for breast cancer).

But the truth is, what most people (including many medical experts) know about these so-called "bad" foods is...wrong. A close look at the latest research shows that they're actually good for you. *Here's what's really known...*

WHITE PASTA

How could white pasta possibly be good for you? Because it's loaded with *resistant starch*, formed when starch-containing foods such as pasta, rice and potatoes are cooked and then *cooled* to room temperature or lower. It's called *resistant* because it resists being completely digested and absorbed in the small intestine, a process that helps balance blood sugar.

Standout scientific research: Insulin is the hormone that ushers glucose out of the bloodstream and into cells—and healthy people are *sensitive*, not *resistant*, to the action of insulin. In a study published in *The Journal of Nutrition*, insulin sensitivity in overweight men improved by up to 73% when they ate more resistant starch. And in a study of people with diabetes, four weeks of including resistant starch in the diet also improved insulin sensitivity.

Tip: You don't have to be overweight or have diabetes for resistant starch to improve your body's ability to handle blood sugar.

Why it works: Some scientists theorize that resistant starch improves insulin sensitivity and balances blood sugar levels because it's a *prebiotic*—it provides fuel for probiotics, friendly bacteria in the colon. When those friendly bacteria flourish, there's less insulin resistance.

My recommendation: Don't be afraid to eat white pasta salad, white rice salad or potato salad two or three times a week—as long as the pasta, rice or potatoes have been cooked and cooled. It's OK if you reheat these foods after cooling—the starch remains resistant.

EGGS

For nearly four decades, the government warned us against eating eggs because of their high level of cholesterol, a supposed risk factor for heart disease and stroke.

Important update: There was never any credible evidence linking eggs to either high blood cholesterol levels or cardiovascular disease. And in the government's latest "Dietary Guidelines for Americans," there are no limits on daily consumption of cholesterol. In fact, the most credible scientific research shows that eggs actually help prevent cardiovascular disease.

Recent finding: A study published in *Journal of the American College of Nutrition* found that eating eggs does not increase heart disease risk—and decreases the risk for stroke by 12%. The researchers concluded their study by noting that eggs deliver lots of protein, essential fatty acids, antioxidants, vitamins and minerals.

Protein in eggs is an efficient muscle builder—crucial in seniors, who can lose up to 5% of their muscle mass each decade.

The antioxidants in eggs—primarily *lutein* and *zeaxanthin*—protect the eyes from age-related macular degeneration, a leading cause of vision loss in people age 50 and older. In one study, published in *The Journal of Nutrition*, eating one egg per day boosted blood levels of lutein by 26% and blood levels of zeaxanthin by 38%.

Eggs also are good for people with diabetes—a three-month study published in *British Journal of Nutrition* showed that people with diabetes who ate two eggs daily reduced their blood sugar and blood pressure.

And eggs can help you lose weight—a recent study from researchers at University of Minnesota shows that eating an egg at breakfast helps you feel less hungry during the morning and eat less at lunch.

My suggestion: Enjoy one egg dish daily. Look for organic eggs or eggs from chickens that are fed omega-3 fatty acids. People who ate these types of eggs had even higher blood levels of eye-protecting lutein and zeaxanthin compared with people who ate regular eggs, according to a study from researchers at Loma Linda University.

FULL-FAT DAIRY

Full-fat cheese, butter and other dairy foods rich in saturated fat are bad for your heart, right? Not according to a recent study published in *The American Journal of Clinical Nutrition.*

Researchers studied 92 people, giving them four different diets over four-week periods—a diet rich in saturated fatty acids, including 13% of calories from either cheese or butter...a diet rich in monounsaturated fatty acids, such as those found in olive oil and avocados...a diet rich in polyunsaturated fatty acids, such as those found in vegetable oils...and a low-fat, high-carbohydrate diet.

Results: Compared with the other diets, the diets with cheese or butter did not cause more inflammation, higher blood pressure or higher blood sugar—all risk factors for heart disease.

And in a landmark study published in *The BMJ*, researchers analyzed results from studies involving more than 300,000 people and found there was no link between saturated fat intake and getting type 2 diabetes or heart disease, having a stroke or dying from heart disease or any cause.

One possible explanation for these results: Dairy products such as full-fat cheese and butter are rich in heart-protective anti-inflammatory conjugated linoleic acid (CLA).

My recommendation: Go ahead and eat organic butter and organic full-fat cheese from grass-fed cows. (Buying organic spares you the pesticides and growth hormones found in full-fat dairy products from conventionally raised cows.)

SOY

Soy foods stand accused of causing a wide range of health problems, from breast cancer to thyroid damage. But soy is a very healthy food if you pay attention to the *kind* of soy you consume.

Traditional soy foods such as miso (fermented soybean paste) and tofu, eaten in amounts consumed by Asian people for thousands of years (two to three times weekly), pose no threat to your health. In fact, a multitude of scientific studies shows that these soy foods—rich in health-giving *isoflavones*—may help protect you from many chronic diseases, including heart disease, breast cancer, prostate cancer, osteoporosis and kidney disease.

But there are soy foods—organic or not—that are bad for you. The worst are soy margarines and shortenings made from partially hydrogenated soybean oil, which contain trans fat.

Another bad-for-you form of soy is *processed soy protein*, such as soy protein isolate, soy protein concentrate, texturized vegetable protein and hydrolyzed vegetable protein. In these forms, the soy has been stripped of nearly all nutrients.

My recommendation: Eat traditional organic soy foods two to three times weekly. Besides miso and tofu, these include edamame (green, immature soybeans), soy milk, tamari (fermented soy sauce), tempeh (fermented soybeans formed into a burgerlike patty) and natto (boiled fermented soybeans).

TAKE NOTE...

Good News for Chocolate Lovers!

In a recent study of 55,000 people, those who ate two to six one-ounce servings of chocolate per week had a 20% lower risk for *atrial fibrillation* (AFib), an irregular heartbeat that raises risk for stroke, heart attack and dementia, than those who indulged only once a month.

Why: Flavonoids in cocoa may improve blood vessel function.

Important: It's the cocoa—not milk and sugar—that's good for you, so the higher the cocoa content, the better.

Elizabeth Mostofsky, MPH, instructor in epidemiology, Harvard T.H. Chan School of Public Health, Boston.

Medical Marijuana—It Can Help Parkinson's, Pain, Anxiety and More

David Bearman, MD, vice president of the American Academy of Cannabinoid Medicine and author of the forthcoming book *Abridged Guide to Cannabinoid Medicine Practice*. He is in private practice in Goleta, California.

Now legal in 29 states, medical *cannabis* (aka marijuana) can treat a wide variety of ailments from cancer pain to seizures. But what if you don't want to get high to get relief?

That is where *cannabidiol* (CBD), a compound that's derived from marijuana, comes in. Unlike its more famous cousin, *tetrahydrocannabinol* (THC), CBD does not cause even mild euphoria...or give you the munchies.

Yet CBD is the subject of some of the most exciting medical research in the field today—it has numerous potential therapeutic applications that may turn it into the next wonder drug for treating epilepsy, anxiety, Alzheimer's and a host of other diseases and ailments.

Case in point: Epidiolex, a newly developed drug (*key ingredient:* CBD), reduces seizures by 39% in children with a rare form of epilepsy, Dravet syndrome. It was approved by the FDA in April 2018.

CBD is widely available in many states as well as online, even though the Federal Drug Enforcement Agency classifies it as an illegal narcotic.

To learn more about its medical uses, we spoke with David Bearman, MD, a leading authority on cannabinoid medicine. He emphasized that people with medical conditions who are interested in CBD should first discuss it with their doctors. *His answers to our questions...*

- **Isn't CBD actually psychoactive—the reason medical marijuana is so controversial?** It is—but not the way people might think. Like THC, it crosses the blood-brain barrier and binds to receptors in the brain—that's how it can reduce pain. It also affects the immune system to reduce inflammation. But unlike THC, CBD doesn't cause euphoria or dysphoria—feeling uneasy, anxious or too out of touch with reality.

- **What forms does CBD come in?** It's available in a wide variety of forms including a liquid tincture, capsules, an oil for use in a vaporizer (aka vaping) and in sprays that can be inhaled or sprayed under the tongue. There also are topical CBD creams to help with muscle pain. Some companies also produce synthetic forms of CBD.

• **Is CBD addictive?** No. There is no addictive aspect to CBD whatsoever—or, for that matter, to THC.

• **What do we know currently about what kinds of patients CBD can help?** The list of diseases and conditions that CBD can improve and the symptoms that it can relieve actually is quite long. *I'll discuss a few...*

Epilepsy. Research shows that CBD helps prevent seizures. Many doctors now are not waiting for an FDA-approved drug—they already are recommending it in tincture or capsules.

Anxiety. A New York University School of Medicine review found that CBD can treat anxiety disorder, obsessive-compulsive disorder (OCD) and post-traumatic stress disorder (PTSD). Other research has found that it has effects similar to some antipsychotic drugs—it may be effective in treating patients with schizophrenia.

Alzheimer's and Parkinson's. CBD's neuroprotective properties may help stem the progression of Alzheimer's disease and Parkinson's disease, among other brain diseases. While more research is needed, I believe that people at high risk for either disease—and certainly those in the early stages—should use CBD.

Other conditions. CBD is being studied for its possible therapeutic effect on diabetes, stroke, rheumatoid arthritis, psoriasis, multiple sclerosis, fibromyalgia and osteoarthritis. It also contributes to the inhibition of cancer cell growth. But more research is needed in all these areas.

• **There always are drawbacks with any drug—what are CBD's?** CBD may cause fatigue, nausea and changes in appetite. A more serious concern is that CBD reduces the speed at which the body metabolizes the blood thinner *warfarin* (Coumadin)—if you're taking the two together, let your doctor know. He/she will want to monitor your blood-clotting factors closely and may need to reduce your warfarin dosage.

• **Are there conditions for which using CBD in combination with THC is more beneficial than CBD alone?** Absolutely. In my experience, CBD paired with THC works better for treating epilepsy and for reducing chronic pain. CBD's principle contribution to treating chronic pain is its anti-inflammatory properties. Often the THC dose can be low enough (5 mg or less) that there's no sense of being high. Plus, CBD partially reduces the euphoric effect of THC. A patient may want to start with CBD and then, if needed, add a little THC to see whether it makes a beneficial difference.

• **How can doctors and patients tell the right amount of CBD to take?** There's not enough research to make any definitive statements about dosing. Every individual is different—your size, age and the illness you're treating will affect how much you require for treatment.

My advice: Work with a knowledgeable health professional who can help you adjust the dose, the THC/CBD ratio, discuss whether to include other cannabinoids, explore the best way for you to take CBD, address possible side effects—and follow your medical progress. My advice to my patients is to start at a low dose and increase it slowly if needed.

• **What's the best form to take?** I generally advise taking CBD orally, not by inhalation or topically. You'll get the fastest effects with inhaling/vaping, but those effects last only about three hours. Taking CBD orally means that the effects can last up to seven hours.

The route of CBD administration depends on how rapidly you need it to start working... and how long you want the therapeutic effects to last. Different patients prefer different routes of administration—respiratory (vaping)...oral (tinctures, edibles, pills)...topical or suppository. But with so many routes of administration, it is best to discuss your preference with your physician.

The 4 Best Supplements to Prevent Alzheimer's

James M. Greenblatt, MD, psychiatrist and chief medical officer and vice president of medical services at Walden Behavioral Care in Waltham, Massachusetts. He has 30 years of experience treating adults for cognitive decline and mental health challenges. He trains medical professionals on integrative medicine and is a clinical faculty member at Tufts University School of Medicine and at the Geisel School of Medicine at Dartmouth College. His most recent book, *Finally Focused,* covers the integrative treatment of ADHD.

Many biochemistry factors contribute to the "neurodegeneration" that leads to Alzheimer's disease. These include brain inflammation...high levels of insulin in the brain, triggered by high blood sugar...nutritional deficiencies...and poor breakdown and elimination of the waste products generated by normal brain activity.

The four supplements I recommend work together to balance brain biochemistry, thereby preventing, stopping or even reversing neurodegeneration. They are safe for anyone to take, but always check with your doctor first. The best time to start supplementation is today, even if you have no symptoms. It takes decades of neurodegeneration to develop Alzheimer's disease.

LOW-DOSE LITHIUM

Nutritional lithium (*lithium orotate*...not *lithium carbonate*, which is best-known as a pharmaceutical treatment for bipolar disorder) in low doses can shield you against neurodegeneration.

Research with animals shows that lithium can stop the development of beta-amyloid and tau, the abnormal proteins in the brain that are the hallmarks of Alzheimer's disease...double the activity of an enzyme that protects the membranes of brain cells—an enzyme that is low in people with Alzheimer's...and prevent the onset of Alzheimer's in mice that have been genetically programmed to develop the disease.

More remarkably, several studies on people show that low-dose lithium can help prevent and even treat Alzheimer's.

Standout research: In a study published in *The British Journal of Psychiatry*, Brazilian researchers studied 45 seniors with mild cognitive impairment, the stage of memory loss and mental decline that precedes Alzheimer's. The researchers divided the seniors into two groups, giving one group low-dose lithium and the other a placebo. After one year, more of the people taking lithium had "stable cognitive performance"—meaning no mental decline. And fewer of those taking lithium developed Alzheimer's disease.

Another important recent finding: In a small study recently published in *Alzheimer Disease & Associated Disorders*, doctors from Columbia University Medical Center gave 150 milligrams (mg) to 300 mg of lithium daily to people with typical Alzheimer's symptoms, such as agitation, psychosis (hallucinations, delusions) and sleeping problems. After two weeks, the researchers noted improvements including a "normal sleep cycle, with a marked decrease in paranoia, auditory hallucinations, agitation and aggression."

If low-dose lithium can *treat* mild cognitive impairment and Alzheimer's, it's likely that it can *prevent* it.

My advice: If you are over age 50, talk to your doctor about taking 10 mg of lithium orotate daily. If you are under age 50, ask about taking 5 mg. Brands of lithium orotate include Pure Encapsulations, Swanson, KAL and many others.

VITAMIN D

Vitamin D influences more than 200 genes including many that play a role in maintaining a healthy brain. It also reduces neuroinflammation—a chronic inflammation of the central nervous system and a key driver of Alzheimer's disease. And vitamin D is a must for the manufacture of *serotonin,* the neurotransmitter that regulates memory and mood. Not surprisingly, vitamin D plays a key role in preventing Alzheimer's.

Recent scientific evidence: A 12-year study of 916 seniors, published in *Alzheimer's & Dementia: The Journal of the Alzheimer's Association*, found a link between low vitamin D levels and cognitive decline. Seniors with low blood levels of vitamin D had faster cognitive decline and were nearly three times more likely to develop Alzheimer's, compared with people with normal blood levels of vitamin D. The only way to determine if your blood levels of vitamin D are normal is a vitamin D blood test. You can have your physician order the test.

My advice: Maintaining a blood level of 50 nanograms per milliliter (ng/ml) is best for preventing Alzheimer's. If your blood level is lower, talk to your doctor about taking 5,000 IU of vitamin D-3 daily for three months. If levels still are lower than 50 ng/ml, continue this dose and check again in three months. Once you have achieved 50 ng/ml, take a maintenance dose of 2,000 IU daily. Have blood levels checked yearly.

VITAMIN B-12

Vitamin B-12 plays a key role in the synthesis of every neurotransmitter—the chemicals that relay messages from neuron to neuron. It also is a must for the health of the myelin sheath, which protects neurons. B-12 also helps lower levels of *homocysteine*, an amino acid that is toxic to brain cells. But as you age, your ability to absorb vitamin B-12 decreases—and if blood levels are low, you're more likely to get Alzheimer's.

Standout scientific research: A study published in *Current Alzheimer Research* found a link between B-12 and Alzheimer's—people with low blood levels of B-12 were about *four times more likely* to have Alzheimer's disease. (People with low levels of B-12 and high levels of homocysteine were about 30 times more likely to have Alzheimer's.)

And in an eight-year study of 501 people age 60 and older, published in *JAMA Psychiatry*, those with the highest blood levels of vitamin B-12 had the slowest rate of brain atrophy—that is, the higher the B-12 level, the less the brain shrank with age. That's an important finding because brain atrophy is another hallmark of Alzheimer's disease.

My advice: Anyone who wants to prevent Alzheimer's should take at least 1,000 micrograms (mcg) of vitamin B-12 daily—for maximum absorption, take a *sublingual* form. (A sublingual capsule or liquid supplement is put under the tongue.) Brands include Pure Encapsulations, Nature Made and more.

Beware: In the US, B-12 levels are considered "normal" as long as they are above 200 picograms per milliliter (pg/ml). In Europe and Japan, normal levels are at 500 pg/ml and above. I consider the US "normal" range one of the tragedies of American medicine, dooming many people to cognitive decline. If your physician tells you that your B-12 levels are "normal," ask what your levels are.

CURCUMIN

Curcumin is the principle component of turmeric, the spice that flavors curries. Research indicates that curcumin is neuroprotective in many ways, including stopping the formation of beta-amyloid.

Standout research: People age 40 to 60 who took a daily curcumin supplement had lower blood levels of beta-amyloid, according to a study conducted by researchers at The Ohio State University and published in *Nutrition Journal*.

My advice: Take 500 mg of curcumin two times daily with meals. Good brands include Doctor's Best, Jarrow Formulas, Now Foods, Source Naturals, Thorne Research and many others.

My favorite brain-protecting curcumin supplement is one that I've formulated myself—CurcumaSorb Mind from Pure Encapsulations. It contains Meriva, a highly absorbable form of curcumin, as well as many other plant extracts shown to be neuroprotective.

ALERT...

Alzheimer's Clue

Increased sleep may be a sign of Alzheimer's. Older adults whose sleep duration increased to more than nine hours a night had twice the risk for dementia a decade later as those who slept nine hours or less. The effect was not seen in people who always had slept more than nine hours.

Sudha Seshadri, MD, professor of neurology, Boston University School of Medicine, and senior author of a study published in *Neurology*.

You Have More Control Over Your Alzheimer's Risk Than You Think

Gayatri Devi, MD, director of New York Memory and Healthy Aging Services and an attending physician at Lenox Hill Hospital, both in New York City, and clinical professor of neurology at SUNY Downstate Medical Center in Brooklyn. A board-certified neurologist, Dr. Devi is author of more than 50 scientific studies on memory loss and three books for consumers, including *The Spectrum of Hope: An Optimistic and New Approach to Alzheimer's Disease.* NYBrain.org

Older adults fear Alzheimer's disease more than cancer. But how worried do you really need to be?

Let's start with the good news...if you have a first-degree relative with the disease (a parent or sibling), you're only at a *slightly* greater risk than someone who does not have a first-degree relative with Alzheimer's. That's because there are many factors that affect your risk for Alzheimer's...not just your genes (more on this later).

Poor lifestyle choices (such as an unhealthy diet and/or not exercising regularly) also increase your risk—much more so than genetics. That's why one twin in a set of identical twins can get Alzheimer's while the other twin stays healthy.

There's even more good news—a diagnosis of Alzheimer's is not necessarily the disaster you probably imagine it to be. Alzheimer's is now viewed by most medical professionals as a so-called "spectrum disorder," rather than a single disease, because different people experience different symptoms and different rates of progression.

Most people diagnosed with Alzheimer's are not on the catastrophic end of that spectrum—they are not going to forget who they are or the names of their loved ones. Most will live at home and die at home, particularly if the disease is detected early and symptoms are well-managed with treatments such as medication, a healthy diet and regular exercise.

Bottom line: Even if you are at genetic risk, you can use lifestyle modifications to reduce your risk to below that of someone who has no family history of Alzheimer's.

HOW TO TWEAK YOUR LIFESTYLE

Most cases of late-onset Alzheimer's disease are preventable—with simple lifestyle changes that reduce one's risk for the disease.

The brain changes of Alzheimer's (the so-called *plaques* and *tangles,* which are accumulations of toxic proteins) can start 20 to 30 years before the onset of symptoms. But research shows that preventive measures can stop plaques and tangles as well as symptoms from ever developing...and even prevent symptoms if your brain is riddled with plaques and tangles.

Factors that increase Alzheimer's risk for everyone—regardless of one's genetic predisposition—and how to counteract them...

- **Sedentary lifestyle.** Exercising for 45 minutes, at least three days a week (at an intensity that is 50% higher than your resting heart rate) is a must for reducing your risk for Alzheimer's. It stimulates blood flow to the brain, allowing new neurons to grow. Research shows that it decreases your risk for Alzheimer's by 40%.

Surprising fact: Cognitive abilities such as memory improve by 10% immediately after exercise.

- **Poor diet.** A diet loaded with saturated fats, refined sugar and processed foods increases the risk for Alzheimer's. A Mediterranean-style diet—rich in whole foods such as vegetables, fruits, beans, whole grains and fish—is proven to reduce the risk for Alzheimer's by 50%.

Also helpful: A healthy breakfast, which consists of protein, fiber and fruit. Research shows that if you take in less than 7% of your daily calories at breakfast, your risk for heart disease and Alzheimer's more than doubles.

- **Limited mental stimulation.** Regular mental stimulation reduces Alzheimer's risk—in fact, research shows that even reading a newspaper every day can help prevent the disease.

Best: Engage in a type of mental stimulation that is *different* from what you do at work, thereby stimulating a different part of your brain. *Example:* If you are a computer programmer, learn how to play golf.

• **Social isolation.** Healthy social relationships—with family, friends and in the community—decrease the risk for Alzheimer's disease. Feeling lonely *doubles* the risk...living alone raises it fivefold.

• **Heart disease.** Circulatory problems cause heart disease and Alzheimer's disease. Medical and lifestyle treatments for cardiovascular issues, including high blood pressure, reduce Alzheimer's risk.

Bottom line: What's good for your heart is good for your brain.

• **Diabetes.** Some experts label Alzheimer's "type 3 diabetes" because of the established link between chronically high blood sugar and the risk for Alzheimer's disease—a person with diabetes has a 57% higher risk of developing the disease. Controlling high blood sugar with medical and lifestyle treatments is crucial for reducing Alzheimer's risk.

Helpful: Keep your glucose level below 100 mg/dL.

• **Insomnia.** Poor sleep increases risk for Alzheimer's, probably because brain plaque is cleared most effectively during sleep. But sleep medications aren't the answer—they also interfere with the clearance of brain plaque.

What works better: Good sleep hygiene, such as going to bed and waking up at the same time every day.

Also helpful: Don't work on your computer in bed or keep your cell phone on your bedside table.

WHAT'S YOUR GENETIC RISK?

Genetics is a strong factor when Alzheimer's begins at a young age. The early-onset form is an aggressive familial illness that can occur, in extremely rare cases, as early as in one's 20s, with most people developing the disease in their 50s or 60s. The child of a parent with early-onset Alzheimer's has a 50% chance of developing the disease. Fortunately, early-onset constitutes only 5% of all cases of Alzheimer's disease.

On the other hand, most cases of late-onset Alzheimer's (beginning after age 65) are not inherited. Instead, many medical and lifestyle factors contribute to the development of the illness.

Compelling scientific research: In one of the largest scientific studies that I have ever completed, published in *Archives of Neurology*, I looked at more than 5,500 siblings and parents of patients with Alzheimer's—alongside age-matched adults who did not have the disease.

Presuming (for uniform statistical analysis) that everyone in the study lived to age 90, I found that those with a first-degree relative with Alzheimer's had about a one-in-four chance of developing late-onset Alzheimer's—whereas those *without* an afflicted relative had a one-in-five chance of doing so.

In other words, if neither your parents nor siblings have (or had) Alzheimer's (and you live to age 90), you still have a 20% chance of getting the disease—while a person whose parent or sibling had Alzheimer's has a 26% chance.

Takeaway: Having a parent or sibling with Alzheimer's puts you at a relatively small increased risk for the disease.

Exception: A person with late-onset Alzheimer's who also has a variant of the *apolipoprotein E gene*—APOE e4 (the most damaging of the so-called "Alzheimer's genes")—is more likely to experience rapid progression of the disease.

GENETIC TESTING

My take on genetic testing for Alzheimer's: It may be appropriate only for individuals who have a family history of early-onset Alzheimer's disease (before age 65). If a parent has early-onset Alzheimer's, as mentioned earlier, the child has a 50% chance of developing the disease. An estimated 200,000 Americans have the early-onset form of the disease.

If you have this type of family history, consult your doctor and a genetic counselor about genetic testing. Not all the genes that trigger early-onset Alzheimer's are known, but some are. If you decide to have a genetic test—and the test finds that you have one of the genetic mutations for Alzheimer's—you and your family can take that fact into account in various ways.

For example, you would want to create a step-by-step action plan for dealing with the disease, even before symptoms develop, by preparing for the future with advanced directives and financial planning...and perhaps consider entering one of the clinical trials that are testing new drugs to slow Alzheimer's development. (To find such a trial, consult ClinicalTrials.gov and search "early-onset Alzheimer's.")

Important: If you don't have a family history of early-onset Alzheimer's, I typically do not recommend genetic testing. The results would not accurately quantify your risk, and it's crucial that you implement key medical treatments (such as those for high blood pressure or diabetes) and lifestyle changes to reduce your risk for Alzheimer's whether or not you have a genetic variant for late-onset Alzheimer's.

FUN FACT...

Book Lovers Live Longer

People who read books for more than three-and-a-half hours per week were 23% less likely to die during a recent study's 12-year follow-up period, compared with those who did not read at all. On average, book readers lived 23 months longer than nonreaders.

Study of 3,635 people by researchers at Yale University, New Haven, Connecticut, published in *Social Science & Medicine*.

ADHD Strikes Adults, Too: 4 Natural Therapies That Help

James M. Greenblatt, MD, psychiatrist and chief medical officer and vice president of medical services at Walden Behavioral Care in Waltham, Massachusetts. He has 30 years of experience treating adults for cognitive decline and mental health challenges. He trains medical professionals on integrative medicine and is a clinical faculty member at Tufts University School of Medicine and at the Geisel School of Medicine at Dartmouth College. His most recent book, *Finally Focused*, covers the integrative treatment of ADHD.

If you hear about someone suffering from attention deficit hyperactivity disorder (ADHD), you'll probably assume that it's a child or adolescent. That's understandable—more than six million youngsters have been diagnosed with the disorder. But that's only part of the ADHD story.

Surprising statistic: More than 10 million adults may have ADHD, according to research that was published in *The American Journal of Psychiatry*.

What's more, research shows that less than 10% of adults with ADHD have ever received a diagnosis to explain their symptoms—problems such as an inability to focus and/or impulsivity...traits that may have led to marriage troubles, a stalled career or depression. The majority of adults with ADHD have struggled since childhood.

Even worse, many adults who suspect they have ADHD may forgo diagnosis and treatment because the go-to therapies include stimulant prescription drugs, such as *methylphenidate* (Ritalin) or *dextroamphetamine* and *amphetamine* (Adderall), with many possible side effects such as irritability, agitation, anxiety, insomnia and facial tics.

A better approach: Science-based *natural* therapies that restore biochemical balance to the brain. Over the past three decades, I have treated thousands of adults and children with these therapies—and found them to be highly effective.

Important: If you think you have ADHD, seek out a professional (such as a psychologist, psychiatrist or social worker) who has experience treating people with the problem. If you are diagnosed with the condition, talk to your doctor about using one or more of these natural treatments before taking a prescription drug. If you and your doctor determine that you do require a prescription medication, these nondrug therapies may help such drugs work more effectively.

Among the best natural therapies, based on research and my clinical experience, for adults with ADHD...*

OPCs

Nutritional supplements known as *oligomeric proanthocyanidins*, or OPCs for short, are usually made from grape seeds, pine bark and/or green tea.

What OPCs do: These plant extracts appear to regulate brain waves, as I've observed using an *electroencephalograph* (EEG), a device that records electrical activity of the brain. My patients using OPCs become more focused in conversation, and I've even seen illegible handwriting become readable.

Good advice: The best supplements combine several OPCs. One such product is CurcumaSorb Mind, made by Pure Encapsulations. It contains pine bark extract, green tea extract, blueberry extract and grape extract. Another good product is OPC-3 from Isotonix.

MAGNESIUM

At least half the people in the US don't get enough of this nutrient, which is involved in more than 300 biochemical reactions in the body.

What magnesium does: Low magnesium can undercut the functioning of glutamate receptors, areas in brain cells that assist the movement of neurotransmitters. The possible results include poor concentration and irritability, anxiety, depression, mood swings, fatigue and sleeping problems.

Good advice: Ask your doctor whether you should be taking a magnesium supplement.

Also: Add magnesium-rich foods to your diet, including nuts, seeds, dark chocolate, leafy greens, such as spinach, and avocado.

OMEGA-3 FATTY ACIDS

Sixty percent of your brain is fat, which means that this vital organ depends on a steady supply of *essential fatty acids,* the building blocks of fat, for its health and function.

*These therapies are generally safe and best tried in the order they appear here, but check with your doctor first, especially if you take medication or have a chronic medical condition.

What omega-3s do: Just about every aspect of *neurotransmission*—the movement of information from brain cell to brain cell that supports every thought, emotion and action—is affected by omega-3s. Fatty fish and fish oil supply two of the most important omega-3 fatty acids—EPA (*eicosapentaenoic acid*) and DHA (*docosahexaenoic acid*).

Good advice: Eat at least two weekly servings of omega-3–rich fish and take a high-quality (molecularly distilled and tested for environmental contaminants such as heavy metals and PCBs) fish oil or krill oil supplement (1 g to 2 g daily).

LOW-DOSE LITHIUM

If your symptoms of ADHD include irritability, anger and impulsivity, low-dose lithium may help.

What low-dose lithium does: High doses of this mineral are prescribed for bipolar disorder. But *very low doses* of lithium can be a safe and effective nutritional treatment for ADHD when taken to calm the turbulent emotions that may agitate people with the disorder.

Good advice: Ask your doctor whether it makes sense for you to take 5 mg of *lithium orotate,* available over the counter, each day.

Also helpful: A diet that limits refined sugar and carbohydrates and emphasizes protein, which promotes the production of *dopamine*—one of the neurotransmitters that aids focus and attention.

DO YOU HAVE ADHD?

Adults who have attention deficit hyperactivity disorder (ADHD) often experience difficulty paying attention, feelings of restlessness and impulsive behavior. These symptoms can result in dangerous driving, poor financial decisions, missed deadlines and substance abuse, among other issues. If you have one or more of the following symptoms that is ongoing and severe enough to negatively impact your life, talk to your doctor...

Impulsiveness...lack of focus...mood swings ...easily frustrated...inability to handle stress... problems planning, prioritizing, multitasking or completing tasks...restlessness...quick temper...disorganization.

Surprising Benefits of Acupuncture: It Works for Asthma, Stroke Rehab, More

Stephen Chee, MD, MPH, MA, MTOM, LAc. He is dual-trained and dual-licensed as a medical doctor and acupuncturist. He is quadruple-board-certified in family medicine, integrative medicine, medical acupuncture and acupuncture, and Traditional Chinese medicine. Dr. Chee has a private practice in Beverly Hills, California. DrSteveChee.com

A recent *Vanity Fair* cover story about actress Angelina Jolie revealed that she had suffered from Bell's palsy (temporary weakness or paralysis and drooping of one side of the face). But Jolie said she no longer had the disorder—and credited acupuncture for her full recovery.

It took acupuncture a very long time to move from its roots as an ancient Chinese therapy to being accepted as "real medicine" in the West—and even today, most people, including most doctors, think of acupuncture mainly as a treatment for pain such as low-back pain, headaches and pain from arthritis. And acupuncture does treat pain effectively, probably because its placement of very fine needles into the skin in particular spots blocks the transmission of pain signals to the brain and also releases the body's natural endorphins.

What most people don't know: Acupuncture also is an excellent treatment for a wide variety of other illnesses and conditions.

Research shows that acupuncture reduces inflammation...improves circulation...regulates the autonomic nervous system (which controls heart rate, breathing, digestion and other body functions)...and balances the production of neurotransmitters, brain chemicals that control mood—all therapeutic keys to treating many health problems.

Here are surprising conditions that acupuncture can treat...

OVERACTIVE BLADDER SYNDROME (OAB)

This problem afflicts one in six Americans and becomes more common with age. You feel a sudden, uncontrollable urge to urinate (which can lead to incontinence), and you may have to urinate many times a day and even several times overnight.

How acupuncture helps: When medications cannot control the problem, electroacupuncture—in which the needles conduct a very mild, nonpainful electric current—often can. The proven approach is using electroacupuncture to stimulate a point in the ankle along what Traditional Chinese medicine practitioners call the "kidney meridian." This also happens to be the location of the posterior tibial nerve, which controls the bladder.

Recent finding: A team of researchers from several leading institutions—including Johns Hopkins School of Medicine, Columbia University Medical Center and Brown University—reviewed studies on nondrug treatments for OAB, publishing the results in *American Journal of Obstetrics Gynecology*. The researchers found that electroacupuncture was effective for the problem and improved quality of life.

What works best: Weekly electroacupuncture for 12 weeks. Discontinue the treatment if it isn't improving the condition after four or five weeks. Patients who respond to the treatment may require additional therapy at individually defined treatment intervals (for example, every three weeks) for sustained relief of symptoms.

Acupuncture may help for incontinence as well: Stress urinary incontinence—passing urine inadvertently when you cough, sneeze, laugh, exercise or lift a heavy object—afflicts an estimated 35% of women, most of them older. A recent study of about 500 women with this condition, published in *JAMA,* showed that electroacupuncture decreased urine leakage after six weeks. (Using electroacupuncture to treat stress urinary incontinence is still being researched.)

DIABETIC PERIPHERAL NEUROPATHY

An estimated 50% of older people with diabetes develop this nerve disorder, which can cause numbness, burning, tingling and pain in the feet, legs, hands and/or arms—and also increases the risk for infected diabetic foot ulcers and the need for amputation.

GOOD TO KNOW...

Finding an Acupuncturist

Word of mouth is the most effective way to find a competent acupuncturist. Ask your doctors, family members and friends for recommendations. You also can use the "Find a Practitioner" feature at the website of the National Certification Commission for Acupuncture and Oriental Medicine (NCCAOM.org).

Talk to the acupuncturist before your treatment to see if you feel comfortable with him/her, which is a key element of healing. (Avoid treatment from any acupuncturist who isn't willing to talk to you or answer your questions before charging you or starting treatment.)

Recent finding: A study published in *Journal of Acupuncture and Meridian Studies* showed that 10 weekly sessions of acupuncture improved the symptoms of diabetic peripheral neuropathy in three out of four patients.

Another recent finding: Acupuncture also may help control high blood sugar itself. In a study published in *Nutrition & Diabetes*, treatment with a diabetes medication (*metformin*) and acupuncture controlled high blood sugar more effectively than the medication alone.

What works best: Electroacupuncture and scalp acupuncture weekly for 10 weeks. (Scalp acupuncture utilizes advanced acupuncture needling techniques and points on the scalp that have been identified not by Traditional Chinese medicine but by neuroanatomy. In my clinical experience, it often is the most effective type of acupuncture for treating neurological problems such as neuropathy, stroke and mental decline and usually requires additional training by the acupuncturist.)

ASTHMA

I have used acupuncture to treat a number of patients with asthma, helping them decrease the frequency and severity of asthma attacks—and reduce the dosage of their asthma medication. (As with all the medical problems discussed here, I almost always use acupuncture in combination with other medical and nondrug treatments—in the case of asthma, those nondrug treatments include certain supplements, conscious breathing, meditation and eliminating environmental and potential food triggers.)

Recent finding: In a study published in *The Journal of Alternative and Complementary Medicine,* German and Swiss researchers added acupuncture (15 sessions over three months) to standard asthma treatment in 184 patients, comparing them with people who had asthma but did not receive acupuncture. Compared with those not getting acupuncture, those receiving it had a 70% greater improvement in asthma symptoms and in limits to their daily activity. They also had two to four times greater improvement in perceived physical and mental health.

What works best: Any style of acupuncture can be effective for asthma, with treatments once a week for 10 to 15 weeks. Patients who respond to the treatment may require additional therapy at regular intervals (for example, every three to four weeks) for sustained relief of symptoms.

POST-STROKE REHABILITATION

Research shows that acupuncture can treat a variety of post-stroke symptoms including pain, depression and insomnia—and can help restore the basic nerve and muscle function that strokes rob from patients.

Recent finding: Researchers from Australia and China analyzed the results from 22 studies on 1,425 stroke patients, publishing their results in *Archives of Physical Medicine and Rehabilitation*. They found that electroacupuncture reduced spasticity (in which muscles involuntarily shorten or flex, causing stiffness and tightness) by more than 40% and improved everyday functioning.

What works best: Scalp acupuncture combined with either electroacupuncture or standard acupuncture.

Some Like It Hot: Saunas Cook Up Sizzling Health Benefits

Jari A. Laukkanen, MD, PhD, cardiologist and professor in the School of Medicine at the University of Eastern Finland's Institute of Public Health and Clinical Nutrition, Kuopio. He has published numerous articles about the long-term health effects of sauna use.

Every now and then something that feels great turns out to be great for your health. This time, it's the modern sauna—a room that radiates dry heat.

Saunas have had a healthy reputation for a long time, to be sure, but scientific evidence has been scant—mostly small, short-term studies. Now there's compelling new research that has tracked the long-term health of thousands of sauna-taking men and women over a period of more than 20 years—and it found wide-ranging benefits for the heart, the respiratory system and the brain.

Not surprisingly, the new studies are coming from Finland, where the sauna has been a part of home life for millennia. But even in the US, there's a sauna at many gyms, and new kinds of home saunas are increasingly affordable and popular—imagine taking a relaxing dry sauna any time you want! *Here's a look at the proven benefits of dry sauna—and how to get them for yourself...*

FOUR WAYS SAUNAS MAKE YOU HEALTHIER

Saunas are such a part of Finland's culture that nearly everyone uses one. So rather than comparing people who use them frequently with those who never use them, researchers compared frequent users with infrequent ones. They then took steps to control statistically for the fact that people who use saunas often might live healthier lives in other ways as well, such as exercising more or smoking less. *Among the health benefits of taking saunas regularly...*

- **Healthier heart.** A 20-year study published in *JAMA Internal Medicine* found that people who took saunas four to seven times a week were 50% less likely to develop cardiovascular disease than those who took saunas only once a week or less. Regular sauna use increases blood flow and heart rate in much the way that cardiovascular exercise does—and improves the function of the inside layer of blood vessels in ways that are beneficial for blood pressure.
- **Protection from dementia.** Research published in *Age and Ageing* found that middle-aged men who took 15-minute saunas four to seven times per week were 66% less likely to develop dementia than men who took one sauna per week or less. One reason may be the cardiovascular benefits that improve blood flow to the brain.
- **Less respiratory disease.** A study published in *European Journal of Epidemiology* found that middle-aged men who took at least four saunas per week were 41% less likely to develop certain serious respiratory conditions over time including chronic obstructive pulmonary disease (COPD), asthma and pneumonia.
- **Longer life.** A healthier heart, brain and lungs may add up to preventing premature death. The study published in *JAMA Internal Medicine* also found that middle-aged men who took saunas four to seven times each week were 40% less likely to die from any cause during the 20-plus-year study than were men who used the sauna only once a week or less.

YOUR SAUNA STRATEGY

Taking the occasional sauna when you visit a hotel or spa is not enough to derive significant health benefits. The secret to saunas is to use them often—ideally every day or every other day.

How long you spend in the sauna and how hot the sauna is matter as well.

Example: Studies show that sauna use is associated with a lower overall risk for sudden cardiac death—and that risk was 52% lower for men who habitually spent more than 19 minutes in the sauna than for those who spent 11 minutes. Various studies confirm that the best sauna temperature for health is about 175°F at head level.

Spending that much time in a hot sauna is likely to make your heart rate accelerate, and it might no longer feel completely comfortable—but maybe that's the point. With cardiovascular exercise, our bodies derive the greatest benefits when we push ourselves beyond the point where the exercise is easy. That's true with saunas, too.

Warning: People who have high or low blood pressure or other cardiovascular problems should speak with their doctors before taking saunas—and in fact, that's a good idea for everyone just to make sure that the heat won't be risky for you.

So far, almost all of the research on health benefits has been done on the traditional "dry" sauna—often called a "Finnish" sauna in the US. This type of sauna features very little steam and humidity levels of just 10% to 20%. Popular "infrared" saunas, which also are dry but work on a different principle to heat the body, have been shown to reduce blood pressure and have other short-term health benefits, but there is no long-term data. Nor do we know much about the health effects of steam rooms, although they, too, create a passive cardiovascular workout.

SAUNA BEST PRACTICES

For safe, effective use of a sauna...

- **The best temperature is around 175°F,** although you'll get benefits over 160°F. Avoid going as high as 195°F—that is not safe for anyone.
- **Twenty to 30 minutes is ideal.**
- **After a sauna, let yourself cool down** for a few minutes by sitting in a normal-temperature room—and drink two to four eight-ounce glasses of water.
- **Saunas are places where people sit or stand and perspire**—so they should be cleaned regularly.
- **Don't drink alcohol an hour or two before a sauna—or during.** The combination of heat and alcohol can make blood pressure drop too low.

How Compassion Relieves Chronic Pain

Emma Seppälä, PhD, science director, Center for Compassion and Altruism Research and Education, Stanford University School of Medicine, California, and author of *The Happiness Track: How to Apply the Science of Happiness to Accelerate Your Success.*

If you suffer from chronic pain, and perhaps the angry emotions that may result, there's a drug-free treatment that takes only 15 minutes a day and can bring real relief.

It's called *compassion meditation.* It's not like "regular" meditation. Rather than simply calming your mind, you actively direct your thoughts—toward kindness and altruism. Do not believe this could relieve your pain? Rigorous scientific studies have found that it can—and it may even help you live longer.

THE SCIENCE OF KINDNESS

At the Center for Compassion and Altruism Research and Education at Stanford University School of Medicine, we study the health effects of compassion and altruistic behavior. *Recent research at our center and other institutions has found that compassion meditation helps...*

- **Chronic pain—and anger.** Among people who have chronic pain, a nine-week compassion meditation program at Stanford University led to significantly reduced pain severity and greater pain acceptance by the end of the program.

One benefit was that it reduced levels of anger, based on self-evaluations of the patients. Anger has been shown to be an important predictor of chronic pain symptoms, and cultivating compassion has been shown to positively influence how we process emotions, reducing the tendency toward negativity, including anger.

- **Post-traumatic stress disorder (PTSD) symptoms.** In a study at the Veterans Administration's Puget Sound Health Care System in Seattle, researchers found that when veterans with PTSD practiced loving-kindness meditation (a form of compassion meditation) for 12 weeks, they experienced a reduction in PTSD symptoms and depression. The benefits were still evident three months later.

• **Migraines.** A study from the University of Massachusetts Medical School in Worcester found that migraine sufferers who learned loving-kindness meditation in a *single session* experienced a 33% decrease in pain and a 43% reduction in emotional tension.

• **Longevity.** While there's certainly no conclusive evidence that learning to be compassionate to yourself and to others will help you live longer, there are intriguing clues that it might.

The connection: Telomeres, which are "caps" on the tips of each strand of DNA on your chromosomes.

A study from Massachusetts General Hospital and Harvard Medical School found that people experienced in practicing loving-kindness meditation had longer telomeres, which are associated with greater longevity.

HOW TO PRACTICE COMPASSION MEDITATION

Compassion meditation aims to strengthen feelings of compassion and empathy toward yourself and other people—to generate feelings of kindness toward yourself and others. It's different from the well-known "mindfulness" meditation, which is mostly focused on calming the mind and increasing awareness. In compassion meditation, rather than letting your thoughts come and go without judgment, you focus your attention in specific ways as you silently repeat benevolent phrases or visualize kind wishes.

The goal is to express your intention to move from judgment or dislike to caring, compassion, acceptance and understanding. Compassion meditation involves bringing to mind people you know and love, feeling their love and spreading caring feelings toward strangers or even people you find challenging.

It isn't hard to do.

What to do: Sit quietly, close your eyes, breathe gently and silently repeat a phrase designed to evoke a feeling of goodwill toward yourself, such as *May I be happy, healthy and strong.* Then, extend the good wishes to someone you feel thankful for, then to someone you're indifferent toward, then to someone you find challenging and finally to the world at large.

Practicing loving-kindness or compassion meditation is a way to stretch the "muscles" of kindness, caring and empathy toward everyone and to remember our common humanity. The key is to give your "compassion muscles" a workout by practicing regularly, just as you might any other skill. Doing so will help you cultivate more loving relationships, greater happiness and better health...and could noticeably reduce your chronic pain.

Ready to do it now? You can use my YouTube video, "A Gift of Loving Kindness Meditation," which runs for less than 15 minutes. Close your eyes and follow the prompts. Once you know it by heart, you can do it in your own time and voice.

End Shoulder Pain *Without* Surgery

Beth E. Shubin Stein, MD, associate attending orthopedic surgeon and a member of the Sports Medicine Service at Hospital for Special Surgery in New York City.

The shoulder is the most movable and complex joint in the human body. And it's basically unstable.

Imagine a golf ball perched on a tee. That's your shoulder. The humerus (upper arm bone) is the ball and the scapula (shoulder blade) is the tee. It doesn't take much to knock them apart.

So it's no wonder that as you get older, normal wear and tear often leads to shoulder pain. You might notice the discomfort while serving a tennis ball, reaching for a jar on a shelf, carrying a heavy suitcase or simply putting on a sweater or fastening a bra. *The most likely culprits...*

Impingement: The rotator cuff, a collection of muscles and tendons surrounding the humerus, gets pinched between that bone and the scapula.

TAKE NOTE...

Better Bones in 60 Seconds

Just one or two minutes daily of high-intensity weight-bearing exercise was associated with 4% and 6% better bone health, respectively. This degree of improvement can be enough to decrease fracture risk. Exercise intensity levels were the equivalent of medium-paced running for younger women or a slow jog for older ones.

Takeaway: For better bones, pick up your pace for at least a minute whenever you're out walking.

Victoria H. Stiles, PhD, senior lecturer, sport and health sciences, University of Exeter, UK.

Frozen shoulder: Tissue around the shoulder joint gets inflamed and stiff.

Tendinitis: Rotator cuff tendons become inflamed or irritated.

Bursitis: Tiny fluid-filled sacs (called bursa) that act as a gliding surface to reduce friction between shoulder tissues become inflamed.

Each condition is caused by inflammation, often as a response to tiny injuries that you didn't notice when they happened. Each can get so painful that surgery seems like a good idea. But why go through that discomfort, recuperation and expense if you can avoid it?

Surprising truth: With pain management and physical therapy, two-thirds of patients get better on their own.

But if your shoulder is bothering you, that doesn't mean you can just do nothing. Your pain will continue and even may intensify the next time you overstress the shoulder. Worse yet, you could get a rotator cuff tear, which definitely requires surgery and then four to six months of recovery.

To learn the best way to avoid shoulder surgery, we interviewed orthopedic surgeon Beth E. Shubin Stein, MD. *Her advice...*

If you feel pain in a shoulder and your movement is restricted, see an orthopedist right away to rule out a rotator cuff tear. As long as your rotator cuff is intact, you have a very good chance of making your shoulder feel better and avoiding surgery if you, in consultation with your doctor, follow these steps.

MANAGE YOUR PAIN

The first step is to manage your pain so that you can start physical therapy. Ice your shoulder for 20 minutes at a time, two or three times a day. Also, take a nonsteroidal anti-inflammatory drug (NSAID), either over-the-counter or prescription, to reduce inflammation and pain (don't exceed the recommended dosage).

If that's not enough to ease pain and allow exercise, your doctor can give you a cortisone shot. It's a potent anti-inflammatory, but repeated shots can limit a tendon's healing ability.

My protocol: If a first cortisone shot works for two months or more and you can exercise, I typically recommend a second shot and continuing physical therapy.

But if the first cortisone shot doesn't ease pain and allow exercise, I offer patients platelet-rich plasma (PRP) injections ($1,000 to $2,500). It's experimental and generally not covered by insurance. If PRP doesn't work, another option is to use donor stem cells from amniotic membranes to help regenerate tendon tissues. This can be about twice as expensive as PRP, and insurance most likely won't cover it either. These treatments don't work for everyone, but if they do, shoulder discomfort should subside within three days to a week.

Tip: You also may want to consider acupuncture as a complement to any of the above approaches.

Once pain isn't holding you back, it's time to get your shoulder moving. You can complete this stretching/strengthening program in 15 minutes. Do it twice a week. It's also great for anyone who wants to avoid shoulder problems.

Important: You should never feel pain when doing either stretching or strengthening exercises.

These exercises might sound like a lot of work, especially if you've become accustomed to avoiding using your shoulder because of pain. But take it from someone who both performs necessary shoulder surgery and does my best to help patients avoid it—it's well worth the effort to avoid the knife. I do these exercises myself two or three times a week—I've had shoulder pain in the past, but these exercises let me stay strong and pain-free.

STEP 1: GET LIMBER

Much of the work of supporting the shoulder falls to the rotator cuff. *These stretches improve rotator cuff flexibility and support normal range of motion...*

- **Wall crawl.** Stand facing a wall. Place the palm of one hand in front of your chest and "walk" it upward along the wall. Go as high as you can without feeling pain, hold for three to five seconds, and walk your hand back down. Perform five to 10 repetitions. Switch hands and repeat.

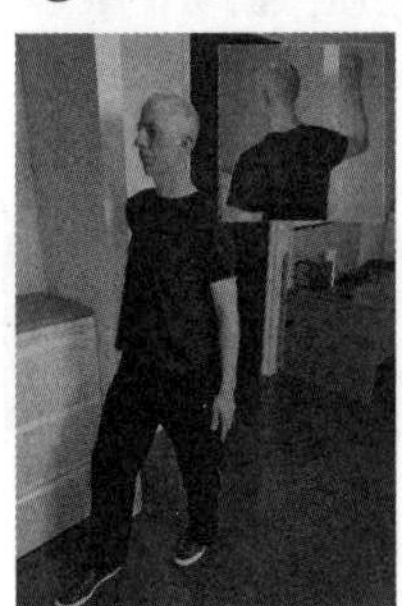

- **Doorway stretch.** Stand in an open doorway, and place your right hand flat against the wall next to the right side of the doorway frame at shoulder height, with your elbow bent. Keeping your right hand in place, step forward with your right foot, bending your right knee (as in a lunge), with your left leg stretched behind you. You should feel a stretch in your shoulder but not any pain. Hold for three to five seconds, and do five to 10 repetitions. Repeat with the left arm on the left side of the doorway and left foot stepping forward.

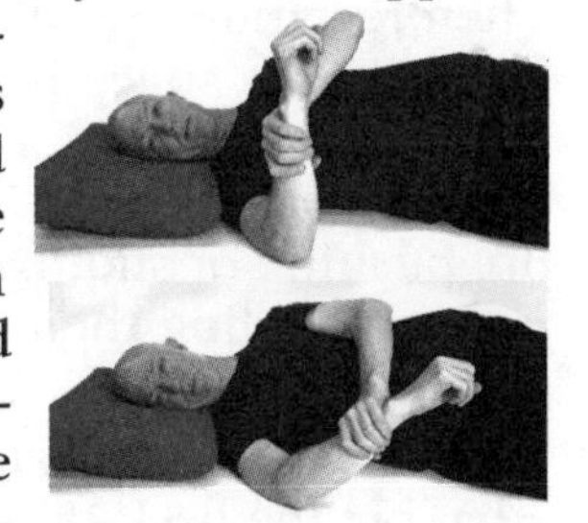

- **Side stretch.** Lie on your side on the floor (on an exercise mat or rug), your painful shoulder on the floor and your head supported on a pillow or bolster so that your spine is in a straight line. Bend the arm that's on the floor at the elbow, with the forearm and hand raised and palm facing your feet. Now use your other hand to gently push the wrist of the bent arm toward the floor. Hold for three seconds and release. Do a total of 10 reps. Repeat with your other arm.

STEP 2: STRENGTHEN THE RIGHT MUSCLES

While impingement, frozen shoulder, tendinitis and bursitis often are referred to as overuse issues, I prefer to call them "understrength" issues. The problem isn't the 100 times you serve during a typical tennis match—it's that your muscles aren't strong enough to handle the stress you're placing on them. Even people who lift weights often focus on the biceps and triceps and ignore the rotator cuff.

Caution: Stay away from military presses and other exercises that require you to lift weights overhead—that can injure your shoulder. Skip kettle bells, too—they require swinging that can inflame your shoulder.

My recommendation: To build the strength of your rotator cuffs, use resistance bands, which do the job and are safer. *Try these three stability builders...*

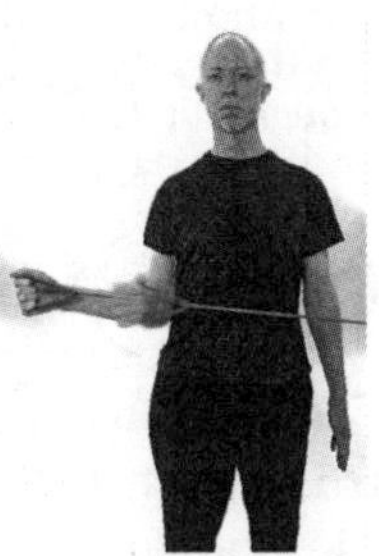

- **External rotation.** Loop a resistance band at waist height around a secure anchor such as the base of equipment at a gym or a strong door handle of a locked door at home. Standing sideways to the anchor, grab both ends of the band with one hand so it's taut. Keep your elbow bent and against your side and your hand near your stomach. Now pull the band away from your stomach, keeping your elbow against your side, until you feel light tension on the outside of the shoulder.

Hint: Your shoulder blade should move toward your spine. Hold for one second. Do a total of 10 reps. Then repeat with your other arm.

- **Internal rotation.** This is the reverse of the external rotation. Keep the resistance band looped around a secure anchor, and stand in the same position as above. But this time, grab the band with the hand that is closest to where it's anchored. Keeping your elbow bent and at or near your side, pull the band across your torso toward your belly button. Hold for one second. Do a total of 10 reps. Repeat with your other arm.

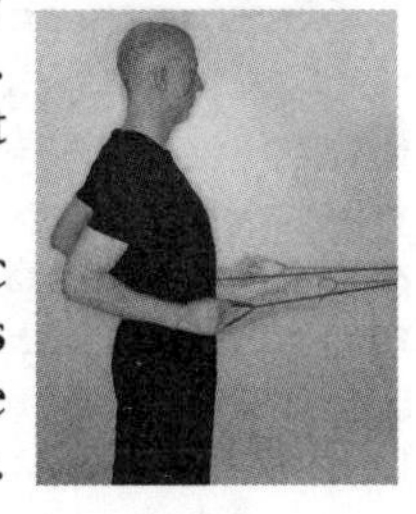

- **Rowing.** With the elastic band securely anchored as above, grab one end of the band in each hand so it's taut.

Pull both arms back, bending your elbows and keeping them close to your sides. Hold for one second. Do a total of 10 reps. Repeat with your other arm.

Stretch Away Your Pain: It Takes Only Minutes a Day!

Joseph Tieri, DO, an osteopathic physician, adjunct professor at Touro College of Osteopathic Medicine in Middletown, New York, and co-owner of Stone Ridge Healing Arts in Stone Ridge, New York. Dr. Tieri is also author of *End Everyday Pain for 50+: A 10-Minute-a-Day Program of Stretching, Strengthening and Movement to Break the Grip of Pain*. His website is EndEverydayPain.com.

Those everyday aches and pains that we all experience are commonly chalked up to arthritis. But that condition is the true cause far less frequently than most people realize.

While your doctor may order an MRI, discover arthritis or a bulging disk, and blame your musculoskeletal pain on that, studies reveal that arthritis and other degenerative conditions often can be detected on the films of *pain-free* middle-aged and older people. Age-related musculoskeletal aches and pains that result from tension and misalignment are far more common than arthritis but *don't* show up on film. As a result, many patients resort to medicine or even surgery for arthritis or herniated disks when that's not the real source of their pain.

Instead, it's poor posture combined with the inactivity of everyday living and underused joints that leads to stiffness and pain, whether it's shoulder pain, hip pain, back pain, etc.

Good news: Doing strategic stretching, strengthening and range of motion exercises for *just a few minutes a day* is enough to keep your muscles supple, your joints lubricated and everyday aches and pains at bay. Incorporate each of these moves into your daily routine to prevent various types of pain and to help relieve it.

Note: Hold each stretch for 30 seconds if you're younger than age 65...and for 60 seconds if you're 65 or older.

Most of the benefit comes from the first stretch, so *one repetition is sufficient*. However, you can repeat these stretches throughout the day whenever your back, neck, hips and/or shoulders feel tight or stiff...

- **Shoulder and chest stretch.** This is one of the most important—and simplest—moves you can do to reverse the rounded-shoulder posture that affects so many people.

What to do: Lie on the floor (on an exercise mat, if you like), face up, arms straight out to the sides in a "T" position with palms up. That's it! Believe it or not, this very simple stretch helps loosen the tight, shortened muscles in the front of your neck, shoulders and chest.

- **Neck stretch.** This will help to reverse the tension caused when one's head juts forward—so common when driving or typing. It also elongates and aligns the neck, creating space for disks between the vertebrae, which lessens the odds of a bulging or herniated disk.

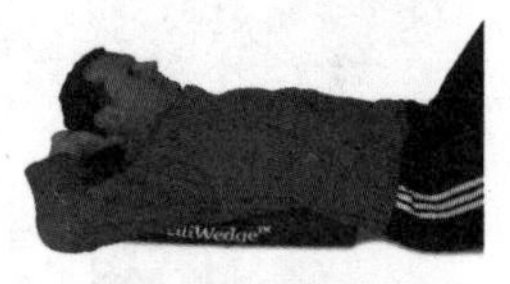

What to do: Begin by lying flat on your back on a bed or a mat on the floor (a wedge mat as shown in the photo above may be more comfortable for older individuals). Allow your head to relax for a few seconds. Then reach up and place the fingers of both hands in the space beneath your neck. With fingertips touching, move them to the bottom of your head. Now move your fingers up, pushing or sliding the back of your head upward, feeling the back of your neck elongating. Then hold.

Note: This movement may tilt your head down a bit, but the back of your head should stay in contact with the bed or mat at all times.

- **Psoas stretch.** The psoas (pronounced "SO-az") is the most important muscle you've never heard of—it's the main muscle connecting the spine to the legs, and it works with other muscles to stabilize the lower spine and promote proper body alignment. The psoas often weakens with age and inactivity, leading to lower back and hip pain and poor posture.

What to do: Start by lying flat on your belly (on an exercise mat, if you wish) with your forehead resting on the backs of your crossed hands. Allow your stomach to relax and notice the natural curve of your lower back. For many older patients, this provides enough of a stretch—if so, continue doing this daily for a week or two until you no longer feel the stretch in your lower back, which means you're ready for the next step—slowly press up onto your forearms (Sphinx) or your palms (Cobra). Remember, keeping your belly relaxed as your lower back gently stretches is more important than trying to lift higher.

• **Piriformis stretch.** The piriformis is a small muscle that runs diagonally from the bottom part of the spine to the upper thighbone on each side of the body. Asymmetry can develop after years of driving with your right foot on the gas pedal, crossing your legs the same way or sleeping in the same position, which can cause pain in the hips and lower back.

What to do: Sit in a chair with both feet on the floor. Rest your right ankle on top of your left thigh, just above the knee. Keeping your back straight, gently bend forward at the waist until you feel a stretch in your right thigh and glute. Then repeat on the other side.

For Cancer Fatigue, Try Exercise

If you suffer from cancer-related fatigue, consider skipping antifatigue medications. A recent meta-analysis of 113 studies including 11,000 men and women found that exercise alone (such as walking or yoga) reduced cancer fatigue significantly, especially when started before or during treatment. Psychological counseling, such as cognitive behavioral therapy, was also effective.

Karen M. Mustian, PhD, MPH, University of Rochester Medical Center, New York.

Yoga as Good as PT for Back Pain

Yoga works as well as physical therapy for back pain. When patients took yoga classes every week for three months, then attended more yoga sessions or practiced at home for nine months, they reported the same improvement in pain and activity limitation after one year as patients who had 15 visits with a physical therapist during the three-month period, then for the nine months had further sessions every two months or did prescribed home exercises.

Robert B. Saper, MD, MPH, director of the program for integrative medicine and health disparities, Boston Medical Center.

Yoga Fights Depression

In a recent finding, when 21 male veterans took a twice-weekly yoga class over eight weeks, those who were depressed at the outset of the study saw a significant and clinically meaningful reduction in symptoms after the study period—regardless of whether they were in counseling or taking an antidepressant.

Theory: Yoga's stress-reducing effects help fight depression.

Lindsey B. Hopkins, PhD, research fellow, San Francisco Veterans Affairs Medical Center, California.

A Little Bit of Exercise Helps Depression a Lot

Just *one hour of exercise weekly* can reduce depression risk. People who do one hour a week of any type of exercise, at any intensity level, have a 44% lower risk of developing depression over a decade than people who do not exercise at all. More exercise or more intense exercise is not better from a mental-health standpoint. Any type of physical activity, including simple walking, had the same benefit.

Samuel Harvey, PhD, associate professor, School of Psychiatry, University of New South Wales, Sydney, Australia, and leader of an analysis of a Norwegian survey of nearly 34,000 adults, published in *American Journal of Psychiatry.*

Feeling Down? That's OK!

People who acknowledge and accept feeling depressed or anxious—without berating themselves—feel better than those who ignore their emotions or judge them as negative, according to a study of 1,300 adults.

Study participants, who reported feelings after journaling or delivering a three-minute videotaped test, had lower levels of distress and fewer symptoms of depression if they accepted these feelings.

Iris Mauss, PhD, associate professor of psychology, University of California, Berkeley.

The Power of Meditation

Anxiety can be reduced in *one* mindfulness meditation session. This form of meditation focuses on breathing and awareness of one's thoughts. In a study of 14 people, mindfulness meditation reduced anxiety in 11 participants in the first hour after the guided session—and all 14 reported lower anxiety one week later.

John J. Durocher, PhD, assistant professor of biological sciences and affiliated assistant professor of kinesiology and integrative physiology, Michigan Technological University, Houghton.

EASY TO DO...

Tap Your Toes for Better Health

Sitting for hours at a desk or in front of the TV reduces circulation and can lead to increased risk for cardiovascular disease and other medical problems.

What helps: Toe-tapping and other leg fidgeting. In a recent small study, the legs of study participants who moved one foot an average of 250 times per minute had significantly improved blood flow, compared with those of participants who did not move their feet. Taking frequent breaks to walk and/or stand also helps.

Jaume Padilla, PhD, assistant professor of nutrition and exercise physiology, University of Missouri, Columbia.

6

Very Personal

The Sex-Starved Marriage: How to Make Both of You Happier

It has been two months since Janet and Mark have had sex. They're hardly speaking to each other. If you asked Janet about this, she would say that their home has become a battle zone—they fight about every little thing. Janet goes out of her way to avoid Mark to protect herself from his wrath.

Mark tells a different story. His anger, he believes, is justified. He is fed up with Janet's lack of interest in their sexual relationship. "She never initiates sex. She recoils when I try to kiss or hug her. I'm tired of being rejected." To cope with his unhappiness, Mark spends longer hours at work and busies himself on his computer at night, deepening the chasm between them.

Both Mark and Janet think that the other one is to blame for the problems between them. They have hit an impasse.

The result: A sex-starved marriage. And sex-starved marriages are surprisingly common. In fact, in about one in three marriages, one spouse has a considerably larger sexual appetite than the other. This in and of itself is not a problem—it's how couples handle their differences that matters.

Here's what you need to know to fix a sex-starved marriage and make you both happier...

YEARNING FOR CONTACT

In a sex-starved marriage, one partner is longing for more touch—both sexual and nonsexual—and the other spouse isn't interested

Michele Weiner-Davis, LCSW, founder of The Divorce Busting Center in Boulder, Colorado, which helps on-the-brink couples save their marriages. She is the best-selling author of eight books including *Healing from Infidelity*, *The Sex-Starved Marriage* and *Divorce Busting* and is a TEDx speaker. DivorceBusting.com

and doesn't understand why such a fuss is being made about sex. The less interested spouse thinks, *Is this just about having an orgasm? That's not such a big deal.* But the spouse yearning for more physical contact sees it differently. Being close physically is more than a physical release—it's about feeling wanted and connected emotionally.

When a misunderstanding of this magnitude happens and the less interested spouse continues to avoid sex, marriages start to unravel. Couples stop spending time together. They quit putting effort into the relationship. They become more like two distant roommates. Intimacy on all levels ends, which puts the marriage at risk for infidelity or divorce.

Typically, the spouse with the smaller sexual appetite controls the frequency of sex. If she/he (contrary to popular belief, men also can have low sexual desire) doesn't want it, it generally doesn't happen. This is not due to a desire to control the relationship—it just seems unthinkable to be sexual if one is not in the mood.

Furthermore, the lower-desire spouse has the expectation that the higher-desire spouse must accept the no-sex verdict and remain monogamous. The higher-desire spouse feels rejected, resentful and miserable.

How do two people with differing sexual appetites begin to bridge the desire gap? Regardless of where you stand on the sexual-desire spectrum, it's important to keep in mind that loving marriages are built on mutual caretaking. Don't wait for your spouse to change first. Be the catalyst for change in your marriage. *Here's how...*

IF YOU ARE THE LOWER-DESIRE SPOUSE

• **Just do it—and you may be surprised.** Over the years, countless clients in my counseling practice have said, "I wasn't in the mood to have sex when my spouse approached me, but once we got going, it felt really good. I had an orgasm, and my spouse's mood really improved afterward."

Why would that be? For many people, the human sexual response cycle consists of four stages that occur in a certain order—*desire* (out of the blue, you have a sexy thought)... *arousal* (you and your partner touch, and your body becomes aroused)...*orgasm*...and *resolution* (your body returns to its normal resting state).

But for millions of people, stages one and two actually are *reversed.* In other words, desire doesn't come until after arousal. These people must feel turned on *physically* before they realize that they actually desire sex. Therefore, being receptive to your partner's advances even from a neutral starting place—when you do not feel desire—makes sense because chances are that sex will be enjoyable for both of you.

• **Give a "gift."** Let's face it, there are times when people—even people with the typical desire/arousal pattern—simply don't feel like having sex. It's perfectly acceptable to decline your partner's offer from time to time. But when "no" substantially outweighs "yes," you are creating deep feelings of frustration and rejection—guaranteed.

What's the solution to an "I'm not really in the mood for sex" moment? Give a gift—a sexual gift—or to be more blunt about it, pleasure your spouse to orgasm if that's what he/she wants, even if you're not in the mood for the same. This is an act of love and caring and completely appropriate within a marriage.

IF YOU ARE THE HIGHER-DESIRE SPOUSE

• **Speak from your heart.** If you're feeling frustrated that your spouse hasn't understood your need to be close physically, chances are you've been irritable and angry. Anger is not an aphrodisiac—it pushes your spouse further away. Press your mental-reset button, and approach your spouse differently. Speak from your heart—express your vulnerability (yes, you are vulnerable, no matter how "tough" you are!) and your hurt.

Example: Instead of saying, "I'm angry that we haven't had sex in so long," it's better to say, "When we don't have sex for this long, I miss being close to you. I feel disconnected. It hurts my feelings that you don't seem interested in me sexually."

• **Rather than complain, ask for what you want.** Complaining, even when it's justified, leads to defensiveness. Instead, ask for what you want in a positive way.

Example: Instead of saying, "You never initiate sex," say, "I'd really love it if once in a while, you threw your arms around me and said, 'Do you want to make love?' That would make me feel great."

- **Figure out what turns your spouse on.** If buying sex toys or downloading X-rated videos has failed to entice your spouse to nurture your sexual relationship, there's probably a reason. Your spouse might need to feel courted by you first. You might be married to someone who feels more connected to you when you have meaningful conversations…spend enjoyable, uninterrupted time together other than having sex…are more affirming and complimentary…or when you participate in family activities together. This is how your partner feels loved—and the truth is, there are many people who want sexual intimacy only when they feel loved first.

If you're uncertain about *your spouse's* way of feeling cherished by you, ask. Say, "What can I do to make you feel loved?" Believe it or not, meeting your partner's needs, though different from your own, may be a turn-on for him/her. Try it.

TAKE NOTE…

A Good Night's Sleep for Better Sex

A good night's sleep improves the sex lives of postmenopausal women. A study of nearly 100,000 postmenopausal women ages 50 to 79 found that those who got seven to eight hours of sleep each night were more likely to be sexually active and sexually satisfied than those who got fewer than six hours a night. The sleep/sex connection was particularly strong for women who weren't taking hormone therapy…and in women over age 70.

Juliana M. Kling, MD, MPH, division of women's health, Mayo Clinic, Scottsdale, Arizona.

What to Do When *He's* Not in the Mood…

Michele Weiner-Davis, LCSW, founder of The Divorce Busting Center in Boulder, Colorado, which helps on-the-brink couples save their marriages. She is the bestselling author of eight books including *Healing from Infidelity, The Sex-Starved Marriage* and *Divorce Busting* and is a TEDx speaker. DivorceBusting.com

When you hear the words, "Not tonight, dear, I have a headache," do you envision a woman politely rejecting her husband's sexual advances?

You almost certainly do. But contrary to popular belief, about 15% of men say they simply aren't in the mood for sex. Low desire in men can be caused by many different factors. One of them, of course, is erectile dysfunction (ED) or ejaculation problems—anticipating undesirable outcomes can make sex anxiety-producing rather than enjoyable, eventually leading to not being interested. *Other reasons include…*

RELATIONSHIP ISSUES

Although most people believe that it's women who need to feel close to their spouses emotionally before they're interested in sex, believe it or not, men often feel this way, too. *The following factors contribute to emotional distance…*

- **Men brood.** Rather than confront relationship conflict head-on, men hold their feelings inside and brood—and often lose desire. Keeping anger and resentment inside is a surefire way to diminish desire for intimacy.

- **Men are visually oriented.** Men often say that they have lost interest in sex with their wives because they're no longer attracted to them. They complain that their wives have "let themselves go" and stopped caring about health and fitness. Men tend to be very visually oriented when it comes to sexual desire.

- **Men get bored.** Sometimes men lose interest in sex because it has become routine or simply unsatisfying. Less-than-rewarding sex can be due to either partner's unwillingness to experiment with new and potentially exciting ways of having satisfying sex. Sometimes couples lack information about ways to improve their sex lives. Other times, they're simply too uncomfortable to talk about what might make their sexual relationship more vibrant and passionate. This problem is compounded if one person is eager to explore creative sexual solutions and the other partner is not.

PSYCHOLOGICAL ISSUES

Sometimes disinterest in sex can be traced to self-sabotaging thoughts and feelings such as dissatisfaction with the changes in one's body, feeling stressed out about work or excessive worry about finances, the kids, in-laws, health issues and so on. *Also...*

- **Questioning of sexual orientation.** Sexual orientation is not necessarily etched in stone. For a variety of reasons, some happily married people eventually do sexual U-turns, seeking same-sex sexual partners and avoiding marital sex. Wives often are unaware of the reason why their husbands' interest in sex with them has waned.

- **Excessive use of porn.** Many couples use pornography to enhance and enrich their sexual relationships. But an excessive porn and masturbation habit can lead to difficulty becoming aroused "in real life."

- **Infidelity.** Countless married people have affairs. Frequently, marital sex suffers when an affair is ongoing. Because of the clandestine nature of infidelity, wives often are in the dark as to the reasons their husbands have pulled away emotionally and stopped initiating sex.

- **Depression** can have debilitating effects on one's sex life. Seventy-five percent of people who are depressed confirm a loss of sexual desire. It is important to note that signs of depression in men often are different from those in women. Women tend to turn their emotions inward, becoming sad and tearful, feeling guilty and worthless. Men, on the other hand, often are uncharacteristically irritable and angry, sometimes resorting to abusing alcohol and other substances to self-medicate.

BIOLOGICAL ISSUES

As people age, sex drive often changes. Although many men enjoy sex well into their 80s, over time, there is a decline in testosterone, the primary hormone responsible for sex drive. As a result, men often feel less focused on their sexual relationships. Also, they require more—and different—stimulation to achieve and maintain an erection. Orgasms tend to be less intense. These changes can be disconcerting and anxiety-producing to men who, in the past, have had sizable sexual appetites and can lead to a pronounced reduction in the desire for sex. *Other biological issues that affect desire...*

- **Illness.** Cardiovascular disease wreaks havoc with a man's blood flow, which in turn makes it difficult to achieve or maintain an erection. This can lead to a feeling of sexual inadequacy that dampens desire.

Other illnesses that can impact sexual desire include endocrine disorders (diabetes, hypothyroidism, hyperthyroidism), liver disease, kidney disease, pituitary disease, Parkinson's disease, anemia and arthritis. Chronic pain can take a toll, too.

- **Medications.** Many prescription and over-the-counter medications can greatly affect a man's sex drive. These include antidepressants, antihistamines, tranquilizers, antihypertensives, antipsychotics, antiarrhythmia and anticonvulsant drugs.

- **Unhealthy lifestyle.** If a man abuses alcohol or drugs, doesn't exercise or eat healthfully or fails to get adequate sleep, sex may become unimportant.

HOW TO BOOST DESIRE

What a man needs to do to boost his libido depends on the reasons for the loss of desire. *That said, it makes sense to begin by taking two commonsense actions...*

- **Get a medical checkup.** Rule out biological causes of low libido. *Example:* A blood test can offer information about testosterone levels and suggest the need for testosterone supplements, frequently a helpful remedy. Similarly, if medications are causing the drop in desire, alternative drugs can be prescribed.

- **Adopt a healthy lifestyle.** To feel more vibrant physically and mentally, you know the drill—you must eat healthfully, exercise regularly, get sufficient sleep and avoid excessive alcohol and other harmful drugs.

Once you have taken these prophylactic measures, here are some other steps...

• **Learn skills to overcome ED and other sexual problems.** If ED or performance anxiety is a problem, men can learn new skills to help them relax and maintain their erections by going to a licensed sex therapist. A sex therapist is specially trained to educate couples who are experiencing difficulties in the bedroom. The American Association of Sexuality Educators, Counselors and Therapists (AASECT.org) offers a directory of qualified sex therapists. Also, drugs such as Viagra, Cialis and Levitra are effective in helping men keep erections, which can help relieve anxiety about performance.

• **Talk about the changes you would like to make to your sexual relationship.** Let's face it—talking about your sexual needs can be dicey and uncomfortable. Plus, too many people expect their partners to be mind readers about what might turn them on. The fallout from this lack of communication is unsatisfying sex.

If you want to feel more enthusiastic about sexual encounters, be specific about what might turn you on. Talk about your fantasies, your likes and dislikes. Describe what you would like your spouse's "come on" strategy to be—grabbing you, asking if you want to fool around, sexting earlier in the day. Discuss what you like about foreplay. Since what arouses people changes over time, share updated information about your sexual turn-ons. Also, talk about your need for nonsexual touch such as snuggling, holding hands, and giving and getting back rubs.

• **Take a relationship skill-building class.** If a drop in desire is caused by underlying feelings of anger and resentment, get some new tools for your relationship toolbox. There are excellent marriage seminars where couples can learn specific techniques to stop arguing and start loving each other again. These classes are not group therapy—you won't have to discuss your personal issues in front of the group. You will be given information about ways to improve your relationship that you can practice privately with your partner.

INTERESTING FINDING...

Is Heart-Stopping Sex for Real?

Heart-stopping sex does happen but is very rare. In a study of 4,557 cases of sudden cardiac arrest over a 13-year period, only 34 cases were linked to sex—about one in 100 cardiac arrests in men and about one in 1,000 cases in women.

Sumeet Chugh, MD, associate director, Cedars-Sinai Heart Institute, Los Angeles, and senior author of a study published in *Journal of the American College of Cardiology*.

• **Just do it.** It also is important to keep in mind that desire sometimes needs a jump-start. Rather than wait until the mood strikes you, start touching each other in sensual ways. Frequently, the desire to have sex follows rather than precedes touching.

It's important to note that when there is a sexual-desire gap in a relationship, the person with lower desire tends to control the sexual relationship—if that person isn't in the mood, sex usually does not happen. When the frequency of sex is a unilateral decision, resentment builds and the relationship suffers. The higher-desire spouse feels intense rejection, hurt and anger. These unpleasant emotions are ever-present, leading to frequent arguments and general unhappiness.

An antidote to this relationship logjam is for a man to be willing to pleasure his partner even if he's not feeling in the mood himself. Healthy, loving relationships are built on mutual caretaking. Helping one's spouse feel wanted and attractive is an essential part of feeling connected emotionally.

Stay Sexually Active...Even with a Chronic Health Condition

Barry McCarthy, PhD, a psychologist, sex therapist and marital therapist who is a professor of psychology at American University in Washington, DC. He is coauthor, with Michael Metz, PhD, of *Enduring Desire: Your Guide to Lifelong Intimacy.*

There are a multitude of reasons why some couples stop having sex as they age. But a chronic health problem is definitely a big one. Fortunately, it doesn't have to be that way.

Sexual satisfaction remains within reach for just about everyone who wants it...and most people still do want it. Not only that, sexual activity has its own health benefits—for example, it helps lower blood pressure, improves sleep and relieves pain.

ADOPTING A NEW MIND-SET

If you're depriving yourself of sexual intimacy because of a health problem, the key is to start thinking about sex in a new way. Instead of viewing a sexual encounter as a pass/fail test that involves intercourse and mutual orgasm, it's time to think of it as an opportunity for sharing pleasure. How you achieve this is largely up to you. *To get started, you'll want to talk to...*

- **Your doctor.** Schedule a single consultation for you and your partner to meet with your internist, cardiologist, oncologist or other physician who is treating your health problem. Ask him/her to explain how your condition might affect your sexual intimacy and to give you any advice on what you can do medically to minimize those issues.

- **Your partner.** It's crucial for you to be able to talk about sex with your partner. Don't wait until you're in bed...or after a negative experience. Instead, bring up the subject (ideally on the day before a sexual encounter) while you're on a walk or having a glass of wine together. Avoid any blaming, and be clear that you're simply making sexual requests so that the experience is more comfortable and pleasurable.

In addition to what you learn by talking to your doctor and your partner, consider these specific steps to get your sex life back on track if you are affected by...

BACK PAIN

Take a man with low-back pain and have him engage in intercourse the way 70% of Americans do—with the man on top of his partner performing short, rapid thrusts—and you've got a perfect recipe for uncomfortable sex.

A better approach: The man with the bad back can invite his partner to go on top, and they can try a circular, thrusting motion. If a woman has back pain, the couple might try the side rear-entry position and long, slow thrusts. If your partner also has back problems, take lovemaking to the shower, where the warm water can loosen sore muscles.

Also helpful: If you're in chronic pain, such as that caused by arthritis, your doctor can refer you to a physical therapist, who can give you additional positioning tips.

Taking your favorite over-the-counter pain-reliever or using a heating pad about 30 minutes before sex also helps. This approach often reduces back *and* joint pain for an hour or more.

Even if your pain is not entirely eliminated, you may get enough relief to enjoy yourself. And after orgasm, your pain will likely be less intense for a period of time.

CANCER

Cancer treatment, such as surgery, radiation and medication, can create pain, fatigue and all kinds of psychological and physical fallout.

With breast cancer, it's common for a woman to worry about her partner's reaction to her altered body and how her breasts will respond to touch, particularly if she has had reconstructive surgery, which reduces sensitivity.

What helps: When talking about these issues, don't be afraid to get specific. Some women will not want to be touched on the affected breast or breasts, at least for a while. Others will crave that touch. Some might feel uncomfortable about nipple stimulation but fine about touching on the underside of the breast.

Cancers that affect other parts of the body, such as cervical or testicular malignancies or even mouth cancer, can also interfere with intimacy. If a man has been treated for prostate cancer, for example, he may want to focus more on pleasure-oriented sexuality rather than the traditional approach of intercourse and orgasm. Whatever the situation, talk about these vulnerable feelings and enlist your partner's help as a sexual ally.

EXCESS BODY WEIGHT

Too much body weight can get in the way—both psychologically and physically.

It's common for a person who is overweight to think: *I don't feel sexy now, but I will when I lose some weight.* While weight loss is a healthy idea, putting your sexuality on ice until you reach some ideal state is not. Learn to love and care for the body you have.

What helps in bed: Think beyond the missionary position, which can get pretty awkward and uncomfortable if one or both parties carry a lot of weight around the middle. Try lying on your sides instead. Or try a sitting and kneeling combination—a woman might sit on the edge of a sofa, supported by pillows behind her back, while her partner kneels before her.

HEART AND LUNG PROBLEMS

The fatigue often associated with heart and lung disease can douse your sexual flames. But a bigger issue is often the fear that a bit of sexually induced heavy breathing will prove dangerous or even fatal.

If this is a concern, ask your doctor whether you are healthy enough for sex. A good rule of thumb is to see if you can comfortably climb two flights of stairs. If the answer is yes, then almost certainly you're healthy enough to have sex.

What helps: If you still feel nervous, you can gain some reassurance by pleasuring yourself. A bout of masturbation produces the same physiological arousal as partnered sex. And it gives you a no-pressure chance to see how that arousal affects your breathing and heart rate.

PARKINSON'S AND RELATED CONDITIONS

People with frequent tremors, muscle spasms and other conditions in which a loss of control over the body occurs can still enjoy sex.

What helps: When talking to your partner about sex, decide between the two of you, in advance, on what you will say if, during lovemaking, your body becomes too uncooperative. It might be just a single word—"spasm," for instance—that tells your partner you need to pause.

Then agree on a "trust position" you will assume as you take a break to see if you want to return to sexual activity. For example, some people will cuddle or lie side by side.

Hormonal Birth Control Linked to Depression

Women who used birth-control pills, hormonal patches or IUDs containing progestin were from 23% to two times as likely to start taking an antidepressant, compared with women using nonhormonal birth control. The likelihood was even greater for teenagers ages 15 to 19.

Self-defense: Women with a history of depression should talk to their doctors about nonhormonal birth control.

Study by researchers at University of Copenhagen, Denmark, published in *JAMA Psychiatry.*

Sexual Bereavement

Alice Radosh, PhD, research psychologist and coauthor of the study "Acknowledging Sexual Bereavement: A Path Out of Disenfranchised Grief," published in *Reproductive Health Matters.*

The death of a spouse is not just the loss of a life partner. It also is the loss of a sexual partner. Unfortunately, most widows and widowers must cope with the emotional impact of that loss of sexual intimacy alone, and the isolation only deepens their suffering. Cultural taboos and personal embarrassment often prevent them from raising their feelings of what is called "sexual bereavement." But there's a way to help yourself psychologically if you are in this situation...or help a loved one who is.

Recent finding: A survey of 104 partnered women age 55 and older published in *Reproductive Health Matters* found that 72% anticipated missing sex with their partners after their partners died, and most said that they would want to discuss this feeling of loss with a friend. But the majority reported that they would feel more comfortable about the conversation *if the friend raised the subject.*

The problem: Most of the women surveyed also admitted that they would not raise this topic if it were one of their friends who had been widowed.

What to do: If you are the close friend of someone who has been widowed, raise the topic of the loss of sexual intimacy. If it makes you uncomfortable to ask your friend about his/her sex life, you could mention that you would grieve the loss of your sex life if you were widowed...or you could say that someone else you know who was widowed experienced these feelings. Don't assume that your recently widowed friend is too old to have had an active sex life—many couples remain sexually active into their 80s.

If you are recently widowed and are experiencing sexual bereavement, understand that these feelings are perfectly normal. Raise the topic with a friend or relative without shame. If you are not comfortable doing this, you could raise the topic with a therapist or support group...or with a friend by mentioning a recent sexual-bereavement article you read about (such as this one).

Unexpected Health Risks of Menopause... and Beyond

JoAnn V. Pinkerton, MD, NCMP, executive director, North American Menopause Society, Pepper Pike, Ohio, and professor of obstetrics and gynecology and division director of Midlife Health at the University of Virginia Health System, Charlottesville.

If you're approaching menopause or are postmenopausal, you already know about bothersome symptoms such as hot flashes and night sweats. And you're likely aware that your risk for serious health conditions, including osteoporosis and heart disease, is now higher.

What you may *not* know is that the shift in hormone levels that occurs during menopause and continues into postmenopause may be behind other physical and emotional changes—everything from achy joints to dry skin.

We asked Dr. JoAnn V. Pinkerton, executive director of the North American Menopause Society, about some of the less obvious effects menopause and postmenopause may be having on your life and your health...and what you can do.

• **Changes in your skin.** Your biggest organ, the skin, takes a hit from menopause-related hormonal changes in several ways...

You lose *collagen*, a protein that gives skin its elasticity. Women lose up to 30% of skin collagen in the first five years after menopause, although the exact link to menopausal estrogen loss isn't clear. The less collagen you have, the looser, drier and flakier your skin looks and feels.

Also, *acne*, which probably has not been a problem since you were a teen, may rear its head again. Blame a shift in the balance between estrogen and androgen. This hormone-related acne usually develops on your lower face or around your chin, jawline, neck and even upper back.

A more rare, yet disturbing, skin issue that can be related to menopause is *formication*—an itching, tingling sensation that feels like ants crawling on your skin! It usually develops during early postmenopause. Short-term hormone therapy—two to 12 weeks—may relieve symptoms. It also can have nonhormonal causes, such as allergens or side effects from medications.

What you can do: Follow basic rules of good skin care—drink plenty of water, exercise, eat well, get a good amount of sleep and avoid sun exposure. If you take estrogen in the first five years after menopause (the safest time to do so), it may help you maintain collagen and avoid some of the issues of aging skin...but not all studies agree that it helps.

Dr. Pinkerton's advice: Don't take hormone therapy for the sole purpose of skin care. But it might be an added bonus.

• **Achy bones and joints.** Waking up with more than your usual aches and pains? It's a normal part of aging, but women after menopause have it worse than men. Compared with men their age, twice as many postmenopausal women develop osteoarthritis—a "wear and tear" degenerative joint condition. Although how estrogen affects women's joints is not well understood, it is known that there are estrogen receptors in muscles, tendons and cartilage, which all support and protect joints. So it stands to reason that there would be some effect when estrogen levels dip.

Observational studies reveal clues. In the Women's Health Initiative study, the largest US study of postmenopausal women, women on estrogen therapy had fewer hip replacements than women who didn't take estrogen. Those who were taking both estrogen and progestin had less joint stiffness and pain. Finally, women who take aromatase inhibitor drugs to block estrogen (usually to treat estrogen-fueled cancers) commonly do have joint pain.

What you can do: As with skin issues, while hormone therapy *may* help ward off arthritis, it is not a good reason to start taking it. Instead, whether you take hormone therapy or not, remain as active as you can, since moving your muscles and joints is key to preventing arthritis. Look for low-impact activities that don't stress joints, such as brisk walking, swimming or tai chi. If you're overweight, losing even a small amount of weight can relieve stress on joints. A healthy Mediterranean-style, anti-inflammatory diet may help even if you don't lose weight.

• **Sleep apnea.** Sleep problems are common in menopause, especially if hot flashes and night sweats interrupt sound sleep. And after menopause your risk of developing *sleep apnea*, a sleep disorder characterized by repeated pauses in breathing during sleep, also rises. Sleep apnea makes you more vulnerable to heart disease and stroke, among other problems.

Postmenopausal women are twice as likely to develop sleep apnea as premenopausal women. In one large study, researchers found that postmenopausal women had different apnea symptoms than men. Men's apnea symptoms were primarily snoring or interrupted breathing at night, while women were more likely to suffer from insomnia, morning headaches, tiredness, depression or anxiety—or even bed-wetting. The increased risk after menopause is believed to be related to hormonal decreases, which may be associated with weight gain. But it can happen even if you don't gain weight.

What you can do: Lifestyle approaches, such as losing weight, not smoking and sleeping on your side, may help. An oral appliance

GOOD NEWS...

Natural Help for Hot Flashes and More

A modest exercise program can help you to navigate those sometimes-turbulent waters of menopause. A recent study followed 166 postmenopausal sedentary women (none were using hormone therapy). Half of these women participated in a cardio/strength fitness program three hours per week for 20 weeks. They also got psychological counseling to help them set goals and deal with setbacks.

Results: Compared with the sedentary women, the active women had fewer hot flashes and better moods, lost weight, reduced blood pressure and increased flexibility.

JoAnn V. Pinkerton, MD, NCMP, executive director, North American Menopause Society, Pepper Pike, Ohio.

that shifts your jaw position may help, too. But if these approaches don't work, you may need to use a *continuous positive airway pressure* (CPAP) machine to keep your airway open so that you can breathe normally all night long. If you even think that you *might* have sleep apnea, talk to your doctor to get diagnosed. In small trials, hormone therapy improved sleep-disordered breathing and sleep disruption.

• **Changes in your senses.** Some women report that their sense of taste, specifically for salty, peppery or sour foods, shifts after menopause. And some women report a strange burning mouth sensation.

There is also evidence that declining estrogen may hasten hearing loss. Your eyes undergo changes, too—they may become dry and itchy after menopause.

What helps: In the case of sensory changes and complaints, research isn't clear about the role of estrogen—or hormone therapy. But understanding that they may be related to the normal menopause process can ease your mind.

Note: Just because *some* of these health issues are more likely after menopause doesn't mean they'll happen to you! But if you are concerned, talk to your doctor.

And although declining estrogen levels can trigger these conditions and symptoms, the best treatment may not be hormone therapy. Always weigh the benefits against your individual risks.

Anxiety After Menopause

JoAnn V. Pinkerton, MD, NCMP, executive director, North American Menopause Society, Pepper Pike, Ohio, and professor of obstetrics and gynecology and division director of Midlife Health at the University of Virginia Health System, Charlottesville.

Anxiety is common in perimenopause. But recent research finds that it's common in postmenopause, too—and is linked to severe symptoms that can interfere with your quality of life.

According to a recent study of 3,503 postmenopausal women ages 40 to 59, published in *Menopause*, the likelihood of having severe menopausal symptoms—especially hot flashes, sleep problems, a racing heart, and muscle and joint pain—was five times higher in those who reported that they felt anxious. One possible explanation is that anxiety boosts the stress-related neurotransmitter norepinephrine, which can trigger symptoms such as hot flashes.

What to do: Find ways to decrease menopausal symptoms and anxiety. A number of approaches could help, including regular exercise, breathing exercises, relaxation techniques such as mindfulness meditation and reducing caffeine. Using the supplement hops and aromatherapy with neroli oil may also offer relief.* If anxiety symptoms persist, be sure to seek professional help.

*Hops can cause drowsiness—do not combine with alcohol or sedatives. If you have allergies or asthma, check with your doctor before trying aromatherapy.

---

9 Ways to Prevent Breast Cancer—Before and After Menopause

Anne McTiernan, MD, PhD, research professor at Fred Hutchinson Cancer Research Center in Seattle, Washington, and author of *Starved: A Nutrition Doctor's Journey from Empty to Full.* She was a member of the World Cancer Research Fund International/American Institute for Cancer Research panel that issued the report titled "Continuous Update Project Report: Diet, Nutrition, Physical Activity and Breast Cancer 2017."

What are the *most effective* things that women can do to avoid getting breast cancer? A team of researchers at the World Cancer Research Fund asked that question. *Here's what they found...*

Background: Each year, 315,000 American women are newly diagnosed with breast cancer. Although new treatments have improved survival, breast cancer remains the second-leading cause of cancer deaths in American women. Many known risk factors are hard to change—such as getting your first period before age 12...not ever having children or having your first child after age 30...hitting menopause after age 55...a family history of breast cancer...being exposed to high levels of radiation. But many lifestyle factors do make a difference—some, a *big* difference.

Study: The World Cancer Research Fund International and the American Institute for Cancer Research gathered an international panel of experts to review 119 scientific studies involving 12 million women about the ways diet, weight and physical activity affect a woman's risk of developing breast cancer. They then determined which of those factors protected women *the most* from getting the disease—both before and after menopause. (Since men account for only 1% of breast cancer cases, the panel limited its recommendations to women.)

Convincing evidence found that...

- **Physical activity and breastfeeding** *decrease* the risk for breast cancer.
- **Drinking alcohol** *increases* the risk.
- **Eating certain kinds** of vegetables and fruits *reduces* risk.

Surprisingly, women who were overweight or obese between the ages of 18 and 30 were *less likely* to develop breast cancer, either before or after menopause, compared with women who were of normal weight between the ages of 18 and 30. The reasons aren't well understood. But while being overweight or obese throughout adulthood was still associated with less risk for premenopausal breast cancer, a pattern of *adult weight gain*—defined in different studies as after age 35 or age 50—was strongly associated with increased *postmenopausal* breast cancer risk.

Bottom line: These evidence-backed lifestyle habits can help prevent breast cancer...

BEFORE MENOPAUSE

- **If you have children, breastfeed if you are able to.** The longer you nurse and the more children you nurse, the more you reduce breast cancer risk thanks to the resulting hormonal changes that reduce estrogen exposure throughout your life.
- **Watch out for weight gain in your 30s, 40s and 50s.** Being overweight before age 30 is protective against breast cancer. But take steps to prevent the weight gain that tends to creep up after age 30.

AFTER MENOPAUSE

- **Redouble efforts to keep weight under control.** Once through menopause, obesity increases breast cancer risk by a whopping 40%, according to some studies. Women who get and eliminate breast cancer have a higher chance of their cancer returning and a higher chance of dying of the disease if they are obese.
- **Whittle your waistline.** It's not just how much you weigh, but where weight lodges on your body. Extra fat around your middle can lead to inflammation, increased levels of estrogen (produced by the fat) and higher insulin levels—all of which can set the stage for breast cells to mutate and turn cancerous. It's tough to avoid turning apple-shaped after menopause. Try to keep your waist measurement less than 32 inches by eating healthy foods and staying active.

AT EVERY AGE

These lifestyle factors can help prevent breast cancer throughout life—and it's never too late to start them...

- **Curb your drinking.** Even just one drink a day increases breast cancer risk by 5% if you're premenopausal—and by 9% if you're postmenopausal. Each additional daily drink increases risk, on average, by the same percentages. So if you like to have a glass of wine with a meal, do not pour more than five ounces—that is one drink.
- **Step up your activity level.** Any type of exercise reduces breast cancer risk. Aim to get about 30 minutes at least five days a week. While moderately intense activity such as brisk walking counts, exercising vigorously—running versus walking, kickboxing versus yoga—is particularly protective.

Higher-intensity workouts not only help you get rid of harmful belly fat but also boost the immune system so your body is better able to kill mutating cells before they form a tumor. (Exercise also can improve outcomes for people who have cancer, research finds.)

- **Get your calcium.** Diets rich in calcium protect against breast cancer both before and after menopause. *One reason:* Calcium helps regulate cell growth, especially in breast tissue.

• **Load up on nonstarchy veggies.** There is evidence that eating nonstarchy vegetables—such as broccoli, leafy greens, summer squash, asparagus, tomatoes—is especially helpful in reducing the risk of *estrogen-negative breast cancer,* which tends to grow at a faster rate than hormone-positive cancers. Aim for at least one cup a day. (Starchy veggies such as potatoes don't count.)

• **Eat your carotenoids.** When choosing fruits and vegetables, be sure to go for color. Animal and test-tube studies have shown that *carotenoids*—fat-soluble pigments that give produce its coloring—have protective properties. Choose red, orange and yellow fruits and vegetables such as berries, beets, peppers and carrots.

How much can these healthy lifestyle habits help reduce breast cancer risk? By about one-third, the researchers estimate. That would be about 100,000 US women every year.

Study Reveals Breast Cancer Caution

There's an increased risk for breast cancer in women who are using or have recently used birth control pills, implants, injections or intrauterine devices that release hormones.

In a study of 1.8 million women, ages 15 to 49, breast cancer risk was increased by 20% among women who used hormonal birth control. Still, risk is low in these ages, so absolute risk was small—an extra 13 cases for every 100,000 women using hormonal contraceptives for one year. Women should balance breast cancer risk with the health risks of nonhormonal contraceptive methods, such as IUDs.

Anne McTiernan, MD, PhD, research professor at Fred Hutchinson Cancer Research Center, Seattle, and author of *Starved: A Nutrition Doctor's Journey from Empty to Full.*

BREAST CANCER ALERT...

Hair Dye and Breast Cancer Risk

The use of brown or black hair dyes by black women was tied to a 51% greater risk for breast cancer. White women who used dark dyes had 31% higher risk. The study found an association between using hair products and the risk of being diagnosed with breast cancer, but it does not prove cause and effect.

Adana Llanos, PhD, MPH, assistant professor of epidemiology with Rutgers School of Public Health, New Brunswick, New Jersey, and leader of a study of more than 4,000 women, published in *Carcinogenesis*.

Safer Hormone Therapy

The latest research on vaginal estrogen for menopausal symptoms shows that these creams, inserts or rings are safer than oral estrogen, which may increase stroke and breast cancer risk. A study of 45,663 women, followed for more than six years, found that those who used vaginal estrogen, compared with women who didn't use any hormonal product, had no greater risk for breast cancer, stroke, heart disease or hip fracture. Vaginal estrogen relieves symptoms including vaginal dryness, itching and urinary urgency.

Carolyn J. Crandall, MD, MS, professor of medicine, David Geffen School of Medicine at the University of California at Los Angeles.

More Fruit = Less Breast Cancer Risk

Women who ate at least three servings a day of apples, bananas and grapes as teenagers were 25% less likely to have developed breast cancer in middle age than women who said that they ate only a half serving of those fruits daily. There also was some benefit—but less of it—linked to eating oranges and/or kale. Fruit juice of any type did not seem linked to lower breast cancer risk.

Study of the questionnaires of more than 44,000 women by researchers at Harvard T.H. Chan School of Public Health, Boston, published in *The BMJ*.

New Breast Cancer Care

A device that treats early-stage breast cancer tumors by targeting them with precisely focused beams of radiation, minimizing damage to surrounding tissue, received FDA clearance in December 2017. The GammaPod is expected to shorten the standard three-to-six-week radiation treatment and may eliminate the need for surgery. To find a hospital using GammaPod, go to xcision.com and click on "patients."

William F. Regine, MD, Isadore and Fannie Schneider Foxman Endowed Professor and Chair of Radiation Oncology, University of Maryland School of Medicine, Baltimore, and GammaPod coinventor.

Prostate Cancer Treatment and Heart Disease

Prostate cancer treatment may increase risk for certain heart diseases. Androgen deprivation therapy (ADT) reduces male hormones to stop them from stimulating prostate cancer cells to grow.

Recent finding: Men on ADT with early, localized prostate cancer had an 81% higher risk for heart failure and a slightly increased risk for heart rhythm disorders, compared with those not on ADT. If you are on ADT, be monitored closely for heart disease.

Reina Haque, PhD, MPH, research scientist in the department of research and evaluation at Kaiser Permanente Southern California, Pasadena.

TAKE NOTE...

Nonsurgical Prostate Fix

In a study of 1,000 men, an outpatient procedure called *prostate artery embolization* (PAE) resulted in long-term improvement in urinary flow and erectile function for 78% of patients with enlarged prostate glands.

How it works: A catheter is used to insert microscopic plastic beads into blood vessels beside the prostate gland, which cuts off blood flow and begins shrinking the gland within two weeks. No major complications, such as sexual dysfunction or urinary incontinence, were indicated.

To find a trial: Go to ClinicalTrials.gov and search "PAE."

João Martins Pisco, MD, interventional radiologist, St. Louis Hospital, Lisbon, Portugal.

New Treatment for Advanced Prostate Cancer

Adding the medication *abiraterone acetate* (Zytiga) plus *prednisolone/prednisone* to standard prostate cancer treatment (androgen-deprivation therapy, ADT) lowers the risk for death by 37%. Abiraterone already is used to treat some men whose disease has spread, but the recent findings mean that more men could benefit by using abiraterone with ADT as soon as they are diagnosed.

Nicholas D. James, MBBS, PhD, honorary professor of clinical oncology at Institute of Cancer and Genomic Sciences, University of Birmingham, UK.

Testosterone Warning

Abuse of testosterone can cause heart attacks, personality changes and infertility. Testosterone supplements are prescribed for men whose testosterone levels are low. But millions of others use testosterone and other anabolic steroids to try to boost physical health or libido. Athletes and body builders are especially likely to take these substances at high levels. This can hurt the heart, brain, liver and endocrine system and can have an impact on mental health as well. The FDA plans to revise labeling guidelines on all prescription testosterone products to make warnings of their dangers clearer.

US Food and Drug Administration, Silver Spring, Maryland.

4 Dangerous Myths About Testicular Cancer

Ajay Nangia, MD, professor of urology at University of Kansas Medical Center, with a practice at the University of Kansas Hospital, both in Kansas City. He is a leading male infertility specialist.

Women learn early about breast cancer. It's got ribbons and races. But men tend to know almost nothing about testicular cancer...and some of what they think they know is actually wrong—which could be putting their health and even their lives in danger. *Here's the truth regarding four common myths about this male cancer...*

***MYTH #1:* Testicular cancer is mostly a problem for older men.**

Truth: Not even in the ballpark. Even though *prostate* cancer rates rise with age, especially after age 60, the majority of the approximately 8,850 cases of testicular cancer diagnosed each year in the US are found in men ages 15 to 40. It's the most common cancer to strike young men. It does occur in older men, though—about 7% of new cases are in men over age 55.

***MYTH #2:* Testicular cancer is less "serious" than other types of cancers.**

Truth: Testicular cancer *does* have a relatively high cure rate—even if the cancer has spread. The five-year survival rate is 95%. When caught early and localized to the testicles, it's 99%. If it has spread to nearby tissue and/or lymph nodes, the survival rate is 96%. Even if the cancer has spread to other parts of the body, the five-year survival rate is 73%.

But these statistics mask the bigger truth that this is indeed a serious cancer. For starters, testicular cancer can't be easily diagnosed via a biopsy—the removal of a tiny piece of a potentially cancerous tissue for testing—because it could cause the cancer to spread.

Note: Biopsies do not cause most other types of cancer to spread.

So if symptoms (see below) or a physical exam lead to a suspicion of testicular cancer, and serum tumor marker blood tests and testicular ultrasound also point to cancer, an accurate diagnosis often involves removing the entire affected testicle—a procedure called *radical inguinal orchiectomy.*

That's traumatic enough...leaving men self-conscious about their altered appearance. Then there's chemotherapy or radiation, and sometimes a second surgery to remove nearby lymph nodes.

What's more, both the cancer itself and treatment (especially chemotherapy) can lead to infertility—even in the 97% of cases in which only one testicle is removed. As a result, men who may wish to father children in the future are advised to bank sperm before treatment—or if they haven't, to wait for a year or two after chemo before attempting impregnation to reduce the likelihood of having DNA-damaged sperm.

Finally, sexual performance may be affected. Treatment often leads to low testosterone levels, which can increase the risk for high cholesterol and high blood pressure—and erectile dysfunction.

***MYTH #3:* Injuring your testicles ups your chances of getting testicular cancer.**

Truth: There's no evidence that a swift kick or some other assault you-know-where impacts your testicular cancer risk. Nor will certain sexual practices, having a vasectomy or infection with *human papillomavirus* (HPV) increase your risk.

What are the risk factors? There's a strong genetic link, so family history matters. Being born with an undescended testicle also is a risk factor. Sophisticated new genetic tests can help identify, for example, the risk that a man born with undescended testicles actually has of developing the cancer. Unfortunately, there are no preventive steps a man can take.

***MYTH #4:* Testicular self-exams are a waste of time and effort.**

Truth: This is where there's some disagreement. The US Preventive Services Task Force (USPSTF), an independent panel of national experts that makes recommendations about health-screening practices, has concluded from a review of studies that the benefit of self-exams is small. But I, along with many other doctors in the field, disagree. The USPSTF's rationale is that there's no evidence that self-examination is effective at reducing mortality. Even without screening, if testicular cancer is discovered, "current treatment options provide very favorable health outcomes." But I see men who are dealing with the aftermath of testicular cancer, chemotherapy and/or surgery, and who are infertile and regret not having frozen their sperm. Plus, what harm is there in doing something that's free and can be handled, so to speak, in the shower?

HOW TO DO A TESTICULAR SELF-EXAM

Testicular self-exams are easy and painless. The hardest part is remembering to do it once a month. *Here are some guidelines from the Testicular Cancer Society...*

1. Do the exam during or right after a warm shower or bath, when the scrotum is most relaxed and easy to examine by hand.

2. Use both hands to examine each testicle. Place your index and middle fingers on the underside and your thumbs on top. Firmly yet gently roll the testicle between your thumbs and fingers to check for surface or texture irregularities (see below).

3. Find the *epididymis,* a ropelike structure on the back of the testicle. Become familiar with how it feels so you won't mistake it for a lump.

4. If you do the exam outside the shower, stand in front of a mirror and check for any visible swelling of the skin on your scrotum. It's not essential but provides an additional check.

5. If you notice irregularities or changes in your testicles, make an appointment to see your doctor as soon as possible.

TESTICULAR CANCER SYMPTOMS

Testicular cancer is often diagnosed when a man notices something unusual and goes to his doctor. *If you have any of these signs, it's best to get checked out...*

- **A painless lump or swelling,** usually hard, on the surface of either testicle.
- **A dull ache in the lower abdomen or in the groin**—especially if it lasts for more than an hour. It could be something else such as an infection or a physical twisting, but it's worth checking out, even going to the ER. Most guys wait too long—hours, days or even months!
- **A sudden buildup of fluid in the scrotum,** forming a soft or hard swelling.
- **Pain or discomfort in a testicle** or in the scrotum.

Red Meat Warning

Diverticulitis happens when the gut wall bulges and forms a sac that becomes inflamed. Six or more servings of red meat weekly, on average, was associated with a 58% increased risk during a 26-year period.

Yin Cao, ScD, research associate, Harvard T.H. Chan School of Public Health, Boston, and leader of a study of 46,461 men, published in *Gut.*

INTERESTING FINDING...

Coffee and Colorectal Cancer

People with colorectal cancer who drank at least four cups a day of regular or decaf coffee after their diagnosis had 52% lower risk for death from colorectal cancer, compared with people who drank no coffee. Previous studies have shown that drinking coffee may prevent colon cancer in the first place.

Yang Hu, doctor of science candidate, department of nutrition and epidemiology, Harvard T.H. Chan School of Public Health, Boston, and leader of a study published in *Gastroenterology.*

Tree Nuts Linked to Colon Cancer Survival

Stage-3 colon cancer patients who ate at least one ounce of tree nuts (such as walnuts and almonds) twice a week had a 42% lower chance of cancer returning and a 57% reduced chance for death from the disease, compared with patients who did not eat nuts. No benefit was found from peanuts, which are legumes. All patients studied already had surgery and chemotherapy—diet, including nuts, is not a substitute for standard therapy.

Temidayo Fadelu, MD, postdoctoral fellow at Dana-Farber Cancer Institute, Boston.

Help for Alcoholics

Less than 10% of alcoholics get treatment even though medicines help some patients reduce alcohol cravings and cut back on drinking episodes. *Naltrexone* is an FDA-approved medicine (long used to help people addicted to opioids) that can help patients who abuse alcohol—other medications are *acamprosate* and *disulfiram*, which may be tried if patients do not do well on naltrexone or cannot use it.

George F. Koob, PhD, director of the National Institute on Alcohol Abuse and Alcoholism, National Institutes of Health, Bethesda, Maryland.

Eye Color Linked to Alcoholism?

European Americans with light-colored eyes—especially those who have blue eyes—had a higher rate of alcohol dependence than those with dark brown eyes.

Study of more than 10,000 people by researchers at University of Vermont, Burlington, published in *American Journal of Medical Genetics: Neuropsychiatric Genetics (Part B).*

Dementia and Alcohol

In a study of 57,000 people with early-onset (under age 65) dementia, 57% of cases were related to chronic heavy drinking—defined as four to five alcoholic drinks a day for men and three for women. People who ceased drinking heavily lived longer than people who continued to drink excessively but were still at risk for early dementia.

Takeaway: Alcohol abuse is the strongest modifiable risk factor for the onset of all dementia, especially early onset. If you drink heavily, seek help.

Michaël Schwarzinger, MD, researcher, Translational Health Economics Network, Paris.

Take Action Against Loneliness

Loneliness is detrimental to both mental and physical health. *To help prevent it...*

Make some small talk with strangers—simply chatting in person, not online, boosts well-being. *Have as much face-to-face contact* with friends and family as possible—use video conferencing if distance or health issues make that impossible. *Use social media* such as Facebook to create your own social networks, such as a book club where you share personal reactions with other readers. *Invite neighbors over for coffee*, and help them with small chores when you can. *Try throwing a dinner party*—eating together is a long-established method of connecting with people. *Creative group endeavors*, from craft nights to choral singing, also can improve connection with others.

Roundup of experts on preventing loneliness, reported in *Psychology Today.*

Moneywise

5 Common Financial Fibs That Can Get You into Big Trouble

Honest people know—without being told—that they should avoid obvious fraud such as writing bad checks or using someone else's credit card without permission. But even bending the financial truth with small misrepresentations and exaggerations that seem like white lies can lead to big trouble. And even if the fibs give you an advantage in the short-term, they could end up costing you big before long.

Five financial "fibs" that can hurt you...

LYING ABOUT YOUR INCOME (UPWARD)

When people overstate their incomes, it's often to secure bigger loans or higher lines of credit. But even if you succeed in getting the ability to spend more by exaggerating what you earn, you may face high interest rates on balances that you can't pay off...penalties if you don't pay on time...and lower credit scores. Lenders (including credit card issuers) care mostly about getting paid, not using the courts to punish borrowers who lie on applications. However, when out of options, a lender may sue to recover what is owed.

What to do: Don't fudge your income upward to secure a loan or line of credit that is more than you can realistically repay.

LYING ABOUT YOUR INCOME (DOWNWARD)

When people say they earn less than they do, it's often to obtain a government benefit

Note: Prices, rates and offers throughout this chapter and book are subject to change.

Joann Needleman, an attorney heading the consumer financial-services regulatory and compliance group at the law firm Clark Hill PLC in Philadelphia. She is immediate past president of the board of directors of the National Creditors Bar Association (NARCA). She serves on the Consumer Financial Protection Bureau consumer advisory board, and she has been recognized by the courts for her pro bono work with consumers facing lawsuits. ClarkHill.com

reserved for lower-income people such as Medicaid, rental assistance, etc. That's fraud, which is a prosecutable offense. It also can mean that there are fewer benefits available for people who genuinely need them, so it's a moral offense as well. But even if you think that a government program should be available to you despite the fact that you don't technically qualify, you are playing with fire by claiming it.

What to do: Never misrepresent income to receive a benefit meant for people who earn less than you, especially when dealing with an official agency or a government entity.

LETTING SOMEONE USE YOUR CREDIT CARD

Generally, it is not against the law to lend someone your credit card, although doing so likely breaks the contract you signed with the card issuer, which agreed to extend credit to you—not to a friend or relative of yours. In effect, you are causing the other person to lie about who he/she is—you are condoning a misrepresentation. And even though it is the other person who is misrepresenting himself, you are ultimately responsible for any use of the card by the person you give it to—even if he ends up charging much more than you expected. Legal responsibility would fall on the other person only if you could prove that he used the card without permission. If you don't pay the bill, you face the same legal repercussions as if you defaulted on your own purchases. That could include being sued.

What to do: Don't lend your credit card to someone unless you absolutely trust that person and the person's judgment. Even better, if you want to give or loan someone money for a purchase, make the purchase yourself using your credit card or give the person cash.

FUDGING AN INSURANCE CLAIM

After a car accident, it might be tempting to lump in the cost of preexisting mechanical problems with the cost of repairs from the crash when filing an insurance claim. You heard a rattle in your exhaust for a few weeks, then you got rear-ended. Why not just say that the rattle started with the accident? But misrepresenting damage in a claim to an insurance company is illegal. It's also very possible that you will get caught. Insurance companies employ expert investigators to examine anything suspicious, whether it's related to a car accident, a house fire or a burglary. Insurance companies are regulated by the state, and lying on a claim can be a felony.

What to do: Resist the urge to overstate damage or loss when filing an insurance claim, and never falsely attribute loss or damage to an incident or accident.

FABRICATING A HARDSHIP

If someone owes more than he is able to pay back without undue hardship, in certain cases, especially when the bill is from a doctor or hospital, the amount might be reduced or an extended-payment plan might be arranged. However, if someone with adequate means finagles his way into such a hardship program, the organization may seek to recover the full debt, which might include suing the debtor, if the dishonesty is discovered. Even worse is fabricating a hardship to avoid court-imposed payments or fines. Whether it's a municipality, a county, a state, etc., misrepresenting your finances while under oath to avoid a payment—even for something as minimal as a

BETTER WAY...

Make Sure You Have a Written Financial Plan

Although 64% of Americans say they have a financial plan, only 18% of baby boomers say it is in writing—compared with 21% of Generation X and 34% of millennials. People with written financial plans are more likely to accomplish the goals in the plans. And they more often have good financial organization in other ways, too.

Example: 51% of those with written plans have a household budget, compared with 40% of those who do not have a written plan...45% of those with written plans have an emergency fund to cover at least three months of living expenses, compared with 26% of those without a written plan.

Modern Wealth Index study conducted by Charles Schwab Corp.

traffic ticket—is considered perjury, a serious offense.

What to do: Never claim to be destitute to avoid paying a fine or bill that you actually can afford. If you're facing a legitimate hardship, be open about it and ask the creditor to work with you.

The 5 Mental Traps That Make You Throw Away Money

Dan Ariely, PhD, the James B. Duke Professor of Psychology and Behavioral Economics at Duke University in Durham, North Carolina. He is coauthor of *Dollars and Sense: How We Misthink Money and How to Spend Smarter.* DanAriely.com

Why do otherwise smart people sometimes make foolish purchases and fail to save for the future but then also frequently penny-pinch in ways that hurt them? The problem is not necessarily a lack of willpower or a failure to stop and think before making spending decisions.

What often happens is that even when we do think before we act, our instincts and emotions steer us wrong again and again. Why? In a nutshell, evolution did not shape the human brain to evaluate things such as retirement accounts and 40%-off sales at stores.

Here is a look at five ways that your normal human instincts and emotions can lead you to make costly money mistakes—and how you can do better...

***TRAP:* You know what you want today, but you have trouble connecting with a version of yourself that will exist many years from now.** When psychology researchers ask study subjects to imagine themselves years in the future, the results are startling—the subjects struggle to picture those future selves and feel surprisingly little connection to them.

Example: One study found that the typical person feels less empathy for the 20-years-later version of himself/herself than he feels for a homeless person he sees on the street but never meets. This lack of empathy for our future selves greatly decreases our drive to save for the future.

What to do: Use a free app such as *Aging Booth* or *Oldify* (Oldify costs $0.99 for iOS) to age a photo of yourself by 20 years. Spend a minute looking at this aged image before making any major spending or saving decisions (such as filling out 401(k) retirement account contribution forms at work). A 2011 study published in *Journal of Marketing Research* found that people who look at pictures of their aged selves feel a deeper connection with their future selves and save more money.

***TRAP:* You use past spending decisions as a guide when you make new spending decisions.** When we decide whether a product or service is worth its price, we tend to use the financial decisions we have made in the past as reference points, often without realizing we are doing so. So if you ever paid $5 for a coffee...$100 for a pair of jeans...or $60,000 for a car, the odds dramatically increase that you will convince yourself that it is acceptable to do so again. After all, if these weren't reasonable spending decisions, you wouldn't have made them the first time—right?

What to do: Unfortunately, most of us already have plenty of overspending lurking in our pasts, ready to inspire overspending in the future. One way to break the cycle is to conduct a more conscious review of your previous spending by reviewing your credit card statements and checkbook (and any other spending records) at the end of each year and asking yourself, *Which of these expenditures did not serve me well?*

This will make you a better, more objective judge of future spending choices.

***TRAP:* You worry too much about "fairness" when you spend.** Imagine that you call a locksmith because you are locked out of your house. He tells you that he can come right away and unlock your door for $150, and you agree. If you're like most people, you'll consider this fee acceptable if the locksmith sweats over your lock for two hours...

but you'll feel cheated if he opens it in two minutes. But why? Afterall, he opened your lock, and he didn't leave you standing outside for hours as a slow, incompetent locksmith would have.

Or imagine that you're walking down a city street and it starts raining. As you approach a street vendor to buy an umbrella, you see her increase the price from $10 to $15. Do you feel outrage at this price increase and walk away? What the umbrella previously cost should not be relevant—either it's worth $15 to you to stay dry or it isn't.

What to do: If you feel your sense of moral outrage rising when confronted by a price, focus on the benefit that this product or service is providing, not the amount of effort that was required to provide it to you or how much it might have cost under different circumstances. And view quick work done for you as a positive—tell yourself, *Wow, he not only got the job done, he also saved me time.*

***TRAP:* You think there's no downside when you hear the word "free."** One day each year, Ben & Jerry's gives out free ice-cream cones, and many people stand in line for a half hour or longer to get a snack that they could have purchased for $4 on any other day with barely any wait. This values their time at below the hourly minimum wage.

Similarly, when people are asked to choose between a 99-cent app that does something very well and a free app that does that same thing much less well and perhaps requires more time and/or effort, most people will choose the free app—even if the 99-cent app would add much more than 99 cents worth of convenience or pleasure to their lives.

When people see the word "free," they stop thinking in terms of cost/benefit and instead think, *This is free—there's no reason not to.* But free things often do have a cost—they can consume time or detract from quality of life.

What to do: When you see that something is "free," mentally assign a minimal price to it instead, such as a dollar. Ask yourself, *Would I go to the trouble of buying/using this if it cost a dollar, or would I pay a slightly larger amount for a different option?* Assigning even this very low price tends to encourage our brains to think through the nonmonetary cost of something that's free rather than get hypnotized by the word "free."

***TRAP:* You think of your income in the wrong way.** When you think of your annual income, which might be a relatively large number, you may feel pretty well-off...which makes you more likely to overspend.

At the other end of the spectrum, when you think of your income on, say, a per-hour or per-day after-tax basis, which is a much smaller figure, you are more likely to feel poorer... which makes you think that you don't have enough room in your budget to save for the future.

What to do: When you are about to make any sort of choice between saving and spending, reflect on your annual income. But before spending money, think about how much you earn after taxes on a per-hour or per-day basis.

If you are already retired, before making a purchase, think in terms of your monthly, weekly or daily budget. You'll make wiser decisions!

TAKE NOTE...

Podcasts to Boost Your Money Smarts

Listen Money Matters, from finance writer Andrew Fiebert and productivity expert Thomas Frank...*Planet Money* from National Public Radio...*Stacking Benjamins*, with advice designed to be immediately useful and actionable...*The Money Tree*, focusing on investments...*Money Box* from the BBC...*HerMoney* with Jean Chatzky, a personal-finance specialist...*Freakonomics Radio*, with storytelling and psychology from Steve Levitt and Stephen J. Dubner...*The Dave Ramsey Show*, which focuses on reducing money-related stress.

WiseBread.com

How to Zap Money to a Friend, Relative or Dinner Companion

Lou Grilli, director of digital payment strategies for CSCU, a payment-solutions consultant to the credit union industry, Tampa. Formerly, he oversaw mobile-payment strategies at Fidelity National Information Services and was the director of mobile-payment solutions at American Express. CSCU.net

You are used to paying at stores with a plastic card…switching money from savings to checking with a click…and having paychecks or Social Security payments deposited electronically into your bank account. So how long are you going to keep forking over your cash or paper checks when you want to give money to friends, relatives, household help or other individuals?

There now are more convenient ways to exchange money than the centuries-old practice of passing pieces of paper back and forth! "Peer-to-peer," or "P2P," electronic-payment services allow you to use your smartphone to send and receive cash. By 2021, more than 129 million US consumers are expected to use these services to exchange hundreds of billions of dollars, according to Javelin Strategy & Research, a digital-money consulting firm. So even if you're content using old-fashioned cash, someone is likely to want to make a P2P payment to you before long.

Is this type of payment really safe and easy enough to replace cash in your wallet? We asked digital-money expert Lou Grilli for the smartest ways to use these cash-transfer services and which ones offer the best combinations of speed, safety and convenience for your needs…

HOW TO GET THE MOST OUT OF P2P SERVICES

There are more than a dozen P2P services to choose from, with snappy names such as Venmo and Zelle. Many are small tech start-ups, but Internet giants such as Google and Facebook have gotten into the business, as have more established digital-payment providers such as PayPal and, most recently, a consortium of more than two dozen major banks and credit unions.

Almost all of these P2P services work the same. To send money to someone, the service acts as a middleman, making an online transfer from your bank account and typically storing the cash in a digital escrow account for the recipient, who then is notified. The money then can be transferred to the recipient's bank account, either automatically or at the recipient's request. You and the recipient must each have downloaded the P2P service's app to your mobile device…input contact information…set up a password…and for most services, provided your bank routing and account numbers. Some services also allow you to request that the cash be drawn by taking an advance on your credit card or by linking the service to your debit card—both of which might make the transaction go through faster. Once your account is established, you exchange money simply by entering the person's cell-phone number and/or e-mail address, filling in the amount and tapping "send."

FOUR DRAWBACKS

Keep the following in mind when deciding whether to use a P2P service…

- **P2P cash transfers are not instantaneous.** They typically take one to three days to complete, similar to clearing a check. That's because most P2P transactions still go through the Automated Clearing House (ACH) network that banks have been using for 40 years. Only Zelle (see below) moves cash directly from your bank account to another person's bank account within minutes.

- **Using P2P services can incur charges.** If you link to your bank account, transactions usually are free. But the services charge the sender up to 3% of the amount of the transaction if you link to a credit card or, with some services, to a debit card. Also, you typically do not get rewards points or miles if you draw cash from your credit card using a P2P service.

- **There are limits to how much you can send.** The limits vary widely among services, ranging from $300 a week to $10,000 per transaction, and sometimes individual banks set their own limits.

• **You should use P2P services to exchange cash only with trusted parties, not with strangers.** *Reason:* A scammer might, for instance, pretend to buy something from you and then cancel payment. Or you may make a purchase from a scammer who doesn't send the item. Although the services use similar security technology as banks do to keep transactions safe from hackers, if a thief does steal your money through a P2P service, federal law does not require the service to reimburse you or to follow a dispute-resolution process, although the service may choose to do so.

You also might be vulnerable to losses if a thief steals your phone and if access to your phone and P2P app do not require a password, PIN or thumbprint. If the thief transfers money using a credit card, debit card or bank account, federal regulations greatly limit your liability. If the transfer is shifting money that already is in your P2P escrow account, however, you have to abide by the payment service's own resolution process, which may or may not result in getting the money reimbursed.

Self-defense: You can activate extra levels of security that P2P services provide such as PINs and/or fingerprint authentication.

P2P SERVICES WORTH CONSIDERING

You may want to sign up for several of these services and keep multiple apps on your phone, depending on which ones are used by the friends and relatives you plan to exchange cash with the most.

• **PayPal.** If you use just one service, this one makes the most sense because it has the most users and is widely trusted. Nearly 200 million individuals already link their credit cards to a PayPal account to facilitate consumer-to-business online purchases.

Fees/limits: 2.9% of the amount of the transaction is charged when you link to a credit or debit card...$5,000 limit per transaction. PayPal.com

• **Venmo.** Owned by PayPal, this service is geared toward (but not limited to) millennials, 20-somethings who like to split the cost of meals and other expenses with roommates and friends. The average Venmo transaction is less than $10. The app features a popular Facebook-style news feed that encourages users to share their spending activities with their friends on the service.

Fees/limits: 3% of the amount of the transaction for credit cards, free if using your Venmo balance bank account, debit card or prepaid card...$2,999 transaction limit per week. Venmo.com

• **Zelle.** This P2P service is jointly owned and operated by a growing list of banks and credit unions including Bank of America, Chase, Citi, TD Bank, Wells Fargo and First Tech Federal Credit Union, one of the largest credit unions in the US. The Zelle service, embedded in each member institution's own online banking app, allows any account holders at its member banks to transfer money directly from one bank account to another.

Fees/limits: No fees. Transaction limits are set by individual banks. Zelle's instant transfers with a minimal holding period make it seem like an obvious winner, but there are drawbacks. You cannot link a credit card to the service. Also, for fast transfers, the sender and receiver must each have an account at one of the major institutions in the Zelle network. Otherwise, it takes the same one-to-three-day processing time as at other P2P services. ZellePay.com

• **Google Pay.** If you already have a Google account and the Google app, you can just log in and sign up for this service. Google Pay synchronizes with other Google accounts, including Gmail, and you can send or request money by clicking the $ icon at the bottom of any Gmail you send.

Fees/limits: No fees. You may send up to $9,999 per transaction...no more than $10,000 every seven days. As with many Google products, Google Pay gleans general information from the transactions you make and can use it for targeted advertising unless you adjust your privacy settings to opt out. Google.com/pay

• **Facebook Messenger.** Facebook has embedded the ability to pay other Facebook users in its instant-messaging service. You sign up for the P2P service, then open the chat feature in Messenger and press the $ icon in the toolbar.

Fees/limits: No fees, but you can link only your debit card and PayPal account to the service. Transactions are limited to no more than $9,999 in a rolling 30-day period. Like Google Pay, you have to opt out to avoid having your activity scanned for targeted advertising. Messenger.com

• **Apple Pay.** This P2P service uses the Messages app.

Transaction limits: Up to $3,000 per transaction...$10,000 limit per week.

Fees: No fees when using a debit card...3% of the transaction when using a credit card. Apple's cash-sending and cash-receiving features are limited to users of an iPhone, iPad or Apple Watch. Support.Apple.com/apple-pay

Better Choices Than a Personal Loan

Personal loans are a way to finance almost anything you want, but because of high interest rates, they are not always a good idea...

Paying for college or refinancing student debt: Federal or private student loans usually have lower rates than personal loans, and interest on them is tax-deductible.

Financing a car: Auto loans secured by the car you are buying are easier to get and carry lower rates than personal loans.

Consolidating credit card debt: Consider a balance transfer to a zero-interest credit card—but watch carefully for fees and how long the zero-interest offer lasts.

Roundup of experts on personal loans and alternatives, reported at Forbes.com.

Most Family Loans Aren't Repaid!

People who lend to relatives are repaid only about 57% of the amount loaned, on average. The average amount people report lending is $5,022, of which $2,857 is repaid. Despite the lack of full repayment, only 26% of the people surveyed said they would never lend money to family members again.

Study by online loan site LendingTree, reported at CNBC.com.

Best Place to Get No-Strings Free Checking

No-strings free checking is more than twice as common at large credit unions as at large banks. About 84% of large credit unions offer no-fee checking accounts without requiring such things as direct paycheck deposits or maintaining a minimum balance, although a minimum opening balance may be required. That's up from 72% two years ago.

To find a credit union with free checking, go to MyCreditUnion.gov (click "CU Locator").

Greg McBride, CFA, chief financial analyst for the personal-finance website, Bankrate.com.

Online Savings Fees to Look Out For

Transfer fee: Some online banks charge a fee for outgoing transfers, so look for a section in the account agreement referencing "ACH transfer fees" to make sure that transfers are free for both incoming and outgoing transfers.

Excessive withdrawal fee: Most savings accounts have a withdrawal limitation—for example, if you make more than six electronic withdrawals in one statement period, you will be charged a fee. Read the fine print, and stay aware of any limit on withdrawals.

Wire-transfer fee: Wire transfers are the fastest way to move your money, but most online banks charge a fee of around $20 for the service. A few banks offer free wire transfers, and others will waive the fee if the customer maintains a large bank balance.

Monthly maintenance fee: Some online savings accounts have minimum balance requirements to qualify for the top interest rate or to avoid a monthly fee.

Account inactivity fee: If you do not have any withdrawals or deposits in a span of six to 24 months (depends on bank), your bank may charge a monthly fee for each month the account remains inactive.

Money.USNews.com

Money-Stealing Malware from Your Bank

Trickbot, a Trojan-horse program, is spreading through phishing e-mails. Scammers send messages supposedly from victims' banks. The e-mails look like bills and have a PDF, Word or Excel document attached. Clicking on the attachment installs Trickbot, which runs in the background until the victim tries to get to a banking site—the malware redirects to a realistic-looking phony site where the victim enters banking credentials that are then used by thieves to empty the person's bank account.

Self-defense: The same as with other malware—be cautious before clicking links, have strong security software and keep it updated, set up two-factor authentication for added protection, use a unique and strong password for every site you visit, and never hand over personal data if you receive any unsolicited e-mail unless you are 100% sure that the message is legitimate.

Komando.com

10 Tricky Credit Card Terms

Jill Gonzalez, consumer finance expert and "Wallet Guru" for WalletHub, a consumer finance and credit card evaluation website operated by Washington, DC–based Evolution Finance. WalletHub.com/credit-cards

In the world of credit cards, *almost everything* that you are told can be confusing or misleading—and that includes ads, promotional offers, the contract you sign and even your monthly statement. And credit card issuers *like it* that way.

Don't let credit card companies fool you. *Here are 10 tricky terms that credit card applicants and users need to understand...**

- **"Grace period."** A credit card's grace period is the time between the end of its monthly billing cycle and the date when payment is due. Many people think they have "a month," but by law, grace periods can be as short as 21 days. Pay your bill before this grace period ends, and you typically will not face interest charges.

What's tricky: Grace periods generally do not apply if you carry a "revolving balance" on the credit card—that is, if you failed to pay off the entire balance by the end of the prior billing cycle.

What to do: Pay off your credit card balance in full whenever possible—having even a tiny balance left over at the end of a monthly billing cycle means interest charges will be imposed not only on this balance but also on new purchases made during the following billing cycle starting the day that those purchases are made.

- **"Due date."** This is the day by which your credit card payment must be received.

*Credit card offers change frequently, so check the card issuer's website for the latest details.

What's tricky: If you have been carrying a balance on a card, waiting to pay close to the due date—*even if you pay on time and in full*—will cost you money. That's because credit card interest *compounds* daily, so every day you wait to pay means additional interest.

What to do: If you carry a balance, pay as soon as possible rather than waiting until the due date nears.

• **"0% interest rate."** Credit card promotions often promise that you will pay 0% interest, usually referred to as an "introductory" rate, for a certain period—which sounds like a no-lose proposition.

What's tricky: The 0% rate might not apply to both new purchases and balance transfers (see below), and it almost certainly won't apply to cash advances. If you're late with a payment, your 0% rate could skyrocket, potentially all the way to a "penalty" rate that could be 25% or higher.

What to do: Read the fine print of any 0% offer so that you understand exactly what this rate does and does not apply to—it can vary widely from offer to offer.

• **"0% on balance transfers."** This is similar to the 0% purchase rate discussed earlier except that it applies specifically to a balance transferred from a different credit card, not to new purchases.

What's tricky: A 0% balance-transfer rate does not mean a balance transfer will have no cost. Most card issuers impose a "balance-transfer fee," typically around 3%. The other tricky aspects of 0% rates discussed above apply here, too.

What to do: Use a balance-transfer calculator (like WalletHub.com/balance-transfer-calculator) to make sure it's worth paying the card's balance-transfer fee. Or apply for a card that offers an introductory 0% interest rate on balance transfers and charges no balance-transfer fee for some period—a recent example is the Chase Slate card.

• **"5% cash back."** So-called cash-back cards offer small refunds on purchases, generally 1% or 2%—but card issuers know that there's something compelling about increasing the offer to 5% back.

What's tricky: Cards that offer 5% cash back inevitably do so only with purchases in certain spending categories and usually up to a preset limit. Even worse, these spending categories might change every few months, and cardholders might have to contact the card issuer to "opt in" to the savings each time they do. It's easy to lose track, and lots of cardholders don't end up getting nearly the amount of cash back they envisioned when they signed up.

What to do: If you don't want to have to jump through hoops, choose a cash-back card such as Citi Double Cash that offers 2% cash back on virtually all purchases. If you tend to carry a balance, skip rewards cards entirely and instead choose a card that offers a low interest rate.

• **"Deferred interest."** Retailers sometimes advertise special programs that allow shoppers who use store-branded cards to pay "no interest if paid in full within six [or 12] months." These "deferred-interest" offers can be a good way to postpone payment.

What's tricky: If you do not pay off the whole balance by the end of the deferred-interest period, you will be charged interest retroactively to the date of purchase on the entire purchase amount—losing all the advantage of the offer.

What to do: Take advantage of a deferred-interest offer only if you are certain you will pay off the bill in its entirety by the end of the deferred-interest period. Do not make additional purchases using this store card until you have paid off the deferred-interest purchase. Otherwise, your payments to the card issuer might be applied to these additional purchases, making it more difficult to pay off the deferred-interest balance by the deadline.

• **"Convenience checks."** Credit card issuers sometimes send their cardholders blank checks that they can use to obtain cash...pay off other cards' balances...or make payments in places where credit cards are not accepted.

What's tricky: If these checks are used to obtain cash or make payments, your credit card's cash-advance interest rates likely will apply—and these rates typically are very high, often 25% to 30%. You likely will be charged this interest rate starting the day that you use the check with no grace period...and probably will be charged a fee as well, often 5% of the check amount. If the marketing materials provided with the convenience checks cite attractive terms, such as "0% interest," these terms almost certainly apply only if the checks are used to transfer balances from other cards.

What to do: Understand that the word "convenience" is intended to put you off guard. Do not use convenience checks to obtain cash or pay bills.

• **"Preapproved."** Consumers often receive marketing materials from credit card issuers informing them that they have been "preapproved" (or "preselected") for a card.

What's tricky: "Preapproved" does not mean that you already are approved to receive the card. If you apply, you still could be rejected or approved under less attractive terms than described in the marketing. And because applying for a credit card can reduce your credit score, you could lose two ways if you are swayed to apply by a "preapproved" promise.

What to do: Apply for a card because that card offers rates, rewards or other features that are better than the cards you already have, not because an issuer tells you that you're preapproved.

• **"Foreign-transaction fee."** Most credit cards impose a fee, often between 2% and 4% of the purchase, when transactions are made outside the US.

What's tricky: Foreign-transaction fees can apply even to purchases made in the US if the company you buy from is based abroad—as many Internet retailers are.

What to do: Use a card that charges no foreign-transaction fees at all. These include cards issued by Capital One, Discover and certain cards from other issuers.

• **"Currency conversion."** When you use a credit card to pay for something in a foreign country or to buy from a merchant in a foreign country when you are in the US, the merchant might offer to convert the purchase into US dollars as part of the purchase transaction rather than have the credit card issuer do the conversion.

BETTER WAY...

Secure Online Credit Card Payments

Privacy (Privacy.com) lets you create virtual credit cards for online transactions. Users register at the site or through the iOS or Android app and link a bank account. Privacy lets users generate a unique credit card number for any website that accepts Visa with monthly, yearly or total spending limits or "burner cards" that are closed after one use.

MarketWatch.com

What's tricky: If you agree to this currency conversion, the merchant likely will charge you a fee and/or impose an unfavorable exchange rate. You might end up paying 3% to 7% more than you expected—and that's on top of any foreign-transaction fee that might be charged by your card issuer.

What to do: Just say no when asked by a merchant whether you want a purchase converted into US dollars. Your credit card issuer will automatically convert the purchase into dollars on your credit card statement at a more favorable rate.

5 Common Mistakes That Can Sink Your Credit Score

John Ulzheimer, president of The Ulzheimer Group based in Atlanta. He is a nationally recognized credit expert who has served as an expert witness in more than 270 cases in both federal and state court. He held positions with both Equifax and Fair Isaac, which created the most popular credit score, and authored four books, including *The Smart Consumer's Guide to Good Credit: How to Earn Good Credit in a Bad Economy.* TheUlzheimerGroup.com

You're nothing but a number—that's the title of a book by credit expert John Ulzheimer. Whether you are seeking a good deal on a loan, a credit card or an insurance policy, the number that represents your credit score can determine whether you get it.

You can keep your credit score high by avoiding these five common mistakes...

PAYING MORE THAN 30 DAYS LATE

We all know that late payments can sink credit scores. What a lot of people don't realize, however, is that everyone gets a 30-day grace period before any lender can report delinquency to the credit bureaus.

Even if you are hit with a late-payment fee from your credit card issuer, you still can save your score if you pay within this grace period.

What to do: If you missed a credit card payment, don't panic...but do be sure to pay at least the minimum amount due within 30 days of your original due date, preferably giving yourself a cushion of a few days so that you don't accidentally miss the deadline that would allow a delinquency to be reported.

PLAYING GAMES WITH REVOLVING DEBT

You know that paying only the minimum owed on a credit card invites hefty interest charges and ever-growing debt. But there's another big problem that comes with carrying a revolving credit card balance—even if you periodically pay off that balance.

Lenders and the credit bureaus frown upon too much revolving credit card debt and favor borrowers with low "credit utilization ratios" (the percentage of your available credit that you currently are using). In the past, loan applicants with revolving credit card debt could get big bumps in their credit scores by simply paying what they owed in full just before applying for loans or credit.

But now lenders have a new weapon in the form of a 24-to-30-month chronology called "trended data." Trended data reveals whether applicants have consistently carried revolving debt over the past 24 to 30 months. And trended data soon will make it impossible to quickly fix the damage that carrying revolving debt does to your credit score. Fannie Mae, the government-backed mortgage giant, already uses this technique, and an updated scoring system called VantageScore 4.0 gives trending data capabilities to all lenders.

What to do: If possible, use credit cards only for purchases that you have the cash to cover, and pay the bill in full—or close to it—each month.

IGNORING LETTERS AND CALLS FROM CREDITORS

If you fall behind on payments, it might be tempting to ignore letters and calls from creditors because eventually they'll give up. That's technically true, but it's not the best outcome that you could achieve.

Just because your phone stops ringing doesn't mean that your problems are over. Some lenders eventually will write off some uncollectible debt as a loss, but many times they'll hand it off to collection agencies or sell it to debt buyers, which are likely to hound you even more ruthlessly.

A default looks terrible on your credit report and can crush your credit score for up to seven years.

What to do: Don't hide. Engage your creditors. Explain your situation to them, and ask them to work with you by reducing your minimum payments, lowering interest rates, eliminating penalties and/or extending your grace period. This will help to preserve your credit score and prevent default, which is all but inevitable if you ignore your creditors.

LETTING GOOD CARDS COLLECT DUST

Credit-scoring systems like to see lots of unutilized credit. But not using a credit card at all, even if you think of it as an "emergency" card, can encourage the card issuer to classify the card as unused. If this happens, the issuer may cancel the card because of inactivity.

When this happens, not only does the borrower lose the ability to use that card's credit line, but he/she also forfeits the positive effects of having that available credit.

The more unused credit that a cardholder has, the lower his credit-utilization ratio is. Scoring systems like to see credit-utilization ratios of no more than 10%.

What to do: For any credit card that you want to keep so that it counts toward your overall credit limit, use it for a small purchase every few months so that it is not canceled.

Then pay your bill in full to avoid any finance charges.

And if you have strong credit, you might ask a credit card issuer to increase the credit limit on your card so that your overall credit total expands and, as a result, your credit-utilization ratio drops.

LETTING UNPAID TAXES RUIN YOUR CREDIT

Many people think that not paying their taxes and having the government issue a tax lien—which is imposed on a person's property to secure payment of their taxes—won't affect their credit scores because the taxes did not involve borrowing money. This is wishful thinking.

Not only are tax liens visible to lenders on credit reports, they also serve as warnings to potential lenders that the IRS has a legal right to the applicant's property, which makes the applicant a greater credit risk.

Federal debt generally is in a class by itself, and it includes federally guaranteed student loans. Unlike virtually all other types of debt, unpaid tax liens and defaults on federally guaranteed student loans can stay on your credit report indefinitely instead of just for seven years.

Also, almost all debt can be statutorily discharged through bankruptcy—but not tax liens or federal student loans. When the bankruptcy dust settles, they'll still be there.

What to do: Place federal debt and tax liens at the top of your if-you-can-pay-only-one-debt priority list.

Avoid Setting Off a Fraud Alert on Your Own Credit Card

Certain activities are closely monitored by card issuers and may trigger alerts even if *you* are the one doing them.

Examples: Making a purchase in a place far from where you usually shop...making unusually large purchases...spending a lot just after getting a new card...buying the types of luxury items that thieves favor, such as designer tote bags, electronics and expensive headphones...making a small purchase and then a large one—thieves often do this to test a card they have stolen.

Self-defense: Keep your credit card issuer informed of changes in personal information, travel plans and any spending that is likely to be significantly different from your usual pattern.

GoBankingRates.com

4 Strategies for Settling Credit Card Debt

Roundup of experts on debt settlement, reported at WiseBread.com.

Below are four ways to settle credit card debt...

- **Hardship repayment or forbearance** may be available if you have had a significant change in life circumstances such as a divorce or job loss. Ask your lender how it handles customers with financial hardship.
- **A modified payment plan** can reduce monthly payments by extending the time to pay—although your interest rate may increase. Negotiate with your credit card company.
- **Debt settlement** means offering a lump sum of less than you owe in return for erasing your debt. Negotiate with the credit card issuer or work with a debt-settlement company.
- **Debt management** involves paying a counseling organization monthly—the agency helps negotiate terms and pays bills on your behalf. For advice on choosing a credit counselor, go to Consumer.FTC.gov and click on "Money & Credit," then "Dealing with Debt."

Caution: With any of these approaches, your card accounts may be closed...your credit score may drop...you may owe taxes on forgiven debt...and higher interest may mean that you end up paying more over a longer time.

Recover from Credit Card ID Theft

Adam Levin, JD, chairman of Scottsdale, Arizona–based cybersecurity firm CyberScout and former director of the New Jersey Division of Consumer Affairs. He is author of *Swiped: How to Protect Yourself in a World Full of Scammers, Phishers, and Identity Thieves.* CyberScout.com

All that an identity thief needs to open credit cards in your name is your full name and your Social Security number. Then the thief can make thousands of dollars in fraudulent purchases, leaving you to cope with threatening phone calls from collection agencies and shattered credit scores when the bills are not paid.

If you learn that a credit card has been opened in your name, you are not legally responsible for the fraudulent charges, but you will have to take quick steps to stop this fraud and remove the account from your credit reports. *Do the following immediately...*

1. Call one of the three major credit-reporting agencies. The one you contact will pass the word to the other two. Report the fraud, and ask to have an initial fraud alert placed on your account. This will force creditors to take additional steps to confirm your identity before issuing credit in your name for the next 90 days.

2. Contact the card issuer's fraud department. Say that you did not open this account and that you want it closed.

3. Call your police department. A police report can spur the card issuer to more quickly remove fraudulent charges from your bill.

4. Contact your homeowner's insurance company. An increasing number of insurers offer ID-theft victim assistance or coverage, usually at no additional charge. Also contact your employer's human resources department and/or your credit union to see whether it offers an ID-theft victim assistance program. It might help you shut down additional attempts to steal your identity and/or compensate you for out-of-pocket expenses.

5. Freeze your credit before your 90-day fraud-alert period expires. If a credit card account has been opened in your name, your Social Security number is in the hands of at least one ID thief. The best way to prevent additional fraudulent accounts from being opened in your name is to permanently freeze your credit with each of the three major credit-reporting agencies—Equifax (Freeze.Equifax.com)...Experian (Experian.com/freeze/center.html)...as well as TransUnion (TransUnion.com/credit-freeze/place-credit-freeze).

Freezing or unfreezing a report may cost up to $10 but usually is free for victims of ID theft and/or seniors—either age 62 or age 65. (The fee and age for seniors vary by state.)

Tip: When you want to apply for credit after triggering a freeze, ask the lender or credit card issuer which credit-reporting agency it uses and then unfreeze only that agency's credit report. Then refreeze it once your application is approved.

Or request a onetime-use PIN or code from the agency and provide this to a lender so that only it can access your report. Only mortgage lenders typically check all three credit reports.

Know Your Rights After a Data Breach

Steven J.J. Weisman, Esq., an attorney and author of *Identity Theft Alert* and founder of the scam-information website Scamicide.com.

When a company suffers a massive data breach that exposes personal information of millions of customers, do those customers have the right to sue that company? The answer typically is yes, but don't expect a windfall even if the lawsuit is successful.

The question has come up in connection with several high-profile breaches in recent years, the most notable involving Equifax. That credit-reporting agency revealed that information about as many as 147 million US consumers had been hacked, exposing names, Social Security numbers, birth dates, addresses and driver's license numbers. By early 2018, over 250 class-action lawsuits had been filed against the company. *Consider these comparable cases...*

• **In early 2017, health insurance company Anthem Inc. agreed to a $115 million settlement** stemming from a 2015 hack of about 79 million customers' information. Under the settlement, victims of the hack could receive an extra two years of credit-monitoring and identity-protection services—in addition to the original two years the company offered. If someone is already enrolled in credit monitoring elsewhere, he/she instead can opt to receive up to $50 in cash. And $15 million was designated to pay victims' out-of-pocket expenses resulting from the incident.

• **In 2016, Home Depot agreed to a $13 million settlement involving a 2014 breach** affecting information on more than 50 million customers. Those who had credit or debit card information stolen could have collected up to $10,000 from a fund that covered documented losses such as fraudulent charges on a card as well as time spent remedying issues related to the data breach...and they could have received 18 months of credit monitoring.

If you are eligible to participate in a data breach class-action suit, look for a notice in the mail, but also look for updates on the website of the company that experienced the breach...in the press...or at Consumer-Action.org/lawsuits, which tracks class actions.

Also, be sure to read the fine print in any offer from a company that suffers a breach. Initially, when Equifax offered one year of free credit monitoring, there was a catch. A clause in the offer appeared to strip people who signed up of their right to sue the company, but in the face of tremendous pressure, Equifax dropped that condition.

Documents to Keep in a Safe

It's important to keep these essential documents in a safe...

Birth certificates or adoption papers...Social Security cards...copies of ID cards...naturalization papers...original marriage certificate and divorce papers...your living will...your last will and testament...power-of-attorney papers that name you on behalf of someone such as an elderly parent...proof of eligibility for any government benefits or assistance programs...professional appraisals done on your house and on any high-value items you own...mortgage papers...real estate deeds...titles and registrations for cars, boats, trailers and tractors...a list of all your financial accounts, including account numbers, institutions and the user names and passwords needed to get online access to the information.

WiseBread.com

TAKE NOTE...

Free Secure-Password Apps for Smartphones

Dashlane lets you have one master password that unlocks all others. It can generate passwords and update them regularly and has a secure, built-in browser. *Keeper* provides separate folders for filing personal and work-related passwords as well as other confidential information. *1Password* stores passwords/credit card info, offers auto-filling for online shopping and has an Apple Watch app for wrist display. *LastPass* has a bright and attractive interface and stores data such as credit card numbers in addition to passwords.

All these apps are free in basic versions for iOS and Android devices—additional features are available at various prices.

Roundup of experts on smartphone password protection, reported in *The New York Times*.

"Health-Worker" Scam

Scammers are posing as government health workers to get personal information and steal identities. The thieves make phone calls that can show up on caller-ID as "HHS Tips" or "Federal Government." The callers ask for personal information—and if they get any, they use it to steal a victim's identity. The Department of Health and Human Services does not use phones if it needs personal information—it contacts people via US mail.

If you get a scam HHS phone call: Report it to the FTC at 877-FTC-HELP and to HHS at 800-447-8477 or by e-mail at spoof@oig.hhs.gov.

Consumerist.com

Beware This Netflix Con

A recent Netflix e-mail scam can fool even sophisticated users. Millions of Netflix users have received a fraudulent notification that their Netflix accounts will be suspended if they don't click on a link to restart their memberships. The link prompts customers to enter their credit card numbers, which the con artists then use or sell. Netflix never sends e-mails requesting financial information.

Steven J.J. Weisman, Esq., an attorney and author of *Identity Theft Alert* and founder of the scam-information website Scamicide.com.

Latest Hacker Target: Cell-Phone Accounts

John Sileo, president of The Sileo Group, Denver, a cybersecurity training company. He is author of the eBook *Smartphone Survival Guide: 10 Critical Security Tips in 10 Minutes.* Sileo.com

Hackers are hijacking cell-phone numbers as a way to take over financial and social-media accounts.

How it works: A hacker calls your mobile-phone service provider, claims to be you, says that your phone was lost or broken and asks to have the phone number and account transferred to a different cell phone—one that the hacker controls. If the customer service representative doesn't fall for the ruse, the hacker keeps calling back until he/she reaches a rep who does.

To verify customers' identities, many sites send a onetime security code to a phone number that the customer provided—which now may be the number that the hacker controls. If accessing an account also requires a password, the hacker may claim to have forgotten this password and ask to have it reset, knowing that a new temporary code will be sent to the number he now controls. Using this method, he might be able to loot your financial accounts, take over your social-media accounts and/or send messages in your name to your contacts.

What to do: Ask your cell-phone service provider whether it's possible to add a special verbal "call-in" password or PIN to your account that will have to be provided by anyone trying to make changes to the account over the phone. Most providers now will do this upon request. Also avoid entering your cell-phone number on forms unless it's mandatory—prying eyes at many companies could be collecting numbers. Supply a landline phone number instead.

Ask your financial companies whether they offer *"app-based" two-factor authentication*, and sign up for it if they do. With this, the onetime code needed to access your account is sent to your phone not as a text message but through a password-protected app on your phone, creating an additional layer of security.

If your phone screen says "no signal" or "emergency calls only" when you are somewhere where you usually have reception, and turning the phone off and back on does not fix the problem, immediately contact your cellular provider from a different phone to ask whether any changes have recently been made to your account.

GOOD TO KNOW...

Best Day to Buy a Home

The best day to buy a home is *February 7.* Statistically, that is the day when prices are lowest—12% below average. The two next-best days to buy are February 4 and 5—in fact, eight of the top 10 days to close on a home are in February. In all, the median price per square foot is 6.1% lower than average in February, 5.6% lower in January, 3.6% lower in March and 1.8% lower in April. In all other months, median sale price is above average.

It is highest, at 3% above average, in July and August, which makes those the best months for sellers but the worst for buyers.

Analysis by real estate research firm Attom Data, Irvine, California.

Open House Advice

Two key questions to ask during a real estate open house...

- **What are the average utility costs?** Older homes tend to be less energy-efficient, but the previous owners may have installed energy-saving upgrades such as a new heating/cooling system or double-paned windows.
- **Has the price changed?** A lower listing price may save you money now, but it could be a sign of issues with a home.

WiseBread.com

6 Items Home Buyers Want Most

Laundry room, which would cost $1,000 to $10,000 to install...*exterior lighting,* $65 to $135 per fixture...*energy-efficient windows and appliances,* $270 to $800 per window, appliance costs vary...*a patio,* about $961 per 120 square feet of concrete...*hardwood floors,* $1,473 per 120 square feet, unfinished...*an eat-in kitchen,* $1,000 to $10,000.

Kiplinger.com

Scammers Steal Down Payments

Steve Kenneally, vice president, cybersecurity policy, American Bankers Association, Washington, DC. ABA.com

If you're buying a house or an apartment, you know that you have to satisfy your financial obligations on the day of the closing. And if you get an urgent e-mail from the title company that day telling you where to wire your down payment, you're likely to follow those instructions, right? If you do, you might end up losing that down-payment money to a con artist.

Thieves impersonating real estate title companies are scamming home buyers out of their entire down payments. Complaints to the FBI about this online scam, which can cost victims tens of thousands of dollars, have skyrocketed.

How the scam works: Thieves hack into a title company's client list, learn the details of pending sales and wait until the day of a closing when a buyer is required to send a down payment and closing costs to the appropriate parties. They then send a fraudulent but real-looking e-mail to the buyer purportedly updating the bank account numbers where the money should be wired. It's easy to be fooled because you're juggling so many details on closing day. Unfortunately, because you authorized the wire transfer, standard protections covering fraudulent withdrawals from your bank account don't apply, and you might have to bear some or all the liability.

Self-defense: Be suspicious of any e-mail with last-minute changes related to your closing and wire transfers. You should have received information and instructions on the closing weeks before it happens. Verify any changes directly with your title agent and real estate agent and/or lawyer. And don't call any phone number provided in any e-mail sent to you by a title company before independently checking that it is the number for that company, because phone numbers also can be illegitimate. If you do wire money to an account that you then discover is fraudulent, contact the manager at your bank as soon as you find out. Even if the wire has been sent, ask the manager to request that the receiving bank put a temporary freeze on the money if it's still in the thief's account until the problem is sorted out. File a local police report detailing what happened, as well as a complaint with the FBI's Internet Crime Complaint Center at IC3.gov.

How to Make Escrow Go Smoothly...

WiseBread.com

Escrow is a period, usually 30 to 40 days, when a third party holds the buyer's funds until both you and the buyer meet contractual requirements.

• **When you receive an offer,** add in the clause "Exact legal description to follow in escrow" to the offer. This gives you time to address any issues found during the escrow process—such as a clerical error that affects the deed of your property.

• **Limit closing adjustments** by striking out the phrase "any other acceptable to buyer" in the contract, which can lead to you being charged costs that are not your responsibility. Also delete that phrase if it appears in the list of exceptions—any exceptions, such as easements, should be clearly spelled out.

• **Ask your agent what time is reasonable** for the buyer to review your seller disclosure, which discloses problems such as a large stain on the carpet or termite damage.

• **Remove any buyer language** asking for copies of all instruction manuals for appliances, original blueprints and other documents, which you may not have.

Basics of Investing in Rental Property

• **Know what your costs will be** if the property sits vacant for some time.

• **Balance anticipated income against debt taken on** to make the purchase and against likely ongoing operating costs.

• **Learn about property classes**—Class A is top quality for a market, although this means different things in different places...Class B properties usually are older but well-maintained...Class C properties often need renovations and are outside the prime rental areas.

Roundup of experts on investing in rental properties, reported at RealEstate.USNews.com.

Avoid These Costly Mistakes When Saving for Education

Kathryn Flynn, content director, SavingForCollege.com, which offers college-savings tools and strategies.

A 529 savings account can be a great way to save for your child's or grandchild's education costs while getting big tax breaks.* But with these accounts, it's easy to make a mistake that would reduce your savings...force you to pay tax and even a penalty...or cause you to miss out on financial aid. *Here are today's common 529 account mistakes and how to avoid them...*

MISTAKE: **You assume that your state's 529 plan is your only option.** Nearly every

*Prior to 2018, 529 plans could only be used for qualified college expenses. The new tax law now allows 529 plans to pay qualified costs for kindergarten through high school education. Check with your tax adviser to see if your state has adopted federal rules.

state sponsors its own 529 plan, which allows you to permanently avoid income tax and capital gains tax on any investment profits when you use the money for qualified education costs. But you are allowed to invest in a different state's 529 if you prefer—and sometimes that is the best option.

If you live in a state that offers a significant state income tax break on contributions to its 529 plan, it's probably best to stick with that state's plan. But there's no reason to do so if you have reached the limit for a tax break in a particular year or if it is a state that...

- **Doesn't provide an income tax break,** such as California, Delaware, Hawaii, Kentucky, Maine, New Jersey and North Carolina.
- **Has no state income tax,** like Alaska, Florida, Nevada, New Hampshire, South Dakota, Tennessee, Texas, Washington and Wyoming.
- **Offers the same tax break whether you choose its plan or a different state's plan,** such as Arizona, Kansas, Missouri, Montana and Pennsylvania.

Exception: An uncommon type of 529 plan known as a "prepaid plan" generally is open to only in-state residents. Most savers do not opt for prepaid plans even when they are available, however, because they tend to be very restrictive, using financial incentives to steer students to enroll in specific state university systems. Conventional 529 plans are far more flexible—money saved in them can be used at essentially any US college plus many foreign colleges.

If you shop out-of-state for a 529 plan, lean toward plans that offer low-expense investment options with strong track records. *Among the states with the best plans...*

- California (ScholarShare529.com).
- Iowa (CollegeSavingsIowa.com).
- Maine (MerrillEdge.com/offers/529).
- Michigan (MISaves.com).
- Nebraska (Nest529Direct.com).
- Nevada (Investor.Vanguard.com/529-plan/vanguard-529-plan).
- New York (NYSaves.org).
- Utah (My529.org).
- Wisconsin (Edvest.com).

For ratings and descriptions of 529 plans, visit SavingForCollege.com.

It's not too late to make a change if you already have invested in your own state's 529 plan and then realize that there might have been a better option. You can make one 529 rollover per beneficiary in any 12-month period without generating any taxes or penalties.

***MISTAKE:* You are not the student's parent, and you withdraw money for college payments from your 529 account early in the student's college career.** This can unintentionally undercut the student's financial aid. When a student's grandparent (or uncle or anyone else other than a parent) withdraws money from a 529 account, the college financial-aid system treats the money as untaxed income for the student even if it is appropriately used to pay college costs—and the more income the student has, the less financial aid he/she is likely to receive.

To get around this, if the parents are able to cover expenses for the first two years, nonparents can wait to withdraw money from their 529 accounts until the student's final two calendar years of college. A student's financial aid in any given year is calculated using the family's "prior prior" tax return—2017's return affects 2019's financial aid, for example. So if the nonparent waits until the final two calendar years that the student is in college, the income from this 529 should not affect the student's aid at all.

Another option for grandparents and other nonparents is to put money into a 529 account owned by the student's parents. The financial-aid system will consider this money parental assets, which has a smaller impact on financial aid than does student income.

Note: Contributing this way could cost the nonparent a state tax break on 529 contributions...and it means that the nonparent loses legal control over the assets after they are contributed. A small number of plans do not accept "third-party" contributions, so a nonparent would have to give the money to a parent and have the parent make the contribution.

***MISTAKE:* As a parent or other person claiming a student as a dependent, you take excessive advantage of a 529 plan while**

getting education-related tax credits at the same time. If you claim an education-related tax credit such as the Lifetime Learning or American Opportunity credit, tax law requires that you subtract the education costs covered by that credit from your qualifying education expenses when you determine how much to withdraw from your 529 account that year. Fail to do this properly, and you could end up owing income tax and a 10% penalty on a portion of your 529 withdrawal. It's easy to go wrong here because, counterintuitively, the amount you need to subtract from your 529 withdrawal can be greater than the amount you receive from the tax credit.

Example: If the credit is 20% of the qualifying educational expenses up to $2,000, you would need to subtract the full $2,000 used to "support" the credit, not just the $400 credit you receive.

***MISTAKE:* You withdraw money from a 529 account for expenses that will not be paid until the following calendar year.** Do not withdraw money in December to pay for spring-term tuition unless you are certain that this money will be paid to the institution before the end of December. If the qualifying education expenses that you pay during a calendar year are less than the amount withdrawn from your 529 account during that year, the IRS likely will insist that you pay tax and a penalty—even if the excess is used to pay qualifying expenses in the first few days of the following year.

***MISTAKE:* Withdrawing money from a 529 to cover the expense of the student's travel to or from campus.** Money can be withdrawn from 529 accounts for a range of education expenses including tuition, fees, room and board, books, computers, equipment related to computers and Internet access—but not travel costs.

***MISTAKE:* You assume that you cannot withdraw 529 money to cover the student's housing and food costs if the student lives and dines off campus.** Off-campus housing and food costs are qualifying expenses up to the amount that the college charges for on-campus room and board as long as the student is enrolled in school half-time or more.

TAKE NOTE...

Best 529 College Savings Plans

The best 529 college savings plans come from just four states, according to a survey from Morningstar Inc.

These gold-rated plans, with strong investment menus and low fees, are open to investors in all states—Bright Start College Savings Plan (Illinois)...Vanguard 529 College Savings Plan (Nevada)...Utah Educational Savings Plan (Utah)...and Invest529 (Virginia).

Two of the 62 plans in the survey received negative ratings—Arizona's Ivy Fund InvestEd 529 Plan and New Jersey's Franklin Templeton 529 College Savings Plan.

For the complete survey, search "Best 529 College Savings Plans" at Morningstar.com.

Leo Acheson, CFA, senior manager research analyst at Morningstar Inc., Chicago, which conducts the annual survey. Morningstar.com

MISSING-BENEFICIARY MISTAKE

Here is one of the worst mistakes you could make in a 529 plan...

You pay tax and a penalty to liquidate all or part of a 529 plan because the beneficiary doesn't go to college...the beneficiary drops out of college...or the college ends up costing less than you saved in the 529. Liquidating a 529 is not the only option, and often not the best option, when the 529 can't be used for college. You could instead use 529 savings to send the beneficiary to a trade school—many of these are eligible under 529 rules. If you have money left in your 529, you also could change the beneficiary to another member of your current beneficiary's extended family without penalty. (See SavingForCollege.com for details on what constitutes eligible "family.") Or you could name yourself as beneficiary and use the money to go back to school yourself—everything from grad schools to local community college classes to culinary schools could be eligible. (For a list of eligible institutions, select "Find 529 Eligible Institutions" under the "Tools & Calculators" menu at SavingForCollege.com.)

Some good news: If you do pull money out of your 529 account for nonqualifying expenses, only the portion of the withdrawal stemming from investment gains within the 529 will face income tax and that 10% penalty. The money you originally deposited in the account will not.

Helpful: If your 529 beneficiary earns tax-free scholarships, you have the option of removing from the account an amount up to the amount of those scholarships and using the money for nonqualifying expenses without paying the usual 10% penalty, though you would have to pay income tax on the earnings. (Similar rules apply if the beneficiary attends a US military academy that does not charge tuition.)

Types of Student-Loan Forgiveness...

GoBankingRates.com

- **Public Service Loan Forgiveness Program** forgives all direct loans after 10 years of monthly payments if you work full-time for the government or certain nonprofits.
- **Perkins Loan forgiveness** gives partial or total forgiveness to teachers, nurses, firefighters, police officers and members of the armed services.
- **Teacher Loan and Stafford Loan forgiveness** are available to highly qualified teachers working for five years in a qualifying elementary or secondary school. Special rules apply if you teach math or science in some schools or work in special education.
- **Nurse Corps Loan Repayment Program** makes 60% of your qualifying loan balance eligible for forgiveness after you work in an underserved area's facility for two years... and another 25% after three years.
- **Student loan forgiveness for doctors and lawyers** is available in certain states in differing amounts. Do careful research—requirements for programs vary and may change anytime.

Money Well Spent

It does pay to buy time-saving services and spend the time saved with your partner to strengthen your relationship. *Spending money on home-related needs that both of you dislike*—which may include cleaning, yard work, preparation of meals or other tasks—relieves tension in the home and allows more time to be spent on happiness-boosting activities. *Outsourcing some tasks*—for example, hiring someone to cut your lawn or hiring someone to clean your house—increases overall life satisfaction noticeably, assuming that your finances permit this.

Ashley Whillans, PhD, assistant professor, Harvard Business School, Boston, and lead author of a study of 6,271 people from Canada, Denmark, the Netherlands and the US, published in *Proceedings of the National Academy of Sciences.*

3 Big Challenges When Taking Over a Loved One's Finances

Shirley B. Whitenack, Esq., a partner with Schenck, Price, Smith & King, LLP, Florham Park, New Jersey, and former president of the National Academy of Elder Law Attorneys. SPSK.com

Taking over a family member's finances can be challenging in the best of circumstances. In the event of a loved one's sudden illness or mental decline, you not only have to deal with myriad financial issues but with the emotional challenges as well. And before you can even start your day-to-day financial role, you might need to overcome a number of common hurdles such as obtaining the legal authority to act on behalf of your loved one and coordinating efforts with other family members.

To help you get started managing a loved one's finances—and succeed over time—here are the most common issues you'll likely discover, and how to tackle them successfully...

1. Your loved one hasn't planned for not being able to handle his/her own finances. Many people put off estate planning and end-of-life planning so it is possible that no one has been officially named to make financial decisions for them when they are no longer able to do so themselves. Even if your loved one appointed someone years ago, that person may no longer be able to fulfill the role.

In these cases, you'll need to work with your loved one to obtain the legal authority to handle his finances. If your relative is completely incapacitated, you will have to go to court to petition for guardianship, a process that often involves a psychological evaluation to declare your loved one incompetent. Such extreme efforts are rare, though, since most elderly people—even those with memory problems—are able to execute basic estate-planning documents. *Those papers include...*

• **Durable power of attorney (POA).** This is the most important document you will need in order to become your loved one's financial caregiver. It will declare you the person's "agent" and provide the legal authority for you to sign tax returns...write and deposit checks...sell assets such as stocks, bonds and real estate...and make other financial moves on the person's behalf. It may cost roughly $150 to $250 to have an attorney draft a POA. This is money well-spent because an attorney can draft a POA document that addresses your relative's specific needs.

Example: If your loved one wants to transfer assets to a spouse and/or children while he is alive, you may need a gifting provision, which isn't included in a standard POA.

In many cases, a parent may decide to name two or more adult children to share power of attorney. If multiple siblings are serving as agents, consider writing the POA to specify that each of you can act independently. If not, all agents will have to sign every check, which may be tricky if you and your siblings live far apart. Keep in mind that rules governing POAs vary from state to state.

Caution: Keep your own financial accounts separate from the loved one's accounts so that no family member or other person can accuse you of misusing that person's money. For instance, your loved one's Social Security checks and other income should be deposited directly into his checking account, not yours, even though you have control of that checking account. Keep meticulous records of all transactions and bills paid to answer any potential questions that arise.

• **Will.** You might want to help your loved one create a will if he doesn't have one or update an existing will that no longer serves its purpose well. If you help with a will, be careful that you don't open yourself up to accusations that illness or frailty made the incapacitated person susceptible to your "undue influence" in shaping the will in your favor.

Example: If you isolate the person from friends and family members and what he chooses to leave you is drastically increased in the will, that might make you more vulnerable to such accusations.

• **Health-care POA.** If you are making financial decisions for your loved one, you also may end up being the person to make health-care decisions for him. To do so, you'll need to set up a separate health-care POA with your loved one's attorney and a living will, which directs doctors about end-of-life medical care.

2. Your family member's finances are disorganized. Ideally, your loved one would have meticulously organized files, making it easy to find all the financial information you need...or he would be able to tell you about various accounts and where to find records. Often, though, financial agents have to do some detective work, which can include looking through files, sifting through mail and even going through closets or an attic. You want to obtain a clear picture of your loved one's income, assets and insurance. *This includes identifying...*

• **All bank and brokerage accounts.**

• **Social Security payment information.**

• **Retirement benefits statements** for pensions and retirement accounts such as 401(k)s and IRAs.

• **Copies of your loved one's insurance policies** including, potentially, health, life, disability, long-term care, auto and homeowner's policies.

If you aren't sure that your search has uncovered every bank and brokerage account, look at your relative's tax return to review the interest and capital gains reported to the IRS. You can call your loved one's former employer to find out whether he should be receiving a pension or, if the employer no longer exists, contact the Pension Benefit Guaranty Corporation (PBGC.gov) for help finding a lost pension.

Next, examine your loved one's expenses to create a household budget. You'll need to gather your loved one's monthly bills and receipts for such things as medical care, credit cards and other basic living expenses such as food and utilities. If your loved one hasn't saved past bills, your POA provides you the authority to call local utilities and other creditors to get information.

Helpful: To make sure that your loved one is taking advantage of all federal, state and private benefit programs he qualifies for, ranging from income assistance and tax relief to utility payments and help with transportation, go to BenefitsCheckUp.org, a free service of the National Council on Aging.

You also can check for assets that he may have abandoned, such as old bank accounts, pension benefits and insurance payouts. Most states maintain a database of such assets—to find your state's, search online for "unclaimed property" and your state's name.

3. You need special designations to deal with Social Security and veterans benefits. A POA won't help you if you need to manage your relative's Social Security payments and provide information to the Social Security Administration. Instead, you need a "representative payee" designation. To get this, you must complete Form SSA-11 and apply in person at your nearest SSA office.

Similarly, to manage your relative's veterans benefits, you must apply to be a "VA fiduciary." To do so, submit a written request with your loved one's name and VA file number (typically the same as his Social Security number without dashes) at your nearest regional VA office. The VA will contact you to assess your qualifications. This will include a credit-report review, a criminal background check and an interview, typically in person.

Helpful: Download the guide "Managing Someone Else's Money: Help for Agents Under a Power of Attorney" from the Consumer Financial Protection Bureau's website (ConsumerFinance.gov). It includes tips on avoiding financial scams and hiring an accountant, attorneys and other professionals to help your loved one.

8

Insurance Adviser

Why You Should Always Check Those Medical Bills!

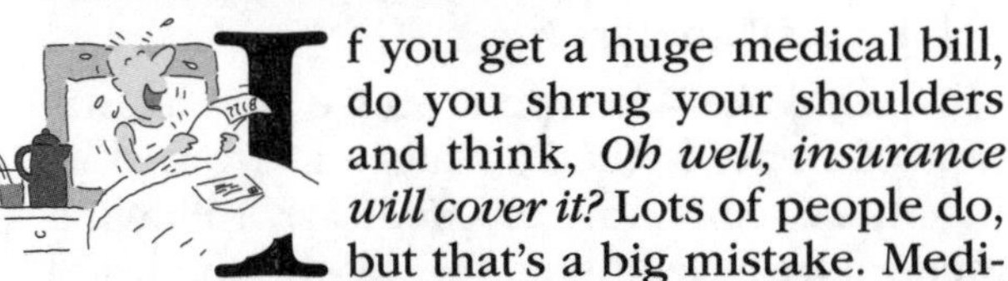

If you get a huge medical bill, do you shrug your shoulders and think, *Oh well, insurance will cover it?* Lots of people do, but that's a big mistake. Medical bills—particularly those for a hospitalization or outpatient surgery—have always been difficult to decipher. For that reason, far too many people don't even make the effort. But with health-care expenses continuing to skyrocket, it's more important than ever to closely examine these bills.

Here's why: As your health insurance premiums continue to rise, it's not just your insurer who suffers. You are paying ever-increasing amounts for out-of-pocket deductibles and co-pays. And don't make the mistake of thinking that there's an advantage to meeting your deductible faster. If you have to pay $4,500 before your insurance kicks in, for example, and there is a $2,000 mistake (not uncommon), you're paying for services not received. The idea of a deductible is to lower the cost to the insurer by passing along part of the payment to you. By reviewing your bill carefully, you're making sure that you're actually buying something for your money.

Now that you can see how much of a hit you're taking when a medical bill is wrong, here are simple errors to look for—and what to do if you find one...

• **Check the basics.** First off, make sure that all the administrative information on the bill is correct. Is your name spelled correctly? Is your date of birth accurate? Also, check that

Note: Prices, rates and offers throughout this chapter and book are subject to change.

Charles B. Inlander, a consumer advocate and health-care consultant based in Fogelsville, Pennsylvania. He was founding president of the nonprofit People's Medical Society, a consumer advocacy organization credited with key improvements in the quality of US health care, and is author or coauthor of more than 20 consumer-health books.

the insurance account number is the same as the one on your card, including any "group number." If you have two policies, such as Medicare and a Medigap supplement plan, there should be an account number for each plan listed. They are almost never the same. If it's a hospital bill, make sure the admission and discharge dates are correct. If it's just one day off, it could cost you $1,000 or more. You should also make sure that if your hospital and/or providers are in-network that they're listed that way...and make sure that any required pre-authorizations are acknowledged.

• **Get an *itemized* bill.** Most hospital bills list only a summary of charges. For example, it might list $5,500 for "Medications" or $8,200 for "Operating Room." Never accept such a vague bill. Contact the hospital's billing office and ask for a completely itemized bill, which will list every charge separately. The provider is required by law to give it to you. This bill will be hard to read, but you can often pick up mistakes or excessive charges. I was once billed $370 for a "patient tray" (with little amenities such as a toothpaste and razor). When I called, I found out it should have been $37.

• **Ask for a corrected version.** Remember, a lot of the costs are coming out of your pocket, so if you spot an error or don't understand something, call the health-care provider's billing office. If there's a product or service you don't think you received, ask who ordered it. If it was your doctor, you can call him/her if you think something is amiss. You should also call your insurance company's claims department and notify the representative that you are disputing or questioning a charge. Insurance companies have personnel devoted specifically to reviewing bills for obvious errors—such as listing you as male when you're female, or charging maternity services for a man—who then contact the hospital directly to get it corrected.

If there's an error, you'll be glad you followed these steps!

Medical Coding Mistakes Can Cost You Big

Pat Palmer, who has more than 20 years of experience contesting medical bills as founder of Medical Billing Advocates of America, a patient-advocacy company, Roanoke, Virginia. She is author of *MBAA's Guide to Surviving Your Medical Bills: What You Need to Know Before You Pay a Dime.* BillAdvocates.com

There is a five-digit "CPT" code for every medical procedure that health-care providers perform. If one of these Current Procedural Terminology (CPT) codes is entered incorrectly by your provider on a claim submitted to your insurance company or Medicare, the result could be big out-of-pocket costs for you—and errors such as these are extremely common. One recent study by the US Department of Health & Human Services found that a staggering 42% of Medicare claims for "evaluation and management" were incorrectly coded.

Insurance companies and the Medicare system shoulder much of the cost of miscodings, but patients can face inflated bills, too, in the form of higher co-pays...overcharges that must be paid out of pocket before deductibles are met...or outright denials of coverage because misentered codes refer to procedures deemed not medically necessary.

What to do: When you receive an Explanation of Benefits (EOB) statement from your insurance company or Medicare following medical treatment, read the description listed for each service provided. (If an EOB does not provide descriptions, just a series of five-digit alpha-numeric codes, enter these codes into a website such as HealthcareBlueBook.com to find descriptions. If your EOB provides neither codes nor descriptions, contact your insurer and request the CPT codes—these must be supplied upon request.)

Be especially wary if...

• **The same code appears more than once.** It's possible that you received the same treatment multiple times...but it also is possible that you have been double-billed.

• **A straightforward office visit is coded as something more extreme.** A "level 5" office visit—with the CPT code 99215—should be listed only if you had a life-threatening condition, for example.

What to do: Enter any code you think is questionable into Medicare's National Correct Coding Initiative Edit (CMS.gov/NationalCorrectCodInitEd). If a description does not sound like the procedure or treatment you received, call the provider's office and ask if the code is accurate. Sometimes office personnel acknowledge miscoding when prompted this way and will make corrections.

If you are told that the original coding is correct but you remain skeptical, send a letter to the provider's billing department officially disputing the bill. Or you can hire a medical billing advocate to contest the bill for you.

The Right HSA for You Now

Leo Acheson, CFA, senior manager research analyst covering multiasset strategies at Morningstar Inc., Chicago, which tracks 544,400 investment offerings. Morningstar.com

Just because your employer offers a particular health savings account doesn't mean that you have to choose that one. As long as you are enrolled in a qualified high-deductible health insurance plan, you can set up a health savings account (HSA)—an account that lets you avoid paying tax on earned income and then use it to pay health-care expenses—with any of the hundreds of qualified providers that offer them. And there may be excellent reasons for choosing an HSA not provided by your employer—a choice that could end up meaning hundreds or even thousands of dollars in extra money in your tax-advantaged account over the years.

The best HSA for you depends, in part, on whether you tend to spend your HSA money fairly soon for current health-care expenses ...or invest the money and spend it in later years.

To help people choose the right HSA, investment research firm Morningstar Inc. recently assessed how suitable the largest ones are for these two types of HSA users. (Search online for "2017 Health Savings Account Landscape" to get the full rankings. The 2018 rankings were unavailable at press time.)

• **For immediate spenders,** the research firm focused on the maintenance fees charged by each plan, which ranged from nothing to $4.50 monthly, and on interest rates offered by the providers' checking accounts, which ranged from 0% APY to 1.05% APY.

Top ranked: Alliant Credit Union...The HSA Authority...Select Account.

• **For people who tend to hold and invest their HSA balances,** Morningstar focused on the range of investment options offered by various HSA providers and the quality, cost and performance of these investments.

Top-ranked: HealthEquity...OptumBank... The HSA Authority...and Bank of America.

All paycheck contributions to HSAs are triple-tax-advantaged (you fund your HSA with pretax dollars...the money grows tax-free... and withdrawals for both you and your spouse are tax-free for qualified health-care expenditures). If your HSA contributions do not come directly out of your paycheck and you make them yourself with after-tax dollars instead, you can claim an income tax deduction for them on Form 1040 of your tax return.

EASY TO DO...

Cut Your Medical Bill

Some health-care providers, including hospitals, let patients under private insurance pay less than their co-pays and deductibles if they pay very quickly. Once you get a bill, ask the billing department for a "prompt-pay discount."

Bottom Line Personal research.

Get the Most from Medicare

Charles B. Inlander, a consumer advocate and health-care consultant based in Fogelsville, Pennsylvania. He was founding president of the nonprofit People's Medical Society, a consumer advocacy organization credited with key improvements in the quality of US health care, and is author or coauthor of more than 20 consumer-health books.

If you are already on Medicare—or will be soon—it's important that you carefully review the various options available to you under the program. It's not as simple as you may think. If you let cost be your only determining factor, for example, you may find that you are limiting your choice of services available, including some of the best specialists and hospitals in the country. Each fall (for 2018, from October 15 to December 7), Medicare runs an "Open Enrollment" period. *Beneficiaries have the option to...*

- **Do nothing and keep their current Medicare medical and drug coverage.**
- **Switch to a Medicare Advantage plan** (programs run by private companies approved by Medicare, which are similar to HMOs in that they have a preset roster of doctors and hospitals you must use or pay more out-of-pocket for your care). *When to consider:* If you want to save money. One-third of Medicare-eligible beneficiaries choose one of these plans for that reason.
- **Switch from a Medicare Advantage plan to traditional Medicare** (which allows you to see any doctor or hospital in the country that accepts Medicare). *When to consider:* If you live part of the year in another state...or you don't want to be restricted to an Advantage plan's limitations via their network.
- **Change Medicare Advantage plans.** *When to consider:* The selection of doctors or hospitals doesn't include ones you want to use. To find out what plans are available, call Medicare at 800-633-4227...or go to Medicare.gov.
- **Change Medigap plans** (insurance that supplements the traditional Medicare program). *When to consider:* If you're looking for a less expensive plan...or want to switch to a more comprehensive plan. *Note:* If you are in an Advantage plan, you do not need—and cannot buy—Medigap coverage. Also, based on your health, you can be turned down or charged more by an insurer other than your current Medigap plan.
- **Change Part D prescription drug plans...** sign up for a drug plan (if you don't have one now)...or drop drug coverage. *When to consider:* If the drug formulary changes or does not include one or more of your medications.

To ensure that you make the smartest choice for your situation...

- **Don't be cheap!** Choosing a less expensive plan may cost you more in the long run—*and* limit your access to quality care. A friend of mine enrolled in a Medicare Advantage plan that cost him no additional premium than that taken each month out of his Social Security check. He thought he was relatively healthy, so why pay more? In the next year, he had four unexpected surgeries and more than 40 doctor office visits. Between the hospital co-pays and all the doctor visits, his out-of-pocket costs exceeded $7,000. Had he selected the original Medicare program and a maximum-coverage Medigap plan, the same scenario would have cost him $3,500 for the premium and less than $500 in co-pays.
- **Get access to the best care.** Research shows that health insurance plans that offer low premiums and limited networks of hospitals and doctors are more likely to exclude doctors affiliated with National Cancer Institute (NCI)–Designated Cancer Centers (widely considered the best places for cancer care). In other words, low premium costs may limit your access to excellent care—even if it's available in your own community!

Beware a New Medicare Card Scam

In phone calls, scammers posing as Medicare representatives demand your Medicare number plus fees and financial information to get a new card that is meant to reduce ID theft. They claim you risk losing coverage if you don't comply.

Self-defense: Hang up on the caller. If you currently have a Medicare card, you will receive an official redesigned one automatically.

Micki Nozaki, director, Senior Medicare Patrol, a California-based advocacy group. CAHealthAdvocates.org

Genetic Testing Could Torpedo Your Insurance

Lee J. Slavutin, MD, CLU, principal of Stern Slavutin-2 Inc., an insurance and estate-planning firm in New York City. Prior to entering the life insurance business in 1983, he was a surgical pathologist at Lenox Hill Hospital in New York City. SternSlavutin.com

If you expect to apply for life insurance, disability insurance or long-term-care insurance, think twice about getting a DNA test.

DNA testing has become so inexpensive in recent years that many people are having it done as a precaution—or simply out of curiosity. For $250 or less, companies such as 23AndMe (23AndMe.com) and Color Genomics (Color.com) will analyze a sample of your saliva and tell you about your heritage and/or your health.

Example: Some people learn that they have inherited genes that put them at high risk for breast, ovarian, colorectal or prostate cancer. If knowing this inspires them to make anticancer lifestyle changes or to be checked for cancer more frequently, it could help them stay healthier.

But if a DNA test reveals that you have a genetic predisposition to a serious health problem, you may be required to inform life, disability and long-term-care insurers of this when you apply for coverage. (Genetic testing that explores only your ancestry and not your health should not create this problem.) And insurance companies may respond by imposing higher premiums or declining to cover you at all. The federal Genetic Information Nondiscrimination Act bars health insurers from requesting the results of genetic tests or discriminating against applicants based on such tests, but this law does not apply to other forms of insurance.

What to do: If your doctor advises you to get a genetic test because of a specific, pressing medical concern, do so. But if there is no pressing health concern and you intend to apply for life, disability or long-term-care insurance in the future, delay DNA testing until after you have been approved...or choose a test that reports on your ancestry only and not on your health.

Life Insurers Could Misread Your Medical Records

Lee J. Slavutin, MD, CLU, principal of Stern Slavutin-2 Inc., an insurance and estate-planning firm in New York City. Prior to entering the life insurance business in 1983, he was a surgical pathologist at Lenox Hill Hospital in New York City. SternSlavutin.com

Apply for a life insurance policy, and you authorize the release of your medical records to the insurance company—but what if those records are misunderstood or misinterpreted and the insurer thinks you have a health problem that you don't have? This can happen, and the consequences may be costly. If the insurer mistakenly believes that you have a health issue that could reduce your life expectancy, it might set your premiums 10% to 30% above the "preferred" premiums, if not more, or decline to cover you at all. And if the insurer reports this perceived issue to the Medical Information Bureau (MIB) database, other insurers will learn of it, too, and they also will quote you higher premiums or deny you coverage.

Example: A woman was quoted a steep premium because an MRI scan in her medical file appeared to show a carotid artery abnormality. Upon reviewing the file, her insurance broker realized that she was a perfectly healthy person with this one exception blemishing her medical profile. The broker asked a more senior radiologist in the department that conducted the scan to review the initial finding—and this radiologist discovered that there actually was no significant abnormality. The initial report had "overreported" a minor abnormality. A letter from the radiologist to the insurance company allowed the underwriter to offer the policy on a preferred basis.

What to do: When you choose among potential insurance brokers, ask, "Who do you have on your staff or on call who has medical or underwriting experience?" Lean strongly toward brokers who confirm that they do have such people available. If you are denied coverage or quoted a steeper-than-expected rate because of a medical issue of which you previously were unaware, ask your broker to have his/her medical staffer or consultant review your exam findings. Insurers generally are willing to reconsider their health assessments when brokers they work with demonstrate that these assessments could be mistaken.

TAKE NOTE...

Easy Way to Calculate Your Life Insurance Needs

Take your salary and multiply it by 20—if your salary is $50,000, that means you need $1 million in insurance. Buy a 20-year term policy for that amount. Term insurance is the least expensive kind and is pure insurance—not an investment or savings account. In most cases, it is the best type to have to protect your loved ones against an economic loss, which is the purpose of life insurance.

The New York Times.

Surprising Things Your Homeowner's Insurance Covers

Laura Adams, senior insurance analyst at InsuranceQuotes.com. She also is host of the free "Money Girl" podcast, which has been downloaded more than 40 million times.

Your homeowner's insurance covers more than just your home. These policies also provide protection for things that few policyholders would expect them to—in some cases, even things that occur thousands of miles away from home.

There is a catch—making a claim may lead to increased premiums for the next five to seven years. As a result, it generally is not worth making claims that result in payouts of less than $500 to $1,000 after accounting for the policy's deductible. (See page 160 for additional details about the risk of filing a claim.) But there are good ways to use your policy that you probably never thought of. (Of course, check your policy for specific coverage.)

Here are nine unexpected things covered by most homeowner's policies...

COMMON COVERAGE

• **Lawsuits against you stemming from incidents that did not occur on your property.** The liability section of your homeowner's insurance does not just provide coverage if a guest slips and falls in your kitchen or your dog bites a deliveryman in your front yard. It generally will pay settlements and judgments against you and provide legal representation even if someone sues you over an incident that occurs elsewhere.

Examples: You break someone's nose playing pickup basketball...your dog bites someone at the park. Personal liability coverage included with homeowner's insurance usually has a cap that is low by today's standards—perhaps $100,000—but it is there if you need it.

Exceptions: Homeowner's insurance usually will not cover you if a suit against you involves a motor vehicle or watercraft...business activities...intentionally causing injury or property damage...and in certain other situations. Read the "Liability Coverage" section of your policy for details.

• **Sheds and gazebos.** Most policies cover outbuildings on a property up to either 10% or 20% of the amount of coverage provided for the primary structure. That generally is more than enough to replace a shed or gazebo. This component of your coverage also might cover any freestanding guesthouses, barns, retaining walls, swimming pools and other things built on the property aside from the main house, so if you have pricey outbuildings, a wall and/or a pool, check the "Other Structures" section of your policy to confirm that you have sufficient coverage. If you don't, find out how much it would cost to increase this coverage.

• **Possessions stolen from storage units, hotel rooms, cars, luggage or kids' dorm rooms.** Your homeowner's insurance provides coverage for your stuff even when that stuff is not in your home. In fact, it protects your possessions even overseas.

This away-from-home coverage typically is capped at 10% of the maximum amount that the policy would pay to replace the contents of the home. Losses due to theft or disasters such as fires typically are covered (though usually not losses due to floods or earthquakes, which typically are specifically excluded from homeowner's insurance). Note that possessions in dorm rooms, or stolen from children who live in dorm rooms, are covered, but possessions in off-campus apartments, or stolen from students who live in off-campus apartments, are not. A student living off campus would need his/her own renter's policy to have coverage. Look for the section of your policy labeled "Off-Premises Coverage" for details.

Helpful: Items stolen from people when they are not at home sometimes are items those people have only just purchased. If so, contact the issuer of the credit card used to make the purchase before contacting your insurance company. Many cards offer coverage for the theft of recently purchased items.

• **Spoiled food.** Your policy probably provides coverage if a prolonged power failure ruins your frozen and/or refrigerated food. Some policies even offer a lower deductible or no deductible at all. The coverage typically is capped at $500 or less. *Exception:* Food ruined by a power failure caused by an event specifically excluded from coverage in your policy, such as a flood or earthquake, likely will not be covered. Details about this coverage might be in the "Property Coverage" section of your policy or in a "Special Endorsements" section. Insurers generally do not raise a policyholder's rates because of spoiled food claims, but there are no rules prohibiting them from doing so, and proof generally is not required.

• **Home upgrades required by new laws and ordinances.** If your home is more than a few years old, new building codes and ordinances might have taken effect since it was constructed. If you try to have the home repaired or rebuilt following a disaster, you might be required to comply with those new rules, potentially increasing your costs. Most homeowner's policies will pay some or all of these additional costs, though details and limits vary. Look for a section of your policy labeled "Ordinance or Law" or a similar phrase for details.

A small percentage of policies will pay a portion of the cost of upgrading the home to meet current codes and ordinances even when the upgrade is unrelated to a disaster that's covered by the policy.

• **Landscaping.** Your trees, shrubs, flowers and other landscaping probably are covered by your insurance. This coverage usually is capped at 5% of the home's coverage limit. And the coverage might provide protection only if landscaping is damaged by specific causes listed in the policy—and wind, a common cause of landscaping damage, sometimes is not listed. Typically only trees and plants you purchased for the property will be covered, not plants that grew on the property on their own. Look for a section of your policy labeled "Trees, Shrubs and Other Plants"... "Landscaping"...or something similar for details. Take photos of your landscaping so that you have evidence of the damage and/or save receipts and invoices from landscapers, nurseries and home centers.

LESS COMMON COVERAGE

These are included in some, but not most, policies. *Be sure to check yours so you'll know...*

• **ID theft and counterfeit money.** Some homeowner's insurance policies include a limited amount of coverage for losses related to ID theft and/or accidentally accepting counterfeit currency. This coverage often is capped at around $500, however, and usually covers only very specific types of ID-theft losses. A cynic might say that it's more a marketing gimmick than real insurance. Look for a section of the policy with a label featuring terms such as "ID Theft," "Credit Cards" or "Counterfeit Money" to see how much, if any, coverage you have. If you want more extensive coverage, you're likely better off buying specialized ID-theft coverage from a company that offers it.

- **Fire department service charges.** Your homeowner's insurance might pay some or all of the bill if a fire department charges you after it responds to a call to protect your property. If you have this coverage, there should be a section of your policy labeled "Fire Department Service Charge" or words to that effect. When offered, it typically has a lower deductible than the policy's standard deductible, if it has any deductible.
- **Grave markers.** Your homeowner's insurance might cover the cost of repairing or replacing a loved one's grave marker or mausoleum—even if the grave is not located on your property. Look for a section of your policy labeled "Grave Markers" or similar for details. Cemeteries typically are responsible for repairs to grave sites but not grave markers unless cemetery equipment caused the damage.

THE RISK OF FILING A CLAIM

When a home owner files a single claim, his/her homeowner's insurance premiums increase by an average of 9% for the next five to seven years, according to a study. But this is just an average. *Some policyholders have discovered that their rate increases are significantly higher or lower, often because of...*

- **Where they live.** Rate hikes for filing one claim were 17.5% or more on average in Wyoming, Connecticut, Arizona, New Mexico, California, Utah, Illinois and Maryland. They were 5% or less in New York, Massachusetts, Florida and Vermont. *Warning:* Filing multiple claims within a five-to-seven-year period will lead to substantial rate increases everywhere.
- **What type of claim they filed.** A claim related to liability, fire, theft, vandalism or water damage typically results in an increase of 12% or more. But a claim related to weather damage to the home (especially weather damage unrelated to hail or wind) or a medical bill stemming from an injury suffered by a guest on the property usually results in an increase of just a few percentage points.

Beware These Costly Homeowner's Deductibles

For damages related to a hurricane, deductibles in 19 states may range from 1% to 5% or more of the home's insured value. That typically would mean a deductible much higher than the flat $500 or $1,000 that is common for damages related to most other causes. (For a full list of states and rules, go to III.org and search for "hurricane deductibles.")

What to do: Ask your insurer whether you have the option of paying a higher premium in exchange for a lower hurricane deductible.

Michael Barry, vice president at the Insurance Information Institute, New York City. III.org

How Auto Insurers Trick You with Their Language

J. Robert Hunter, director of insurance for the Consumer Federation of America, Washington, DC, and former commissioner of the Texas Department of Insurance. ConsumerFed.org

When buying auto insurance, do you really know what you are getting and why? The language used in auto insurance ads and policies often is misleading or confusing—and can lead you to be *underprotected or overcharged.*

Solution: Do what the insurance industry hopes you *won't* do—understand the tricky auto insurance terms explained below. Then you will be able to ask the right questions when buying auto insurance...reject the options you don't need...avoid hidden auto insurance traps...and get the best price for the protections you do need...*

TERMS YOU MAY THINK YOU UNDERSTAND BUT DON'T...

- **"New-car replacement."** If your car is totaled in an accident, you typically get only its depreciated value, which may be less than

*Availability and details of various types of coverage in this article may vary by state.

what you still owe on your car loan. New-car-replacement coverage is an option that pays the full cost (minus your deductible) for the latest make and model of your vehicle, up to 110% of the manufacturer's suggested retail price.

What's tricky: New-car replacement can increase your premiums by 15% or more. Plus, the coverage is available for only a limited time for any given car. *Example:* Ameriprise and Liberty Mutual offer new-car replacement until cars are one-year old or have been driven 15,000 miles (whichever comes first).

What to do: From a financial standpoint, most drivers should skip this coverage. It's unlikely to pay off, considering that there is less than a 1% chance in any given year of having an accident in which one's vehicle is totaled.

- **"Gap coverage."** This option frequently is pushed on people who have made small down payments on their vehicles. It pays the difference between the balance of a loan due on your totaled vehicle and what your insurer pays you if the car is totaled.

What's tricky: What this covers can vary. *Example:* Most gap coverage does not include your out-of-pocket deductible. However, Allstate's gap coverage pays deductibles up to $1,000. And although gap coverage typically pays off your car loan regardless of your car's value, Progressive's version pays a maximum of just 25% of the car's actual cash value at the time of the accident.

What to do: This might be a cost-effective add-on for some drivers who still owe a lot on their cars because it typically costs just $30 a year and the premium decreases as the vehicle ages. And you can drop it after a few years as you pay off the loan. Before you buy it, be sure to clarify with the insurer the extent of the coverage.

- **"Decreasing deductible."** This feature, also known as "vanishing deductible," reduces the deductible on your collision insurance without increasing the premium if you remain accident-free. *Example:* At Travelers, the Premier Responsible Driver Plan will reduce your deductible by $50 every six months that you go without an accident, up to a total reduction of $500.

What's tricky: To qualify, all drivers covered by the policy must remain accident-free. That includes accidents that aren't your fault, such as another car hitting yours. If you have an accident, your original deductible is reinstated and you must reestablish a clean record to qualify for future reductions. This feature typically is available only as part of an upper-tier insurance package that adds 5% or more to your premiums.

What to do: It's not worth that extra cost on its own, so be sure you think it's worth paying for the package, which can include new-car replacement and/or accident forgiveness.

- **"Accident forgiveness."** This feature will help you avoid a rate increase following your first at-fault accident. Without this benefit, some insurers push up base premiums by 10%, 20% or more after just one accident, and the higher rates can last as long as five years.

What's tricky: The coverage may exclude teenage drivers. If you do have an accident, it may take three to five years to requalify for this feature.

What to do: This essentially is asking you to pay up front for accidents you might have in the future. Avoid this coverage unless you are a very bad driver.

- **"Appraisal clause."** If you and the insurer can't agree on how much will be paid to repair or replace your vehicle after an accident, this clause allows for the appointment of an appraiser by each side. If the two appraisers can't agree, they can jointly choose a third appraiser as umpire.

What's tricky: Under an appraisal clause, the insurer might be able to force you to accept arbitration rather than take the matter to court. Also, the appraisers may have a conscious or unconscious bias in favor of the insurer.

What to do: You always want to retain the option to get a lawyer and go to court. Twenty-six states prohibit or restrict insurance companies from imposing this type of arbitration on drivers. Check with your state's department of insurance. If your state allows forced arbitration, this is an important consideration in choosing insurers. Check whether a potential insurer includes an appraisal clause in its policy.

• **"As defined by us."** This phrase can refer to a variety of different terms or concepts in a policy. Watch out when it's used to give the insurer the right to make its own determination about the proper cost for a repair even if that is a below-market rate. Look for this phrase in the limits of liability section of your policy.

What's tricky: You might be stuck paying the difference if you want to use a repair shop that's more expensive than the insurer deems necessary.

What to do: If you have a favorite auto-repair shop, ask the insurer whether it has approved and paid for work at that shop in the past. If not, find out which shops the insurer knows in your area that will accept its rates and make sure that you are OK with using them...or seek another insurer.

• **"Collision" and "comprehensive."** You probably already know the basic meaning of these auto-insurance terms—but it's not their meaning that often trips up drivers. Collision includes damage to your car when you hit another car or an inanimate object such as a tree or fence or you drive over a hazard such as a deep pothole. Comprehensive (really not comprehensive in its extent of coverage) covers loss or damage caused by an event other than what collision covers, such as fire, theft, vandalism or hitting an animal.

What's tricky: Despite what many people think, no state requires either of these two types of coverage. What's required by most states is liability coverage, which protects you if you're at fault for an accident and the other car is damaged or if the driver and any passengers in either vehicle are hurt. However, if you have a loan on your car, the lender probably requires that you carry both collision and comprehensive.

What to do: In general, drop collision coverage, which can be about three times as expensive as comprehensive, when the value of your car is less than 10 times the annual cost of the collision coverage. Set aside what you save on your premiums for buying your next vehicle.

• **"Uninsured/underinsured motorist."** This coverage protects you if you're in an accident involving an at-fault motorist who has no insurance (or not enough) to pay for your damages and/or medical care for injuries. Or if the other driver cannot be located (a hit-and-run). If you live in one of the dozen states with no-fault insurance, insurers typically don't offer this option. (In no-fault states, if you are injured in an accident, your auto insurance covers both your vehicle damage, regardless of who was at fault, and your medical expenses through a personal-injury-protection policy that you are required to buy.)

What's tricky: Of the states that do assign fault in accidents, 23 do not require drivers to have uninsured/underinsured motorist coverage. Insurers in those states generally offer this coverage as two separate policy options—one for uninsured/underinsured motorist property damage (UMPD), the other for uninsured/underinsured motorist bodily injury (UMBI).

What to do: Everyone should consider having UMBI, even in a no-fault state, if the option is offered. *Reason:* About 15% of cars are uninsured, and many insured cars are covered by low-tier policies with low coverage limits. If you are hit by an uninsured or underinsured driver and incur medical expenses, your UMBI coverage kicks in before your health-care insurance coverage does. That means you typically won't face out-of-pocket deductibles and co-payments. UMBI also will cover some lost wages, depending on the policy, if your injuries prevent you from working and may compensate you for your pain and suffering, which your health-care insurance may not. How much UMBI coverage you need will depend on what other insurance you already carry, including any short-term disability insurance, and the out-of-pocket requirements of your health insurance. Consider getting at least "100/300" coverage (a maximum of $100,000 for your injuries and up to $300,000 total for injuries to everyone in your car).

• **"Credit-based insurance score."** Yes, there is a score related to your credit that can affect your auto insurance rates.

What's tricky: This special credit score, used by almost all auto insurers, comes from the same company that issues the FICO credit score used by mortgage lenders and other lenders, but it's not the same score. Government studies have shown a correlation between credit scores and the likelihood of filing auto insurance claims. The lower a customer's credit score, the greater the likelihood he/she will make a claim. Car insurers believe that this is because people who manage their money responsibly also are more careful in how they drive. (*Note:* Three states—California, Hawaii and Massachusetts—prohibit auto insurers from using consumer credit information to determine premiums.)

What to do: You cannot get access to your credit-based insurance score. However, you should monitor your regular credit reports to make sure that they are accurate, and ask to be reevaluated by your insurer if you have found and corrected errors in your reports.

- **"Multipolicy discount."** Some insurers reduce your auto-coverage premiums as much as 10% to 15% if you buy one or more other types of insurance from them such as a homeowner's policy.

What's tricky: You don't necessarily save money bundling policies. An insurer that specializes in insuring cars may have its homeowner's business handled by a third party and offer uncompetitive rates or less coverage.

What to do: Shop for the best rates on comparable policies, including discounts and bundles at various insurers.

GOOD TO KNOW...

What *Not* to Say to Your Auto Insurer After an Accident

Be careful when talking to your auto insurer after an accident...

- **Don't say you're fine**—soft-tissue injuries may not show up immediately.
- **Don't mention whiplash**—it is a red flag that you might be trying to scam the insurer.
- **Avoid saying "sorry"** or accepting blame for the accident.
- **Before letting the insurer tape-record the conversation,** make sure you know exactly what you want to say.
- **Stick to the facts** as you remember them to be.
- **Do not volunteer information** beyond what is requested.
- **If you are injured, see a doctor to get documentation**—insurers will not pay without it.
- **For damage to your car,** most states let you have repairs done where you choose—if your insurer refuses, contact your state insurance department.

Amy Bach, executive director, United Policyholders, a consumer-advocacy group, quoted in *USA Today*.

Auto Insurance You Don't Need

J. Robert Hunter, director of insurance for the Consumer Federation of America, Washington, DC, and former commissioner of the Texas Department of Insurance. ConsumerFed.org

A recent disclosure involving scandal-plagued Wells Fargo bank underlines how important it is to read the fine print of auto insurance coverage.

The disclosure involves "guaranteed asset protection" (GAP) insurance, which Wells Fargo and other lenders sell aggressively through dealerships when consumers take out car loans. Because the vehicle quickly loses much of its value, GAP insurance is meant to compensate lenders for that diminished value if the vehicle is totaled, stolen or repossessed. Wells Fargo charges a onetime fee of $500 to $700. In nine states—Alabama, Colorado, Indiana, Iowa, Maryland, Massachusetts, Oklahoma, Oregon and South Carolina—when borrowers pay off the loan early, lenders are required by law to refund part of the fee.

Wells Fargo has reportedly come under regulatory scrutiny for failing to refund GAP insurance fees to many consumers whose auto loans were paid off early.

If you are paying off a vehicle loan early in one of those nine states and are having trouble getting a GAP refund, contact your state insurance commissioner (NAIC.org/state_web_map.htm).

If you don't have GAP insurance coverage, which is not required by law in any state and can't be forced on you by a lender, you don't need it. *Here's why...*

In the unlikely event that you suffer a total loss of your vehicle during the life of your loan, your insurer will always pay the current value of the vehicle at that time. If you can't afford to buy a new vehicle for the original price of the lost vehicle and pay off the remaining loan balance, you could buy a less expensive new or used vehicle and take out a new loan. *Example:* Your new $20,000 car is totaled in an accident...your insurer covers $18,000, reflecting the current value...you buy a used car with a similar number of miles for no more than $18,000 and you still owe the same total of $20,000. Also, if you shop around, you can get a variation on GAP coverage without an extra fee. *Example:* Car loans from State Farm Bank automatically come with a Payoff Protector provision.

Extra-Safe Cars Cost More to Insure

The high-tech features that make them safer are very expensive to replace if they are damaged or destroyed, so insurers often raise premiums significantly.

Example: A conventional left mirror on a 2015 Mercedes-Benz ML350 costs $166 to fix, but when the mirror contains collision-avoidance technology, the repair cost is $925—an increase of $759.

Self-defense: Carefully consider insurance costs when deciding whether to buy cars with autonomous braking, multiple cameras, sensors and microprocessors. The technology often is in bumpers, fenders and external mirrors—areas that frequently are damaged in crashes.

The Wall Street Journal.

Get the Right Pet Health Insurance

Frances Wilkerson, DVM, who has practiced veterinary medicine since 1992. She founded the independent website Pet-Insurance-University.com.

If you own a cat or dog, you probably aren't spending the average $40 per month that pet health insurance costs. Fewer than 1% of pets are insured. If you can dip into your emergency fund to pay for expensive care, you can pass on a policy. But routine surgery can cost $3,000, and newer advances in veterinary medicine to treat cancer, heart disease and other chronic illnesses can cost much more.

Best bet: Starting insurance when a dog is a puppy or a cat is a kitten. Since your pet is unlikely to have a preexisting condition, you won't be excluded for one. It's true that premiums often rise with age, but some insurers also offer discounts for annual renewals.

If your dog or cat is older or already has a health problem, your insurance options may be more restricted. *Pet insurance tips...*

- **Accident/illness policies,** if your pet is eligible, are better than accident-only policies. Your pet is far more likely to need medical care for an illness.
- **Think twice before you pay for "wellness" coverage.** This covers routine care, including annual exams and vaccinations. Check what your vet charges—it may be cheaper to pay for these out of pocket.
- **Make sure your policy covers** cancer...chronic disease (it should be continual coverage, not for just one policy year)...hereditary and congenital diseases...and medical conditions common to your pet's breed and species.
- **Compare policies carefully.** Research the underwriters' financial strength by checking A.M. Best's rating center (AMBest.com/home/ratings.aspx). It is free, but you must register.

Your premium will vary based on what you choose for the deductible (generally $100 to $1,000 per year), copay (generally 10% to 30% of the cost of services) and the total amount that your policy will reimburse, which can vary from $2,500 up to an unlimited amount.

9

Tax News & More

5 Strategies to Save Money Under the New Tax Law

The new law overhauling the federal tax code changes much of what you've learned throughout the years about how to minimize your taxes. To keep our readers from overpaying under the new rules, we asked tax and financial expert Greg Rosica, CPA, CFP/PFS, to analyze the specifics and how they might affect you. Most of the changes go into effect starting with the tax year that began January 1, 2018, and are set to expire at the end of the 2025 tax year.

Here are five important strategies you need to consider right away...

INVESTING

The new rules affect decisions about your retirement accounts and education expenses.

• **If you want to convert a traditional IRA to a Roth IRA, don't do it all at once.** Contributions to a traditional IRA typically are tax-deductible, but you pay income tax on withdrawals...while contributions to a Roth IRA are not deductible, but you don't pay tax on withdrawals. Sometimes it makes sense to "convert" a traditional IRA to a Roth IRA by paying tax on the money converted. That's because you'll never have to pay tax on withdrawals from that IRA again, even as the assets grow bigger.

Under previous law, if you converted a traditional IRA to a Roth IRA and then those investments fell substantially in value, you could reverse the conversion and turn the Roth back into a traditional IRA—a process known as

Note: Rates and figures throughout this chapter and book are subject to change.

Greg Rosica, CPA, CFP/PFS, a partner with the accounting firm Ernst & Young who specializes in private client services and tax consulting, Tampa. He has 29 years of experience in the field and works with high-net-worth families. EY.com

"recharacterization." Then you could reconvert the traditional IRA to a Roth IRA with the value of the investments—and the resulting tax bite—lower than when you did the original conversion, thereby paying less tax.

The new rules eliminate this option to recharacterize, which makes converting a traditional IRA to a Roth IRA a riskier proposition because you will have to stick with it.

What to do: Without this do-over option of recharacterization, some people simply may decide to never convert a traditional IRA to a Roth. Instead of abandoning the idea, however, consider spreading out the conversion to a Roth IRA into equal portions over two or three years. That way, you could pay less tax on a portion of the converted assets if the value of those assets drops before you convert them.

One last chance: If you converted a traditional IRA into a Roth IRA in 2017, you still have until mid-October 2018 to undo your Roth conversion by recharacterizing under the old law.

• **Invest in a 529 college savings plan with an eye toward more than just college expenses.** Under previous law, money from a 529 plan could be withdrawn tax-free only to pay qualified college-related expenses. Under the new law, you can withdraw up to $10,000 per child each year tax-free while a child is in grades kindergarten through 12 to pay tuition for private or religious school or to pay for expenses involved in home schooling.

What to do: Start a 529 account right away if your child or grandchild is attending or may enroll in a nonpublic school. Also consider funding a 529 if you have a disabled child. The new rules allow you to roll 529 assets into ABLE accounts—tax-advantaged savings accounts for individuals with disabilities.

HOME BUYING AND BORROWING

Tax treatment of homes under the new law might have a big impact on which home you purchase...as well as loans you take out using the equity in your home as collateral.

• **Reevaluate whether you want to buy that big, expensive home.** Unless you are paying cash, one of the factors that goes into evaluating whether you can afford a home is your ability to deduct the interest payments on your mortgage. In the past, you were able to deduct mortgage interest on up to $1 million in debt.

A new rule, which applies to mortgages issued on December 15, 2017, or later, allows you to deduct interest on only the first $750,000 of mortgage debt. *Example:* If you take out an $850,000 mortgage, you can deduct a prorated amount of the interest you pay each year—about 88%—over the life of the loan. (This rule includes a "qualified residence" such as a motor home or boat in addition to your primary residence.) *Related:* The interest on home equity lines of credit (HELOCs) and home-equity loans, a relatively cheap form of borrowing, used to be deductible on loans up to $100,000 even if you didn't use the loan for home improvement. But starting with the 2018 tax year, home-equity interest will no longer be deductible unless the loan is related to home improvement or acquiring or building a home.

What to do: Consider buying a less expensive home or trying to reduce the size of the mortgage by increasing the down payment. Also, before you take out a home-equity loan, calculate the cost of doing so if there is no tax deduction on the interest you pay.

INCOME TAX DEDUCTIONS

The new law attempts to get more taxpayers to take the standard deduction rather than itemizing. But this might cost you money.

• **Even if you have itemized in the past, you and/or your accountant should run scenarios to see whether it makes sense to continue itemizing.** About one-third of US taxpayers have typically itemized, but under the new rules, that number could drop to as low as 5%. That's not just because the new law nearly doubles the standard deduction to $12,000 for single taxpayers and $24,000 for joint filers, but also because it eliminates or caps some popular deductions that taxpayers itemized in the past.

Examples of changes: In addition to the changes described above, there now is a $10,000 cap on deductions for state and local taxes that are paid starting in 2018, which can include any combination of property, income and/or sales taxes. And deductions are no longer allowed for unreimbursed employee expenses...tax-preparation expenses...moving expenses...or fees that you pay to an investment adviser or money manager. And for alimony agreements or decrees that start after December 31, 2018, the alimony you pay is not deductible.

Certain other deductions now have much narrower eligibility. *One temporary bright spot:* Just for tax years 2017 and 2018, medical expenses in excess of 7.5% of your adjusted gross income are deductible (down from 10% in previous years). But in 2019 and beyond, that threshold returns to 10%.

What to do: Don't assume that you should itemize for the 2018 tax year and beyond even if you have a lot of deductions that still are allowed (such as charitable contributions and student loan interest). Add up all your allowable deductions to decide whether they still save you more than the standard deduction.

BUSINESS TAX BREAKS FOR INDIVIDUALS

You may not think of yourself as a "business," but you might qualify for a business deduction under the new tax law.

- **Consider becoming a pass-through entity.** Certain kinds of businesses get big tax breaks under the new federal tax law...and if you currently are an employee, you might be able to get a slice of that tax-cut pie yourself by technically turning yourself into a business.

Background: Many small-business owners and other individuals who don't work for employers (such as freelancers and independent contractors) operate as pass-through entities, which can be in the form of a sole proprietorship, a partnership or a limited liability company (LLC). That means they earn income not in the form of a salary but as a profit distribution.

Under the old tax law, pass-through entities were taxed the same way as employees of a business—based on individual income tax rates. The new law, however, generally allows pass-through entities to take a deduction on 20% of their taxable income. For example, if your total annual income lands you in the 24% tax bracket, you would pay that 24% rate on only 80% of your income and pay no tax on the other 20%. There are some restrictions on the kinds of businesses eligible for the full deduction, but most pass-through filers qualify for the full 20% deduction as long as their taxable income is less than $157,500 (or $315,000 for joint filers). Above that, the deduction typically phases out.

What to do: If you are a salaried employee, it's worth exploring whether you can pay less tax by becoming a pass-through entity and working as your own business. To do so, you file paperwork with the state where the business is based and pay a fee.

Of course, you need to factor in the drawbacks of such a move. For instance, if you operate as a sole proprietorship, the simplest and most common type of pass-through entity, you're responsible for paying for your own health insurance and you are personally liable if your business runs into financial trouble.

BETTER WAY...

Deploy Tax Refunds Wisely

Give the tax refund a purpose instead of having the money vanish in the blink of an eye.

Possibilities: Use it to boost holdings in IRAs or other tax-sheltered accounts...pay down high-interest debt...purchase extra insurance (flood, umbrella liability, etc.)...increase emergency funds.

How to Stay Off the IRS Radar—Tax Return Red Flags

Abby Eisenkraft, CEO of Choice Tax Solutions, Inc., New York City. She is a federally licensed enrolled agent, an accredited tax preparer and a chartered retirement-planning counselor who specializes in federal and state tax audits. She is author of *101 Ways to Stay Off the IRS Radar.* RealLifeTaxAdvice.com

Anyone can get audited by the IRS. An audit can be random...it can be related to a transaction you made with someone else who is under audit...or it can result from something you did. The IRS says it has cut the number of auditors by 25% since 2010. But there still are some things that tend to make the IRS want to take a closer look at your tax returns. By recognizing and avoiding these red flags, you might be able to protect yourself from triggering an audit.

DEDUCTIONS THAT SLASH TAXABLE INCOME

Itemized deductions, including charitable donations as described below, can reduce your tax bill, but they also can raise suspicions when they're disproportionately high relative to income. A taxpayer who came to me after he ran into a problem had earned $21,000 one year and yet attempted to write off $17,000 in itemized deductions, including local taxes, real estate taxes, mortgage interest, charitable deductions and work-related out-of-pocket expenses. This lopsided claim naturally drew scrutiny from the IRS, which wanted to know how the client could afford to survive for a year with so little remaining income.

What to do: *Substantiation* in itemized deductions is the key to staying in the good graces of the IRS. Make sure you can account for shortfalls that likely won't make sense to the IRS. *Example:* The client who wrote off all of his annual income except for $4,000 might satisfy an IRS inquiry by proving that he tapped his savings to survive the lean times.

EXCESSIVE CHARITABLE CONTRIBUTIONS

The tax code allows taxpayers to write off some charitable contributions, which are among the most common itemized deductions. This reduces your taxable income and ultimately your tax bill. But some taxpayers tend to overvalue what they give, particularly with nonmonetary donations such as clothing. Excessively high valuations can make the IRS take note, which could increase the likelihood of triggering an audit.

The IRS also tends to take note when taxpayers claim charitable deductions that are high relative to their incomes. *Examples:* One of my clients triggered an audit by claiming $4,000 in charitable deductions on an income of $40,000—an unusually high 10% of income.

What to do: Resist the urge to highball the estimated value of your nonmonetary donations. In IRS publications 526 and 561, available at IRS.gov, the IRS outlines several methods for determining fair market value, which is roughly the amount that you should deduct. There is no set formula, but the estimated value should reasonably match the price that a consumer would be willing to pay for the item in a secondhand shop.

Also, make all donations verifiable whenever possible. Instead of putting money in a charity's sidewalk bucket, leave a paper trail by writing a check or donating the money online with a credit card. You also need a contemporaneous written acknowledgment for donations of $250 or more. And you need an appraisal if you donate property worth more than $5,000...or art worth more than $20,000.

APPEARANCE OF UNDER-REPORTED INCOME

The central function of IRS audits is to ensure that taxpayers accurately report what they earn. One of the surest ways to invite a tax audit is to give the IRS a reason to think that you're concealing income. *Example:* The IRS questioned one couple who reported a relatively low income that couldn't have reasonably supported their life in an expensive neighborhood in New York City.

What to do: Never try to conceal income, and be sure to gather and maintain documentation to explain any discrepancies between your income and your lifestyle. *Example:* The couple in New York had just gotten married, and they were able to provide proof that they had received large cash gifts and parental assistance that temporarily enabled their lifestyle.

SUSPICIOUS ENTERTAINMENT WRITE-OFFS

The IRS generally allows taxpayers to write off up to 50% of qualified business-related entertainment expenses. The key word, however, is *qualified.* Questionable entertainment write-offs are among the biggest red flags for auditors. And the new tax law has drastically changed the rules for deductible business entertainment expenses starting in 2018. Many entertainment "experience" expenses such as golf outings, concerts and ball games are no longer deductible. But it may be acceptable for a business owner to write off part of a dinner with a potential client if the purpose of the dinner was to secure the client's business. Two friends who are talking about starting a business over dinner, however, doesn't count.

What to do: Familiarize yourself with IRS publication 463 and tax topic 512—Business Entertainment Expenses—on the IRS website (IRS.gov). Also, keep all associated receipts, bills and other documentation. Business entertainment write-offs require a higher level of substantiation than many other business deductions and often attract more intense scrutiny.

CLAIMS OF 100% BUSINESS VEHICLE USE

If you use a vehicle for business purposes, you can deduct some related expenses. But if you also use the car for personal use, you must distinguish the two and deduct only expenses related to business use of the vehicle. The IRS is likely to become suspicious anytime taxpayers claim 100% vehicle deductions for cars they personally own.

What to do: Always be accurate and honest when claiming mileage or other expenses, and claim a 100% deduction only on a dedicated work vehicle. For example, you can't claim 100% business use of a work truck if you occasionally drive it to ball games. Maintain a mileage log or use an app for this purpose, and keep all supporting documentation, including gas and toll receipts.

DEDUCTIONS FOR CABLE- AND SATELLITE-TV

In some situations, the IRS allows taxpayers to write off some portion of cable- or satellite-TV subscriptions. These deductions, however, are known to make the IRS suspicious. You should pursue these deductions only if you bought the subscription purely for work, as in the case of a restaurant owner who keeps a television on for his customers at the business location. People get in trouble when they try to write off some arbitrary percentage of their home cable bills because it indirectly pertains to their work, such as actors watching movies or journalists watching the news.

What to do: A good rule of thumb is that if it's a cable-TV subscription that you would have had anyway, then no portion is deductible, since business usage does not cost any more. In most cases, this includes your cable at home—unless you can successfully prove to the IRS that you had to obtain a different level of service for business usage and then only that portion would be deductible.

THE REAL ESTATE RED FLAG

Real estate investors are not real estate professionals. The IRS allows tax-saving exemptions called passive activity losses—but this allowance is reserved solely for industry professionals who spend a certain percentage of time actively participating in the development or management of the property. This does not apply to investors attempting to write off losses associated with properties in which they own stakes.

What to do: Learn the guidelines for passive activity losses (Internal Revenue Code Section 469 or Publication 925) before claiming real estate deductions aside from those associated with your primary residence. If you seek tax deductions as a real estate professional, the IRS is likely to ask how much time and money you spend dealing with the property.

THE "SHARING ECONOMY" RED FLAG

From Uber drivers to Airbnb hosts, there's confusion about how "sharing economy" money is reported to the IRS. There's so much confusion, in fact, that the IRS dedicated a web page specifically to the topic. Search IRS.gov for the "Sharing Economy Tax Center."

The IRS is paying closer attention to independent contractors as the sharing economy goes mainstream. Even though you don't get a Form W-2 and may not receive a Form 1099-Misc, income from gigs is considered independent contractor earnings, which must be reported.

What to do: Avoid the common mistake of assuming that you don't have to report income earned as an independent contractor because you "didn't earn that much." A single dollar may be reportable.

They Beat the IRS—and So Can You

Edward Mendlowitz, CPA, a partner with Withum-Smith+Brown in New Brunswick, New Jersey (Withum.com). Mendlowitz is admitted to practice before the US Tax Court, and he writes a blog for Bottom Line called "The Pay-Less Tax Man." BottomLineInc.com/blogs/pay-less-tax-man

A taxpayer who takes on the IRS may feel a bit like David going against Goliath. But don't forget—David won, as taxpayers end up doing in almost 20% of legal challenges, according to the latest analysis by the National Taxpayer Advocate's office. Once a court case is decided in favor of a taxpayer, it becomes easier for other taxpayers to claim and get the same tax breaks.

Here are some notable recent cases where taxpayers fought the IRS and won—and how you can benefit from the precedents those cases set...

• **Alternative medical treatments can be deductible.** Victoria Malev's painful spinal disease wasn't helped enough by a chiropractor, and she feared that conventional treatments were too risky. Instead, she began alternative treatments, unreimbursed by insurance, from four individuals who were not recognized as conventional medical caregivers. She took tax deductions for the cost of these treatments as unreimbursed medical expenses.

The IRS disallowed those deductions and said she owed back taxes and a penalty for underpayment of taxes.

IRS Reasoning: Malev's treatments were not provided by individuals licensed to practice medicine.

Tax Court Ruling: Malev could deduct the expenses for her alternative treatments largely because the language of the tax regulations surrounding medical deductions makes the patient's *state of mind* regarding her condition relevant. Malev's testimony that the treatments had greatly improved her medical condition demonstrated her sincere belief that she incurred those expenses to cure or mitigate her symptoms. What's more, those expenses were something that an individual would not routinely incur for nonmedical reasons. Finally, the court determined that the law does not require those services to be provided by a licensed medical practitioner.

Note: After receiving notice from the IRS of her tax deficiency, Malev had obtained a new diagnosis from a medical professional and a recommendation that she pursue "integrated medical treatment." Had Malev received that recommendation before seeking alternative treatments, the case would have been even easier to resolve in her favor, since the alternative treatments would have clearly fallen under the recommendation of a medical professional.

Lesson: You can deduct expenses for unreimbursed alternative treatments provided that they are clearly directed to address a specific medical condition. But it's helpful to first receive a diagnosis from a licensed medical professional who recommends a course of integrative medicine.

Malev v. Commissioner, No. 1282-16S

• **Qualify as a real estate professional and reap more deductions.** Mohammad M. Zarrinnegar and his dentist wife owned a dental practice in California. They worked their joint dental practice in shifts. Mohammad worked at the dental practice 14 hours a week, but he spent the rest of his time managing the couple's real estate business, which included four rental properties and a brokerage. For three years, the couple claimed tax deductions for real estate–related losses ranging from $221,000 to $242,000 against income from their dental practice.

The IRS denied these deductions.

IRS Reasoning: Zarrinnegar was employed in a non–real estate field and could not claim to be a real estate professional who was entitled to deduct real estate losses from total income. Instead, the losses from his investment properties should be considered "passive" and could be used to offset only passive income.

Tax Court Ruling: The court applied the two tests that may qualify a taxpayer as a real estate professional—whether the person spent more than 750 hours during the year actively participating in real estate work...and whether the time spent amounted to more than half of total working hours for the year. Zarrinnegar offered detailed logs showing that he spent more than 1,000 hours per year on real estate activities and fewer than 1,000 hours per year at the dental practice. Several witnesses testified, corroborating his logs.

As a result, the court found that he satisfied both elements of the real estate professional test and could deduct the full real estate losses during the years in question against his dental practice income.

Lesson: Taxpayers who hold full- or part-time jobs in a non–real estate industry still can deduct all losses from a real estate business as long as they document that they have met the two tests that qualify them as real estate professionals.

Zarrinnegar, T.C. Memo. 2017-34

• **An owner's estimate of a property's value may be acceptable to determine a casualty loss.** Howard Bruce Coates and his wife owned two properties in Oklahoma, one that included the couple's home and two barns and another that was undeveloped woodland. A tornado damaged their home and barns and flattened their woodland.

Coates estimated that the first property lost $210,000 in value and that the undeveloped land lost $88,000 in value. Insurance covered part of the loss on the first property, but his second property was uninsured. After subtracting their insurance payout, the couple reported a deductible "casualty loss" of about $128,000 for both properties.

The IRS disallowed the casualty loss and assessed a penalty of more than $6,000 for inaccuracy in reporting the loss.

IRS Reasoning: Coates wasn't a certified appraiser and had not explained his method of determining his properties' values.

Tax Court Ruling: Although the law requires that before-and-after fair market value for a casualty loss be determined by a competent appraisal, the appraisal does not have to be done by a professional. Coates had bought and sold many properties in the area over many years, so his assessment of the value of the property that included his house and barns was credible. The court did, however, reject a casualty loss for the woodland property, saying that Coates had not proved its value...but siding again with Coates, the accuracy-related penalty was rescinded because the tax return had been prepared in good faith.

Lesson: If there's no recent appraisal of your property before a disaster strikes, your own informed opinion of the value of your home and land might suffice, particularly if you have had experience buying and selling property in your area. Without extensive experience, you should obtain a credible outside appraisal for losses.

Coates v. Commissioner, T.C. Memo. 2016-197

Avoid Airbnb Tax Trouble

Natalie Rasmussen, a Las Vegas–based enrolled agent. She is tax senior manager at Shared Economy Tax, which specializes in tax returns for people who have earnings from companies such as Airbnb and Uber. SharedEconomyCPA.com

Renting out your home, or even a single room, through a short-term rental service such as Airbnb, HomeAway or VRBO could earn you some cash—and a big tax headache. That's because special tax rules apply. *Here's how home-rental hosts can minimize the tax hassles and dodge some potentially expensive tax traps...*

• **Think twice before renting out your home for more than two weeks.** The federal tax code offers a wonderful way to avoid paying any income tax on short-term rentals. If the property is your personal residence and you rent it for a total of no more than 14 days in a calendar year, no income tax is due. This provision can let you make substantial tax-free income if there is tremendous demand for rentals in your area during a particular window of time, such as when a big sporting event takes place nearby.

However, if you rent out your home or a part of your home for a total of more than 14 days in a given year, *all* of your rental income becomes taxable and you have to navigate some complicated tax-reporting rules for claiming deductions.

TAKE NOTE...

Pets That May Bring Tax Deductions

•**Guard dogs** can lead to a business expense for upkeep and veterinary bills if you keep careful records and the dog seems suited to guard duty—large breeds may be acceptable, but small ones will not be.

•**Cats** kept mainly for pest control can bring deductions if their use is provable.

•**Hobby-income offsets** are available if you make money from pets by winning a prize at a dog show, for example, and report it—then the expenses of maintaining the hobby can be deducted if you itemize and track costs carefully.

•**Expenses related to your foster care** of pets can be deducted as charitable donations if you itemize and the animals come from a qualified nonprofit.

•**Guide dogs and service animals** can be deducted as medical expenses if you itemize and have proof of medical necessity.

Ask your accountant or go to IRS.gov for more information.

Roundup of tax experts, reported at GoBankingRates.com.

•**Don't assume that you don't have to report rental income because you didn't receive a 1099-K form from the rental service.** Rental services such as Airbnb are required to mail you this form only if you earn more than $20,000 and have more than 200 transactions during the year. But even if this form is not mailed to you, the IRS will be informed about your earnings.

•**Set money aside to pay self-employment taxes.** In 2016, the IRS clarified that home-rental hosts who rent out for more than 14 days and "provide substantial services" for tenants should report their income on Schedule C, *Profit or Loss from Business*, rather than Schedule E, *Supplemental Income and Loss.* "Substantial services" includes things that most Airbnb hosts do such as cleaning, changing linens or performing repairs. Self-employment taxes of 15.3% typically must be paid on Schedule C income.

•**Don't forget to deduct your home's depreciation.** Although real estate itself often appreciates in value, buildings depreciate throughout their useful lives, and people who earn income renting out their homes (or portions) can deduct a portion of that depreciation. For details see IRS Publications 527, *Residential Rental Property*, and 946, *How to Depreciate Property.*

•**You might have to pay lodging tax or "transient occupancy tax."** Not all localities have these local and state taxes, but if yours does, they likely apply even if you rent out your home for no more than 14 days. Contact your town, city and/or county to check whether any such taxes exist—and if so, make sure these taxes get paid.

How Blended Families Can Avoid a Financial Train Wreck

Martin Shenkman, CPA, JD, founder of Shenkman Law, which specializes in wealth planning and protection, Fort Lee, New Jersey. ShenkmanLaw.com

Deciding on how your assets will be distributed after your death is always challenging. But the process can be especially fraught for individuals who remarry once or multiple times.

Consider that about 40% of new marriages in the US include at least one spouse who is remarrying, and many of these spouses have children from previous marriages. With ex-spouses, step-siblings, half-siblings and other family members in the mix, estate planning is complicated not only by the sheer number of potential beneficiaries but also by the complex emotional relationships among the members of these blended families. It can be difficult for couples to find equitable ways to support children from multiple marriages.

Likewise, protecting family homes or businesses becomes complicated when multiple parties feel strong connections to the assets.

Navigating these challenges requires a special approach to estate planning. *Consider these strategies for developing a fair division of assets for a blended family...*

1. Realize that your situation is unique. There is no one-size-fits-all estate plan for couples in second and later marriages. Blended families come in endless configurations, and what works for another family might not suit your needs.

Start by acknowledging the specific facts of your situation, then establish goals that feel right to you and your spouse. Among the factors to consider are how much in assets each spouse enters the marriage with...how much income and expenses each generates during the marriage...how many children there are and what ages...and the particular needs of each child.

Example: If one or both of you have children from a prior marriage and you also have children together, you might have a goal of dividing your assets equally among all of them to minimize the potential for disputes. However, if children from a previous marriage are adults and financially well-established, you might plan to leave a larger portion (or all) of your assets to young children from your current marriage. Families with adult children who already are well-off also might want to prioritize charitable giving, whether through a trust, foundation or other means. Starting from these goals, you can work with a financial adviser and estate planner to create a plan that fits your family's situation.

2. Get a "postnup." If you're already in a blended family but don't have a prenup, you haven't lost your chance. A postnup can serve most of the same functions as a prenup. Check what your state's laws are regarding postnups. Prenuptial or postnuptial agreements may not be necessary for all first marriages, but they are critical for couples who are coming from previous marriages.

These agreements are the most effective way to specify which assets—including future earnings—are considered to be marital property and which belong to each spouse and his/her respective children.

Examples: You can choose to protect money that you already have saved for a specific child's college education while agreeing to set aside shared money for children that you might have with your new partner. Similarly, one spouse can waive the rights to certain properties, such as a vacation home or a family business, that the other partner wishes to save for his/her children from a previous marriage. This ensures that assets with special value or meaning can be passed on to specific people, without having to keep all your accounts separate.

To avoid potential legal disputes over the prenup or postnup if the marriage ends in divorce, each partner should hire a separate attorney for the drafting process. Both partners and their lawyers should make a list of all assets each spouse is bringing to the marriage and agree on whether those assets will become marital property or remain separate property.

If either partner has children from a previous marriage, the agreement can outline specific directions for financial support or the inheritance of certain assets.

3. Consider establishing trusts. For remarried couples, trusts can serve several purposes. They can provide a formal structure to keep the assets of one spouse separate from the other's...ensure a source of income for a surviving partner after the death of the other...and preserve assets for children from previous marriages.

Example: One popular option for remarried couples is a qualified terminable interest property (QTIP) trust. This type of trust provides lifetime income for the surviving partner, while also designating where the trust's remaining assets will go once the surviving partner dies—whether it is to children from that marriage...to children from previous marriages...or elsewhere.

4. Use insurance to support different members of the family. Having a life insurance policy can be an effective way to direct money toward a particular beneficiary while preserving other assets for different uses. Policies also can be kept separate from other agreements such as prenups or wills, which rules out possible misinterpretation or lawsuits in the event of divorce. Life insurance policies can be especially helpful for couples with one significantly older spouse.

Example: Each spouse can purchase a new life insurance policy and name children from a previous marriage as the beneficiaries. That allows him/her to leave other assets to the new spouse and/or any children they might have together. Alternatively, each spouse could buy two life insurance policies, one for the children from a previous marriage and one for the new family.

5. Update beneficiaries on all your financial accounts. Most people understand that their wills should be updated when entering a new marriage. But many individuals neglect to update beneficiaries in other documents, including retirement accounts, bank and brokerage accounts, life insurance policies and real estate and vehicle documents. Even if these crucial updates are discussed before the marriage, it's easy to neglect following through on them...and the consequences can be serious.

Example: If the husband does not remove his ex-wife as beneficiary of his pension, she may have a claim on that account even if the new will says that all assets go to children from the new marriage.

Beneficiary designations can be updated online for many accounts. Others might require you to sign and mail a paper form. Some require spousal approval. Check with each of your financial providers for their specific process. Once you update your beneficiary designation, be sure to let the named individual know.

6. Be specific but also build in flexibility. Specificity is key for estate plans for newly remarried couples. Say you and your new spouse decide to keep your previously held assets separate but share all new income generated during your marriage. In that case, you must spell out in writing what exactly counts as income, considering not only salaries but potential income sources such as investment returns and capital gains.

Likewise, you should decide on the specific mechanisms that are involved in sharing your income, ranging from setting up a joint account to having your adviser structure your investments so that all dividends or income goes directly into that shared account.

Caution: Too much specificity can cripple an estate plan, especially if you try to construct complicated rules to handle changes in your family structure or financial situation. *Example:* Rather than attempting to calculate adjustments in the percentage of assets that each child from previous marriages will inherit in the event that you and your new spouse have a new child, simply write into your estate plan that you will revisit this agreement with each major change in your family's makeup. Even if nothing substantial has changed, it's a good idea to revisit your estate plan every two to five years to ensure that it still meets your goals and intentions.

7. Have honest conversations with your family. Even the most carefully crafted estate plans can result in frustration and resentment if you don't discuss them with your family members. This is especially true for blended families, which can include step-siblings who don't fully trust one another and half-siblings who may have such a big age difference that they don't really know one another.

Once you have completed your plan, arrange meetings with the named family members (either as a group or individually if the siblings don't get along) to review your rationale for each decision in your plan. Such conversations can be difficult, but they will help answer questions your heirs might have and can go a long way toward avoiding ill will in your family many years down the line.

Protect Dead Relatives from ID Theft: Here's Why...and How

Adam Levin, JD, chairman and founder of cybersecurity company CyberScout, Scottsdale, Arizona, and former director of the New Jersey Division of Consumer Affairs. He is author of *Swiped: How to Protect Yourself in a World Full of Scammers, Phishers, and Identity Thieves.* CyberScout.com

---

Don't assume that the risk of having your identity stolen lasts only as long as you are alive. More than two million dead Americans become victims of identity theft each year.

To an identity thief, the recently deceased are ideal targets. Unlike the living, the dead never notice that they are being victimized and don't take steps to stop these crimes.

There is a system in place that is supposed to prevent this—when Americans die, their Social Security numbers are added to the Social Security Administration's "Death Master File." Once that occurs, credit-reporting agencies note the deaths in their files and credit issuers should not issue new credit.

But this process can take months, leaving plenty of time for identity thieves to strike. During these months, it falls to surviving spouses, heirs and executors to protect the identities of the deceased. It's in their best interests to do so.

Although these spouses, heirs and executors are not legally responsible for financial losses caused by postmortem identity theft—it's the duped creditors who are left holding the bag—these crimes can cause them major headaches as they struggle to convince creditors and bill collectors that the debts are not the responsibility of the estate.

And if the executor of the estate is not paying close attention, identity theft could even go unnoticed, meaning that fraudulent account withdrawals might not be corrected and/or fraudulent bills might be paid, reducing the size of the estate.

Here's what you should do...

SAFEGUARD SENSITIVE INFORMATION

If you're a surviving spouse or heir, take the following actions to decrease the odds that identity thieves will steal the deceased's identity...

• **Edit the obit.** Do not mention the deceased's home address, birthday or mother's name in his/her obituary. Some identity thieves scour the obituaries for potential targets, and this information could be useful to them.

• **Watch the wallet.** There have been cases of hospital or emergency services personnel stealing credit cards from the wallets of the deceased. These thieves sometimes leave most of the contents of the wallet in place in order to decrease the odds that a loved one will realize anything is amiss. *What to do:* Cancel the deceased's credit cards as soon as possible. Carefully check the final bill for charges that occurred after the deceased went to the hospital and/or passed away.

• **Discard the deceased's documents with care.** Identity thieves have been known to pick through garbage cans outside the homes of the recently deceased. They're hoping that heirs threw out sensitive paperwork while cleaning out the house. Documents that should be shredded with a paper shredder include tax returns...financial account statements...credit card statements...bank account statements... and anything with a Social Security number.

• **Relocate the wake.** If you hold a wake or reception in the deceased's home, an identity thief (or burglar) could show up, claim to be an old friend of the deceased and then slip away from the crowd to steal sensitive information, credit cards and small valuables. Also, an employee working for the caterer, florist or cleaning company you hire for the event could be a crook bent on ID theft.

• **Prevent oversharing on social media.** Some identity thieves search the social-media accounts of the recently deceased to find the facts they need. If the deceased has Facebook and/or other such accounts, log into each of these and either delete the accounts (assuming that you can gain access)...or, if you prefer to leave the accounts open as a way to remember the deceased, at least confirm that the account settings restrict access to only a small circle of family members and friends.

Also read through the posts, deleting any that mention ID-related information such as mother's maiden name or birth date. If you do not log into the account because you don't have the password and cannot find it near the deceased's computer, report the death to the social-media site. This often leads to the account being shut down or "memorialized" in a way that could at least limit access, though this can vary depending on the site and the settings that the deceased selected.

• **Have the deceased's mail held at the post office or forwarded to the estate's ex-**

ecutor. Otherwise, mail containing account information and other sensitive data might sit in the deceased's mailbox where an identity thief could grab it. *Exceptions:* This is not necessary if a spouse or some other trusted loved one still lives at the deceased's address...and/or the deceased has a post office box or locking mailbox.

SPREAD THE WORD

Even if you take all the right steps to safeguard your deceased loved one's sensitive information, he/she still could be victimized by an identity thief. There have been so many data breaches of retailers, financial institutions, government agencies and others in recent years that the information an identity thief needs might already be in circulation. What's more, postmortem identity theft sometimes is committed not by a stranger, but by a family member who has access to the deceased's sensitive information.

Informing key agencies and institutions about the death can at least contain the damage that a postmortem identity thief can do. Obtain copies of the death certificate as soon as possible—death certificates typically are available through the funeral home or mortuary—and send them along with letters reporting the death to...

- **Government agencies** including the IRS, Social Security Administration, Department of Motor Vehicles and the tax authority in the deceased's state. This should prevent identity thieves from having duplicate driver's licenses, Social Security cards or other documents issued to them in the deceased's name. Notifying the IRS and state tax authorities promptly should prevent an identity thief from filing a phony tax return in the deceased's name and receiving a refund.

- **The deceased's creditors and other financial institutions.** This includes investment companies and advisers, banks, credit unions, credit card issuers, lenders and insurance companies. If you are not certain which financial companies the deceased used, go through his recent mail, checking account registers, filing cabinets, recent tax returns and wallet in search of clues. Or identify these creditors and financial companies by obtaining a free copy of one of the deceased's credit reports at AnnualCreditReport.com.

To obtain this report, you will have to provide identifying information about the deceased, including his Social Security number. It generally is easier to obtain the credit report before the credit-reporting agencies are informed of the death. After they learn of it, extra steps might be required for the estate's executor to obtain a copy.

- **The three major credit-reporting agencies.** Ask Equifax, Experian and TransUnion to place a "deceased alert" on your loved one's file. This is like putting a security freeze on the file—it prevents the credit-reporting agency from releasing the file, which should, in turn, prevent new credit accounts from being opened in the deceased's name. Send certified copies of the death certificate along with brief letters identifying the deceased by full name, Social Security number, last five years of addresses, date of birth and date of death to...

  - Equifax, PO Box 740241, Atlanta, GA 30374
  - Experian, PO Box 4500, Allen, TX 75013
  - TransUnion, PO Box 2000, Chester, PA 19016

Helpful: If there are signs that identity theft is occurring despite your efforts—these signs might include money disappearing from the deceased's accounts...or account mailings arriving from creditors that the deceased did not have—the estate's executor should call the credit-reporting agencies and the deceased's financial institutions as quickly as possible to confirm that they received the death certificate and placed a death alert on the file or account. The executor also should call the Social Security Administration and ask whether the deceased's Social Security number has been added to the Death Master File. If it hasn't, explain that identity theft is occurring and ask whether anything can be done to speed along the process.

10

Investments Now

4 Money Pros Reveal Their Biggest Money Blunders

Everyone has made a costly money mistake at some point in his/her life—even shrewd financial experts who deal with money for a living. We spoke with four money mavens to find out their most unfortunate mistakes and what they learned that could be helpful for investors and consumers.

PAM KRUEGER
Weathramp.com

MISTAKE: **I got caught up in a stock market craze even though I thought I knew better.** Back in 1999, I got my own financial talk show on satellite TV. I had a front-row seat to what was making Internet stocks skyrocket in price because every day, people called in to tell me how they were investing in companies such as Pets.com that were steadily losing money. Mostly, they assumed that there must be something great about these companies because the stock prices kept climbing. As a former stockbroker, I thought I was too financially savvy to get sucked in, but finally I couldn't resist purchasing the stock of Pets.com and several other early Internet ventures—all of which turned out to be doomed. I lost big.

Lesson learned: Even well-educated investors can be easily dazzled by a soaring stock price and assume that there must be hidden reasons why a company making little or no profit is attractive. To keep yourself grounded, you need to create a tangible reminder of your long-term objectives. Make a specific, written statement of your goals, asset allocation, risk tolerance and what you've decided you can and can't do. Review it whenever you're tempted to make an irrational investment decision.

Pam Krueger, CEO, Wealthramp.com, an online service that matches investors with registered financial advisers, and executive producer of *MoneyTrack: Money for Life,* which airs on PBS stations. PamKrueger.com

Note: Rates, prices and offers throughout this chapter and book are subject to change.

KAREN C. ALTFEST, PhD, CFP
Altfest Personal Wealth Management

***MISTAKE:* I didn't focus when it came to a big financial transaction, and the oversight could have put us on a rocky road.** When my husband and I started our investment advisory firm and moved to lower Manhattan, an important client asked me to sell $20,000 worth of corporate bonds from his portfolio. I prized myself on multitasking and getting a lot done, so I called in the order to his brokerage firm while juggling other client accounts. The next day, my colleague wanted to know why the client had made a $2 million sale. I had mistakenly requested to sell 20,000 shares, not $20,000 worth of shares! Fortunately, the price of the bonds hadn't moved. We were able to cover the transaction costs and unwind the trade without having any impact on the client's portfolio.

Lesson learned: Slow down and triple check. Busy people prize being efficient. But with vital money transactions, be a little inefficient. For example, instead of putting your credit card bill and other large bills on autopay so that they are paid directly from your bank account, actually handle the paper bill. Go through your credit card transactions each month. It takes a few extra minutes, but you may catch a lot of errors...and notice when companies quietly raise their monthly recurring charges.

Karen C. Altfest, PhD, CFP, a principal and executive vice president at Altfest Personal Wealth Management, New York City. She has appeared on the *Forbes* magazine list of America's Top 200 Women Advisors. Altfest.com

JONATHAN D. POND
Jonathan D. Pond, LLC

***MISTAKE:* I assumed that the more risk I took in the stock market, the higher the returns.** When I was a business major in college, I took an $18,000 inheritance I had received from my grandmother and put 100% of it into hot, fast-growing stocks. I figured that I had such a long time horizon that I should be as aggressive as possible to get the best returns. However, many of the young companies I bet on went out of business. Within a few years, my inheritance was gone. Since then, I have never put more than 60% of my portfolio in stocks, and I have kept the rest in high-quality government bonds.

Lesson learned: Being conservative costs you much less in long-term portfolio performance than you think. Over a 40-year period, the Standard & Poor's 500 stock index has returned 10.4% on an annualized basis. But a mix of 60% stocks and 40% short- and intermediate-term US Treasuries has returned an annualized 10% with only about half as much volatility. At any age, you need some exposure to lower-risk, dependable investments to preserve your capital.

Jonathan D. Pond, president, Jonathan D. Pond, LLC, Newton, Massachusetts. He is an Emmy Award–winning PBS TV financial host and author of *Safe Money in Tough Times*. JonathanPond.com

JANET M. BROWN
FundX Investment Group

***MISTAKE:* I wanted to give financial help to a friend who was starting a business—but I didn't think about the consequences to the relationship if the business failed.** It was a long-time friend, and she had asked me to invest $50,000 in her custom tailor shop. I wrote her a check. The business survived for several years but wound up closing. I never got my money back, and my friend moved away. And the same kind of thing has happened more than once to me!

I do enjoy supporting my friends' entrepreneurial ambitions, but ultimately I realized that my relationships with them would have survived just fine—and probably ended up better—if I hadn't provided them with money for their businesses.

Lesson learned: It's OK if you don't give money to a family member or friend, especially if you think that person's business idea isn't viable or if the person would have to dramatically change his behavior or work ethic to make the business succeed. If you do give money for a business venture, decide on an amount that wouldn't ruin the relationship if you lost it all.

Janet M. Brown, president of the FundX Investment Group and managing editor of the *NoLoad FundX* newsletter, San Francisco. FundX.com

5 Stock-Picking Secrets from a Legendary Fund Manager

Joel Tillinghast, CFA, manager of the $38 billion Fidelity Low-Priced Stock Fund, Boston. Over the past 15 years, the fund had annualized returns of 12% vs. 9% for the S&P 500. He is also author of *Big Money Thinks Small: Biases, Blind Spots, and Smarter Investing*. Fidelity.com

Legendary fund manager Joel Tillinghast says you don't have to be a bold, daring investor to succeed. Great long-term portfolio performance isn't about choosing the most exciting stocks, adds Tillinghast, who has managed the Fidelity Low-Priced Stock Fund since its inception 28 years ago. Whether you are the manager of a giant fund or an individual investor with a small portfolio, the best strategy is to avoid big mistakes and to find overlooked companies that have what Tillinghast calls, in his understated manner, "a high likelihood of a decent outcome."

Tillinghast's fund is proof of how effective the strategy can be. In real money terms, $10,000 invested in the fund in 1989 would be worth more than $350,000 today, compared with $128,000 for the Standard & Poor's 500 stock index. His prudent, disciplined approach seems particularly useful in today's aging bull market, in which many stocks are considered overvalued and a few flashy large companies seem to draw all the attention.

We interviewed Tillinghast to find out his secrets to picking good stocks without taking a lot of risk and how our readers can benefit from his approach…

TAKE NOTE…

Apps That Help You Invest

If you want to invest using spare change, try *Acorns*. This app will round up purchases on linked credit or debit cards to the nearest dollar and invest that amount. ($1/month charge for balances below $1 million.)

If you want to choose your own portfolio of stocks, *Robinhood* offers commission-free trading of US-listed securities on mobile devices and is rolling out cryptocurrency trading. (No minimum or account fee, but certain trades, such as buying foreign securities, incur costs.)

For investors looking for "socially conscious" investments, *Swell Investing* offers portfolios that invest in renewable energy, green technology, clean water and similar sectors. ($50 minimum investment, 0.75%/year fee.)

USNews.com

MY SECRETS

When I was interviewed by renowned fund manager Peter Lynch for my first job at Fidelity back in the 1980s, I didn't believe that I was ever going to match his uncanny ability to pick huge stock winners at the tremendously successful Magellan Fund. In fact, my first job at Fidelity was as an analyst researching the coal industry. But laboring in that unglamorous sector helped me clarify what to look for in stock investing.

What I've learned that can help anyone who chooses stocks…

- **Invest in businesses with long-term advantages over competitors.** A company should dominate its market niche and have low levels of debt…a distinctive brand that consumers trust and seek out…and a business model that isn't buffeted by the ups and downs of the economy. These guidelines make it easier to forecast a company's profitability without being dangerously wrong.

Example: A decade and a half ago, I started investing in a California company now called Monster Beverage. I paid an average of eight cents per share (adjusted for splits) over the years. This company made energy drinks, sodas and juices using unusual ingredients such as guarana seed extract and ginseng that have powerful mood-boosting effects. It was a simple but outstanding concept. In 2018, the company will have revenue of close to $4 billion, and its stock recently traded at more than $60 a share.

Energy drinks are an example of a product that has a long runway of growth ahead. I avoid industries that I think are headed for obsolescence (such as the coal industry) or that have commodity-like products with so few differences from one another that price becomes the only basis for competition (such as airlines).

• **Make your initial purchase in a stock when it is trading at $35 a share or less.** My fund typically keeps at least 80% of assets in low-priced stocks (which currently means stocks purchased initially at or below $35 per share). This is a somewhat crude way to point me in the direction of bargain-priced small- and mid-cap stocks, but the discipline it has imposed has served me well. Focusing on low-priced stocks often is a good way to find companies that are either too small for Wall Street analysts and big institutions to pay attention to or whose prices are temporarily depressed due to short-term problems. (Of course, a low price alone doesn't mean that a stock is worth buying—there are plenty of stocks priced under $35 that I would never touch.)

Important: I don't sell a stock just because it appreciates beyond $35 per share. I hold my winners as long as their long-term growth potential looks attractive.

• **Stay within your circle of competence.** Back in 2000, I became very curious about a well-respected investor named Bernie Madoff. Even in sloppy markets, Madoff's funds seemed to be perennially profitable. I wanted to learn from and incorporate his strategies into my own investing, so I met with a Boston money manager named Harry Markopolos who was trying to "reverse engineer" the returns of Madoff's funds to figure out the formula. Markopolos, who later helped expose Madoff's Ponzi scheme, couldn't do it. I had no idea about the malfeasance and criminality involved in the Madoff fund at the time. But I was wise enough to know that if I didn't understand it, I should just stay away.

You have to understand a company enough to be able to forecast with confidence how the business will make money in the next decade.

Example: One of my fund's largest holdings is Ansys, which makes simulation software that allows engineers to save time and money by testing multiple concepts when designing products. An aerospace company, for instance, can simulate the effects of wind and stresses from vibration, temperature and velocity on new plane wings. Although Ansys software is highly technical, the business isn't. The company has a proprietary product, a leading market share in a highly fragmented industry and a 95% renewal rate among customers.

• **Avoid "story" stocks.** These companies are so exciting, you are tempted to suspend your normal investing criteria.

Example: Investors have piled into the electric-car company Tesla. Its CEO, Elon Musk, is a visionary who has created a very cool, marvelously designed product. At the same time, the company is losing money on every single car...is saddled with $18 billion in debt...and its stock has a price-to-earnings ratio of 3,600 based on expected earnings for the next 12 months (versus 19 for the S&P 500). Tesla could disappoint for many reasons, including its fading competitive advantage (every major car company is racing to produce electric vehicles) and its limited potential for long-term profitability.

• **Get serious about increasing your exposure to foreign stocks.** The bull market in the US has left many investors overallocated to US stocks as their prices have soared. About 40% of my fund now is invested in foreign stocks, which offer investors more chances to find undervalued buys. I'm finding good opportunities in Asian stocks. My fund owns shares in Hon Hai Precision Industry Co., a Taiwanese electronics manufacturer that makes mobile phones and is expanding into nanotechnology. The fund also holds some Canadian companies such as Metro Inc., one of the country's largest grocery and drugstore operators.

RECENT STUDY...

Sudden Financial Loss Can Be Deadly

Middle-aged or older people who lost 75% or more of their total net worth within a two-year period were 50% more likely to die over the next 20 years than those whose wealth stayed stable or grew.

Study of 8,714 people by researchers at Northwestern University's Feinberg School of Medicine, Chicago, published in *JAMA*.

5 Companies That Will Change the World: You Could Profit Big

Laird Bieger, comanager of the Baron Discovery Fund (BDFFX), based in New York City. The fund, launched in 2013, had annualized returns of 12.2% over the past three years, compared with 10% for the S&P 500, and 34% over the past year, putting its performance in the top 1% of its category. BaronFunds.com

The young, little-known companies that Laird Bieger picks for the mutual fund he comanages like to shake things up a lot. They don't offer just a slightly better product or cheaper service than competitors do. Their innovations actually disrupt how industries operate, tapping into powerful emerging trends and offering customers something brand new that may quickly become essential to their lives or businesses. And they offer attractive opportunities for investors who are willing to take a chance on stocks that largely fly under the radar.

Among the products and services these companies provide: A long-lasting, nonaddictive drug for knee arthritis pain...microchips the size of grains of sand that allow businesses to tag and track millions of items...and virtual doctors who can treat you almost anytime and anywhere. Several of the stocks held by Bieger's Baron Discovery Fund have doubled in price recently...but they have plenty of room for further gains.

We asked Bieger how to identify disruptive companies and which stocks he thinks are most attractive now...

SPOTTING DISRUPTIVE COMPANIES

Disruptive companies can be found in many sectors, ranging from the auto industry (Tesla) and retail (Amazon.com) to lodging (Airbnb) and transportation (Uber). My comanager, Randy Gwirtzman, and I also have discovered companies transforming industries such as advertising, defense contracting and health care. As a result, the stocks have the potential to double over the next five years.

Characteristics I look for in these companies...

- **They are tiny and overlooked by Wall Street analysts.** It's hard for small investors to gain an edge investing in large, well-known companies. About 40% of my portfolio is in stocks with total market values of $500 million or less—considered very small by today's standards for publicly traded companies.
- **Each company has a unique and enduring competitive advantage** and a huge potential market for its products and/or services. Biotech companies possess patents on their drugs and treatments. Other businesses have what I call "first mover" status. They helped create their market niches, and it will take competitors years and enormous sums of capital to challenge them. Many first movers end up being bought by huge corporations that are willing to pay a 50% premium above the share price.

Reality check: As promising as these disruptive companies are, they should be reserved for the most aggressive part of your investment portfolio because they carry higher risk than larger companies do.

MY FAVORITE DISRUPTIVE COMPANIES

These five stocks all have the characteristics described above. Owning one or more can help boost your long-term portfolio returns.

- **Flexion Therapeutics (FLXN).** In 2015, more than 14 million Americans were diagnosed with osteoarthritis of the knee, and there are no safe and effective and long-lasting treatment options short of knee replacement. This small biotech firm's only drug, Zilretta, has completed clinical trials for treatment of knee arthritis pain and was approved by the FDA in October 2017, which could reshape the standard of care in the $5 billion osteoarthritis-treatment market. The nonaddictive corticosteroid is injected into the site of the pain where a patented slow-release formula provides patients with pain reduction that is not only superior to that of traditional, once-a-month steroid shots but also has fewer side effects and lasts three to four months.

Recent share price: $22.*

*Prices as of August 9, 2018.

• **Impinj (PI).** Radio-frequency identification (RFID) uses microchips that transmit radio signals to automatically identify and track the objects they're attached to, ranging from clothing in stores and products in warehouses to hospital supplies, wandering pets and baggage at airports. The concept has been around for a few decades and always had enormous potential, but the cost of the chips was prohibitive. Impinj, which has more than 200 patents on its RFID technology, has been able to reduce the price to just pennies per microchip, and its microchips don't need batteries because they power themselves from the base scanner's wireless signal. The company controls 60% of the RFID-chip market and expects to ship 7.1 billion chips this year to clients ranging from Delta Airlines to the University of Tennessee Medical Center and United Technologies.

Recent share price: $19.50.

• **Mercury Systems (MRCY).** It's fairly certain that US defense spending will rise in the coming years—but how the money will be spent will change dramatically. The military is becoming less reliant on large-scale deployment of troops and focusing instead on electronic warfare. Mercury Systems, whose customers include the 25 top US defense contractors, is a leading supplier of proprietary circuit boards and electric subsystems that are critical to the defensive Patriot missile system, military drones and the navy's antiship missiles. The company, with more than $490 million in annual revenue for the fiscal year ending June 30, 2018, controls about 15% of the defense electronics manufacturing market and has substantial opportunities for revenue growth.

Recent share price: $49.

• **Teladoc (TDOC).** Health-care providers treating patients remotely over mobile devices and the Internet have the potential to become a $30 billion market. Patients get to "see" a doctor within minutes and can have drugs prescribed. And health-care costs for insurers and consumers are substantially lower. Teladoc, the nation's leading provider of remote medicine by telephone and video conference, expects to connect 1.5 million doctor/patient visits this year, mostly for ailments such as colds, flu, earaches and skin rashes as well as behavioral therapy and smoking cessation. While Teladoc's technology isn't proprietary, the 15-year-old company controls 75% of the market including business from corporate clients such as Bank of America and PepsiCo. It draws on a network of more than 3,000 board-certified physicians and other health professionals.

Recent share price: $69.

• **The Trade Desk (TTD).** Many of the ads that you see on your screen when you visit websites are the result of auctions among advertisers taking place in fractions of a second. This is known as programmatic advertising, a field that's expected to grow by about 30% annually over the next four years. It's a more cost-effective way for advertisers to target the right ad for a particular consumer, and it's a radical departure from traditional ad buying—a field that is struggling because of the shift by marketers to online ads. The Trade Desk designs the software program that advertisers use to bid online for ad space. The software allows them to use preset criteria tailored to their budgets and strategies and to automate the entire process. The Trade Desk is likely to generate an industry-leading $320 million in revenue this year.

Recent share price: $93.

Spotting Takeover Targets

Many companies are likely this year to become takeover targets of corporations that benefit from the new federal tax cuts. The companies being acquired will provide new avenues for growth to the corporations acquiring them...and could reward investors with a stock price surge.

To find likely takeover candidates to invest in, look for the same traits that acquiring companies do—a number-one or number-two ranking in a niche type of business...a solid balance sheet...and a stock that appears undervalued due to short-term problems or investor misperceptions. Make sure that the target still can do well on its own in case a takeover does not occur.

Bruce W. Kaser, CFA, associate editor of *The Turnaround Letter*, whose model portfolio has produced annualized returns of 11% over the past 20 years, vs. 7.5% for the S&P 500. TurnaroundLetter.com

How to Invest in Volatile Bitcoins

Brian Kelly, founder of BKCM, a hedge fund firm specializing in currency investing, New York City. He is author of *The Bitcoin Big Bang: How Alternative Currencies Are About to Change the World.* BKCM.co

Of all the widely available investments in the world, the one that has garnered the most controversy lately is the virtual currency called bitcoin, which exists online only...isn't controlled or issued by any bank, brokerage or government...and has become a tremendously volatile form of payment.

There have been sharp declines and rallies in this currency. The price of each bitcoin went from $2,500 in July 2017 to more than $19,000 in December 2017, up from just $1 in 2011.

Along the way, however, it has had drops of more than 80%. As of August 2018, it fell to around $6,470. It's right only for investors comfortable with big risks...and only in amounts you are willing to lose, perhaps entirely.

Steps to take if you want to delve into bitcoin investing...

- **Buy during pullbacks.** They have happened every year since 2010.
- **Buy bitcoins directly.** There's only one SEC-approved fund that invests in bitcoins, Bitcoin Investment Trust (GBTC), but it has traded at more than double the value of its underlying assets recently.

Instead, be sure to use a reputable dealer such as Coinbase.com, the leading online US platform for buying, selling and storing digital currency. You establish an account and fund it with cash or use a credit or debit card. You can buy a portion of one bitcoin divided out to the eighth decimal place.

Coinbase, which typically charges 1.5% of your transaction amount when you buy or sell, is regulated by state and federal laws on money transmissions. It has insurance covering any losses due to a breach of Coinbase physical security or cybersecurity or employee theft, but not losses due to your own negligence.

Beware: Discount Brokers Pushing Higher-Cost Products

At Fidelity, Charles Schwab and TD Ameritrade, the brokers are encouraged to put customers into investments that make the companies more money—and the brokers get paid more when they succeed.

Example: Fidelity representatives receive 0.04% of the assets if their clients invest in most types of mutual and exchange-traded funds. But they receive 0.10%—more than twice as much—if they get customers to invest in higher-cost managed accounts and annuities and make referrals to independent financial advisers.

The three firms say that they remain focused on finding appropriate investments for clients. The fourth major discount firm, Vanguard, does not use sales incentives.

Interviews by *The Wall Street Journal* with dozens of former employees of Fidelity, Charles Schwab and TD Ameritrade.

For a Better Financial Adviser...

Beware of financial advisers taking advantage of volatility to market themselves. They may use e-mail, LinkedIn or other services to reach users with limited investment experience—those who have not dealt with big daily market swings in the past. Be careful about replying to these advisers. They are not allowed to make unsubstantiated claims. Advisers appealing to fear should be avoided—look for ones calling on positive emotions, such as enjoying retirement and having long-term financial security.

Advisers registered with state regulators or the SEC must operate in good faith and keep clients' needs foremost. When considering an adviser, ask whether he/she is a fiduciary. If the answer is yes, you can confirm this and check any disciplinary actions through the National Association of Personal Financial Advisors (NAPFA.org) and the Certified Financial Planner Board of Standards (CFP.net).

Roundup of experts on financial advisers, reported at MarketWatch.com.

GOOD TO KNOW...

Fees from Financial Advisers Are Falling

Take advantage of falling fees from financial advisers. A recent study found that 79% of fee-only advisory firms expect their fees to drop over the next five years. *Why:* Increased competition from "robo" advisers, online services that use software to generate ETF portfolios for a typical annual fee of 0.25% of invested assets.

What to do: For a human financial adviser, negotiate an annual fee of no more than 0.7% for personalized investment advice...up to 1% for comprehensive financial advice including more complex matters such as real estate transactions and insurance.

Pam Krueger, CEO, Wealthramp.com, which matches investors with financial advisers.

Investment Scam

Con artists are posing as regulators who pitch investments.

How the scam works: You get an official-looking letter by mail or e-mail from someone purporting to be a Financial Industry Regulatory Authority (Finra) official. The letter asks you to send to money to Finra for extremely risky "penny stock" investments. But the fraudsters just pocket your money. Remember that Finra personnel never offer or recommend investments.

Self-defense: If you are unsure about a solicitation, call Finra toll-free at 844-574-3577.

Gerri Walsh, JD, senior vice president for investor education at Finra, Washington, DC. Finra.org

Free Way to Learn About Investing in Municipal Bonds

The Municipal Securities Rulemaking Board, a Washington, DC–regulatory group, has launched an online course, complete with both slides and lectures on its website. The lessons cover the basics of municipal bonds, including how the bonds back local or state projects and offer numerous tax breaks. The course takes about 45 minutes to complete and is especially helpful for first-time fixed-income investors.

For more information: Go to MSRB.org/EducationCenter.

Barron's.

11

Consumer Guide

Get a Top Exec to Solve Your Customer Service Problem

Trying to get help from a customer service representative often is fruitless. But an executive of a company can cut through red tape and, in some cases, "bend the rules." *Here's how to get hold of the executive...*

1. Locate the names and e-mail addresses of company executives whose roles likely involve customer satisfaction. This might include customer service managers...directors or VPs of customer service (or customer support)...and even the president or CEO of the company. You might be able to find the names of these execs on the company's website but generally not their e-mail addresses. If that's the case, try entering the company name and "executives" or "executive team" into a search engine...check whether you can contact the exec through LinkedIn...and/or check whether the exec's e-mail address is listed on Elliott.org/company-contacts, which contains corporate contact information.

2. If you can't find an exec's e-mail address, try to figure it out. At many companies, everyone's e-mail address follows the same format, so if you find any employee's address, try that format with the name of the exec you want to reach. *If you can't find anyone's address, try the two most common formats:* John.Smith@CompanyName.com...JSmith@CompanyName.com. If an address is not correct, your e-mail likely will just be bounced back to you.

3. Write a brief, polite and unemotional e-mail message to the executive. In just a few sentences, explain what went wrong with the

Note: Prices, rates and offers throughout this chapter and book are subject to change.

Christopher Elliott, a consumer advocate who writes the "On Travel" column for *USA Today* and "The Navigator" column for *The Washington Post.* He is author of *How to Be the World's Smartest Traveler (and Save Time, Money and Hassle).* Elliott.org

product or service and what you suggest as a reasonable step that would set things right, such as replacing a defective item. Mention that you tried the normal customer service channels but that they "let me down."

If you identify multiple execs who might be worth contacting, start with the lowest-level one and work your way up until you find someone who is willing to help. Or if you're in a rush, try the "carpet bomb" approach—send your e-mail to every executive you have located all at once. There is a downside to this tactic, though—if an exec who was inclined to help realizes that you e-mailed others, he/she might assume that someone else will help you.

When Extended Warranties Make Sense

Roundup of experts, including GreenPal CEO Bryan Clayton and auto-sales-and-leasing consultant Matt Tuers, quoted at WiseBread.com.

For many products, extended warranties are not worth their price. But in certain situations they do make sense. *Here are some examples...*

- **Lawn and garden equipment** gets heavy use and often runs on fuel that can degrade parts. Fixing the equipment a few times when you do not have a warranty may cost almost as much as buying something new.
- **Cars** are increasingly complicated and costly to repair even though they are more reliable than they used to be. If you buy a new car and plan to get rid of it by the end of the warranty period, an extended warranty is not important. But if you plan to keep it longer—or buy a used car—consider getting the warranty.
- **Home-improvement projects,** such as new siding, are intended to last many years, so an extended warranty can be worthwhile.
- **Computers** are generally reliable but can be very costly to repair without warranty coverage.

Helpful: Check your credit cards—some issuers offer deals on extended warranties.

Tricky Warranty Protection

Edgar Dworsky, former Massachusetts assistant attorney general. He is founder of the consumer-protection websites ConsumerWorld.org and MousePrint.org.

You might have warranty protection even after a product's manufacturer's warranty expires. An obscure consumer protection called the "implied warranty of merchantability" gives consumers the right to demand a refund, replacement or repair when an item fails to work properly for a "reasonable" period. Another consumer protection called the "implied warranty of fitness for a particular purpose" protects consumers who are told a product will serve a purpose, but it does not.

These warranty protections are written into the laws of every state and Washington, DC—but in many states, there's a loophole that restricts their use. Merchants and manufacturers can "disclaim" implied warranties, opting to not have them apply to their products. This generally is done by "conspicuously" disclosing in writing that the item is being sold "as is" or "with all faults" or by noting in the manufacturer or retailer warranty that "all other warranty coverage is excluded." Big corporations often take advantage of this loophole, but smaller companies might not.

Some states, such as Maine, Maryland and Massachusetts, generally do not let sellers or manufacturers disclaim implied warranties, so if you bought the item there, the odds are very good that you have implied warranty protection. In other states, review seller and manufacturer websites as well as product warranties, packaging and sales literature, if possible, to see if the implied warranty was disclaimed. Or contact your state's attorney general's office (NAAG.org) or consumer-protection department (USA.gov/state-consumer) for details about your state's implied warranty laws.

If you believe that implied warranty protections might apply to your purchase, contact or visit the seller's customer service department and explain that you want to return the item

GOOD NEWS...

Get Paid for Your Opinion

Focus groups will pay for your opinion. You may be paid $100 or more for just a few hours of your time. Volunteers sit at a conference table with a professional moderator who invites participants to give their opinions on new products, marketing initiatives or other research that the company is doing. There is a video camera or two-way mirror through which company officials can watch participants' reactions.

To find focus groups in your area: Look for marketing companies through FocusGroups.org, PaidFocusGroup.net and FocusGroup.com. Fill out a profile, then browse through upcoming panels to see whether you are a good fit for any research, and check back regularly to stay informed about new opportunities.

Clark.com

for a refund, replacement or repair under the state's implied warranty laws.

If you get no satisfaction, file a complaint against the seller with your state's attorney general's office or consumer-protection department. If your case is strong, a mediator from this government agency might contact the retailer on your behalf, which often leads to a resolution.

Forget What You Know About Mattress-Buying: How to Shop Now

Nick Robinson, founder and editor of SleepLikeTheDead.com, which has been offering unbiased mattress reviews and research for 10 years.

For decades consumers have lost sleep over the frustrating intricacies of mattress selection. But there's been a revolution in the once-sleepy mattress industry. New brands have been pouring into the market...foam and memory foam mattresses have been gaining ground on the venerable innerspring...and consumers now can easily buy high-quality mattresses online and in big-box stores such as warehouse clubs, not just in mattress and department stores.

These new options offer the potential for big savings and a more comfortable night's sleep—but you still need to understand the choices and distinguish fact from hype.

Here's what you really need to know now to get a good deal on a mattress you'll love...

- **The "tried-and-true" test is often unreliable.** The standard advice for mattress shoppers has long been to lie on a mattress in a store for at least 15 minutes to determine whether it feels comfortable. But I've studied thousands of consumer mattress reviews and complaints, and when you dig into this data, you discover that people are nearly as likely to be happy with mattresses bought online—mattresses they never tested—as they are with those bought in stores. That tells us that 15 minutes of lying fully clothed on a brand-new mattress in a showroom is not an effective way to judge whether it will be a comfortable place to spend eight hours every night.

Better ways to increase the odds that you will end up with a comfortable mattress...

- **Buy a medium or medium-firm mattress.** Mattresses are sold in "supportiveness" levels ranging from soft to extra firm—but it turns out that almost everyone is happiest with a medium or medium-firm model. And despite the conventional wisdom, a firm mattress usually is not best for reducing back pain.

Rule of thumb: Back sleepers, stomach sleepers and people who weigh more than 230 pounds usually prefer medium-firm...while side sleepers and people who weigh less than 120 pounds usually prefer medium, though this can vary. (You might reasonably opt for firm if you intend to put a "mattress topper" on your mattress—see below.)

- **Buy from a seller that has a liberal return policy.** The truth is, no matter how much you pay for a mattress and no matter which brand and type you select, there is a chance that you won't like sleeping on it. The best solution is to buy from a company that will give you a hassle-free full refund if necessary. The best return policies these days are from direct-to-consumer online foam and hybrid foam/memory foam mattress sellers such as Casper (Casper.com, now also sold at Target)... Leesa (Leesa.com)...Purple (OnPurple.com)... and Tuft & Needle (TuftAndNeedle.com). Each offers 100-day, no-hassle, no-cost returns in the continental US. Usually you just contact the company, which will send a courier to pick up the mattress and donate it to a charity or recycle it if no charity is available.

Warehouse clubs generally have liberal return policies. However, a buyer usually must transport the mattress back to the store.

If you shop elsewhere, confirm that you can return your mattress at low or no cost if necessary after *at least* a month or two. Get this return policy in writing.

• **The most popular type of mattress is the least likely to satisfy.** The classic innerspring mattress is far from the only option these days. New types of foam mattresses, in particular, have been gaining ground. But most people still end up buying an old-fashioned innerspring mattress—it's what they've always slept on, so they assume it's the safest choice. In fact, it's the riskiest.

My research has found that only 64% of innerspring mattress buyers are satisfied with their mattresses—compared with 77% to 80% of buyers of other types of mattresses. One reason—innerspring mattresses are about twice as likely as other types to develop permanent sags, dips or body impressions within three years of use, which is the leading cause of dissatisfaction with mattresses.

Also, some people who opt for innerspring fear that a foam mattress will "sleep hot" (make them feel too warm). But although about 10% of memory foam mattress users complain that their mattresses are uncomfortably hot—because memory foam conforms closely around the sleeper's body—foam mattresses that are mostly or entirely a type of regular foam rather than memory foam actually are even less likely than innerspring mattresses to generate heat complaints.

This doesn't mean that every foam mattress is a good mattress. Foam and memory foam mattresses often fall short on "edge support"—sitting or sleeping near their perimeters can be a problem. And thin foam mattresses can flatten out under sleepers who weigh a lot. As with any type of product, quality varies from brand to brand and model to model.

But what if you've been happy with an innerspring mattress and really want to stick with that type? In that case, buy one—but perhaps not one with a "pillow top," a thick extra layer of cushy padding on top. The pillow top often is the part of an innerspring mattress that develops a problematic dip or body impression. If you want the soft pillow-top feel, consider instead adding a "mattress topper" to a nonpillow-top mattress. Mattress toppers serve the same function as pillow tops but can be removed and replaced if they degrade. This strategy is likely to be a money saver, too—nonpillow-top mattresses tend to be at least 25% less expensive than comparable pillow tops, and highly rated mattress toppers are available online for just $30 to $100.

• **The best-known brands often are not the best.** Mattress maker King Koil and the so-called "S" brands—Sealy, Serta, Simmons and Stearns & Foster—are among the best-known mattress brands, mainly because of their long histories and wide availability in stores. But these well-known brands tend to have some of the lowest customer satisfaction scores in the mattress industry—only 62% to 65% of buyers of these brands are satisfied with their mattresses.

The highest consumer satisfaction scores, ranging from 78% to 80% satisfied buyers, are earned by the new breed of Internet-sold foam and hybrid foam/memory foam mattress makers mentioned earlier—notably Casper... Purple...Tuft & Needle...and Leesa. Among innerspring mattress brands, relatively unknown web-sold Saatva registers the highest satisfaction score—81%—partly because of very strong customer service.

Other innerspring mattress brands that score relatively well in satisfaction include the upscale but little-known Hästens (77% satisfaction) and Aireloom/Kluft (75%)...and economical Ikea (70%).

In two other mattress categories, the most famous brands score well for satisfaction—but not for value—and there are some great alternatives...

Tempur-Pedic, the biggest name in memory foam mattresses, has an 81% customer satisfaction score. But a company called Zinus (Zinus.com) makes memory foam mattresses that have a 78% satisfaction score and cost just $250 to $300 versus $2,000 or more for most Tempur-Pedic mattresses. Zinus mattresses are sold on Amazon.com under the brand names "Sleep Master" and "Best Price"...and on Walmart.com under the brand name "Spa Sensations."

Sleep Number is the biggest name in adjustable-firmness mattresses and has a 77% owner-satisfaction score—but lesser known adjustable brands Boyd (BoydSpecialtySleep.com), Innomax (Innomax.com, sold at Sam's Club as "Dual Digital" mattresses) and Personal Comfort (PersonalComfortBed.com) all earn satisfaction scores of 78% to 82% and typically cost at least 15% less than comparable Sleep Number mattresses.

Better Appliance Shopping

Consider purchasing a refurbished major appliance if it is one or two years old, includes a full warranty and comes at significant savings compared with a new one. But before buying, look for low prices on new appliances through a site such as PriceGrabber. Then compare total costs, including delivery and installation charges. Buy refurbished appliances only at stores you know and trust.

WiseBread.com

GOOD TO KNOW...

Items Never to Buy at the Grocery Store

Greeting cards—grocery stores often overcharge, so go to your local dollar store and stock up on a few.

Batteries—warehouse stores such as Costco and Sam's Club offer great deals on bulk packages of batteries.

Diapers—with Amazon's Subscribe & Save, you can schedule regular deliveries and get a 20% discount off diapers.

Pet food—if you prefer shopping in a store, go to your local PetSmart or Petco for competitive prices and reward programs that can result in free food. If you enjoy shopping online, use the subscription service Chewy.com.

Coffee—Costco and Sam's Club stores, as well as office-supply stores such as Staples, tend to have great deals on coffee.

MoneyTalksNews.com

To Save at the Grocery Store...

Five grocery habits that make you spend too much.

Assuming coupons are money savers: Coupons often encourage consumers to buy more than they need. In most cases, generic or store-brand products will offer a better value.

Staying loyal to brands: If you always buy the same brand, you could be missing out on more competitive brands, significant product improvements and promotional deals.

Ignoring expiration dates: Always check expiration dates to make sure that the food you are buying is fresh.

Falling for clever packaging: Don't pay more for something only because the presentation is better. Examine ingredients, nutritional value and unit price.

Jumping on trends: Save money by sticking to the basics and not falling for temporary food trends that can cost you a lot more than expected.

Wisebread.com

The Truth About Organic Foods

Sharon Palmer, RDN, a Los Angeles-based registered dietitian nutritionist and author of *The Plant-Powered Diet* and *Plant-Powered for Life*. Palmer also is editor of the newsletter *Environmental Nutrition* and nutrition editor for *Today's Dietitian*. SharonPalmer.com

Organic food is on a roll. Sales have doubled in the last decade, and organic foods are now available in three out of four conventional supermarkets.

Rather than being relegated to the "organic produce bin," there is now a wide assortment of organic foods and beverages. You can not only toss organic apples in your cart but also add a few organic gummy bears from the candy aisle, for example, and then pop over to the liquor store for organic vodka!

We are willing to pay more for organics, mostly because we think they are healthier for us. But are they really? What does "organic" on a food label really mean, anyway?

Let's explore a few common myths—and truths.

6 ORGANIC FOOD MYTHS

For such a popular (and pricey) part of our everyday food-buying habits, organic foods are surprisingly misunderstood...

1. *Belief:* Organic foods are more nutritious. *Not exactly.* The science is mixed. In 2012, a meta-analysis of 17 studies done by Stanford University found very little difference in vitamin content between organic and conventional produce. However, other studies have found that organic dairy and meat products contain more heart-healthy omega-3 fats, and organic fruits and vegetables are richer in antioxidant compounds than conventional produce.

The bottom line? While there may be some nutritional merits, the main reason to buy organic is not to get more nutritious fare but to support systems of cultivation that are good for the environment (check *What "Organic" Really Means* on the next page).

2. *Belief:* Organic foods are less likely to cause food poisoning. *Sorry, not true either.* An organic chicken or hamburger meat that you buy from a farmer's market is no less likely to cause food-borne illness than conventional products.

3. *Belief:* Organic foods improve health. *Maybe.* Organic produce is significantly lower in pesticide residues than conventional. Both adults and children who eat more organic foods have lower levels of pesticides in their bodies compared with those who eat little or no organic foods. But whether that translates to healthier lives isn't known.

4. *Belief:* Organic foods are always local and sustainable. *Sometimes, but not always.* The standards do promote "sustainable practices," but do not require foods to be produced locally. The US imported $1.65 billion worth of organics in 2016, both fresh and processed, mostly from Turkey, Mexico, Italy, Peru and Ecuador. Transporting foods long distances means greater use of fossil fuels, which is not a sustainable practice.

5. *Belief:* Organic foods are pesticide-free. *Not necessarily.* It's true that farming practices that promote biodiversity, natural borders, soil health and natural pest predators lessen pest problems, so there's less need for pesticides.

But while most synthetic pesticides are not allowed in organic produce, there are a few exceptions—25 are allowed (compared with about 900 in conventional produce). In addition, "natural" pesticides are allowed, such as soaps or lime sulfur.

6. *Belief:* All organic producers are the same. *Not by a long shot.* Some farms practice techniques that go well beyond the standards—avoiding even "allowed" pesticides and selling locally—while other farms barely squeak under the minimum compliance to standards.

So you may want to seek out local organic producers who are more in tune with the spirit of organic, such as caring for the environment and supplying a local food source. The moral of the story? If buying organic matters to you, do some homework on organic producers before you buy.

TAKE NOTE...

Best Foods to Buy Organic... and What to Skip

According to data analyzed by the nonprofit Environmental Working Group (EWG), these are some of the foods that should be at the top of your organic shopping list...

- **Leafy greens.** Crops such as these, which grow close to the soil, are prone to pests. Spinach samples had twice as much pesticide residue as any other crop.
- **Strawberries,** which also grow close to the soil, had up to 20 different pesticides.
- **Peaches and nectarines** tested positive for at least one pesticide in nearly all samples.
- **Cherries and apples** tested positive for pesticide residues in nearly all of the samples tested.
- **Dairy foods, eggs and meat.** Organically raised beef cattle, dairy cows and chickens are not treated with synthetic growth hormones or antibiotics. Plus, organic dairy, meat and eggs have higher levels of omega-3s, and organic eggs have more vitamins A and E.

If your food budget is limited, don't waste your organic dollars here...

- **Candy and soda.** Organic sugary foods are just as bad for your health as conventional sugary foods.
- **Baked treats, such as cookies, cakes and pies.** A few organic ingredients in a decadent treat won't make it any healthier.
- **Nuts, melons and avocados.** The outer shells of these foods protect them from pests, so few pesticides are needed. They tend to have low residue levels.
- **Carrots and sweet potatoes.** These root vegetables, which grow in the soil rather than above it, can absorb some pesticides through the soil but are usually peeled before eating.
- **Citrus.** Citrus fruit, especially grapefruit, registered among the fruits with the lowest levels of pesticide residues, according to EWG. Thank the thick rind!

Sharon Palmer, RDN, a Los Angeles-based registered dietitian nutritionist and author of *The Plant-Powered Diet* and *Plant-Powered for Life.* SharonPalmer.com

WHAT "ORGANIC" REALLY MEANS

The main reason to choose organic is to support a kind of food cultivation that preserves the soil and promotes a cleaner environment. Nutrition and safety aren't the primary goals. Organic cultivation isn't so much about the *end product* as it is about the *process.*

The USDA's National Organic Program (or NOP) maintains standards for organically produced agricultural products. The purpose is to support a system of farming that encourages recycling of resources within a farm, protects the environment, enhances soil and water quality and conserves ecosystems and wildlife. Most synthetic fertilizers, sewage sludge, irradiation and genetic engineering can't be used.

Only products that have been through a rigorous certification process to show that they meet these requirements may carry the USDA organic seal. Foods with the seal may be labeled "100% organic" (everything in it is organic)..."organic" (at least 95% of the ingredients are organic)...or "made with organic ingredients" (at least 70% of the ingredients are organic). This includes both whole foods (for example, an apple) and packaged foods (such as applesauce).

A Chef's Strategy for Buying Seafood at the Supermarket

Aliza Green, a Philadelphia-based chef and author of more than a dozen books about food including *The Fishmonger's Apprentice* and *Field Guide to Seafood. The Philadelphia Inquirer* inducted Green into its Culinary Hall of Fame in 1988. She currently leads culinary tours and serves as chef manager of Baba Olga's Kitchen in Philadelphia. AlizaGreen.com

The key to preparing delicious seafood occurs *before* you set foot in your kitchen—you must buy a great piece of fish. If the seafood you start with is not high quality and fresh, the meal you make will fall flat.

Unfortunately, many areas do not have top-notch seafood stores. That means most Americans must buy their seafood at supermarkets.

This is not necessarily a bad option—some supermarkets have excellent seafood departments—but quality can vary *dramatically*.

How to decide where to buy seafood and how to pick the best seafood...

WAYS TO EVALUATE A MARKET OR SEAFOOD DEPARTMENT

Before buying from a supermarket seafood department or stand-alone fish market...

• **Take a whiff as you approach the counter.** You should smell ocean brine or nothing at all. If instead you get a low-tide–like fishy odor, walk away—the store does not pay sufficient attention to freshness or cleanliness.

• **Examine whole fish on display—even if you intend to buy a fillet.** The fishes' eyes should be bright and clear, not cloudy...scales should be shiny and metallic-looking, not dull. If you can touch the fish, gently press its flesh—if it is fresh, the depression you create will quickly disappear. It speaks poorly of the store if there are past-their-prime whole fish on display.

• **Look for liquid in packaged fish fillets.** Tip a few packaged fish fillets to one side. If you see liquid sloshing around, the fillet has been sitting around too long—those are juices that have escaped the fish as it aged and dried out. You could simply select a different fillet, but the smarter move is to not buy seafood there at all—liquid in fillet packages is a red flag that a store is not sufficiently focused on freshness.

• **Eye the *ice* in fish display cases.** This ice should look clear. If it is cloudy or yellowed, it likely is not changed very often—another sign of inattention.

• **At a supermarket, ask to speak to the fish-department manager.** I always consider it a warning sign if this manager is summoned from the meat department—supermarkets that take seafood seriously tend to have specialists running their seafood sections. The main point of asking for the manager is to see who he/she is. To that end, you can ask about his background with seafood...and you might also ask, "What's the freshest fish you have today?"

• **Notice fish-department traffic.** The more customers a seafood department or seafood store has, the faster it will turn over its inventory and the fresher its seafood is likely to be. Be wary if you've been to a store several times and rarely see anyone buying fish.

• **Seek out markets that cater to immigrant groups from coastal, seafood-loving nations.** I have found that if there's a market in the area that has a large clientele of people from Portugal, Korea, Vietnam or Italy, for example, it likely is a great place to buy excellent seafood for reasonable prices. Members of these communities tend to be savvy seafood shoppers. And because these groups tend to eat lots of seafood, inventory turnover often is high.

WAYS TO SELECT SEAFOOD

Even at a well-run seafood store or supermarket seafood department, some pieces of fish inevitably will be fresher and better than others...

• **Look for a slight blue tint in white-flesh fish.** A white, flaky fish such as cod, flounder or haddock should be translucent or such a brilliant white that it seems to have a slight bluish tint. If there's a slight yellowish tint instead, the fish has begun to oxidize and won't taste very good.

• **Seek a distant sell-by date.** Prepackaged fish should include a sell-by date on the label. But it's not sufficient that a packaged piece of fish hasn't passed its sell-by date—you want to find fish that is at least two days away from this date.

Warning: If seafood has a far-off sell-by date but seems past its prime, don't buy it—disreputable stores occasionally repackage fish as it nears its original sell-by date.

• **Don't be afraid of the word "frozen."** When it comes to seafood, fresh is best only if you live very near where that fish was caught. Otherwise you may be better off buying frozen, particularly when the frozen fish is vacuum-sealed and the packaging says it was "flash frozen"—that is, frozen almost immediately after coming out of the water.

Warning: When you choose frozen fish, avoid packages that have frost on the fish inside the packaging...and/or where sections of the frozen fish's flesh appear discolored. These are signs that frozen fish has been sitting around too long.

• **Lean toward seafood that is sold in thick steaks.** The higher a piece of seafood's ratio of volume to surface area, the better it likely will hold up over time, whether fresh or frozen. All else being equal, that means the best bet for freshness often is large fish that's cut into thick steaks, which might include tuna, swordfish, salmon or Chilean sea bass. (Be aware that swordfish—and to a lesser extent tuna and Chilean sea bass—sometimes have high mercury levels, so they should not be eaten very frequently, especially by children and pregnant women.)

• **Avoid seafood imported from Southeast Asia.** Fishing industry standards and quality controls are not as reliable in Southeast Asia as they are in North, South and Central America. Among other issues, fish imported from Southeast Asia—including from large exporters such as Vietnam, Thailand, Indonesia and China—might not have been frozen promptly and properly, increasing the odds of flavor and safety problems.

Warning: Virtually all the tilapia sold in the US is imported from Southeast Asia. Much of the shrimp sold in the US comes from Southeast Asia, too, but it is possible to find shrimp from Mexico, Venezuela or the US Gulf Coast instead.

• **Don't automatically skip the fish that's on sale.** Buying bargain fish might sound like a bad idea—because fish sometimes is marked down because it is about to go bad. But sometimes the fish that's on sale is the *freshest* fish in the store because there have been big recent catches of a certain type of fish and distributors must temporarily slash prices to move this inventory.

• **Avoid exotic or obscure fish unless you have great trust in the store.** Some people find it fun to try new foods—but most don't, which means unusual types of fish tend to sit around in stores longer than well-known types of fish. It's fine to buy unusual fish if a store you trust assures you that it's fresh, it's a fish that is popular in the community that frequents the store (such as whiting in an Italian market or monkfish in an Asian market) and/or you have faith in your fish-selection skills.

• **Buy shellfish that grew in northern waters, especially if you're planning to enjoy it raw.** These are less likely than warm-water shellfish to harbor dangerous parasites, and they often have more flavor, too. *Examples:* Oysters and mussels from Atlantic Canada or New England are excellent options.

AFTER YOU BUY YOUR FISH...

It might not be the store's fault when a piece of seafood tastes less than fresh. *How you transport and store seafood after you buy it matters, too...*

• **Ask for ice for the trip home.** Seafood can significantly degrade in the time it takes to get it home from the store, especially on hot days. Most seafood stores and departments will provide a bag of ice upon request.

• **Store seafood on ice in your fridge.** Unless you're cooking seafood as soon as you get home, fill a container with ice and put the seafood on this bowl in your fridge. (Wrap the seafood in plastic wrap first if it is not already sealed well.) This ice provides additional cooling—I find that seafood is best stored at around 28°F, which is colder than a fridge on its own.

• **Defrost frozen seafood in the fridge.** This takes longer than defrosting it at room temperature, but it's safer—there's increased risk for contamination when you defrost seafood at room temperature. Defrosting in the fridge leads to tastier seafood—too much liquid often drips out when seafood is defrosted at room temperature, taking a lot of the flavor with it.

Helpful: The ideal time to cook a piece of seafood that has been frozen is when it is no longer rigid but you can still feel tiny ice crystals in its flesh. If you wait until these ice crystals melt, some flavor will be lost even if you do defrost in the fridge.

• **Don't let seafood languish, even frozen.** Even frozen, most fish should be kept tightly wrapped and positioned in the back of the freezer where it's coldest and used within one month for the best flavor.

What the "Natural" Label on Beef Really Means

The beef label "natural" is misleading. The USDA label simply means that meat is minimally processed and contains no artificial ingredients or added color. But many consumers think that it means much more—for instance, that the meat was raised without antibiotics or growth hormones.

This directly affects consumer costs: Beef consumers who did not know the official meaning of "natural" were willing to pay $1.26/pound more for meat with the label—and $2.43/pound more for meat also labeled as having no growth hormones. But consumers who were made aware of the FDA label's definition were not willing to pay more for beef labeled "natural" unless it had other positive labels, such as "no growth hormones." In these cases, consumers were willing to pay $3.07 per pound more.

Karen Lewis DeLong, PhD, assistant professor, department of agricultural and resource economics, University of Tennessee, Knoxville, and corresponding author of a study published in *Applied Economic Perspectives and Policy.*

Egg Labels That Matter

Organic means that eggs were laid by uncaged hens that have access to outdoors and are fed grains grown without synthetic pesticides. *Free Range* and *American Humane Certified* mean that the birds were not caged—the two labels mean that the chickens had access to outdoors.

Egg labels that do not matter also are sometimes used on eggs and cartons: "No hormones" is irrelevant because all egg-producing chickens must, by law, be raised without hormones. "Farm fresh" means eggs come from a farm—all of them do—and the eggs have not been frozen, which they should never be. "Natural" means nothing—all eggs are natural foods.

Consumer Reports.

The Toxin in Your Chocolate

Tod Cooperman, MD, president, ConsumerLab.com, an independent group based in White Plains, New York, that tests and reports on the quality of health and nutrition products.

The cocoa and chocolate you eat may be contaminated with the toxic heavy metal cadmium. Many people are consuming cocoa products for better health because cocoa and dark chocolate are sources of *flavanols*—200 mg/day of flavanols have cardiovascular benefits...while 500 mg/day may help improve memory.

The problem with cocoa as a flavanol source is that nearly all types are contaminated with cadmium, a toxin that with chronic exposure can damage kidneys. The World Health Organization says that cadmium levels in foods such as cocoa should not exceed 0.3 micrograms (mcg) per gram. Almost all popular cocoa powders that ConsumerLab tested in 2017 exceed that limit.

Example: Bulletproof Chocolate Powder was found to contain 2.2 mcg per gram.

Cadmium occurs naturally in soil, especially in the sort of volcanic soil where cacao trees grow. This means that even organic cocoa contains it. There is cadmium in chocolate, too, although at lower levels than in cocoa powder because chocolate bars contain other ingredients. Still, some chocolate is high in cadmium.

Example: Trader Joe's Dark Chocolate Lover's Bar 85% Cacao had 12 times as much cadmium as another brand, Endangered Species Chocolate with 88% Cocoa. A bar of Trader Joe's contained 29 mcg of cadmium—seven times the daily limit in Canada for adults. (There is no US limit.)

If you like to drink cocoa, having a cup (using one tablespoon of cocoa powder) now and then is unlikely to expose you to too much cadmium. But be especially cautious about drinking cocoa if you have kidney disease.

Another option for getting a large amount of cocoa flavanols without contamination is the supplement CocoaVia, which is made from a concentrated cocoa extract.

How to Save on Generic Drugs

Charles B. Inlander, a consumer advocate and health-care consultant based in Fogelsville, Pennsylvania. He was founding president of the nonprofit People's Medical Society, a consumer advocacy organization credited with key improvements in the quality of US health care, and is author or coauthor of more than 20 consumer-health books.

If you're interested in saving some money on your health-care expenses—and who isn't?—using generic prescription drugs is a great approach. Studies show that generic medications are 80% to 85% cheaper than comparable brand-name drugs. And in most cases, the medical benefits are equal.

In recent years, however, the cost of many generic drugs, including some that have been on the market for decades, has increased dramatically. For example, the generic antibiotic *tetracycline* has recently jumped from approximately four cents per pill to over $4. Other drugs have risen at an even greater pace. There are several reasons for the increasing cost of generics. For example, some large generic drug manufacturers are merging, thus limiting competition…and safety regulations are tightening, forcing manufacturers to adopt better safeguards to ensure quality products. And some companies hike their prices simply to increase their bottom lines—remember the EpiPen controversy? Fortunately, there are ways to save on generic drugs. *What I recommend…*

- **Comparison shop.** Pharmacies can charge whatever they want for a generic drug. The problem is, most of us do not compare the prices of generics from one pharmacy to another. But you should! Prices on generic drugs can vary by up to 100% from pharmacy to pharmacy in a local area. And all you need to do is make a few phone calls to compare prices. Don't forget to check out pharmacies at big discount retailers such as Walmart. It has many generics for less than $4 per 30-day supply.

Insider tip: Even within the same chain pharmacies, such as Walgreens, Rite Aid or CVS, prices can vary.

Caution: If you use several different pharmacies, let each of the pharmacists know all the drugs you use, even the ones not filled at that store. They can then check for any interactions between drugs.

- **Look for discount coupons.** Many drug manufacturers distribute discount coupons for generic medications. This is their way of getting you to use their drug, but if it works for you, take advantage of the savings. The easiest way to get these coupons is by searching online for "discount coupons for (insert the name of the drug)." Savings can be 50% or more but are generally not usable if combined with any drug insurance you may have. You can also use discount coupon websites, such as GoodRx.com, RxPharmacyCoupons.com or BlinkHealth.com, for discounts ranging from 50% to 95%. These coupons can be used at most pharmacies throughout the country.

Insider tip: Using discount coupons while you're still paying off your drug insurance deductible is a great way to get more for your dollar!

- **Buy by mail.** Most prescription drug insurance plans offer mail-order delivery, which is almost always cheaper than other options and handled by a reputable company. I get three different generic drugs in 90-day supplies (90 tablets per order) by mail order and save 33% over what I'd pay at my local pharmacy. So if you take a drug regularly, ask your doctor to send the prescription to your mail-order pharmacy.

Caution: To ensure quality, use only mail-order pharmacy programs affiliated with major insurers...and avoid online pharmacies, including some Canadian sites. Many have been found to be disreputable, sending wrong pills, wrong dosages and wrong quantities.

MONEYSMARTS...

Free Prescription Drugs at Grocery Stores

Some grocery store chains offer specific medicines at no cost...

Bi-Lo, Harveys and Winn-Dixie: Some antibiotics, *lisinopril, metformin.*

Price Chopper and ShopRite: Certain diabetes medicines.

Meijer: Some antibiotics, some prenatal vitamins, metformin immediate release, *atorvastatin calcium.*

Publix: Some antibiotics, *amlodipine,* lisinopril, metformin, *montelukast.*

Reasor's Foods: Certain antibiotics, certain prenatal vitamins, certain children's vitamins.

You typically will need only a doctor's prescription and may have to sign up for the store's free-drug program.

MoneyTalksNews.com

Triclosan Still in Toothpaste

Triclosan still is allowed in toothpaste even though the Food and Drug Administration has banned the antibacterial compound from soaps. Experts warn that triclosan can potentially disrupt hormones in children and promote drug-resistant infections. One of the best-selling toothpastes in the US—Colgate Total—contains triclosan, which the FDA says is effective at reducing plaque and gingivitis. A review of 30 studies found that toothpastes with triclosan plus fluoride outperformed those containing fluoride alone by several measures, reducing plaque severity 41% more effectively over six to nine months. The FDA says that the risk-benefit ratio is favorable for continued use of triclosan in toothpaste.

Roundup of experts on toothpaste, reported in *The New York Times.*

Freebies You'll Actually Want...

Free eye exams and treatments for any disease that's diagnosed are available from EyeCareAmerica.org through a network of nearly 6,000 volunteer ophthalmologists if you qualify. *Free wellness classes* are available at select Lululemon Athletica stores. *Free book downloads* are available at Gutenberg.org and through Amazon.com, BarnesAndNoble.com and the iTunes store. *Free stock trades* are available from the mobile app Robinhood.

Kiplinger.com

6 Tricks Bartenders Use to Rip You Off

Jon Taffer, who provides bar-and-restaurant-consulting services and is executive producer and host of *Bar Rescue,* a reality TV series about revamping bars that are failing. Currently in its sixth season, the series runs on Spike TV on Sunday nights. He has started and owned dozens of bars, has been inducted into the Nightclub Hall of Fame and is author of *Raise the Bar.* Taffer also offers business-management training courses. JonTaffer.com

For many people, the upcoming holiday season also is the drinking season. But be careful not to get taken when you order drinks—dishonest bartenders, bar owners and restaurant owners might attempt to serve you less drink than you paid for. I believe this happens at perhaps 10% to 15% of bars, including restaurant bars.

Experienced drinkers tend to assume that they can spot a watered-down or over-iced drink, but sneaky bartenders and establishments have ways to disguise these tricks, and they have come up with various other tricks to cheat customers.

Here are six warning signs that you might be served a less-than-honest libation or targeted with some other bartender trick...

Warning sign: **Crushed ice or tiny ice cubes.** Putting an excessive amount of ice in a glass is one of the oldest tricks in the book—lots of ice leaves less room for liquor. But drinkers tend to notice and complain if they see that ice virtually fills a glass.

What many drinkers don't realize is that bars have a way to get excessive amounts of ice into a glass without appearing to give you a diluted drink—they use crushed ice or tiny ice cubes. These pack together so tightly that there can be a tremendous amount of ice in the glass and yet that ice reaches no higher than normal.

What to do: Before ordering your drink, glance around at other patrons' glasses to see what type of ice the bar is using. If you see crushed ice or tiny cubes, consider ordering a drink that is not on the rocks...or asking for your ice in a separate glass.

Of course, it's possible you could get an honest pour even at a bar that uses crushed ice. To know for sure, count off the seconds it takes for the bartender to pour liquor into patrons' glasses. An honest 1.5-ounce pour of liquor should take three to four seconds. If it seems quicker, ask, "Do you give a one-ounce pour here or a 1.5-ounce pour?"

If the answer is one ounce, you are getting less liquor than normal for your money. If nothing else, asking this question sends a strong message to the bartender that you're a savvy customer who doesn't want a weak drink.

Warning sign: **The bartender puts on a "long pour" show.** If the bartender holds liquor bottles high up in the air as he/she pours, creating a long stream of liquid in the air, he might be showing off his bartending skills... or he might be pulling a psychological trick on his customers. When people see this long stream of liquor, they tend to assume that they are getting lots of it. But bartenders sometimes do "long pours" that also are quick pours.

What to do: Silently count off the duration of the long pour. If it lasts less than three to four seconds, it's very possible that patrons are not getting a full 1.5 ounces despite the height of the bottle.

Warning sign: **Straws come from a spot below the bar that you cannot see.** In this case, there's a chance the bartender is trying to trick patrons' senses so that they don't notice watered-down drinks. The hidden straws might be soaking in a glass of vodka (or some other high-proof alcohol). That way, when patrons lift their glasses and/or touch their straws to their lips for the first time, they get a strong initial smell and taste of alcohol.

Some bartenders even press a finger tightly over the top of a straw that's standing in vodka and then carefully transfer the straw to a patron's glass with the vodka still inside so that the first sip taken through the straw is extremely alcoholic. First impressions are lasting impressions with drinks, as with people, so this can convince a drinker that a very weak drink actually is a strong one.

What to do: Be suspicious if bartenders retrieve straws from a spot that's out of sight... especially if you notice the bartender's finger pressed on top of straws as they go into glasses. Also, be wary if glasses are stored out of sight below the bar or disappear under the bar for a moment before drinks are served. Sometimes the rim of the glass, rather than the straw, is dipped in vodka.

Warning sign: **The bartender does not enter each transaction into the register...** or you see him ring up an amount lower than what you paid for a drink. You can probably figure out what's happening here—the bartender is pocketing money, stealing from his employer. What you might not realize is that this could mean you are being cheated, too.

Most bar and restaurant owners try to keep their bartenders honest by carefully comparing the amount of liquor that the bar goes through with the liquor sales that are rung up. Bartenders know this, so to get away with shorting the register, they often short drinks, too—a bartender who pockets the cash from every third liquor sale, for example, might put one-third less liquor in each drink.

GOOD TO KNOW...

3 Ways to Avoid Bar Germs

What's worse than getting taken by a less-than-honest bar? Taking ill after drinking at an unhygienic one. Many bars (and even restaurant bar areas) have far lower sanitary standards than restaurant kitchens, opening the door to illness. *To stay safe...*

• **Check the cutting board behind the bar.** These cutting boards typically are made of white plastic. If you see significant discoloration, do not order any drink that includes sliced fruit such as a lime or lemon wedge. The discoloration could be the result of a bacterial contamination.

• **Skip the cherry.** Bartenders tend to take maraschino cherries from a big jar that is kept behind the bar. Although new cherries likely are added to this jar regularly, the juice these cherries sit in might not have been changed in months or even years.

• **Watch how the bartender holds glasses.** If you see the bartender touch the rims or interiors of other customers' glasses, order a bottled beer, which does not require a glass... or walk to the other end of the bar and order from a different bartender.

Jon Taffer, host of *Bar Rescue* and author of *Raise the Bar.* JonTaffer.com

What to do: If you notice a bartender not ringing up sales or underringing sales, watch especially carefully for the drink-preparation tricks described earlier. Consider ordering bottled beer to avoid underpours. Or better yet, drink elsewhere.

Warning sign: **"Top-shelf" liquor bottles have worn-looking labels.** Some bar owners refill empty bottles of expensive liquor with cheaper substitutes. They know that many drinkers won't be able to tell the difference.

It's a bad sign if the labels on one or more top-shelf liquor bottles appear to be old, worn or peeling. That rarely happens during the normal life of a liquor bottle and could mean that these bottles have been refilled, perhaps multiple times.

What to do: Don't pay up for pricey top-shelf liquor if any of the top-shelf bottle labels look worn unless you know and trust the bar or restaurant. Be especially wary about ordering top-shelf vodka and rum—these are especially likely to be replaced with cheaper substitutes because vodka and rum often are combined with juices or other mixers that largely hide their quality...and, in the case of vodka, because few drinkers can tell expensive vodka from cheaper stuff.

Warning sign: **The bartender calls a cab for you.** In this era of smartphones and car services such as Uber and Lyft, unless you literally are too drunk to arrange for your own ride, there's no reason for a bartender to call a cab for you. He might not just be doing you a favor—he might be getting a kickback from the cabdriver who might end up overcharging you to recoup this cost.

What to do: Don't drive if you've had more than two drinks, but arrange your own ride unless you know and trust the bartender.

Save on Wedding Costs

Roundup of experts on wedding planning, reported at CreditCards.com.

If you have strong credit, open a cash-back rewards credit card and charge as much of the wedding costs as you can pay off quickly on the card to get a signing bonus plus points you can use for other wedding-related costs such as travel and hotels. *Other tips...*

• **Look for a venue where you can have both the ceremony and the reception**—that saves on rental cost and also reduces the hours you need a photographer or videographer.

• **Scale back on food**—more noodles and salads, less meat and seafood, and a simpler cake.

• **Get nonwedding, easily available flowers that look pretty** but may cost much less than specific types.

• **Do some things yourself**—possibly favors or a photo booth with selfie sticks.

• **Put $1,000 into a fund for last-minute expenses** so that you do not run up unexpected credit card bills.

• **Read all contracts carefully** so that you are not hit with extra charges for which you did not budget.

Top Picks from the 2018 Consumer Electronics Show

Jonathan Takiff, who has written about consumer electronics for the *Philadelphia Inquirer* and *Philadelphia Daily News* for more than 40 years. He currently is a contributing editor for *Tech50+*, which focuses on consumer electronics products for people age 50 and older. Tech50Plus.com

---

There was no shortage of smart-home devices, smart robots, smart cars, smart TVs and smart digital assistants at the 2018 annual Consumer Electronics Show in Las Vegas. There was even a smart toilet. But how much of the tech cornucopia would be smart to buy?

We asked veteran consumer electronics journalist Jonathan Takiff to sort through all the new tech at the show and pinpoint which products are more than just novelties and would be worth our readers' money...

HOME TECH

***Voice-controlled TV sound bar:* Polk Command Bar.** This two-piece TV speaker system (including a wirelessly connected subwoofer) has the Amazon voice-controlled digital assistant, Alexa, built right in. That means you not only can simply speak to adjust the volume of the show you're watching—you also can ask the sound bar to check your e-mail messages, play music or look up information, just as you would any other Alexa device. And the sound bar's clear, rich sound makes it easy to understand Alexa's responses. *Price*: $299. PolkAudio.com/products/command-sound-bar

***Bathroom digital assistant:* Kohler Verdera Voice Lighted Mirror with Amazon Alexa.** With this wall mirror, you could ask Alexa for weather or traffic updates...to review your e-mails...to play music while you shave or dry off after a shower...or to adjust the -mirror's LED lights, all without cluttering up your bathroom with a stand-alone Alexa device. And unlike most stand-alone devices, it offers stereo sound and is designed to withstand the high humidity of a bathroom. The mirror itself is stylish, 33 inches tall and available in 24-, 34- and 40-inch widths. *Prices:* $1,332, $1,598.70 and $1,732, respectively. US.Kohler.com

***Front door security system that requires virtually no installation:* Remo+ DoorCam.** There are numerous digital security systems available that let you see a video image of the person at the door of your home. DoorCam stands out because you don't have to drill any holes in the door or run any wires to use it—simply clip DoorCam over the top of the door and connect it via Wi-Fi. That's ideal for renters who are not allowed to install permanent systems...people who want security when they stay in vacation rentals...and those who don't want to fuss with installation. It features a wide-angle, motion-sensing, night-vision high-definition camera plus a two-way intercom. *Price:* $199. RemoPlus.co

***Wireless monitor for heating and air-conditioning filters:* Breezi AirPulse.** This small, wireless device attaches easily to your heating-ventilation-and-air-conditioning system's filter and then sends warnings to your Apple or Android device (or through an Alexa-enabled device) when it identifies an air pressure differential that suggests that the filter is clogged and needs to be replaced. Especially if your filter is in a hard-to-see location, this is a potential money saver, since a clogged air filter can make an HVAC system as much as 15% less energy efficient. AirPulse also warns of mold-promoting humidity and unhealthful airborne volatile organic compounds. It will reach the market late in 2018 with a price around $50. Breezi.io

PORTABLE TECH

***Versatile voice-translation device:* Pocketalk.** This pocket-size gadget can translate spoken words in 63 languages almost instantly. There are other pocket translators and apps available but none that handles such a wide range of spoken languages so seamlessly—with Pocketalk, you truly can have a conversation with someone who doesn't speak your language. *The only catch:* It requires a Wi-Fi or mobile data signal. *Price:* $199. Pocketalk.net

Camera that records video of things that already happened: **Roader Time Machine Camera.** Ever wish you'd filmed something that just occurred? This small digital camera, which is designed to be worn around the neck like a lanyard, can do just that. It is constantly buffering video—that is, temporarily saving it—so when you tap its button, Roader can upload digital video of the prior 10 seconds plus the following 10 seconds to your Bluetooth-connected Apple or Android phone. That way you have a record of the hit-and-run accident you just witnessed...or the funny thing your cat just did. *Price:* $199. Roader.com

HEALTH AND SLEEP TECH

Airbag for falls: **Helite Hip'Safe.** Airbags aren't just for cars anymore. This French-made belt is worn around the waist and automatically deploys a pair of airbags to cushion your hip bones when it senses that you're falling. The idea is that it could prevent a hip fracture, a very serious injury. Hip'Safe's battery can last up to 15 days between charges, and unlike car airbags, its airbags can be repacked and reused after they deploy. This device weighs about two pounds. *Price:* About $800. Senior.Helite.com

Hearing aids that are heard but not seen: **Eargo Max.** These hearing aids are so tiny that the only part that extends outside the ear canal is an almost-invisible clear plastic strand that's there so wearers have a way to remove them. Eargo Max feels almost like it isn't there, too, because it does not fill the ear canal—instead it "floats," supported by numerous gentle flexible fibers. The rechargeable batteries can last a day. *Price:* $2,500 per pair, and there's a 45-day money-back guarantee if you're not satisfied. Eargo.com

Better white noise machine: **Nightingale.** This device plugs into a wall outlet so that it can convert that wall into a resonance chamber that blankets the room in soothing white noise. Tests conducted by Harvard Medical School researchers found that Nightingale helps people fall asleep 38% faster, on average, which is comparable to prescription sleeping pills. Nightingale, which is only a little larger than a standard wall outlet itself, can be controlled with an Apple or Android device. *Prices:* $149 (appropriate for bedrooms up to 150 square feet) or $249 (for up to 300 square feet). MeetNightingale.com

Better Smartphone Calls When the Signal Is Bad

For better smartphone calls when the signal is bad, simply enable Wi-Fi calling—this lets you make and receive calls and texts through Wi-Fi instead of through the mobile carrier's cell network. Most but not all carriers offer this. When Wi-Fi calling is enabled, your calls will be routed to any Wi-Fi network—and will go to your mobile network only when Wi-Fi is not available.

Komando.com

Return of the Flip Phone

Flip phones are regaining popularity now. Even though more than three-quarters of Americans have smartphones, some people are sticking with or switching back to flip phones.

Reasons: Flip phones make it easier to avoid news headlines and social-media chatter...discourage instant response to e-mail...do not distract users from getting jobs done.

MarketWatch.com

Phone Case Caution

Liquid-glitter iPhone cases cause chemical burns when they leak. About 263,000 of the cases were sold from October 2015 through June 2017 by such retailers as Amazon, Nordstrom Rack, Henri Bendel, Victoria's Secret and Tory Burch. Prices ranged from $15 to $65. Consumers should return their cases for a full refund.

More information: Call MixBin Electronics, 855-215-4935...or go to PhoneCaseRecall.ExpertInquiry.com.

Carla Coolman, a public affairs specialist at the US Consumer Product Safety Commission, Bethesda, Maryland.

TAKE NOTE...

New Uses for Smartphone Cameras

- **CamFind** is an image-search utility—take a photo, and the app runs a search to identify what is in the picture.
- **Amazon Mobile Shopping App** lets you take a photo of a product or scan a barcode to see if you can buy it for less on Amazon.
- **Photomath** lets you point your camera at a math equation and get an answer—and even works if you write out the equation by hand.
- **Google Translate** works in 38 different languages—start the app, tap on the camera icon, point the lens at what you want to translate, and the translation appears on your screen.

Komando.com

Turn Your Clutter into Cash

Lauren Greutman, author of *The Recovering Spender: How to Live a Happy, Fulfilled, Debt-Free Life.* She writes and speaks about frugal living and household finance on her website and on TV shows including *The Today Show* and *Good Morning America.* LaurenGreutman.com

Craigslist and eBay are not the only online ways to sell your unwanted possessions—and not necessarily the best, either. The following websites and free Android/iOS apps can be safer, easier to use and help you reach *precisely* the type of buyers who will pay you the most for what you have to sell...

Best for selling women's fashion: **Poshmark.** Women's clothes, shoes and accessories sold through this app tend to fetch higher prices than they would on eBay or Craigslist. Poshmark shoppers generally are style-conscious and willing to pay a bit more for pieces they love. The app is ideal for items made by desirable designers such as Michael Kors, Louis Vuitton and Alexander Wang. (You can sell men's and kid's clothes through Poshmark as well, but those categories typically attract fewer buyers.) The app makes selling simple—use your phone to take photos of an item and fill in a few details such as size and price. Poshmark takes a 20% commission on most sales or a flat $2.95 commission on sales under $15. Poshmark.com

Best for selling items that are too big to ship: **5miles.** Craigslist is the most popular site for selling things too large to realistically ship—it connects sellers with local buyers who can pick up their purchases in person. The 5miles app serves a similar function—and makes it easier to weed out thieves, a growing problem on Craigslist. With 5miles, each party in a potential transaction can verify the other's identity by phone or his/her Facebook account and see whether other users' comments on earlier transactions have been favorable. That's not foolproof—comments and Facebook accounts could be faked—but it does reduce the odds of crime. There is no charge for selling or buying through 5miles. To sell, you simply use your smartphone to take photos of the item, then add a few details and your asking price. The main drawback is that the app is not yet heavily used in all markets—sellers in large urban areas are most likely to find buyers. 5milesapp.com

Similar to 5Miles: If 5miles has few or no listings in your area, suggesting that it is not yet widely used there, see whether *VarageSale* has a larger number of listings. Like 5miles, this app offers a safety-first way to sell things locally, with no cost for buying or selling. You can post the items you have for sale from VarageSale's website rather than its app if you prefer. Buyers and sellers initially connect via Facebook so that they can see who they are dealing with before they agree to meet. Local administrators review all the prospective buyers and sellers before they can engage in transactions. VarageSale.com

***Best for selling books:* Amazon Seller app.** Internet retailing behemoth Amazon.com lets you sell things through its very popular site. The Amazon Seller app makes this sales process especially easy—use your smartphone to scan the book's barcode, and most of its details will be automatically entered into Amazon. (You also can type in book titles if there is no barcode. Or items can be listed directly through Amazon's website if you'd rather not use your phone.) You can use this app to sell virtually anything Amazon sells, but the app is especially useful for selling books, given the huge number of book shoppers on Amazon. If your item sells, Amazon typically takes a 15% commission plus a 99-cent per-item fee, although the commission varies by the type of product. (If you're selling a lot of items, you can avoid that 99-cent per-item fee by paying a $39.99 monthly fee to become an Amazon Professional Seller.) Amazon.com

***Best for selling consumer technology:* Kiiboo.** If you are trying to sell a smartphone, tablet, laptop computer, digital camera or some other piece of relatively modern consumer technology, Kiiboo is the simplest option. With Kiiboo you don't have to take photographs, write up a listing, figure out packaging or deal with buyers. Just identify your product on Kiiboo.com (Kiiboo is a website, not an app), and if the product is something that the site thinks it can sell, the company will send you appropriate prepaid packaging so that you can easily ship the device to it. Kiiboo handles everything else and claims an 18% commission if the item sells. (If your item does not sell within 100 days, you can pay the postage to have it returned to you or let Kiiboo donate it to charity.) Kiiboo.com

***Best for selling antiques:* Trove Marketplace app.** Trove is a great app for selling antique furniture to local buyers because it's used by many antiques shoppers. (You can sell modern furniture through Trove as well, but many modern items will do better on 5miles or VarageSale.) Trove may be safer than Craigslist because prospective transaction partners can view each other's profiles and ratings before agreeing to meet. If the item sells, Trove claims a 10% commission, plus additional fees if you have Trove process a credit card transaction for you. You can sell through either the app or Trove's website. Like other "sell local" apps, Trove is most useful for sellers in areas where the app has lots of users—the odds of success are best if you live in a heavily populated area. UseTrove.com

GOOD TO KNOW...

Get Money Back for Your Used Clothes

You can get some money back for your used clothes.

Websites that let you sell to other consumers: Grailed, for young, hip male clothing, charges a 6% commission plus Paypal costs. Poshmark, for fashionable men's, women's and children's clothing and accessories, charges $2.95 for items less than $15, otherwise 20%.

Websites that buy your old clothes: Material World accepts excellent-condition designer clothes—it sends you a prepaid mailer and sends you an offer after it gets the clothing. ThredUp takes clothing of all types, paying 5% to 80% of the anticipated selling price. The RealReal takes only luxury brands and pays you 55% to 85% of the sale price.

The Washington Post.

12

Retirement Report

6 Money Mistakes That Can Jeopardize Your Retirement

Despite the years of planning, retirement often brings many surprises. Along with the excitement and freedom that come from ending a long career, you also might experience snags as you adapt to your new life. You can work them out. But even financial mistakes early in your retirement can be very difficult—or even impossible—to recover from, and they can jeopardize your long-term financial security. Many retirees make these money mistakes—but you don't have to! *Keep your retirement on track by avoiding these common mistakes of new retirees...*

• **First-year spike in spending.** You might assume that you will spend less when you retire, but in reality, nearly half of retirees spend more in the first years of retirement than they did when working.

Reason: With more free time on their hands and all their retirement savings at their disposal, new retirees feel emboldened to spend more on hobbies, dining out, travel and other activities. That is understandable. But overly exuberant spending can deplete your savings much more severely than you might imagine—because every dollar you spend early in retirement represents *multiple future dollars* that you would have earned from investing that money instead.

What to do: You don't have to live beneath your means, but you should develop a sensible retirement budget with a financial adviser *before* you retire. Sticking to these spending

Note: Rates, prices and offers throughout this chapter and book are subject to change.

Bill Losey, CFP, owner of Bill Losey Retirement Solutions, LLC, an independent, fee-only registered investment-advisory firm, Greenwich, New York. He is author of *Retire in a Weekend! The Baby Boomer's Guide to Making Work Optional.* BillLosey.com

guidelines can help keep your retirement on track for years to come. And it's fine to allow for some splurging early in retirement—if you and your adviser plan for it and you save a little extra for those first years of fun.

• **Underestimating the cost of relocating.** Retiring to a home on the beach or other major move is part of many people's retirement dreams. But while some of the costs of moving—such as buying a house or apartment and hiring a moving company—may be obvious, others can sneak up on you. Variables such as local taxes and homeowner's insurance rates can make your new location a lot more expensive than you expected. *Example:* Homeowner's insurance in Florida costs nearly twice the national average.

What to do: Before deciding to move, research your potential new locale carefully. Compare local taxes and typical costs of living with what you're used to paying. You can find data to make these comparisons at websites such as BestPlaces.net or RetirementLiving.com.

• **No long-term-care insurance.** You might have been content to hold only life insurance and disability insurance during your working years. But upon retirement, you realize that you now need insurance to cover the costs of a potentially debilitating illness—costs that might include in-home care or an extended stay in a nursing home. The trouble is, your options now are limited. Long-term-care insurance gets more expensive—dramatically so—as you age. *Example:* A policy purchased jointly by a couple, both at age 55, costs an average of $2,466 annually. In contrast, if they wait until they are both age 60 to buy a policy, they pay an average of $3,381 annually. Worse, you can be rejected for long-term-care insurance altogether if you have a disqualifying medical condition—and the chance of that increases as you age.

What to do: Buy long-term-care insurance as early as possible, even in your late 40s or in your 50s. If you are not keen on the idea of paying premiums for decades, you can consider a policy for which you pay a higher premium for a set amount of time early in the contract and then no premium after that. That way, you could buy a long-term-care policy and pay premiums while you're younger and still working—essentially prepaying for insurance you may need during retirement.

If you are in your 60s and in good health, purchasing a long-term-care policy may be more expensive but likely worth it to protect your other financial assets. If you apply but are rejected by more than one carrier, work with a financial adviser to examine other alternatives, such as annuities that have long-term-care riders. (Alternative long-term-care coverage options often are complicated, and the best approach will depend on your unique circumstances.)

• **Getting divorced in retirement.** Early retirement is a time of transition that can be rocky for couples. Spouses sometimes struggle to adapt their relationships to a new reality in which their careers are over and they are spending more time together. But a divorce, even if it is warranted, is expensive. The legal fees for a divorce without minor children average $12,500 and easily can cost many tens of thousands more. Worse, once assets are divided, what had been enough money to support a couple through retirement may not support two individuals leading separate lives. This financial strain can set your retirement plans back by 10 years or more.

What to do: Consider staying married but living apart. You still will have to face some duplicate expenses—such as covering housing costs in two locations—but your retirement assets may take less of a hit than the full cost of a divorce.

• **Being house-rich and cash-poor.** For many retirees, a home is one of their most important assets. In fact, many people retire with more equity in their homes than cash and investments in their retirement savings. But this situation might not be ideal if it means that you don't have enough income to afford the lifestyle you dreamed about. And waiting too long to remedy the problem is even worse because a large house can rapidly drain your savings due to expenses such as taxes and upkeep.

What to do: If you have more equity in your home than the value of your investment assets, consider downsizing to a smaller home and/or moving to a cheaper locale. However, be sure to conduct sufficient research about the potential costs of that move, as explained above.

Alternatively, a reverse mortgage—which taps the equity in your home to give you cash payments and typically doesn't need to be paid back until you move permanently, sell your home or die—is a good choice for some people. *Example:* If you don't plan on moving and don't want to bequeath your home to any heirs, a reverse mortgage may work for you. Before deciding on a reverse mortgage, work with a financial adviser to explore your options.

- **Still supporting adult kids.** Helping out your adult kids by paying a few bills for them or providing regular cash gifts might not have been a big deal while you were working and earning money. But as a new retiree, you no longer have steady income from a job—and each dollar you provide to your children is one less you will have to support yourself through what can be a long retirement.

What to do: Cutting off financial support for your kids is difficult, but you don't have to do it all at once. You can establish a time frame with them for when you will stop providing the regular support that they may be used to and then gradually reduce the amount you give them. If you must turn down requests for large amounts of money, such as a child asking for help with a down payment on a house, remind your children that spending too much early in your retirement could cause you to outlive your savings and that you don't want to be a financial burden on them as you reach old age.

INTERESTING FINDING...

Best State for Retirees

In a recent analysis, the best state for retirees was *New Hampshire*. This is based on an analysis that considered eight factors, in this order of importance—cost of living, health-care quality, crime, cultural vitality, weather, taxes, senior citizens' well-being and prevalence of other seniors. New Hampshire scored sixth-worst for weather but placed first overall because it came in with high scores for well-being (second best), crime (third) and health care (fourth).

The other top places to retire: Colorado, Maine, Iowa and Minnesota.

Among popular retirement destinations, Arizona came in at number 12, Florida at number 17 and Nevada at number 44.

Analysis by Bankrate.com.

Are You Cheapskating Yourself Out of a Good Retirement?

Meir Statman, PhD, professor of finance at Santa Clara University's Leavey School of Business, California. He is author of *Finance for Normal People: How Investors and Markets Behave.*

Retirees often are warned not to overspend or they could outlive their savings. Rarely mentioned is that some retirees actually have a very different problem—they *underspend.* And their dramatic underspending detracts from their quality of life and, counterintuitively, can lead to money problems (more on that below). But as far as these underspenders are concerned, they are just being frugal and responsible.

Here's what retirees and their families need to know about problematic underspending...

AN OVERBLOWN RISK

We've all heard horror stories about retirees reduced to scraping by on modest Social Security checks. But when you dig a little deeper and investigate *why* these retirees ended up in dire financial straits, you almost always discover that postretirement overspending was not the issue. More likely they were poor throughout their lives...made poor investment decisions... were defrauded by scammers...had massive medical or long-term-care bills...and/or never had much saved for retirement.

You almost never hear about retirees who saved diligently and successfully for retirement but who ended up broke anyway, primarily because of excessive discretionary spending.

Yet it's this unlikely danger that causes some retirees to pinch their pennies.

SIGNIFICANT SHIFT

The retirees most likely to make this underspending mistake are, ironically, those who made few money mistakes during their working lives. These people paid off their credit card balances in full every month and maxed out their retirement contributions. These people are cautious and savvy—in short, they're the last people you would expect to have a bad financial habit.

But shifting from the working world into retirement requires people to make a challenging mental transition—the shift from saving to spending. They struggle to escape the sense that taking money out of retirement savings is wrong, so they withdraw much less than they could and harangue their spouses to do the same.

Many decide that it's OK to spend the income generated by their investments but not to draw down the capital. But with today's low interest rates, the income produced by a typical retirement portfolio often is not enough to finance even a frugal retirement, so these underspenders seek out investments that pay higher yields. They tell themselves that this is the safe play because it lets them preserve their capital and spend only income—but they are focusing on the wrong danger. The real risk is investing a significant portion of retirement savings in assets that are riskier or pricier than is appropriate, which is exactly what they are doing—high-yield investments often come with excessive risks or fees. Ironically, for retirees, the drive to be financially responsible can lead to investment losses.

Examples: There's a reason that high-yield bonds often are referred to as "junk" bonds—they are issued by companies or governments that might not be able to pay the money due, meaning these bonds can be very risky. "Income-focused" mutual funds that emphasize high dividends often have high fees and might generate higher-than-necessary tax bills.

Most underspending retirees also are loath to tap their home equity, either by selling their home or by taking a reverse mortgage. They do everything they can to pass the family home to the next generation debt-free—even if that next generation is just going to sell it.

OVERCOMING UNDERSPENDING

Among the options for overcoming retirement underspending...

• **Set up automated monthly transfers** from retirement investment accounts into a bank account or money market fund. When money appears automatically, it tends to feel like income, not like tapping into savings.

Bonus: Setting up these preset monthly withdrawals also helps overcome stock-sale-timing regret. If you pull money out of a stock fund today and the stock market rallies tomorrow, you are likely to feel pangs of regret about the profits you missed. For some retirees, these concerns are such a significant psychological hurdle that they cannot bring themselves to tap into their retirement capital at all. Automated monthly withdrawals reduce these feelings of regret because there's less of a sense of personal responsibility—the money was withdrawn by an automated process.

Historically, it has been safe for retirees to withdraw 4% of their savings early in retirement—although some experts suggest 3% to be extra safe—and adjust that amount upward to keep pace with inflation as the years pass. Invest in "managed payout" funds. These distribute a small percentage of their value in the form of monthly payments that seem like income, so they are another effective way for retirees to overcome psychological hurdles about tapping into capital.

Examples: Vanguard Managed Payout Fund targets a 4% annual distribution rate (Vanguard.com)...Schwab Monthly Income Funds pay 1% to 8% annually, depending on the fund selected and market conditions (Schwab.com).

• **Treat "required minimum distributions" as required minimum spending.** If you have money in a tax-deferred retirement account, such as a 401(k), traditional IRA or SEP IRA, you typically are required to start withdrawing money starting the year you turn 70½. These withdrawals start at 3.65% at age 70½ and increase over the years. (These rules do not apply to Roth IRAs.)

GOOD TO KNOW...

Stop Postponing Splurges Until Later in Retirement

Retirees often reason that if they might live 25 years in retirement, they shouldn't spend more than 1/25 of their retirement savings in any year. But retirees actually spend significantly less as the years pass by. After around age 70, they travel less, splurge on fewer creature comforts and pour less money into home improvement. Retirement spending falls off even more sharply after one partner in a couple passes away. People inevitably derive the greatest joy from retirement spending early in retirement, while they still are relatively young, healthy and energetic.

Meir Statman, PhD, author, *Finance for Normal People.*

Underspenders sometimes make these required withdrawals but then reinvest the money. Instead, tell yourself, *I've paid taxes on these withdrawals anyway, it's my money, so I might as well enjoy it rather than reinvest and face more taxes later.* Underspenders as a group are perturbed by taxes, so framing spending around tax avoidance such as this can be effective. The required withdrawal rate is very conservative, so it is safe to spend this money.

• **Investigate what forms of spending tend to bring you the most joy.** These might not be the classic retirement activities...and it might not be the things that you splurged on during your career.

Example: Retirees often find out that keeping-up-with-the-Joneses, status-oriented purchases such as luxury cars bring them less joy in retirement.

The good news is that retirees have time to try different things until they stumble upon something that does bring them joy. If spending on yourself does not do the trick, consider making gifts to your kids (or to a charity). They're the ones who will get this money if you don't spend it, and giving gifts now means you get to see the recipients enjoy it.

BUT WHAT IF I NEED LONG-TERM CARE?

Don't let the possibility of a long stay in a long-term-care facility ruin your retirement. It's true that some retirees eventually face staggeringly large medical or long-term-care–related bills—but that doesn't mean that the prudent move is to hang on to as much savings as possible to pay those costs if they do come. If someone lived very frugally in retirement, perhaps he might have $300,000 remaining in his savings when he needed an extended nursing home stay versus $200,000 if he enjoyed his retirement—but the average cost of a nursing home stay is around $100,000 per year and rising fast. At that rate, he is likely to have to turn to Medicaid to pay the bills eventually anyway (unless he has purchased a long-term-care insurance policy). Medicaid won't pay for his care until he has run through virtually all his savings anyway, so the sensible option is to enjoy retirement so that he qualifies for Medicaid a bit sooner.

And while it is worth budgeting for the Medicare deductibles and co-pays you are likely to face based on your typical health-care spending, there really is no feasible way for the average retiree to save enough to be able to pay the massive medical bills that sometimes occur—those are likely to eat up their savings no matter how frugally they have lived. The smart move is to sign up for a Medigap plan or a Medicare Advantage plan that limits out-of-pocket medical costs as much as possible and then enjoy your retirement.

Funds for a Secure Retirement

Dana Anspach, CFP, CEO of Sensible Money, LLC, an investment advisory firm based in Scottsdale, Arizona, that specializes in retirement income planning for clients throughout the US. She is author of *Control Your Retirement Destiny.* SensibleMoney.com

Many investors are surprised to learn that once they retire, investing becomes a lot trickier than when they were still saving for retirement. You have to transform the nest egg you've accumulated into a portfolio that generates a steady, reliable stream of income to live on and still make sure that you never run out of money. And you may need to strike this balance for decades. That's a lot to ask from your portfolio!

Intriguing solution: Invest in a *retirement income mutual fund*. At least 10 major asset-management companies, including Charles Schwab and Vanguard, have introduced these funds as millions of baby boomers retire and the number of Americans over the age of 65 is expected to be 60% higher in 2025 than it was in 2010. The pitch for these funds is that you choose one that can provide the right amount of annual income for your needs, invest enough of your assets to generate that income, then sit back and collect a regular payment every month without worrying about what investments to buy and sell or how much cash to draw from your portfolio.

The funds' promise: You won't run out of money. But are these funds really as safe and easy as they sound?

We asked top retirement-planning expert Dana Anspach, CFP, to lay out the pros and cons of using these funds and how to choose a good one for your personal circumstances...

ADVANTAGES

Before you decide whether a retirement income fund is right for you, take a basic inventory of your retirement finances. First, figure out what your monthly spending needs are likely to be. This includes essential spending (housing, utilities, groceries, insurance, etc.) as well as discretionary spending (restaurant meals, vacations, etc.). Next, subtract from that amount the total amount of relatively steady and reliable post-tax income you expect to receive each month from other sources. This includes income from Social Security, pensions, annuities, certificates of deposit (CDs) and US Treasuries.

The amount left over is what you'll need to draw monthly from your investment portfolio. *Important:* If that amount is more than 4% of your portfolio, you may need to rethink your spending habits and lifestyle. A large body of research shows that 4% is the maximum sustainable annual drawdown from a diversified portfolio of stocks and bonds for a nest egg to have a high probability of lasting the next 30 years.

Most retirement income funds are designed to generate monthly income in similar ways. They all invest in a number of underlying mutual funds so that you wind up with a very broad array of asset classes. The fund income is generated from dividend-paying stocks... bonds...and/or capital appreciation when the manager sells investments in the portfolio. These funds aim to provide an annual payout rate of 4% of the value of the assets typically. *Example:* If you invest $500,000 in a typical retirement income fund, you can estimate an annual payout of $20,000 or a monthly payout of about $1,667. However, payout rates do differ from fund to fund and even can fluctuate within a particular fund over time.

There are two more aspects of retirement income funds that can make them more attractive and useful relative to other types of retirement investments...

- **You are able to sell your shares at any time if you need emergency cash** and to pass on your shares and income payouts to your beneficiaries when you die. This is a significant advantage over long-term annuities, which typically can't be liquidated without paying hefty surrender charges and whose guaranteed payments can cease altogether if you pass away.
- **Expenses are relatively low.** The funds typically charge annual expense ratios as low as 0.34% and require initial minimum investments ranging from $100 to $25,000. In contrast, a financial adviser typically would charge you 1% of your managed assets each year to oversee your portfolio and set up an income flow—that's a cost difference of $660 annually on a $100,000 investment. Annuities typically come with even higher costs.

DRAWBACKS

While the simplicity of retirement income funds is appealing, they are a new type of offering that hasn't been tested in a bear market. *Keep the following in mind when deciding whether to use one of these funds for your retirement...*

- **There are no guarantees of the size or longevity of monthly income payouts.** Even though the fund managers strive to produce stable income, the funds can lose money in bear markets and/or reduce payouts at any time. That means these funds are best-suited for retirees who have the flexibility to cut back on their discretionary spending if necessary or who have other sources of occasional income such as part-time work. If you need absolute, guaranteed monthly income to cover essential spending, it may be worth the costs and restrictions of buying an annuity from a highly rated insurance company.

• **The funds are designed to hold the bulk of your investment money in retirement.** Some investors may find it uncomfortable or inconvenient to cash in their preretirement portfolios and stash everything in one fund, no matter how widely diversified it is. But committing only a small portion of your investment portfolio to a retirement income fund defeats its purpose and forces you to have to manage multiple investments.

For details on retirement income funds from two fund companies, see below.

ATTRACTIVE RETIREMENT INCOME FUNDS

The following retirement income funds have different strategies, but they stand out as offering an impressive variety of solid underlying investments, very reasonable expenses and strong (if relatively short) track records. (Other retirement income funds have higher expenses, focus on a narrower range of investments and/or have even shorter track records. For instance, T. Rowe Price launched its retirement income fund in June 2017.)

• **The Vanguard Managed Payout Fund (VPGDX).** With $2.2 billion in assets, this is by far the largest retirement income fund and has the most aggressive asset allocation with about 60% of its assets in stocks recently. It uses 10 underlying Vanguard funds, strives for a 4% annual payout and requires a minimum initial investment of $25,000. Vanguard avoids sharp changes in monthly fund shareholder payouts by dipping into principal if the income generated by the portfolio falls. Every January, the fund recalculates the dollar amount of the planned monthly distributions for the coming year based on how well the fund has performed over the past three years. The fund is best for investors who are OK with the higher volatility of a stock-heavy fund. *Annual expense ratio:* 0.34%.*

• **Schwab Monthly Income Funds.** Schwab offers three different retirement income funds. Each one offers a different target payout rate, and even that rate will vary depending on the current interest rate environment. All three require minimum initial investments of just $100 and allocate their assets among five in-house Schwab funds.

• Moderate Payout (SWJRX) strives for an annual payout of up to 3%, with 36% of the portfolio recently in stocks. *Annual expense ratio:* 0.58%.

• Enhanced Payout (SWKRX) currently has a target annual payout rate of up to 4%. It recently had 32% of assets in stocks. *Annual expense ratio:* 0.46%.

• Maximum Payout (SWLRX) currently has a target annual payout of up to 5% and recently had 18% of assets in stocks. *Annual expense ratio:* 0.34%.

These funds generate monthly payouts to shareholders through the interest and dividend income from their portfolios and do not expect to touch the principal. This means that the payout rates, which are recalculated each month, may fluctuate a lot. The funds work best for relatively conservative retirees who don't mind fluctuating monthly income.

*Expense ratios as of August 2018.

Mortgage Secrets for Retirees and Near-Retirees

Keith Gumbinger, vice president of New Jersey–based HSH Associates, which publishes consumer loan information. HSH.com

Would you want to have a mortgage for the rest of your life—even as a retiree? Maybe you should. With today's low interest rates, the old idea that a debt-free retirement is a safer and happier retirement is not necessarily valid. In fact, having a mortgage at interest rates of 4.25% to 4.75% (as of August 2018) actually can be a good way to boost the amount of savings a retiree has available to spend or to invest.

The problem: Unfortunately, although lenders are legally prohibited from discriminating against retired borrowers based on their age, mortgage-lending rules favor borrowers who still are in the workforce. Lenders expect borrowers to have significant income, and income is something that retirees often lack—even retirees who have substantial savings.

Here's what retirees and near-retirees need to do to get a new mortgage or refinance an existing mortgage...

- **If you are nearing retirement, apply for a mortgage before leaving the workforce, if feasible.** If you are planning to buy a home as soon as you leave your job—perhaps because you'll want to move to a retirement locale, downsize or both—try to buy one before you leave instead. Likewise, if you are thinking about refinancing on your current home to get a lower interest rate and/or take cash out of your home, explore this option before you leave the workforce. The mortgage process is likely to be quicker and simpler—and a larger number of lenders are likely to be interested in getting your business—if you apply while you still have earned income. Applying before retiring is particularly important if you want a "jumbo" mortgage, typically a mortgage of more than $453,100 in 2018.

Also: Consider applying for a home-equity line of credit before retiring even if you do not currently need to access the equity in your home. Like a mortgage, a HELOC can be easier to obtain while you still have earned income... and it could come in handy down the road.

- **If you are retired and have little income beyond Social Security,** when you initially contact mortgage lenders, ask whether they are familiar with "annuitization of assets" mortgages (also called "asset depletion" mortgages) as a way to overcome income requirements. *Here is an example of how those requirements can block mortgage approval:* A borrower's monthly housing costs, including mortgage, property taxes and homeowner's insurance payments, generally must add up to no more than 28% of gross income...and his/her total monthly debt payments generally must add up to no more than 43% of gross income. Retirees often have some income from Social Security and perhaps a pension, but with little or no earned income, most fall well short of what is required.

Fortunately, Fannie Mae and Freddie Mac, the government-backed agencies that repurchase many mortgages from lenders, quietly added a rule a few years ago designed to help retirees clear the income hurdle—lenders now can treat up to 70% of a borrower's qualified retirement savings as if it were income spread over the length of the loan.

Example: A retiree who has $1,400 in monthly income, all from Social Security, is unlikely to qualify for a mortgage with a monthly payment of more than $392 based on that income, if he qualifies at all. But if that same retiree has $500,000 saved in IRA and/or 401(k) accounts, a lender can credit this borrower with additional monthly income of $972. Based on the 28% rule of thumb noted above, this retiree then might qualify for a mortgage with a monthly payment of as much as $664.

Even though this very helpful Fannie Mae/Freddie Mac rule has been in place for a few years, some lenders still are unfamiliar with it. And even if these lenders are willing to learn about it and work with you, their unfamiliarity with the rule would increase the odds of delays or mistakes—that's why you want a lender who has used the rule multiple times before.

One catch: Fannie Mae and Freddie Mac do not purchase "jumbo" mortgages, which in most housing markets are mortgages of more than $453,100. As a result, lenders are unlikely

TAKE NOTE...

More People Staying Put in Retirement

More people plan to retire where they now live than plan to move. Among 45-to-65-year-olds surveyed, 43% say that they plan to stay in their current residence during retirement versus 33% who say they plan to move. The rest are not sure.

Ipsos/USA Today survey of 1,170 adults, ages 45 to 65, reported in *USA Today*.

to be willing to treat your assets as income with these larger loans.

• **If you already are retired but have not yet started receiving your Social Security benefits (and/or traditional pension plan benefits),** consider delaying your mortgage application until after you begin receiving these benefits if income could be an impediment to your loan. Mortgage lenders will count your monthly Social Security and pension benefits checks as income only if you have begun receiving them.

Related: If minor children in your household receive Social Security benefits based on your (or your spouse's) earnings history, these children's Social Security income typically can be counted as income on your mortgage application as long as the benefits are slated to continue for at least three more years.

• **If you haven't paid close attention to your credit scores lately, check your credit reports.** Do this three to six months before applying for a mortgage and then again as the application date nears. Notify the credit-reporting agencies of any mistakes. *Also:* Do not close credit card accounts even if you no longer use the cards in retirement. Having access to this credit and using it responsibly will benefit your credit scores.

SHOULD RETIREES REFINANCE EVEN WHEN IT WON'T LOWER THE INTEREST RATE?

Home owners typically refinance mortgages when doing so will allow them to lock in lower interest rates. Surprisingly, some retirees anxious to reduce their monthly bills might find that refinancing is beneficial even if it does not lower their rates at all. Refinancing can let them extend their mortgage loans over additional years, reducing monthly payments and freeing up retirement assets and income for other purposes. This does reduce the odds that they will ever entirely pay off their mortgage loans, however.

Example: Say a man took out a 30-year $200,000 mortgage in 2012. This loan had an interest rate of 4.75% and monthly payments of $1,043. Now, six years later, this man is retired and has $179,000 remaining on that mortgage. In today's market, there's a good chance that he could obtain a no-closing-cost 4.75%, 30-year loan for the remaining amount. If he did this, his interest rate would not improve—but stretching the loan out for an additional six years would reduce his monthly payment to $934, freeing up $109 in his monthly budget.

Figure Out If a Former Employer Owes You Retirement Money

Joellen Leavelle, communications and outreach director of the Pension Rights Center, a nonprofit consumer advocacy organization in Washington, DC. She previously worked at a law firm that specialized in employee benefits. PensionRights.org

---

It's easy to lose track of a 401(k) or pension plan over the years. Ordinarily the best way to recover those missing retirement assets is to contact the former employer's human resources department. But what if that employer insists that you cashed out your retirement plan long ago or rolled it into a different retirement account? Or what if you suspect that you are forgetting about one or more of your former employers entirely? *There might be a way to recover your missing retirement savings even in these tricky situations...*

• **If a former employer insists that you cashed out your retirement plan or rolled it into a different retirement account but you have no recollection of doing so,** ask for the date when this transaction occurred and to what institution the money was sent.

If you have a copy of your tax return from that year, any rollover or retirement plan cash-out should be noted on the return even if it did not generate income taxes.

If you still have retirement plan and/or financial company account statements covering the time when the transfer or cash-out supposedly occurred, check these for any record of money moving the way the plan administrator says it did. If your records do not go back far enough, contact the plan sponsor or financial institution that you were told received the transferred assets and ask whether it can provide the relevant records.

If you locate statements or tax returns suggesting that the rollover or cash-out did not occur as your former employer claims, provide copies of these to the plan administrator and ask it to reconsider its position that you removed your money from its retirement plan. If the administrator does not reverse its position, contact the Pension Rights Center (PensionRights.org), a nonprofit, and ask if it can provide assistance.

• **If you can't recall the names of all your prior employers where you might have retirement assets,** dig through your files to see if you can turn up paperwork that mentions such employers or otherwise jogs your memory. Old tax returns are a good bet, as are old résumés, date books, address books and business cards. Even a photo album could provide clues—look for shots taken at company events and/or where people are wearing garb featuring corporate logos.

If all else fails, you could file Form SSA-7050 with the Social Security Administration to request a "Detailed Earnings Report" listing all of your employers (SSA.gov/forms/ssa-7050.pdf). There is a fee of $115, so do this only if you believe there is a good chance you are forgetting a former employer and missing a 401(k) or pension.

Beware the Social Security "Bonus" and Other Big Mistakes

Laurence J. Kotlikoff, PhD, professor of economics at Boston University, a fellow of the American Academy of Arts and Sciences and a former senior economist with the President's Council of Economic Advisors. He is president of Economic Security Planning, Inc., which markets financial-planning software. He is coauthor of *Get What's Yours: The Secrets of Maxing Out Your Social Security.* MaximizeMySocialSecurity.com

---

Every day, about 10,000 Americans between the ages of 62 and 70 start to claim their Social Security retirement benefits for the first time...and most of them make costly mistakes when they do so—or at some point thereafter. They end up collecting less than they could have over their lifetimes. Whether or not you have started collecting your benefits, you owe it to yourself to avoid these six costly mistakes...

***MISTAKE:* Taking the six months' worth of "bonus" benefits that the Social Security Administration (SSA) is offering.** For people who delay starting their Social Security retirement benefits, the monthly payments they receive grow bigger the longer they wait, up to age 70. But some people in their late 60s have received calls from the SSA telling them that if they agree to start their benefits immediately rather than wait until a later age, they can get a lump-sum check equal to six months' worth of benefits. This really isn't a bonus at all—for anyone who takes the offer, the size of monthly checks received will be lower just as if the person had started receiving benefits six months *earlier*. Most people eventually will come out behind if they accept such an offer. Receiving a big onetime Social Security check also increases the odds that a portion of your Social Security income will be taxed during this first year.

What to do: If your plan is to maximize your monthly check by delaying the start of benefits, stick with this plan even if the SSA tries to tempt you into starting earlier with a lump-sum payout. The lump sum isn't really a special offer anyway, despite how the SSA might make it sound—this option always is available to anyone who applies for their benefits six months or longer after they become eligible.

***MISTAKE:* Missing out on "free" spousal benefits.** The Social Security system usually rewards patience. But there is absolutely no reason to continue waiting to claim spousal benefits based on your spouse's earnings record beyond your own full retirement age. Spousal benefits stop increasing once this age is reached, as do survivors benefits, so waiting any longer will only cost you money. There is one valid reason not to claim spousal benefits at full retirement age, however—if your spouse is not currently collecting his/her own retirement benefits, you will not be allowed to collect your spousal benefits until he does (unless he filed for his benefits and then "suspended" them by April 29, 2016).

What to do: If you have reached your full retirement age and your spouse is collecting Social Security retirement benefits, go ahead and claim any spousal benefits that are available to you.

MISTAKE: **Starting your benefits before age 70 because of a short "life expectancy."** If you use an online Social Security calculator to figure out the best age when you should start your benefits, there's a good chance that it will base its answer in part on your life expectancy—an estimate of how long you will live based on factors such as your current health and your parents' life spans. If your life expectancy is not long, the calculator likely will advise you to claim benefits relatively soon. This makes some sense if your goal is to maximize the amount you get from Social Security. But it does not make sense if your goal is to reduce the risk that you will outlive your retirement savings and end your days in poverty—and that is the primary goal most people should pursue with their Social Security benefits. Social Security benefits are an excellent retirement insurance policy because you cannot outlive them—your checks will continue to arrive each month as long as you are alive to receive them. But they might not be large enough to protect you against retirement poverty if you claim them early—the typical person who starts his benefit at age 62 receives just $1,077 a month. But whatever amount you are due to receive, you could get a whopping 76% more each month if you claim at age 70.

What to do: Do not let a retirement calculator convince you to claim benefits early based on a pessimistic life expectancy. (Starting your benefits before age 70 can make sense if it is part of a larger strategy involving multiple types of benefits—for example, if you intend to later switch to spousal or survivors benefits, as explained above.)

MISTAKE: **Accidentally starting both your retirement benefits and your survivors benefits.**

Widows and widowers be warned: If you are eligible for benefits under both your own earnings history and your late spouse's, the SSA inadvertently might start both benefits when you ask to begin just one—even though starting both likely makes absolutely no financial sense for you. Some retirees lose hundreds of thousands of dollars because of an SSA error.

How it works: If you were married for at least nine months before your spouse passed away, you typically are eligible to claim survivors benefits based on that late spouse's earnings history starting as early as age 60 (or age 50 if you are disabled and at any age if you care for a child who is younger than 16 or disabled). Survivors benefits usually increase the longer you wait to claim them, up to your full retirement age, which, when it comes to survivors benefits, is age 66 for anyone born between 1945 and 1956 and progressively higher for those born later. (*Note:* When it comes to your own benefits, the full retirement age of 66 applies to those born between 1943 and 1954.)

Although widows and widowers are eligible to claim either survivors benefits or—starting at age 62—benefits based on their own earnings history, they cannot receive both at the same time. If they file for both, they essentially will receive only the larger of the two, and because they filed for both benefits, *neither* will continue to increase in size as it would have if they had waited. That means the best strategy generally is to start one of these benefits when you become eligible to do so, but let the other remain unclaimed until it reaches its largest possible amount, likely years later. That could mean starting survivors benefits as early as age 60 and waiting to file for one's own benefit as late as age 70...or filing for one's own benefit as early as age 62 and not filing for survivors benefits until full retirement age.

Unfortunately, when widows and widowers ask the SSA to start one of these benefits, Social Security employees sometimes start both, robbing recipients of their chance to allow the other benefit to continue to increase.

What to do: Widows and widowers should write, "I am applying for my retirement benefits. I am NOT filing for my survivors benefits" or vice versa in the remarks section of their benefits applications. That way you can prove that the SSA, not you, made the mistake if you do get signed up for both. The SSA usually will correct its mistake only if you provide strong evidence.

***MISTAKE:* Overlooking dependent parent survivors benefits.** If you're 62 or older and one of your adult children provides at least half of your financial support and claims you as a dependent on his tax return, you likely would be entitled to a survivors benefit based on that child's earnings record if he passed away. This benefit probably would be equal to 82.5% of the child's "primary insurance amount"—the amount that he would have received if had he started his benefits at his full retirement age—though it could be less if multiple survivors are eligible to claim benefits based on his earnings. That could be more than you are eligible to receive from your own Social Security earnings record. Many eligible parents don't know about this option. (If you claim both this survivors benefit and your own retirement benefit, you will essentially get only the larger of the two.)

What to do: If a child who is providing most of your financial support passes away, contact the SSA to check whether your survivors benefits based on this child's earnings would be larger than your own benefits.

If you are providing financial support to your parent, make sure that your parent knows to look into this if you die...and inform other family members about it as well, in case the parent is no longer able to handle complicated financial affairs if and when the time comes.

***MISTAKE:* Not suspending your benefits if you realize you started them too soon.** Some people are under the impression that Social Security rules no longer allow them to suspend their benefits. That's not true. You still have the right to suspend your benefits and—assuming that you haven't yet reached age 70—doing so will increase the size of the checks you receive when you later restart them. (The confusion occurs because recent rule changes mean that married people can no longer receive benefits based on their spouses' suspended benefits.)

What to do: If you have not yet reached age 70 and now regret claiming retirement benefits as early as you did, consider suspending your benefits until you reach age 70 to increase the size of your future checks.

Tools to Help You Maximize Social Security Benefits

Clark.com

There are numerous online calculators that provide you with estimates to make it easier to plan for retirement...

- **The Retirement Estimator calculator** (SSA.gov/retire/estimator.html) provides estimates of your benefits based on your actual Social Security earnings record. This detailed calculator requires you to fill out personal information including your Social Security number, your mother's maiden name and your place of birth.
- **The Quick Calculator** (SSA.gov/oact/quickcalc) requires only your date of birth and current-year earnings to provide you with a benefit estimate.
- **The SSA Online Calculator** (SSA.gov/planners/retire/AnypiaApplet.html) will provide you with an in-depth assessment of your potential benefits. You will need to enter your annual earnings, which you can access at SSA.gov/myaccount.
- **The Consumer Financial Protection Bureau** (ConsumerFinance.gov/consumer-tools/retirement/before-you-claim) has a calculator that helps you determine the optimal time to begin taking Social Security.

Dozens of Senior Discounts Can Save You $$$

Amie Clark, founder of TheSeniorList.com, a website that features ratings, reviews and articles about products and services for older adults. She previously was a social worker specializing in senior housing and care coordination.

Discount programs for seniors have been disappearing. Not long ago, the supermarket chain Kroger discontinued its version. And the National Park Service recently raised the price of its popular lifetime pass for seniors from a heavily discounted $10 to the standard $80. Big restaurant chains increasingly are allowing each franchise to decide for itself whether to offer a senior discount—and many are opting to scale back these programs or end them. Some restaurants are offering "senior menus"—with low prices *and small portions*—rather than bona fide senior discounts.

However, there still are some businesses that offer significant (not just token) senior discounts. These savings usually are available starting at age 60, 62 or 65, but in some cases customers as young as age 50 or 55 can take advantage. Many senior discounts are designated for AARP members, but some of those also are granted to members of other seniors' organizations (see below).

Here are dozens of businesses that still offer attractive senior discounts. Confirm these offers before buying—discount programs can change with little notice...and sometimes not every location in a chain participates.

SUPERMARKETS

Supermarket senior discounts have become rare, but they can be worth seeking out. The typical US household spends about 8% of its budget on groceries, so a 5% or 10% senior discount could be worth a lot of money. Expect certain product categories, including prescriptions, lottery tickets and tobacco, to be excluded. *Two of the largest supermarket chains that still offer senior discounts...*

Fred Meyer: 10% discount for age 55 and up on the first Tuesday of each month.

Harris Teeter: 5% discount for age 60 and up every Thursday.

RESTAURANTS

Within a chain, eligibility and/or other details of senior discounts sometimes vary from location to location. Among the chains that do offer appetizing senior deals and discounts at many or all locations are Arby's...Ben & Jerry's...Burger King...Dairy Queen...Krispy Kreme...Mrs. Fields...Sonic...and White Castle.

The following discounts are available in at least some locations to AARP members...

Bonefish Grill: 10% on select items.

FREEBIES...

Free or Low-Cost Help for Seniors

The federal government's free Tax Counseling for the Elderly program gives specialized assistance to taxpayers age 60 and older. *Additional help...*

- **Complex Medicare information** is explained by the free State Health Insurance Assistance Program, funded by federal agencies.
- **Free local transportation may be available in your community—**although some is available only for seniors below certain income levels.
- **Some prescription medicines** are free at certain supermarket chains, and free or nearly free medicines are available, based on income, through Partnership for Prescription Assistance.
- **Many colleges and universities** offer free or discounted courses to seniors.

MoneyTalksNews.com

Bubba Gump Shrimp Co.: 10%, which also applies to the meals of up to five other guests accompanying the senior and which also is available at several other chains owned by the Bubba Gump parent company, Landry, including Cameron's Steakhouse, Landry's Seafood House, Meriwether's and Rainforest Cafe (though not Rainforest Cafes in Disney theme parks).

Carrabba's Italian Grill: 10%.

Denny's: 15%.

Outback Steakhouse: 10%.

Papa John's: 25% on delivery and take-out orders placed online.

APPAREL AND DEPARTMENT STORES

Here are four apparel and department stores where seniors can save on clothing, housewares and more. (Typically these discounts cannot be combined with any other percentage discounts, but they often can be used together with coupons and "rewards.")

Bealls: 15% for age 50 and up every Tuesday.

Belk: 15% off on most items purchased online (10% on items from the home and shoe departments) for age 62 and up on the first Tuesday of each month. The discount climbs to 20% (15% on home/shoes) if you pay with a Belk charge card in store.

Dress Barn: 10% for age 62 and up one day a week at most locations, in store only. (The day of the week varies, but it usually is either Tuesday or Wednesday.)

Kohl's: 15% for age 60 and up on Wednesdays.

TRAVEL

Many travel-related businesses offer senior savings—but because these discounts often are applied to the full "rack" rate, they are not always good deals. Better deals might be available either through the company or through third-party travel websites such as Kayak.com or Expedia.com. Still, it's worth investigating—sometimes these discounts truly are money savers. *Among them...*

AARP car-rental deals: Alamo, Avis, Budget and Hertz up to 25% off. The top discount rate is not available at all locations.

Train and bus deals: Amtrak offers 15% off for age 62 and up. Greyhound offers 5% off for age 62 and up, and Peter Pan offers 15% off.

Hotel savings: Most major hotel chains offer senior discounts, frequently 5% to 20%, though they might not be available at all locations. These savings are available only when the room is booked directly through the hotel, not through a third-party travel app or website.

The good news is that hotel chains are trying to meet or beat the rates offered on these third-party sites on their own websites these days—and at some hotel chains, the senior discount can be applied to the "best available" room rate, not the steep "rack" rate. After finding the best rate you can on a third-party site, visit that chain's website or call its reservation number to check whether you could do better with the senior discount. *Examples:* Hotel chains where senior discounts often are available and are applied to the "best available" rate include Best Western (age 55 and up)...Hilton (AARP)...Starwood (AARP)...and Wyndham (age 60 and up).

Airline deals: Several airlines, including American, Southwest and United, say that they offer special fares for travelers age 65 and up. Unfortunately, you typically must call the airline and book directly to obtain these rates—and seniors who do so sometimes report that the senior fares they are offered are no lower than the typical fares. Be sure to shop around before booking one of these senior rates.

SHIPPING AND OFFICE SUPPLIES

If you are age 50 or older, you can join senior associations and qualify for attractive discounts at these businesses...

Office Depot and OfficeMax: These retailers offer a 10% discount on most office products—plus lower rates on copying and printing services—to members of the Association of Mature American Citizens (see below).

UPS: AARP members get 15% off many products and services, plus a 5% discount on shipping.

MOVIE THEATERS

Many movie theaters offer senior discounts that can save you a few dollars or more per ticket.

AMC: Many AMC theater locations offer discounted tickets to patrons age 60 and up, but details vary from theater to theater.

Cinemark: Most offer a "Senior Day" with reduced pricing. Details vary from theater to theater.

Showcase Cinemas: $7.50 admission for age 60 and up on Wednesdays. This applies even to 3-D and IMAX showings that ordinarily cost extra—though not on holidays and for certain special engagements.

ALTERNATIVES TO AARP

Many senior discounts actually are discounts offered to members of AARP, formerly known as the American Association of Retired Persons, which is open to people age 50 and up and their spouses (AARP.org, $16/year, spousal membership free).

But some seniors disagree with AARP's politics and prefer not to join. Those seniors might consider joining a different group such as the American Seniors Association (AmericanSeniors.org, $15/year, age 50 and up, spousal membership free) or the Association of Mature American Citizens (AMAC.us, $16/year, age 50 and up, spousal membership free). These groups have arranged some member discounts of their own, and businesses that offer AARP discounts sometimes are willing to extend those discounts to members of these senior associations, too, when asked to do so.

The End of "Old Age"—Change Your View to Live Longer

Marc E. Agronin, MD, vice president, behavioral health and clinical research, Miami Jewish Health Systems, and an adult and geriatric psychiatrist and affiliate associate professor of psychiatry and neurology at University of Miami Miller School of Medicine. He writes about senior health for *The Wall Street Journal* and is author of *The End of Old Age*. MarcAgronin.com

---

"Old age" has long gotten a bad rap. The conventional thinking has been that it's a time for rocking chairs, fading memory, illness and decrepitude.

Now: As an increasing number of Americans are living—and thriving—into their 80s and beyond, it's more important than ever to cast aside those outdated and harmful attitudes.

What the new thinking can mean for you: Older adults who see aging as a positive stage of life have fewer cardiovascular problems and actually outlive those with gloomier self-perceptions by more than seven years, according to landmark research conducted at Yale University.

So what are you waiting for? There are simple steps you can take to make sure that you aren't missing out on the richness of aging—and this uniquely positive life stage.

THE GIFTS OF AGE

As a geriatric psychiatrist, I have worked with hundreds of older adults who have developed life skills and perspectives that, in many ways, enable them to live more successfully than younger adults.

Of course, we can't kid ourselves. Old age does bring some challenges. We become more susceptible to disease. Our brains and bodies slow down. Daily life gets harder in many ways. The flip side is that some of the traits that come with age make us more adept at dealing with adversity and finding purpose in our lives.

Don't believe the myth that older adults get stuck in the past and can't handle new challenges. For example, research has shown that many older adults excel at *divergent thinking*, the ability to generate different solutions to particular problems. A lifetime of experiences helps them sort through complexities and explore novel ideas.

Other significant benefits that come with growing older—and what you can do to cultivate them in your own life...

- **A reserve of wisdom.** You can be smart and capable at any age, but wisdom is something different. It is an amalgam of all the knowledge, skill and attitudes that you have gained over time.

Wisdom is a trait that we often attribute to the world's great thinkers, but it also has a smaller, day-to-day scope.

Example: Mary, a woman in her 90s, had no earth-shattering life experiences. She wasn't known by anyone outside her small circle of family and friends. But within that circle, she had tremendous influence.

She had two Sunday rituals that gave her a sense of purpose—Catholic Mass in the morning and a family dinner in the afternoon. Her son-in-law would take her to church. After that, she would spend hours with her daughter and other family members preparing a multicourse Italian meal. She was the glue that held the family together—the one who shared recipes...passed along family stories...and overflowed with love. These are powerful forms of wisdom.

My advice: People sometimes ask, "How do I achieve wisdom?" *The answer:* You *already* have it. Think of wisdom as your life's résumé. It might consist of knowledge from your previous careers...military experience...being a good listener...a tolerance for different ideas, etc.

• **Resilience.** Hurricane Katrina, which devastated the Gulf Coast, was one of the deadliest hurricanes in history. Older adults were among the most vulnerable and suffered disproportionately. Thousands lost their homes, support networks and even their lives.

Yet subsequent research found that many of them coped just as well with the chaos as younger adults—and, in many cases, even better. Decades of experience increased their stores of resilience, the ability to manage life's obstacles without feeling helpless.

Examples: They didn't sweat the storm-related loss of cell-phone service or the Internet because they tended to view these things as luxuries, not necessities. Shortages of food and water? People who have lived through tough times know how to be resourceful when things are scarce. They could see beyond the chaos and find glimmers of acceptance and hope.

Resilience has physical benefits, as well. Not getting overwrought about difficulties allows the body to quickly recover from stress-related changes—muscle tension, increased heart rate, elevated stress hormones, etc.

Remarkable finding: A study of hundreds of older victims after the storm found that they often had the emotional and psychological strength to deal with the widespread loss of electricity and other basic services. In a way, it's not surprising—these were the same people who went through the Great Depression and World War II. Unlike younger victims, they already knew how to be resourceful in these types of situations. *My advice:* Even resilient adults will eventually hit what I call an "age point," in which their resources and coping skills are temporarily overwhelmed. It's important to get help—from a therapist and/or friends and family members—when you suffer such a potentially serious setback. The ultimate resolution can bring growth and greater resilience.

My advice: Even resilient adults will eventually hit what I call an "age point," in which their resources and coping skills are temporarily overwhelmed. It's important to get help—from a therapist and/or friends and family members—when you suffer such a potentially serious setback. The ultimate resolution can bring growth and greater resilience.

For example, one of my elderly patients had a blood test that indicated abnormal liver enzymes. She was convinced that she had a terminal disease and would be unable to care for her husband who had Alzheimer's disease. Her emotional state started to rapidly deteriorate.

Along with therapy, I treated her with a short-acting tranquilizer, which allowed her to get out of bed, leave the house and function more normally overall. She eventually recovered and was able to go off the medication—and, in some ways, grew stronger.

After further tests showed that she was fine, she recognized that she'd had a turning point that clarified what she wanted from life. She felt that she had been given a second chance to do what *really* mattered—to care for her husband, be a guide for her son, be active in the community and form a close network of friends.

• **Reinvention.** Older adults can do some of their best work late in life. After a serious illness, the French painter Henri Matisse turned his attention, in his 70s and 80s, to the paper cutouts that appeared in the influential book *Jazz* and eventually revolutionized the world of art. He brought a lifetime of experience to the new medium, along with a sense of freedom that's often missing in the young.

Gene Cohen, MD, a well-known psychiatrist, describes an *encore phase* that starts in the late 70s and continues until the end of life.

BETTER WAY...

Time to Take Up Drawing?

Become more resilient with a pen or brush. Recent retirees who made time to paint or draw once a week for 10 weeks were better able to handle the pressures of everyday life than people who did not take the time to create art.

Possible reason: Creating visual art may improve the connections among brain regions associated with resilience.

Study of retired adults by researchers at University Hospital Erlangen-Nuremberg, Germany, published in *PLOS ONE*.

People often take up new activities during this phase. It can be artistic endeavors...more reading...landscape design...or even real estate investing!

Important: You can reinvent yourself even if you're dealing with physical/cognitive issues. In fact, these issues mean that you *should* reinvent. You can shape your interests to circumvent otherwise detrimental changes.

My advice: Start small. Manage your expectations to match your current reality.

For example, one of my clients, a retired professor, suffered from memory loss that made it difficult to keep up with the high-powered, distinguished people she had always spent a lot of time with. She was deeply depressed.

We decided that she should find new intellectual opportunities that didn't require her to be on stage or to "compete." She started taking art and adult-education classes. Family members helped her get used to a computer and an iPad. She was able to pursue her intellectual interests in new (and more comfortable) ways. The opportunities are endless!

Surprising Health Risk for Retired Men

Richard Schwartz, MD, associate professor of psychiatry, Harvard Medical School, Boston, reported by Karen Larson, former editor, *Bottom Line Personal*, BottomLineInc.com.

My husband still sees his old fraternity brother seven times a year—they buy adjacent season tickets for their alma mater's football games. It turns out that they've stumbled on a great solution to a major health problem—the social isolation of retired men.

Social isolation increases the risk for heart disease, certain cancers and dementia while decreasing immune system function. "It has as important an effect on our health as smoking, high blood pressure or obesity," notes Richard Schwartz, MD, associate professor of psychiatry at Harvard Medical School and coauthor of *The Lonely American: Drifting Apart in the Twenty-first Century*.

With the kids grown and no more coworkers, retired men often have few social connections besides their spouses. Retired women face the same situation, but they're better equipped to handle it—women naturally tend to continue to form new friendships throughout their lives.

The best way for men to avoid this isolation trap is to set up *regularly scheduled* get-togethers centered around a shared activity, according to Schwartz. This could be as simple as "let's play golf every Saturday morning." Because these gatherings occur on a schedule, everyone can plan to attend, which increases the odds that the get-togethers will continue. Some travel might be necessary—my husband drives a few hours to get to the games.

How to Get Rid of Your Stuff...for Retirement Freedom!

Adriane Berg, Esq., an advocate for successful aging who has appeared on national TV programs and is host of the syndicated radio show *Generation Bold*. She is also author of 14 books, including *How Not to Go Broke at 102*, and is an attorney who helped found the National Academy of Elder Law Attorneys. Her blog can be found at BottomLineInc.com/blogs/aging-for-beginners.

In her best-selling book, *The Life-Changing Magic of Tidying Up*, Marie Kondo suggests we downsize by keeping only the things we truly love. That sounds smart, except that as we grow older, it may be the very things we do not particularly love, or even dislike, which we feel compelled to keep.

- **First, there's the stuff our now grown children left behind, and which they will never, ever take back.** My daughter Rose may have left for good, but Teddy Ruxpin is still here (as are Rose's rollerblades and massive collection of *Playbills*).

• **Next, there is the surviving detritus of other lives.** How can I ditch my father's old desk, his ribbon for Class Pest, my mother's Persian lamb coat, which she wore every day, or my aunt's now mildewed Singer sewing table? Frankly, I fear reprisal in the form of grief, regret or curses from the grave.

• **Finally, not everything we are saddled with can be blamed on other people.** We also have our own Hall of Shame and Hall of Fame. On the shame side are things like furs, ivory jewelry and maybe even blood diamonds. No one paid attention when we bought these things in the old days. But these are different times and we have evolved. To get rid of these items now, you must bundle them into black plastic bags and stuff them into the trunk of your car in the dead of night.

And we all bought all kinds of nifty stuff in the '60's, '70's and '80's. Some of this stuff may now be called "vintage" and worth some money. We think about selling our personal Hall of Fame items on eBay or on consignment. But in the end, the stuff just sits there waiting for our kids to deal with it.

CAN WE BE THE GENERATION TO BREAK THE STUFF CYCLE?

We can, but it won't be easy. First, we need to acknowledge the deep psychological connection between people and stuff. Even cavemen had stuff, or else there would be no archeologists. Real professors have conducted a study about stuff to prove that we can be damaged and depressed by losing things as well as people. So tread lightly as you divest yourself.

• **Ask first, *Do I use it?*** If the answer is *No,* put it on a hit list. Next ask, *Does anybody want it and will they appreciate it?* If so, give it to them. I get pleasure out of giving my old designer clothing to amateur production companies and donating books to the library. My friend got a suite of Victorian furniture that never fit my decor. The thought of her regard for these pieces gives me a warm feeling that I did right by Aunt Rose.

• **If no one wants the things you don't use, sell what you can and donate the rest.** I've given items to the Lupus Foundation, Big Brothers and Big Sisters and other worthy charities. (Several toilets and wood flooring went to Habitat for Humanity...and they were thrilled to get them.)

• **And what of the items with which you still can't part, yet never use?** Don't delude yourself. You will never use them. At least not in their present form. So maybe you can change their form. I reconstruct old jewelry to be more to my present taste. A friend cuts up old fabric and makes tote bags as gifts.

• **If you still feel stuff-bound, storage can be a temporary solution.** Storage costs money, but the more it costs, the better, as that will force you to be judicious.

Tip: Take a photo of everything you store. A month later, write a list of these items from memory. Now match this list against the photos—and get rid of anything you didn't remember you stored. Two months later, do this again. What's left, you keep in storage or find a place for at home.

You'll never get rid of everything. After all, few of us were born to be minimalist. But, let's do what we can!

13

Travel Hacks

How to Travel Alone... and *Love It*

Are you tired of dragging your partner along on vacations that you know he/she will not enjoy? Leave him/her home instead! Or have you opted out of trips because you don't have a travel partner? Stop waiting to meet that special someone before taking a special journey. You can travel solo and *love* it.

Travel-industry ads feature romantic couples and happy families, but in reality, plenty of people travel alone. Solo travelers represent nearly one-quarter of all leisure travelers.

Unfortunately, most of the travel industry remains set up for couples and families, so going it alone can lead to inflated costs. A solo trip, including food and transportation, may cost less than a couple's trip in absolute terms, but it tends to cost more on a per-person basis. Hotel rooms don't cost half as much, and tour companies and cruise lines often impose "single supplements" that add anywhere from 10% to 100% to the usual per-person rate.

We asked solo-travel expert Janice Leith Waugh how to save money—hundreds of dollars for each trip—when traveling alone without sacrificing quality or feeling lonely...

• **Find tour companies that charge little or no "single supplement."** Most tour operators charge extra on a per-person basis if you will be the only one staying in your room. But a small number of tour operators have no such added fee (or only a modest added fee) on certain trips. These not only save solo travelers money—their popularity with solo travelers means that there likely will be others traveling alone in your tour group, which creates opportunities for camaraderie and makes

Note: Prices, rates and offers throughout this chapter and book are subject to change.

Janice Leith Waugh, founder of SoloTravelerWorld.com, which offers recommendations and links to special deals for solo travelers. Based in Toronto, she is author of *The Solo Traveler's Handbook*.

the solo travel experience less awkward and isolating for all. *Examples...*

- **Overseas Adventure** does not charge single supplements on any of its 70-plus land-based trips, which range from African safaris to Tuscany tours to adventures high in the Himalayas. A modest single supplement does apply on some, but not all, of its ship-based trips. OATTravel.com

- **Exodus Travels** imposes only very modest single supplements on most trips—as low as $10 a night. It offers certain "Solo Departures" trips, such as walks through Andalucia or hiking in the mountains of Morocco, specifically for solo travelers. ExodusTravels.com/activities/solo-departures

- **Road Scholar,** a not-for-profit organization that specializes in educational travel, charges no single supplement on certain trips, among them hiking and canoeing in the Ozarks and exploring the Loire Valley in France. Single rooms on these trips often sell out quickly, however. RoadScholar.org/special-offers/singles-at-no-extra-cost

Another way to avoid single supplements is to ask tour operators and cruise lines whether they offer a "room sharing" program, which many do. With these programs, a solo traveler doesn't pay extra if he agrees to share a room with another solo traveler of the same gender. (Also ask the travel company whether it will waive any single supplement if it cannot find you a roommate—that varies from program to program.) Of course, room sharing isn't for everyone—a recent survey of more than 200,000 solo travelers found that nearly two-thirds prefer not to share a room with a stranger even if it would save them money.

Warning: Although some cruise ships have a small number of one-person cabins that carry no single supplement, demand for these greatly exceeds supply. Price-sensitive solo cruisers usually are better off searching for sale prices on standard cabins even though that means paying a single supplement. There often are great deals available on unsold cabins as the departure date nears.

- **Stay in lodgings designed—and priced—with solo travelers in mind.** Certain hotels have affordably priced compact rooms appropriate for singles.

Examples: Z Hotels in the UK (prices start at around $70* in London or about $50 in Liverpool or Glasgow, TheZHotels.com)...The Pod Hotels in the US (prices start at $85 to $99 at three New York City locations and $104 in Washington, DC, ThePodHotel.com).

Bed & breakfasts are another option. Solo travelers don't pay less than couples, but B&Bs do tend to be more social than hotels, which can be nice for solo travelers who want to have someone to chat with at the start or end of the day.

Want to save a lot of money? Hostels offer beds in shared rooms (and sometimes even private rooms) for a fraction of what you might pay for a hotel room. And despite what you might be picturing, not all hostels are dingy dives for college kids on break. Some are clean, safe and cater to all ages. Hostels also tend to be much more social than hotels, which can be nice for solo vacationers hoping to meet new acquaintances.

Example: The YHA hostels in the UK are excellent. The YHA London Central is especially impressive, with clean, modern facilities and an appealing location near Oxford Street. (Prices start at around $20 per night for a bed in a shared room, YHA.org.uk.)

- **Plan your trip around a class.** You could take a weeklong cooking class and learn to make the local/regional cuisine...or take an intensive immersion language class to learn to speak the local language. These kinds of classes provide something fun and enriching to do during the day...plus a group of classmates with whom to socialize afterward. There likely will be many people taking the class on their own, so your solo status won't feel uncomfortable. To find classes, enter your destination...class topics of interest...and the word "course" or "class" into a search engine.

- **Use Meetup.com to find groups, activities and new acquaintances.** This online service is designed to help people find activities of interest near where they live—but it's also

*Hotel rates are based on weekday stays for one person as of June 1, 2018.

a great resource for travelers. Before your trip, use the site to find groups in the area that have interesting activities planned for when you will be in town, then sign up and join in—many Meetup.com groups and activities are open to anyone who wishes to participate.

Examples: I went on a hike with a local outdoors group when I visited Hong Kong. A woman I know finds jogging groups (also called "run crews") in the cities she visits. Jogging groups often get coffee or beers after their runs (especially on weekends), which makes this a particularly good way to meet and socialize with locals.

• **Attend theater performances or live music in the evening...and/or sign up for nighttime city tours.** Some solo travelers retreat to their hotel rooms at dusk because they feel self-conscious about being out on the town alone after dark. Don't hide! Attend live music and theater performances instead. It won't matter much that you're alone at these performances because even if you were with friends, you would mostly be watching the performers, not chatting among yourselves.

Similarly, when you take a tour, you're basically listening to a tour guide whether you are alone or with friends. Nighttime tours can be a great way to see a city in a different way, too.

Example: Evening walking tours of Paris are unforgettable—the city is vibrant and stunning at night.

Meetup.com also might provide interesting evening activity options.

• **Travel with just one piece of luggage.** Solo travelers don't have anyone to watch their luggage when they need to run to the bathroom, so it's best to bring just one bag (ideally a carry-on) that you easily can keep at your side until you reach your destination.

• **Arrive at your hotel before dark.** It's wise to investigate where your hotel is located before booking a room, but sometimes you can't really get a sense about the safety of a place before you arrive and see it in person. That's why it's best to arrive before dusk, when you can see it in the daylight...and when it might be early enough in the day that you can easily find another room somewhere else, if necessary. Solo travelers can make appealing targets for criminals, so remain in public areas as much as possible during your travels. When you must move through areas that are not crowded after dark, don't walk—take cabs.

MORE FUN...

To Make a Vacation Seem Longer...

Don't plan it to death. Leaving room for spontaneity means you have to think each moment through. Visit a museum...or go for a rambling walk. This seems to make the trip last longer.

Marc Wittmann, PhD, psychologist and time-perception expert, Institute for Frontier Areas in Psychology and Mental Health, Freburg, Germany, interviewed by QZ.com.

Vacation Better Using a Travel Agent

Susan Farewell, owner of Farewell Travels LLC, a Westport, Connecticut, travel design firm. Farewell specializes in custom designing itineraries to destinations around the world. FarewellTravels.com

A lot of people think that travel agents have been put out of business because of the do-it-yourself options on the Internet. But travel agents still are very much around—and a good one can help you plan a better trip than you could on your own and save you money. *Here are the traits of a good travel agent and how to find one...*

• **They make it their business to really get to know you.** They will know, for example, that you want to eventually visit Greece or go on safari. They'll keep their eyes open for you, sending e-mails to alert you to great deals they hear about. Some even will create long-range plans with you.

• **They travel a lot.** Good travel agents personally test-drive experiences as much as possible, so they know which you are likely to enjoy the most, whether it's doing a Vespa foodie tour in Ho Chi Minh City or a museum tour in Italy. Good agents have stayed at the hotels they recommend, and their clients may get perks such as free room upgrades. Obviously, not every agent has gone everywhere. But good ones have networks that cover the globe. Their recommendations can make or break your trips.

• **They are available around the clock.** You've just arrived in Auckland, New Zealand, and your hotel can't find a record of your reservation. The best travel agents pride themselves on being personally reachable 24/7 or having a good backup person who is. Good luck getting that kind of assistance from Hotels.com!

• **They recognize real deals.** The Internet is very good at convincing you that you've found a deal when that isn't necessarily true. Travel agents have an understanding of what exactly is a deal and just how limited inventory might be. They can save you from making bad decisions.

• **To find a good travel agent.** Word-of-mouth always is best—ask your friends and colleagues. Or ask for references from a local community blog or social-media site. There also are professional organizations that list agents, including the American Society of Travel Advisors (ASTA.org). If an agent looks promising, call him/her. Ask him how long he has been a travel professional. How often does he travel? Tell him what you're interested in. Pay attention to his suggestions and how well he listens to you.

• **What will it cost?** Fees range from $150 to $1,500 to design an itinerary, depending on the length and complexity of the trip. Travel agents also charge airline ticket–processing fees, which range from $35 per round-trip domestic ticket to $100 for multileg international trips. As for straightforward bookings, such as booking a hotel room, a cruise or tour package, some agents do not charge fees because they receive commissions from the companies.

Easy Ways to Save on Flights and More

• **Figure out whether a flight is worth the money** with a simple formula—multiply round-trip miles, airport to airport, by $.032, and add $230 to get the average ticket price.

• **Book through Google Flights,** which has a vast amount of information and lets you monitor prices, filter for number of stops and find the cheapest days to fly.

• **If you are completely flexible about where and when to fly,** use Google Flights with only an area or country name, such as Europe or Japan...or try Kayak Explore, Kayak.com/explore, for a map filled with locations and prices.

• **Use Uber or Lyft** at your destination to avoid high-cost taxis.

Komando.com

If You're Planning an All-Inclusive Vacation...

Check the term's meaning at every resort you are considering. Food and nonalcoholic beverages usually are included, but alcohol, activities, water sports, rides to and from the airport, resort fees and other costs may or may not be part of the package. Some resorts charge more for access to more amenities but still call all their tiers all-inclusive. Also be sure to find out what entertainment is included if that is important to you.

To save money, book as a group if you can, and stay brand-loyal if possible—resorts and chains offer perks and discounts to regular customers. And watch for special promotions such as "kids stay free" deals—these can include not only a child's lodging but also the child's food and activities.

WiseBread.com

GOOD TO KNOW...

What Does Trip-Cancellation Insurance Really Cover?

Trip-cancellation insurance will pay only in very *specific* circumstances. For illness, you must see a doctor before canceling—or typically within 72 hours of cancellation. Insurance will not cover you when a threat, such as a big storm, is already known—the insurance protects only against unforeseen events. Canceling a trip because of a delay—even an extended one—may not be covered. You generally must lose more than 50% of your scheduled trip length because of a covered travel delay.

Self-defense: Be sure to read the terms, conditions and exclusions of your policy carefully—you must follow requirements to the letter or your claim can be rejected.

AllianzTravelInsurance.com

Don't Be a Victim of Airline Doublespeak

Brett Snyder, founder and president of Cranky Flier LLC, which operates the Cranky Concierge air-travel assistance service and the CrankyFlier.com website, Long Beach, California. He previously worked for United, USAir and America West airlines. CrankyFlier.com

Sometimes it seems that airlines have a language all their own. Even common phrases whose meanings seem quite obvious really may mean something very different. Don't let seemingly straightforward words cost you extra money and time. Here are 10 ways that airlines (and travel websites that sell air tickets) try to confuse you...and how to see right through their doublespeak...

• **"Direct flight."** If you don't want to worry about catching connecting flights, you might book a "direct flight" on the assumption that this will take you directly to your destination.

What's tricky: Direct flight just means that the flight has the same flight number the whole way, not that it flies directly to your destination. Years ago, it also meant that the entire flight was on the same aircraft, but even that is often not true anymore.

What to do: If you want a flight that will take you from airport A to airport B with no stops or changes in between, find a "nonstop" flight, not a direct flight. If you're OK with a stop as long as you can stay on the same plane, favor Southwest Airlines, where direct flights usually are on the same plane.

• **"Basic economy."** This term begins with the word "basic," so you might reasonably assume that you're booking an ordinary economy-class ticket.

What's tricky: Basic economy actually is a new class of ticket that's significantly more restricted than an ordinary economy ticket. You will not be allowed to obtain a seat assignment prior to departure day...or make changes to your itinerary even if you are willing to pay a fee to do so. On many airlines, you cannot even bring a carry-on bag (you still can bring a "personal item" small enough to fit under the seat in front of you, but not a bag that would have to be stowed in the overhead compartment), and if you try to, it will be diverted to checked baggage and you will face both a baggage charge and a penalty.

What to do: Watch for the words "basic economy" when you book. If you see this, carefully read any fine print. If booking through a third-party website, visit the airline's site to review that carrier's basic-economy rules.

• **"Personal item."** Travelers traditionally can bring into the cabin both a carry-on bag and a "personal item" such as a purse, briefcase, small backpack or laptop bag. Even discount airlines in the US that impose fees for carry-ons and basic-economy tickets that don't allow carry-ons still allow a personal item without any extra fee.

What's tricky: What counts as a personal item varies from airline to airline. The rule of thumb is that the item must fit under the seat in front of you, but how big is that? If you show up at the gate with something that doesn't qualify, you might be hit with fees and penalties totaling perhaps $50 to $100.

What to do: Check your airline's "personal item" rules before packing for your trip. For example, on American, Frontier and Spirit, a bag up to 18-x-14-x-8-inches qualifies...on United, it's 17-x-10-x-9-inches…on JetBlue, 17-x-13-x-8-inches…on Allegiant, 16-x-15-x-7-inches. Some airlines do not disclose a specific size but do list specific types of items that qualify.

• **"Premium economy."** If you want a little more space and comfort than offered in "standard economy" without the steep price of business or first class, premium economy could be an option.

What's tricky: Sometimes premium economy refers to seats that are in a special section of the plane and that have extra legroom, extra width, improved reclining ability, footrests and/or come with better food. But often, "premium economy" simply means a typical seat in the economy-class cabin that has a few extra inches of legroom.

What to do: If you book a premium-economy seat through a third-party website, read the small print or visit the airline's website to check what specific upgrades this seat offers over a standard-economy seat. If you book directly through an airline, seats might not be labeled "premium economy" but instead will sport a label unique to that airline.

Examples: If a seat is listed as "Economy Plus" on United…"Main Cabin Extra" on American or "Comfort+" on Delta, all you're getting is a few extra inches of legroom.

• **"Boarding group 1."** Being among the first to board a plane ensures that there's room for your carry-on bags in overhead bins and means less squeezing through crowded aisles to reach your seat.

What's tricky: You may already know that some people get to board before "Boarding group 1," but on various airlines, those groups can be quite extensive. Some airlines "preboard" many other passengers first, potentially including travelers who have elite frequent-flier status…those who have paid for early boarding…military members in uniform…first-class passengers…handicapped travelers…passengers traveling with young children…and more. In fact, it's not unusual for a plane to be half full before boarding group 1 gets called.

What to do: If boarding early is important to you, you often can pay a fee for "priority" boarding—precisely when passengers with priority boarding get on board varies from airline to airline. This might be worthwhile if you are initially placed in a low boarding group on a crowded flight and you don't want to risk having to check your carry-on bag…or if you are flying on Southwest, which does not have assigned seats. Or you should travel with bags small enough to fit under the seat in front of you so that you never have to depend on limited overhead bin capacity.

• **"Nonrefundable ticket."** Most airline tickets are sold as "nonrefundable"—you cannot get your money back if your travel plans change.

What's tricky: Because of Department of Transportation (DOT) regulations, passengers actually can get their money back even if their tickets are nonrefundable—in certain circumstances. To qualify, you must cancel within 24 hours of booking a ticket that was purchased at least seven days prior to departure (or purchased at least two days prior to departure on American Airlines).

These DOT rules apply only to flights booked directly through the airline (though many travel agencies will apply the same policy) and only for domestic flights and international flights departing from US airports.

What to do: If you might have to cancel a booking, do so at least a week before departure (two days on American) and within 24 hours of booking.

• **"Changeable."** Although most tickets are "nonrefundable," they are at least "changeable"—you can adjust details such as departure date.

What's tricky: Although travelers usually have the right to change their itineraries, most airlines impose "change fees" so steep that it often is not worth doing so—as much as $200 domestic or $500 international. You might be able to buy a new ticket for less.

What to do: If there's a good chance that you will need to change your itinerary, fly Southwest, if possible—it has no change fees (although you still pay the fare difference, if any). Before paying a change fee on another airline, check to make sure that paying it is cheaper than simply buying a new ticket.

• **"No blackout dates."** One of the most common complaints about frequent-flier programs is that it's hard to get an awards ticket when you want one. Thus programs that advertise "no blackout dates" can seem very appealing.

What's tricky: Although no-blackout-date programs do not have any dates on which no awards seats are offered, there might be only a small number of awards seats that inevitably are quickly snapped up. If the program says any open seat is available to awards travelers, the number of miles required for that awards seat will increase with the cost of the ticket, which can be prohibitive during peak travel times.

Example: A plane ticket that costs $1,000 might require 100,000 award miles, four times as much as the standard 25,000 miles for a round-trip domestic ticket.

What to do: Do not be swayed by promises of "no blackout dates" when you decide which frequent-flier programs to participate in. The best programs for you are those offered by airlines that fly to the destinations you travel to most often, blackout dates or no.

• **"Check-in time."** Your flight's departure time is not the only deadline you need to worry about—there also is a "check-in time."

What's tricky: These check-in times vary from airline to airline and airport to airport. Plus, there might be a deadline for reaching the boarding gate in addition to the deadline for checking in. You could reach the gate while other passengers still are boarding and be told that you're too late—you missed a deadline, and the airline gave away your seat.

What to do: Search the name of the airline and "check-in requirements" or "check-in times" to find specific deadlines for your airline and airport. Check in online via the Internet or your phone so that you can focus on only the deadlines for checking your bags and arriving at the gate. Or just arrive at the airport early enough that checking in at least one hour before departure time and reaching the gate at least 30 minutes before departure time will not be a problem. Avoid booking flights that have connections too tight for this.

• **"Hot meals available."** Meals seldom are provided at no extra charge in economy class on domestic flights these days, but on long flights airlines often do say that economy-class passengers can buy meals onboard.

What's tricky: It's not unusual for a flight to run out of economy-class meals before every economy passenger who wants one has had a chance to buy one. Airlines cannot be sure how many passengers on a flight will want a meal, and they would rather run out of meals than carry too many.

What to do: Buy food at the airport to eat on the plane, or bring food from home. Visit the Transportation Security Administration's website to confirm that you will be able to get food from home through security checkpoints (TSA.gov/travel/security-screening/whatcanibring/food).

GOOD TO KNOW...

Safest Airline to Fly

The safest airline to fly is Australia's Qantas. In its 96-year history, it has never had a recorded fatality. Other top airlines for safety—listed alphabetically and based on audits from aviation regulators and governments, crash and serious-incident records, profitability and fleet age—Air New Zealand, Alaska, All Nippon, British Airways, Cathay Pacific, Delta, Etihad, EVA Air, Finnair, Hawaiian, Japan, KLM, Lufthansa, Scandinavian, Singapore, Swiss, United, Virgin Atlantic, Virgin Australia.

Survey and analysis of records of 425 airlines by aviation-analysis firm AirlineRatings.com, reported at MarketWatch.com.

Best US Airline for Overall Service

In a recent survey, Alaska Airlines was tops in certain categories for on-time arrivals, avoiding extreme delays and complaints. Delta scored first on measures of canceled flights and involuntary bumping. Virgin America was tops for minimizing mishandled baggage. Alaska recently acquired Virgin America and is meshing the two carriers' systems.

Middle Seat's annual scorecard of US airlines' performance on seven different measures important to travelers, reported in *The Wall Street Journal.*

How to Keep Your Frequent-Flier Miles from Ever Expiring

Tim Winship, editor-at-large for SmarterTravel.com and author of *Mileage Pro—The Insider's Guide to Frequent Flyer Programs.*

There is no excuse for letting your frequent-flier miles depart without you. Although earned miles typically expire if there is no activity in your account for 18 to 24 months, it is easy to reset the clock without flying anywhere. You can do it by adding or redeeming a single point...using certain credit cards...donating to charity...and other ways that few people know to use. *Here are smart ways to keep your miles active when they are approaching their expiration date...*

• **Join an airline dining rewards program—and agree to receive e-mails.** Dining for miles is an easy way to earn and extend miles. You can register any credit card for free with your airline's dining rewards program—not only mileage cards that earn you points for purchases. Either go to the airline's home page and search for "dining rewards" or search online for the airline name and "dining rewards program." Once you join, many major airlines, including Delta, United and Southwest, let you earn at least one mile for every $2 you spend at participating restaurants, while American Airlines lets you earn at least one mile for every $1 spent. (If you have a mileage credit card, registering it for a dining program can get you double credit—points for eating at the participating restaurant...and points for charging the meal to your mileage card.) Even a cup of coffee should be enough to extend your miles.

If you participate in more than one frequent-flier program, link a different credit card to each one's dining rewards program. This approach will let you extend all your miles on different airlines by using different registered credit cards at different times at various participating restaurants.

Even better: If you agree to receive e-mails from your dining program, you typically will earn three miles for every $1 you spend at participating restaurants—well worth a little in-box clutter. You also can receive bonus miles when you join a dining program, although in some cases you may be required to write short reviews of the first several restaurants you visit to qualify for the bonus. And on the biggest major US airlines, if you attain VIP status, which requires at least 12 dining transactions in a calendar year, you get five miles for every $1 spent.

Caution: Check each restaurant's policy on your airline's dining rewards site. Many restaurants do not offer rewards on certain days of the week.

• **Make a purchase through the airline's shopping portal.** Shopping at an online "mileage mall"—a store where you earn points for every dollar you spend purchasing products from hundreds of retailers—extends the expiration date for your existing miles. If you prefer shopping in a brick-and-mortar store, you can extend your miles by buying a gift card in an online mileage mall from, say, Target or Bloomingdale's or another retailer and using it later. (*Note:* Most mileage-mall retailers won't let you buy a gift card and then spend it at the online mall.)

• **Book your next overnight trip directly with a partner hotel.** Most major hotel chains will offer you airline miles for your stay, which extends the expiration date of your existing miles—but only if you book directly with the hotel. If you book through a third party, such as Expedia.com or Travelocity.com, most chains won't award points.

Exception: If you book through RocketMiles.com, which mostly represents independent hotels, you can earn points. In fact, for most small, independent hotels, you need to book through this service to get points for your stay.

Helpful: Although some frequent-flier programs may allow you to convert your existing hotel points to miles—thus extending the expiration date of your entire airline-miles balance—it is rarely a good idea. The points-to-miles exchange rate usually is unattractive, for example, costing you about five hotel points for one mile. Sometimes, however, airlines offer exchange bonuses that can make a conversion a compelling option to extend miles or can push you over the top to a free flight.

• **Use the best points-earning credit card.** If you tend to fly on one airline, get a co-branded credit card that earns points on that airline. Every time you charge something on the card, it extends your miles, and you even might get a bonus when obtaining the card. For instance, if you prefer American Airlines, you can sign up for a Citi AAdvantage card that typically offers a sign-up bonus (recently 60,000 miles) with a qualifying amount of purchases (recently $3,000) within the first three months. And those purchases are doing double-duty by also extending the expiration date of your existing miles.

If you tend to use various airlines, you can sign up for a credit card that lets you earn miles and transfer them to any of a number of participating airline points programs. When you transfer the miles, it extends the expiration date in that program.

A good card to consider: Chase Sapphire Preferred. Besides the recent sign-up bonus of 50,000 miles after $4,000 in qualifying purchases in the first three months, there is no annual fee the first year ($95 thereafter), and you can transfer points to about a dozen different airline frequent-flier programs.

Helpful: Since most children don't have credit cards, it's harder to keep their miles active. But once you open a credit card account with Chase, you can add your children (no minimum age) as authorized users for no fee. You will remain the primary cardholder responsible for the bill, but now you can transfer points you earn from purchases with that card to their plans, which extends the expiration date of their existing miles. Unlike transferring miles through your airline program, there's no fee and you don't lose points in the exchange.

• **Donate your miles to a good cause.** Earning miles isn't the only way to keep your miles active. You also can give some to a charitable organization such as the American Cancer Society or the Make-A-Wish Foundation. Most airlines require you to give at least 500 to 1,000 miles at a time, but doing so keeps the rest of your miles alive while supporting good causes.

Note: Donated miles are not tax-deductible.

Another charitable option: Some airlines offer limited-time opportunities to extend your mileage expiration dates by making donations of as little as $1 to various charities, typically in response to an e-mail request sent to you or a promotion featured at an airline's online shopping portal.

• **When you need household services, check your airline's list of mileage-plan vendors.** Glance through your airline's list of partners ranging from home-energy companies to florists. You likely will find that any purchase or service you need could net you new miles and extend the ones you already have. As long as the price is reasonable and the service is high-quality, that's a win-win.

Little-Known Tip for Getting a Seat Upgrade

Better-dressed fliers may receive upgrades if better seats are available and no one on board qualifies based on mileage status. Gate agents have discretion about upgrades, and while airlines officially say that they do not take appearance into account, in practice a traveler's wardrobe may make a difference.

Even when upgrades are not provided, better-dressed travelers may receive more courteous service from flight crews.

Roundup of airline crew members and spokespeople, reported in *The New York Times.*

Fly for Free by Getting Bumped on Purpose

Scott Keyes, founder of Scott's Cheap Flights, an e-mail subscription service that searches for airfare bargains, Fort Collins, Colorado. He is author of *How to Fly for Free: Practical Tips the Airlines Don't Want You to Know.* ScottsCheapFlights.com

For the passenger who was dragged off a United Airlines flight in April 2017, getting bumped was a nightmare. But for travelers who have the flexibility to switch flights at the last minute, getting bumped purposely can be desirable. And if you are able to do it over and over, it can be quite lucrative—even more so if you know the best strategies to become a frequent bumpee...

VOLUNTARY VS. INVOLUNTARY BUMPINGS

When airlines need to free up seats, usually because they have overbooked a flight, they offer to bump passengers in exchange for rewards and a seat on a later flight.

To become an expert at being bumped, first you need to know the rules, which differ depending on several factors, including whether you are bumped voluntarily or involuntarily.

• **If it's voluntary,** which is most often the case, the airline usually offers a voucher that can be used to pay for a future flight.

Typically, the gate agent will announce that the airline is willing to give a travel voucher worth perhaps $150 to $250. Sometimes airlines, including Delta and United, ask passengers if they would be willing to be bumped when they initially check in for an overbooked flight.

If not enough passengers accept an initial offer, the value of the travel vouchers will increase—$500 to $1,000 is not uncommon. United recently said it would start offering up to $10,000 if that's what it takes to get someone to give up a seat voluntarily—though in practice, the airline is unlikely to need to offer anywhere close to that amount.

• **If it's involuntary,** FAA rules now require the airline to pay the passenger twice the value of the one-way ticket, up to $675, if the new flight is scheduled to get the passenger to the destination between one and two hours after the original arrival time (one to four hours on international flights)...or four times the value, up to $1,350, if it's more than two hours past the original arrival time (four hours on international flights). Involuntarily bumped travelers have the right to demand this payment in the form of a check or cash rather than a voucher.

Exceptions: The airline does not have to pay if it puts an involuntarily bumped passenger on a different flight that reaches the destination within one hour of the original arrival time...if the passenger is bumped because the airline substituted a smaller plane for the flight...or in certain other situations. Rules also differ on flights departing from foreign airports.

Involuntary bumpings have become rare, however—out of approximately 475,000 passengers bumped last year, only about 40,000 were involuntary, and that figure is likely to fall in the wake of the United incident.

Helpful: Consider what the travel vouchers are truly worth. If you travel on the airline frequently, its vouchers might be almost as valuable to you as cash. Unlike frequent-flier miles, there generally are no restrictions on when these vouchers can be redeemed. But if you do not fly much and/or this airline does not offer many routes you often travel, the vouchers might not be worth the trouble—particularly because these vouchers often expire in 12 months if not used.

PLAYING THE BUMP GAME

Here's how to get the most from getting bumped...

• **Check the "seat map" before heading to the airport for a flight.** If there are no available seats shown for a flight on the airline website a few hours prior to departure, there's a good chance the flight is overbooked. If you are interested in getting bumped, get to the gate at least 45 to 60 minutes before departure time to ensure that you're there when the gate agent requests volunteers.

• **Position yourself as close as possible to the gate agent.** If there are more volunteers than the airline needs, the first ones to reach the agent usually are the ones who get bumped.

• **Do not check luggage unless necessary.** Travel only with carry-on bags if getting bumped is your goal. Otherwise your checked luggage might take the flight you miss and end up lost...or the gate agent might choose a different volunteer to avoid having to redirect your luggage.

• **Evaluate how desperate the airline is.** Often the gate agent will announce how many volunteers are needed. As a rule of thumb, if five or more volunteers are needed, there's a good chance the airline will have to increase its initial offer to find enough volunteers, so the smart strategy might be to decline the initial offer. If only one or two volunteers are needed, the opening offer might be the only one.

Exceptions: The airline might have to increase its offer to find even one or two takers if the flight is the last of the day to its destination...or if it's the last day before a holiday or a major event such as the Super Bowl.

• **Instead of saying, "I accept," say, "What's my new route and arrival time if I accept?"** There's no way to know whether the offer is worth taking until you find out how much of your time you will lose.

Also: If the delay will be lengthy, confirm that the airline will provide vouchers for any meals you need to eat in the airport and/or the hotel room you will need for an overnight stay.

• **If the airline needs multiple volunteers, ask for its final offer.** Rather than accept the initial offer, tell the gate agent that you are willing to give up your seat as long as you receive the same compensation as the next-to-final passenger to accept, which is likely to be a better offer. Gate agents often will agree to this.

• **Ask for upgrades and other perks.** In addition to a travel voucher, the gate agent might be willing to give you a first-class seat on a later flight if one is available...a more direct route with shorter or fewer layovers...and/or airport lounge passes. Such things generally are at the gate agent's discretion, so ask politely.

• **Ask for compensation if you get "unbumped" back onto your original flight.** This is rare, but sometimes a volunteer ends up back on the original flight after the airline discovers that it does not need to bump as many travelers as it first thought. Not only does the unbumped passenger not get the promised travel voucher, he/she often doesn't get the original seat, either—and may end up in an undesirable middle seat. And because unbumped passengers usually are the last to board packed flights, there often is no room in the overhead compartments for their carry-on bags.

What to do: Politely request some compensation, such as a voucher or lounge passes that you can use on a future layover (though they probably are much less than you would have received if successfully bumped). If you don't get anything, later go to the airline's website and send a politely worded e-mail to the airline's executives requesting some sort of compensation. The airlines are so worried about bad press these days that there's a good chance you will be offered something.

Airports with Cheap or Free Attractions

Roundup of experts on travel at GoBankingRates.com.

Don't miss these little-known free or cheap attractions at airports around the world...

• **Austin-Bergstrom International Airport,** in Texas, offers free performances by local musicians for ticketed passengers.

• **Changi Airport,** Singapore's international airport, offers a free 24-hour movie theater, swimming pool, indoor gardens, video-game stations and the world's tallest slide in an airport.

• **Incheon International Airport** in Seoul, South Korea, features play areas and a movie theater.

• **At Istanbul Atatürk Airport,** Turkish Airlines offers any passenger with a layover of six hours or more a free tour of Istanbul.

• **Minneapolis–St. Paul International Airport** is home to the See 18 Film Screening Room, which features free, around-the-clock showings of short films and documentaries by local filmmakers.

• **At Munich Airport,** travelers can take a tour (which includes a tasting) of Airbräu, a microbrewery located inside the airport, for about $10 per person for a minimum of three people.

Lost Luggage? What to Do...

WiseBread.com

Report the loss immediately—there usually is a counter for this near the baggage carousels and bring your baggage ticket to be used for a search. *Then...*

• **Go to the airline's website,** and click on the lost-luggage section if you have not heard anything in 24 hours.

• **Continue to follow up if necessary**—by calling customer service if the website is not enough.

• **Keep your claim updated**—for instance, if you are traveling and change hotels, be sure the airline knows.

• **Ask the airline how much essential spending is covered,** and use the coverage to buy new travel basics such as clothing, shampoo and deodorant—keep all receipts for submission later.

• **Be prepared to negotiate if your luggage is not found**—the airline will not immediately make its best offer.

• **Complain on social media if the airline drags** its feet about reimbursement or makes the whole process harder than it already is—this can sometimes get the airline to speed up the process.

12 Ways to Save on Rental Cars

Christopher Elliott, a consumer advocate who writes the "On Travel" column for *USA Today* and "The Navigator" column for *The Washington Post.* He is author of *How to Be the World's Smartest Traveler (and Save Time, Money and Hassle).* Elliott.org

Don't let a car-rental company take you for a ride. Whether you think the daily rental rate you are quoted is a bargain or steep, even more tricky charges probably lurk down the road. And it's not just the infamous overpriced insurance that rental companies are known to push at the checkout counter.

Here are ways to find lower rates and reduce the odds of being victimized by sneaky rental-car charges...

FIND THE BEST RATES

Travel websites such as Expedia, Priceline, Kayak and Hotwire sometimes offer appealing rental rates and are worth checking. *But if you are willing to invest a bit more time, you could also...*

• **Try a travel agency.** Old-fashioned brick-and-mortar travel agencies often have access to special car-rental rates through the travel agent consortiums they belong to.

• **Search for deals at rental locations that aren't at an airport.** Airport-related taxes and fees can increase the cost of renting there by 10% to 25% or even more in some cases. You often come out ahead if you pick up your car at a lot that isn't right at the airport even after factoring in the cost of taking a cab or car share to this lot.

• **Shop early *and* late.** Is it better to search for car-rental deals long in advance of the trip...or just before the trip? Both. Many rental-car reservations can be canceled without penalty. Reserve the best deal you can find as soon as your travel plans are set, but continue shopping as the travel date approaches. If you find a lower price, book it, too.

If you like, you could call the rental-car company that provided the original price and say, "I'm calling to cancel my reservation because I found a lower price...but before I do, could you match it?" The company often will.

Warning: Confirm that any reservation you make can be canceled without penalty. "Prepaid" rates that are offered by car-rental companies and many third-party travel websites are nonrefundable.

- **Modify pick-up and drop-off times if your timing is somewhat flexible.** Adjusting these by just an hour or two when you search for car-rental rates online could significantly affect the prices you find.

GET ADDITIONAL DISCOUNTS

You don't have to search the entire Internet for rental-car special offers. *Just take a few minutes to...*

- **Search for car-rental coupon codes on AutoSlash.com.** It offers details about dozens of current car-rental coupon codes and other promotions. If you find an appealing offer, just enter its code on the rental company website when you make your reservation.

- **Check whether an organization you belong to offers rental-car savings.** AAA... AARP...USAA...and warehouse clubs BJ's and Costco have partnered with rental-car companies to provide deals. *Examples:* You might save 5% to 30% off the "base" rate...receive free upgrades...or get certain fees waived.

- **Reserve a smaller car, then ask for a free upgrade.** If you would *like* a larger rental but don't *need* one, reserve a smaller, less expensive car and then politely ask for an upgrade at the counter. Rental company employees typically have lots of leeway when it comes to upgrades. This is particularly likely to work if you can point out that you rent from the company often...or that you are on your honeymoon or celebrating a special occasion such as a silver anniversary.

BEWARE OF ADD-ONS AND OVERCHARGES

Questionable rental-car company tactics are more common than ever. *Self-defense...*

- **Reject rental cars that have partially full gas tanks.** If you return a rental car with less gas than you started out with, the rental company likely will charge a very steep per-gallon rate for the difference.

The best option is to reject the gas prepay option and instead fill up the tank at a gas station right before returning the car. But if the car started out with less than a full tank, it will be difficult to refill it to precisely the right level.

To avoid this issue, insist that the car you rent starts with a full tank of gas. Then you simply can top it off before returning it.

Save the receipt from the gas station when you fill the tank, and take a photo of this receipt (in case you misplace the original) and a photo of the car's gas gauge when you return the car. Rental lots have been known to bill customers for gas even though the customers refilled the tank properly.

- **Reject cars that have even small scratches or scuffs.** It's become distressingly common for car-rental firms to charge customers $400 to $499 for minor damage they did not cause.

Why $400 to $499? It's because many people have $500 auto insurance deductibles. The car-rental companies don't want insurance companies getting involved because insurers are aware of this scam and often won't play ball.

The traditional advice is to inspect rental cars very carefully and report any damage to

MONEYSAVER...

Save on Airline Baggage Fees

- **Become an elite flier** if you travel 25,000 or more miles per year on one specific airline.
- **Get a credit card co-branded** with the name of the airline on which you fly regularly.
- **Pack everything in a carry-on bag**—if necessary, wear bulky clothes on the plane to free up bag space.
- **Fly on Southwest,** the only US airline that does not charge for checked bags.
- **Consider upgrading to a higher travel class or roomier seat**—sometimes that will cost less than the cost of checking luggage and typically waives the checked bag fee.
- **Buy ultra-lightweight luggage** to reduce the chance of overweight baggage fees.

WiseBread.com

the rental agent before driving away so that it is noted on the rental agreement.

If possible, demand a different car that has no damage. A car that has visible damage often also has other damage that is not easy to spot.

Whether or not you spot any damage, take numerous pictures of the car from every possible angle, inside and out, before you drive the car off the lot. Do so again when you return the car. An app called *Record360* (free for iOS and Android) can document precisely when and where these images were recorded, improving the strength of your case if you later need to prove that you returned the car in the same condition you got it.

• **Turn down rental company insurance.** The insurance offered by car-rental firms is massively overpriced—and you probably don't even need it. Most drivers already have rental-car coverage through their auto insurance... the credit card they use to rent the car...or both. (Contact your insurer and card issuer before your trip to confirm this, especially because there are exceptions and limits.)

If you do need rental-car coverage—or you prefer to leave no chance that potentially costly gaps might lurk in your coverage—purchase it through InsureMyRentalCar.com prior to your trip. It provides reliable coverage for a fraction of what rental firms charge. Prices start at just $6 per day.

• **Reject the toll transponder, and avoid toll roads.** Rental-car companies often charge $4 or $5 per day for a toll transponder that pays tolls automatically—on top of the cost of the tolls that the renter incurs.

Renters might be given the option of paying for this transponder when they pick up the car...or the transponder—and its daily fee—might be automatically triggered if the car passes through an automated toll plaza during the trip.

The best option is to reject this transponder (if it is optional) and use a map app to avoid toll roads—especially toll roads that do not offer a cash-payment option. When that isn't practical, lean toward renting from Enterprise or Avis, which tend to at least be up front with transponder charges rather than try to trap customers with gotcha fees that show up later.

Another option is to bring your own transponder if you have one that will work on toll roads in the area you will be visiting—but there is a chance that a rental company transponder installed in the car could be triggered as well, leaving you to sort out a double-billing situation.

Similar: If you have your own portable GPS navigation unit (or a smartphone with a navigation app that you are comfortable using), bring it and reject the rental company's optional navigation unit. This may save you $4 or $5 per day.

• **Don't get stuck with an age surcharge.** You may know that young drivers (under age 25) usually are charged more for rental cars. But some rental companies in Europe now charge *older* drivers a surcharge or refuse to rent to them at all. And these companies often do not make these rules clear when people book reservations—older would-be customers are simply turned away when they try to pick up their rentals.

If you are age 70 or older and you intend to rent a car in Europe, contact the car-rental company, perhaps through its website, to ask whether any age limits or age-based surcharges will apply. This surcharge is most common in Bulgaria, Croatia, Greece, Hungary, Ireland and Portugal.

Hotel Fees Turn Even Trickier

Bjorn Hanson, PhD, clinical professor at New York University School of Professional Studies, Jonathan M. Tisch Center for Hospitality and Tourism, New York City. BjornHansonHospitality.com

The bill for your next hotel stay might come with some costly surprises. It might include a daily charge for your in-room safe even if you don't use it...a fee for using the minibar to refrigerate *your own beverages*...and/or a daily "resort fee" even if the hotel is in the middle of a city and nowhere near a casino or beach. And these fees can add up fast. Some are a few dollars a day, but a resort fee alone can be $20 or more per day—$140 a week!

Taking a page from the airline industry's playbook, hotels are imposing a slew of new and/or higher fees to boost revenue. These fees can add 20% or more to your nightly room rate. Although the Federal Trade Commission requires hotels to disclose mandatory fees when you make reservations, disclosures often are buried in small print.

More examples of unexpected fees: Besides the fee for cooling your own beverages, some hotels charge a minibar "restocking fee" of perhaps $2.95 a day. Some charge 5% of the nightly room rate as an automatic "housekeeping gratuity." Hotels are more likely now to charge you a fee for early arrival or late departure—and might even charge you extra for holding your luggage for a few hours. You might have to pay as much as $30 extra to get a room near the elevators or on a high or low floor. Many hotels that advertise "free Internet" charge $5 or more per day to upgrade that access from very low speeds unsuitable for streaming videos or sending files.

SELF-DEFENSE

Check in advance whether the hotel will waive certain charges, such as Wi-Fi fees, if you belong to its loyalty rewards program and if you book directly rather than through a third-party website...or if you make clear that you don't intend to use certain services, such as the pool or gym. Also, ask in advance for a full list of mandatory and optional fees. Then you can avoid certain services that have fees...and if the final bill includes a fee that was not on the list, you have more leverage to get it waived. By using the list, you also can avoid leaving extra tips for housekeeping or other services if you're charged an automatic gratuity.

Boost Your Chances of a Free Hotel Room Upgrade

GoBankingRates.com

Some proven tips for scoring a hotel room upgrade...

Book a midrange room: By booking a room in the middle of the hotel's price range, you're more likely to receive an upgrade to a more luxurious room than if you book the cheapest room available.

Stay at new properties: Hotels are more willing to offer upgrades to those who are willing to stay at a newly built property that is trying to build a reputation.

Contact the competition: Ask competing hotels if they would offer a free upgrade in exchange for staying at one of their hotels instead of the one you originally planned to stay at.

Report legitimate room issues: If there happens to be a problem in the room that you are staying in, contact the front desk in a respectful way to report on the issue. Some hotels will offer free upgrades in order to keep their customers happy and increase the chances that they will stay there in the future.

"I Never Travel Without This": The Items Travel Pros Always Bring Along

Experienced travelers tend to pack light. The less they bring, the easier their luggage is to lug around...and the better their odds of avoiding airline checked-bag fees. So when a road warrior says that he/she won't travel without an item, that's usually something worth bringing.

We recently asked travel experts to name an item or two that always accompanies them on their journeys...

COMPELLING CONDIMENT
Andrew Zimmern

I always travel with togarashi, a Japanese dried spicy chili-blend condiment that I adore for its flavor and heat. Living out of a suitcase sometimes means enduring boring food on planes, in hotels and at highway rest stops. Having my favorite spice on hand really brightens my day—it's a godsend on late-night gas station pizza. I use it on almost every trip at some point.

Andrew Zimmern, host of the food-and-travel program *Bizarre Foods: Delicious Destinations,* which airs Tuesdays at 9 pm ET/PT. TravelChannel.com

BABY WIPES
Christopher Elliott

These aren't just for wiping babies. They are a surprisingly effective—and very portable—way to clean lots of things. When my son got chocolate on the backseat of our car in the middle of the Nevada desert, baby wipes cleaned up the mess so well that the fabric didn't even show a stain. Baby wipes also can wipe sunscreen and sand off skin after a day at the beach...disinfect hotel-room light switches and TV remote controls...and provide a quick shine for shoes.

Christopher Elliott, a consumer advocate who writes the "On Travel" column for *USA Today* and "The Navigator" column for *The Washington Post.* He is author of *How to Be the World's Smartest Traveler.* Elliott.org

USED-UP PLASTIC TUBE FROM DEODORANT
Jeff Yeager

Plastic tubes from used-up stick deodorants make great mini-travel safes—thieves don't steal toiletries, so they don't notice that there's something inside other than deodorant. Once in Mexico, my hotel room was robbed while I was out. I lost my laptop computer but not the extra cash and emergency credit card I had stashed in a deodorant tube in case my wallet was taken by a pickpocket. Any stick deodorant works, but I like to use a tube of Secret-brand deodorant. I find it especially satisfying that thieves don't find my cash when it's hidden in something that is clearly labeled "Secret."

Jeff Yeager, a money-saving expert who has written extensively about frugal travel, including in his book *How to Retire the Cheapskate Way.*

MY PILLOW FROM HOME
George Hobica

I never travel without mine, even though it takes up lots of room in my suitcase. Eileen Ford of the eponymous modeling agency once told me that she always advised her "girls" to travel with their own pillows because they would sleep better and therefore look better. It certainly helps me get a good night's sleep.

Also: Bose Noise Cancelling headphones. These block most cabin noise on planes, which helps me sleep on red-eyes and reduces my stress level on daytime flights.

George Hobica, founder of Airfare Watchdog, a website that reports on airfare bargains including unannounced, unadvertised rates. He previously was a travel writer for *Travel+Leisure* and *National Geographic Traveler.* AirfareWatchdog.com

SMALL POWER STRIP
Gary Leff

Many hotels do not have enough outlets, so it's worth bringing a power strip that converts one outlet into many—especially if you travel with lots of electronics that require recharging. And if all the outlets are taken when I get to my gate in the airport, I pull out my power strip and ask if anyone's willing to share. Someone almost always agrees.

Gary Leff, CEO, Miles and Points Consulting, LLC, in Austin, Texas, and emcee and cofounder of the InsideFlyer.com frequent-flier-mile online community. He writes about air travel on his blog, ViewFromTheWing.com.

POCKET-SIZE FLASHLIGHT
Kevin Coffey

People think that they don't need to carry a flashlight anymore since their smartphones have a flashlight built in. But using a smartphone's flashlight quickly depletes the phone's battery. If there's been a power failure—a common occurrence in many foreign travel destinations—you could be stranded in the dark in an unfamiliar location or on a high floor of a hotel with no flashlight and no phone. Even a tiny flashlight that attaches to a key chain is better than nothing.

Also: Duct tape. This can provide a quick, easy emergency fix when something breaks. I once had the zipper of a piece of luggage break as I rushed to make a connecting flight in an airport. Duct tape held the bag together well enough to reach my destination. There's no need to travel with an entire roll of duct tape—very few travel emergencies require 100 feet of tape. Just wind five to 10 feet of duct tape around a small plastic or wood dowel.

Kevin Coffey, a travel-risk consultant and CEO of Los Angeles–based Corporate Travel Safety. He recently retired from the Los Angeles Police Department, where he founded the department's Airport Crimes Investigations Detail. KevinCoffey.com

RESEALABLE PLASTIC STORAGE BAGS
Patricia Schultz

Resealable plastic storage bags of various sizes serve a million purposes during trips. Put damp swimsuits or muddy shoes in one before packing them in your luggage to protect everything else from getting messy. Save a piece of fresh fruit from the breakfast buffet so that you can have a healthy snack on the road. Use a plastic bag to hold travel receipts. Use another to contain your phone charger and adapters. I never leave home without at least a dozen in various sizes.

Also: Thank-you notes. Hotel staff appreciate tips, but a tip that's accompanied by a handwritten thank-you note means more. One lovely fellow at a small hotel in Istanbul walked for blocks in the rain to find me a cab. When I checked out, I left him a note thanking him for doing this, along with my tip—and he was so touched that he tracked me down on Facebook to say so. That was five years ago, and we're still in touch!

Patricia Schultz, a New York City–based travel journalist with 30 years of experience. She is author of the number-one *New York Times* best-seller *1,000 Places to See Before You Die.* 1000Places.com

PULLOVER OR ZIP-UP SWEATSHIRT
Dori Saltzman

I always pack one of these even when I'm traveling to a warm-weather location. At some point, I'll be glad I have it. Even if there isn't a chilly evening, there's often an over-air-conditioned restaurant or theater. The one time I forgot to pack a sweatshirt, I ended up having to buy an overpriced one in the Bahamas.

Dori Saltzman, senior editor with *Cruise Critic*, which offers cruise reviews and information. CruiseCritic.com

BUNGEE CORDS
Patrick Smith

These always seem to come in handy and can be used for any number of in-a-pinch fixes. They can serve as a clothesline, to help keep hotel-room curtains closed, for securing luggage and other tasks.

Patrick Smith, an airline pilot for a major commercial carrier. He is founder of the Ask the Pilot website/blog and author of *Cockpit Confidential: Everything You Need to Know About Air Travel.* AskThePilot.com

REPORTER'S NOTEBOOK
Jim Loomis

I keep one of these little notepads in my hip pocket whenever I'm on the road. I'm constantly pulling it out to jot down interesting things that happen on my travels...the names of restaurants that are recommended to me...or details I need to remember, such as addresses or departure times. These days you can record details such as these in a smartphone, but I find it faster and easier to use an old-fashioned reporter's notebook.

Also: List of all my medications. I once got very sick in Toronto and had to see the hotel's on-call physician. He wouldn't prescribe anything for my illness until he knew exactly what medications I already was taking, including dosages—and because of time-zone differences, it might have been difficult for him to get this information from my doctor's office. Fortunately, I had prepared this list and brought it with me on my trip, so I got the medicine I needed.

Jim Loomis, author of *All Aboard: The Complete North American Train Travel Guide.* He serves on the board of directors of the National Association of Railroad Passengers. TrainsAndTravel.com

TRAVEL-SIZE BINOCULARS
Don Wildman

I bird-watch out of hotel-room windows. It's relaxing, and it's something to do during downtime. There are birds everywhere, even in the parking lots of the worst two-star motels.

Don Wildman, host of *Mysteries at the Museum,* which airs Thursdays at 9 pm ET/PT. He previously hosted several other travel-related series. TravelChannel.com

BETTER WAY...

Travel Stress Reducer

When you travel, do you find yourself worrying that you left the stove on? Or the AC or the iron, etc.? Before you leave, use your smartphone to take a photo of the item you worry about. A glance at the photo will relieve your mind!

Clark.com, a website that gives free advice on consumer issues.

For Safer Travel...

Avoid in-room hotel safes—too many hotel employees may have access to them with a master combination. If you want something kept locked up, put it in the hotel's central safe, since only a small number of people have access. *Stay alert at all times*—if you need to look at your phone for directions, go into a store or coffee shop instead of stopping on the street. *Do not post pictures on social media* during your trip—thieves monitor accounts, evaluate the way users are dressed to decide whether to target them and have the tools to find your exact location.

Matthew Dumpert, senior director at Kroll, a security consulting company in New York City, quoted in *The New York Times*.

Travel Worry-Free with These Gadgets and Apps

- **Safego portable lockbox** weighs one pound and has enough room to fit your wallet, phone, a small camera and jewelry. It also comes with a heavy-duty steel cable so you can secure it to a fixed object (Safego.us, $39.95).
- **Manything security app** lets you use an old smartphone as a security camera. The camera will alert you when it detects sound or motion and can record and store video in the cloud (Manything.com, basic functions are free, cloud-recording plans start at $2.99/month).
- **Verizon's HumX** gives you Wi-Fi on the road. The device connects to your car's onboard computer and also offers emergency roadside assistance and gives you access to a mechanic hotline (Hum.com, $120 or $69.99 with a two-year contract).

Christopher Elliott, consumer advocate, writing at *USA Today*.

Digital-Detox Vacation Spots

Digital-detox vacation destinations encourage you to enjoy your vacation without social media, smartphone apps and other digital distractions.

- **Camp Grounded, California,** is a summer camp for adults that prohibits use of digital technology.
- **Heron Island, Australia,** on the Great Barrier Reef, has no cell coverage and TV-free rooms.
- **Petit St. Vincent Island and Resort, the Grenadines,** has no phones, TVs or Wi-Fi in its 22 ocean-view cottages and villas.
- **Tabacón Thermal Resort & Spa, Costa Rica,** offers mineral-spring therapy in a location with little or no cell service.

Orbitz.com

Safest Seat on a Train

Amtrak has suffered several accidents recently, resulting in six deaths and hundreds of injuries. Avoid a train's last car (most dangerous in a rear-end collision) and front car (most vulnerable in head-on collisions and derailments). The safest place to sit on a passenger train is an aisle seat in a middle car. An aisle seat decreases the risk of being thrown from the train.

Allan M. Zarembski, PhD, director of the Railroad Engineering and Safety Program in the Department of Civil Engineering at University of Delaware, Newark. CE.udel.edu

14

Fun & Games

Golf Nirvana: Best New Public Golf Courses in the US

Great new public-access golf courses have recently welcomed golfers around the country. All are worthy of golfers willing to travel for new experiences!

SHEPHERD'S ROCK, FARMINGTON, PENNSYLVANIA

World Golf Hall of Fame member Pete Dye remains ageless (not to mention gainfully employed) at 91. He recently opened a second course at the luxurious Nemacolin Woodlands Resort in southwestern Pennsylvania, a little more than an hour from Pittsburgh. Shepherd's Rock joins his celebrated Mystic Rock course, which has been ranked among the top 100 public courses in the country. Built on rolling terrain in the Allegheny Mountains, the front nine of Shepherd's Rock is lined with hardwoods, necessitating precision from the tee and careful approach shots. Meanwhile, the inward nine widens with inspiring vistas of the Laurel Highlands. Large grass mounds, wetlands, rumpled fairways and fortified greens ensure that this nonagenarian hasn't lost his mischievous nature and still enjoys making golfers sweat.

Details: Nemacolin.com, 866-344-6957.

STREAMSONG RESORT, BOWLING GREEN, FLORIDA

Florida golf brings to mind condo-lined fairways, man-made water hazards and tight course boundaries delineating the playing fields from adjacent backyards. However, Streamsong Resort, in the central portion of the state, about an hour east of Tampa, upended the notion

Note: Prices, rates and offers throughout this chapter and book are subject to change.

Joel Zuckerman, author of eight books on golf, including *Pete Dye Golf Courses—Fifty Years of Visionary Design* and *Pro's Pros*, both Book of the Year award winners. VagabondGolfer.com

of golf in the Sunshine State. The resort is a stunning transformation of what at one time was a phosphate-mining site, and the 16,000-acre property, with hills, sand blow-outs and numerous lakes and streams, is unsullied by housing or other developments. The first two courses at Streamsong, the Blue and the Red (the former designed by Tom Doak...the latter by Ben Crenshaw and Bill Coore) quickly made numerous "Best Of" lists. Now a third course has debuted. It was built by architect Gil Hanse, who beat out almost every big name in his profession to land the contract to build the 2016 Olympic course in Rio de Janeiro. This new par-73 Black course is a capacious and strategic layout spread across acres of sandy terrain that reminds some observers of the great courses outside Melbourne, Australia, in what's known as the Sand Belt.

Details: StreamsongResort.com, 888-294-6322.

GARY PLAYER COURSE, RIDGEDALE, MISSOURI

One of golf's ongoing concerns for working people with families is the time drain of a full 18-hole round—often upward of five hours. Some golfers are seeking nine-hole rounds or par-3 courses in the interest of saving time. Johnny Morris, the colorful founder of Bass Pro Shops, is capitalizing on this trend as he continues to expand his impressive Big Cedar Lodge property near Branson, Missouri. The latest addition is a Gary Player short course called The Mountain Top Course. The layout, designed as an accessible experience for families, juniors and newcomers to the game, is a collection of par-3 holes in a setting with miles-long views. It joins the other fine courses at Big Cedar Lodge, the estimable par-3 Top of the Rock course designed by Jack Nicklaus and the championship-length Buffalo Ridge course created by Tom Fazio. This Ozarks oasis will add yet another championship course, designed by Bill Coore and Ben Crenshaw, in September 2018.

Details: BigCedar.com, 800-225-6343.

SAND VALLEY, NEKOOSA, WISCONSIN

Mike Keiser is a greeting-card magnate who now develops golf courses, and his success in developing four world-class courses at Bandon Dunes (coastal Oregon) and two at Cabot Links (Nova Scotia, Canada) proves that eager players will go to great lengths for premium experiences. Keiser's latest project, known as Sand Valley, is set amid more than 1,700 acres of sand dunes in the heart of Wisconsin, about 170 miles northwest of Milwaukee. The first course to debut was designed by the architectural duo of Bill Coore and Ben Crenshaw and brings a dramatic, big-featured style of a seaside links to the epicenter of farm country. The layout has been coined "heathland in the heartland" by the designers because it unfolds through meandering ridges and valleys. A companion course designed by David McLay Kidd is in the works and will debut sometime in 2018.

Details: SandValleyGolfResort.com, 888-651-5539.

BAYOU OAKS, NEW ORLEANS

The Bayou Oaks Golf Course in New Orleans City Park replaced 36 holes that were destroyed by Hurricane Katrina in 2005. The new championship-level course, which joins an existing 18-hole layout (the North Course), was designed by venerable architect Rees Jones. There are hopes that at some point it might host the PGA Tour's Zurich Classic, which has long been domiciled in New Orleans. There also are expectations that this city-owned course might someday be considered in the same breath as San Diego's Torrey Pines or Long Island's Bethpage Black—in other words, on the short list of the most desirable municipally owned courses in the nation. Bayou Oaks includes magnificent oak trees with their magical moss canopies and rippling lagoons that are characteristic of the 1,300-acre park.

Details: CityParkGolf.com, 504-483-9410.

SILVIES VALLEY RANCH, BURNS, OREGON

Talk about getting away from it all—Silvies Valley Ranch is a working cattle ranch in Eastern Oregon about five hours from Portland and two hours from Bend. Visitors can observe cattle production, fence-mending and hay-baling and enjoy fine dining and spa services amidst these 140,000 acres with 100 different species of wildlife sharing the property. The ranch has unveiled what might be the most unique new golf facility—with two 18-hole courses built on a property with 27 greens because nine are shared between the courses. These Dan Hixson designs, known as the Hankins and Craddock courses, reverse direction each day. What this means is that on one day you'll start on the first hole and play through the eighteenth, and the next day you'll start on the eighteenth hole and play backward. That may sound crazy, but the very first golf course in history, the Old Course in St. Andrews, Scotland, was designed in the same manner!

Details: Silvies.us, 800-745-8437.

Clever Tricks for Winning at Monopoly and Other Popular Games

Tom Whipple, science editor of *The Times of London* and author of *How to Win Games and Beat People.* TheTimes.co.uk

Some people claim they play games such as Monopoly, Scrabble and others just to have fun, not to win...but let's be honest, playing games is more fun when we win.

British science writer Tom Whipple interviewed numerous probability experts and then pored through the published research to uncover winning strategies for popular games that range from Monopoly to Rock, Paper, Scissors.

Here are his secrets for success with seven popular games...

- **Monopoly.** Players purchase properties and try to bankrupt opponents in this famous board game. *Smart strategy*: Buy the orange properties—that's New York Avenue, Tennessee Avenue and St. James Place on the traditional American Monopoly board. Build hotels on these properties as soon as possible. If another player snaps up one or more of the oranges before you get a chance, try to trade for them. Why orange? Monopoly players end up on the "Jail" square more than they land on any other space on the board...and when they make their first roll after leaving that square, they land on an orange property 39% of the time. No other color property is landed on as often, so owning orange generates lots of rent—and saves you from paying rent when you land there. (It's worth owning at least one of the oranges even if you cannot complete the set. That at least prevents your opponents from exploiting this orange advantage.)

Also: The light-blue properties—Oriental Avenue, Vermont Avenue and Connecticut Avenue—offer a good return on investment, too. Players don't land here as often as on orange, but the light-blue properties are inexpensive to purchase relative to the rents they generate.

- **Risk.** Players compete in dice-rolling "battles" to capture territory in this classic global-conquest board game. *Smart strategy*: Attack when you face an army equal in size to your own—as long as each army numbers five or more pieces. You already may know that the odds are on your side when your army outnumbers your opponent's, but most players don't realize that Risk usually favors the aggressor when armies are evenly matched, too, according to research by a statistics professor at North Carolina State University.

The math gets complex, but it boils down to this—as long as each of the evenly matched armies is at least five pieces in size, the attacking side will win more often than not. The larger the armies, the larger the attacker's advantage—when there are 10 pieces on each side, the attacker has an impressive 57% to 43% edge. The defender has the advantage if there are four or fewer army pieces on each side of the battle, however.

Also: Try to control Australia and/or South America. These continents are the most difficult for opponents to attack.

- **Scrabble.** Players earn points by using letter tiles to spell intersecting words on a game board. *Smart strategy:* Learn as many of the allowable two-letter words as possible—there are more than 100. *Reason:* Playing long words might be more impressive in Scrabble, but games often are won because a player knows a two-letter word that lets him/her play a high-value tile on a triple-letter score in a tight space. If you don't want to memorize dozens of two-letter words, at least remember "QI"—a word referring to a life force in Chinese philosophy. It is especially useful because it lets you play Q, earning at least 10 points, even when you don't have a U. (Three-letter words containing a Q but no U include QIS and QAT.)

• **Operation.** Players carefully remove "ailments" from Cavity Sam, the game's pretend patient, without setting off a buzzer by brushing their "surgical tweezers" against the sides of tiny openings. *Smart strategy:* Hold the tweezers between your thumb and ring finger, with your forefinger resting on top for added support, rather than between your thumb and forefinger the way most players do. This helps steady the tweezers—some real-world surgeons use the technique.

Brace your elbow against the table or the side of your body. When feasible, brace the heel of your hand or your little finger against the table, too. Practice the movement you need to make in the air once or twice before attempting it on Cavity Sam just as a golfer practices his putting motion.

• **Connect 4.** Players drop colored discs into vertical slots in this well-known game—the first to get four of his color in a line up and down, across or diagonally wins. *Smart strategy:* Set yourself up with three in a line in a spot where the fourth—winning—disc would have to be played at a height that hasn't yet been reached in a column that's still largely or entirely empty. Your opponent probably will notice your three in a row and avoid playing in this column so you cannot get your fourth disc to the height where you need it. (And if you try to fill this column yourself, your opponent likely will block your winning move.) But if you manage to fend off your opponent's attempts to win, the rest of the columns eventually will fill up, and you and your opponent will have to play discs in this remaining column.

Whether you win the game then comes down to whether you or your opponent gets to play in the space that completes your four. That might seem like dumb luck, but it isn't—what most players don't realize is that the player who played the first disc of the game always plays in the odd-number rows in this last remaining column, counting up from the bottom, while the player who went second always plays in the even rows. Remember who played first, and arrange your three in a line accordingly.

• **Jenga.** Players try to remove wood blocks from a tower of blocks without knocking over the tower. *Smart strategy:* Put your elbow on the table at the base of the tower and use your forearm to brace the tower as you remove a block. Jenga's rules specify that you can use only one hand...but they do not ban also using the arm that's connected to that hand in this way. *The best proof that this is legal:* Leslie Scott, the woman who invented Jenga, uses this strategy herself.

But proceed with caution—while bracing the tower with your forearm might win you some games, it won't win you any friends—many players believe it's against the spirit of the game even if it isn't against the rules. If you'd prefer a less controversial strategy, consider trying to nudge one block into a position where it better supports the tower before trying to remove a different block.

• **Rock, Paper, Scissors.** Two players simultaneously select one of the three options listed in the game's name, with rock beating scissors...scissors beating paper...and paper beating rock. *Smart strategy:* Choose paper. Scissors is the least-selected option—played just 29.6% of the time, according to The World RPS Society—so paper wins or ties slightly more than 70% of the time.

GOOD TO KNOW...

Personalized Film Finder

At AGoodMovieToWatch.com, you'll find little-known, highly rated movies and shows from Amazon Prime, Netflix and other streaming services. Search by genre (such as action or documentary), mood (dark, romantic, suspenseful, etc.) or other criteria.

How to Take Great Portrait Photos

Jeff Wignall, a photographer and writer who has written more than 20 books about photography. He is a contributing editor with *Pro Photo Daily* and *Motion Arts Pro Daily* and a former "Camera" columnist for *The New York Times*. JeffWignall.com

Whether you are photographing one person or a small group, all it takes is a little extra thought to create professional-looking portraits. While you can shoot good portraits with any type of camera, from smartphone to DSLR, I prefer using a dedicated camera because the files are larger and I can make bigger blowups. *Here's how to add both visual and emotional impact to your people pictures...*

• **Fill the frame.** There's an adage in photography that when you think you're close enough, take a giant step forward. Tightly framed portraits intensify emotions and create a more intimate atmosphere. Getting very close physically, however, can be awkward for both photographer and subject.

Less invasive solution: Use a medium-telephoto zoom setting or, if you have an interchangeable-lens camera, a medium-telephoto lens (85mm to 120mm in 35mm equivalent) to fill the frame with your subject from a comfortable distance. If you are using a smartphone, get close enough to avoid "finger" zooming because that crops away part of an already small digital file.

• **Use simple backgrounds.** For outdoor portraits, plain backgrounds (a tall hedge or grassy dune or brick wall) are important because you don't want anything drawing attention away from your subjects. Place your subjects several feet in front of the backdrop because the distance between the two helps blur the background, making the people pop out. If your camera has an aperture-priority exposure mode that lets you choose the lens aperture setting, select a lower setting (such as f/2.8 as opposed to f/11) to "soften" (blur) the background. (The lower the aperture number, the more shallow the "depth of field," or near-to-far area, that will be in sharp focus.) Using a low aperture setting can be even more helpful when the only background available to you is visually busy—the setting will blur out much of the busyness.

• **Choose the best daylight.** Hazy or slightly overcast days produce the most flattering light because the softer light eliminates distracting facial shadows. On sunny days, move your subjects into a bit of shade, in the shadow of a big tree, for example—where the light is gentler. (Be careful to avoid dappled light on the face!) Shade has a bluish cast to it, but you can warm the scene by setting your camera's "white balance" control to the "cloudy day" setting. *More lighting tips...*

Try backlighting (my favorite portrait light) in which the sun is behind your subjects. (It doesn't have to be directly behind.) Backlighting creates a pretty "rim light" around hair and eliminates squinting. Sometimes backlighting will cause dark faces, and one way to cure that is with a bit of fill-in flash. Many cameras have a fill-flash mode that will fire just enough flash to lighten dark faces without creating an obvious fake lighting look. *Another simple fix:* Have a helper aim a sheet of white poster board to bounce sunlight onto your subject's face and "fill" shadows.

Shoot during the golden hour. Late-afternoon light (starting about one hour before sunset) is warm and flattering and produces noticeably softer contrast—a big favorite with fashion shooters.

5 Steps for Adorable Pet Photos

Jeff Wignall, a photographer and writer who has written more than 20 books about photography. He is a contributing editor with *Pro Photo Daily* and *Motion Arts Pro Daily* and a former "Camera" columnist for *The New York Times*. JeffWignall.com

What do you give the person who has everything? How about an adorable photo of his/her pet? *Here's how to take winning shots that make great gifts...*

• **Use the camera you're most comfortable with,** even a cell-phone camera, because you'll be able to concentrate on your subjects and not worry about learning camera settings. But a camera with a lens that has a large zoom range (12x or greater) will let you grab great shots from more positions, including from a distance. My favorite lens for photographing my two cats is a 70-300mm telephoto zoom because it lets me shoot close-ups from across the room. That said, the "stretched out" look created by a very wide-angle lens (equivalent to 24mm or wider on a traditional 35mm camera) is a fun way to exaggerate your kitty's morning stretch or your pooch's gaping yawn.

• **Use familiar places and routines.** With dogs especially, the more familiar the locale, the less distracted they'll be. If you're going to shoot around the house, keep the camera with you rather than breaking the spell of quiet moments by getting up to find it.

• **Try playful action shots.** If your pet is in a lively mood, bring out a favorite toy and try to capture action shots. Put your camera in the shutter-priority exposure mode (in this mode, the camera lets you set the shutter speed that you want and will automatically choose the corresponding aperture setting) and choose the highest shutter speed available for the existing light (1/250 second or faster is good) to freeze motion. For the best chance of grabbing a winning shot, use your camera's "burst" mode for firing multiple shots in rapid succession.

• **For formal portraits, get their attention.** For posed portraits, pets look best when they are engaged with you and have their eyes wide-open. Dogs respond well to a favorite squeaky toy and cats to a dangling string, and you can get them to look into the camera or over your shoulder by holding the object up where you want them to look. You may need an assistant to help with this. Pooch Selfie (PoochSelfie.com, $9.99) is a neat little accessory that lets you attach a squeaky tennis ball to your cell phone to get your dog's attention—just squeak the ball and shoot.

• **Shoot at your pet's eye level.** For more natural poses, kneel or lay down and shoot at eye level or slightly up at your pet rather than aiming the camera down. You also can try placing your camera on a tripod (low down) and firing it with a remote shutter release (or have a helper press the shutter button) so that you can primp the pose and then lean out of the frame and shoot.

How to Photograph Beautiful Sunsets (and Sunrises)

Jeff Wignall, a photographer and writer who has written more than 20 books about photography. He is a contributing editor with *Pro Photo Daily* and *Motion Arts Pro Daily* and a former "Camera" columnist for *The New York Times.* JeffWignall.com

Sunsets and sunrises are among nature's greatest visual gifts. But when most people try to photograph them, they end up with shots that are much too dark or much too light...and that lack the rich colors and details of sky and landscape that are so thrilling in real life.

Solution: You can get spectacular sunset and sunrise shots with any camera, even a cell phone, if you know how. *Here's what to do...*

• **Pick the right spot.** Sunsets and sunrises look best over an interesting or thematic foreground. Look for simple, strong shapes—a lone tree on a hilltop or a sailboat at anchor, for example. Water makes an excellent foreground, particularly a still harbor or lake, because it creates a mirror of the sky and doubles the color intensity of the shot. When traveling, I scout locations in the afternoon so that I know where to get into position well before the sun begins to set (or rise).

Important: Be sure to never look directly at the sun through any lens—it can cause serious eye damage.

• **Take care with placing the horizon.** Putting the horizon low in the frame accentuates the sky, while placing it higher focuses more attention on the foreground. If you're unsure where to place the horizon, experiment and shoot some variations and choose your best shots after the fact.

• **Exploit weather.** Arriving and departing storms often create the most dramatic skies. Crepuscular rays, or what photographers call "God rays," are those biblical shafts of light that shoot down from clouds and are common after storms. In cities, high-pollution days often produce especially vivid sunsets because the dense particulate matter in the atmosphere scatters the sun's rays even more, heightening the vibrant colors.

• **Set the exposure carefully.** A wide range of exposures will provide different and pleasing results with sunsets and sunrises, but you typically will not get a very good shot if you simply point and shoot, letting the camera automatically set the exposure.

Reason: The sun's brightness will make the camera think the overall scene is much brighter than it actually is, and it will make your shot very underexposed—all you'll see is the sun and darkness around it. Instead, slight underexposure will generally produce the best shot.

What to do: Before framing your shot, point the camera at the sky on either side of the sun—with the sun not in the frame—and then, if you are using a camera (not a cell phone), press the shutter-release button halfway and hold it there to lock both focus and exposure. Then recompose the scene with the sun in the frame and take the shot. If using a cell phone, try switching to the high dynamic range (HDR) mode. In this mode, the camera will automatically create a series of separate exposures that may compensate for the very bright sun.

EASY TO DO...

For a Better Selfie...

If you want to look thinner and younger, take the photo from above...and if you want to look more dominant, take it from below.

Based on a study led by Anastasia Makhanova, MS, professor, Florida State University, Tallahassee, published in *Psychological Science*.

Facebook Folly

Facebook may be making you unhappy and unhealthy. Researchers found that the more people use Facebook, the less healthy they are and the less satisfaction they feel in their lives. The more times a user "liked" others' posts, clicked on their profiles or updated his/her own status, the higher the likelihood of mental health problems.

Holly Shakya, PhD, assistant professor of public health at University of California, San Diego, and Nicholas Christakis, MD, PhD, MPH, director of the Human Nature Lab at Yale University, New Haven, Connecticut, and authors of a study of more than 5,000 adults over two years published in *American Journal of Epidemiology*.

Avoid This Facebook Mistake...

After you've created a Facebook post for only one friend to see, do not forget to change your "Who should see this" setting back to "Friends," "Public" or whatever audience you usually post for. People who forget may be sending all their posts to only one friend for quite some time!

Bottom Line Inc. editors.

Smartphones Affect Dating Preferences

Owners of iPhones are 21 times more likely to judge Android-phone owners negatively...while Android owners are 15 times more likely to think poorly of iPhone users. And those who have older models of either type of smartphone are 56% less likely to get dates through online matchup sites than those who have the latest models.

Survey of more than 5,500 single people by dating site Match.com and Research Now.

For a More Successful Online Dating Profile...

The best words to add to your dating profile now...

For men: "Physically fit" led to 96% more interaction compared with profiles that did not include the phrase..."perceptive," 51% more interaction..."spontaneous," 45%..."outgoing," 44%..."optimistic," 39%.

For women: "Ambitious" led to 48% more interaction..."perceptive," 46%..."sweet," 33%... "hardworking," 32%..."thoughtful," 28%.

Certain food-related terms that were more likely to lead to interactions: "Guacamole" led to 144% more messages from potential love interests, and for women—not men—the phrase "pumpkin spice" led to 8% greater interest.

Consensus of studies by online dating sites, reported at Moneyish.com.

TAKE NOTE...

Quality That Impresses Online Daters Most

Financial responsibility impresses online daters more than a sense of humor, attractiveness, ambition or courage. In a survey, 69% of participants said financial responsibility is very or extremely important when looking for a person to date, more important than any other quality.

Helen Fisher, PhD, chief scientific adviser for the online dating site Match.com and visiting research associate at Rutgers University in New Brunswick, New Jersey.

Best Wines for Your Holiday Parties

Jeff Siegel, the Wine Curmudgeon, a wine writer, wine critic and wine judge who specializes in inexpensive wine. He is author of *The Wine Curmudgeon's Guide to Cheap Wine* and oversees the award-winning WineCurmudgeon.com website, which annually ranks among the most influential wine sites on the Internet. He also teaches wine, spirits and beer at El Centro College in Dallas.

The holiday season means parties—and parties mean wine. But you don't have to spend a lot for really good wine. *Here are excellent party wines for about $10 a bottle...*

Helpful: Figure on two to three glasses of wine per person. A bottle of wine holds four glasses.

A BARGAIN RED

Veni Vidi Vici Merlot, about $10, is from Bulgaria. Though Bulgaria is not known for great wine, the Veni Vidi Vici is everything a merlot should be. It has a little Old World earthiness, a quality that you don't find in too-fruity California wine and something that adds a complexity that most $10 merlots don't have. There is fresh but not-too-ripe berry fruit, and the tannins—the astringent quality in red wine—are soft, as they should be in merlot. That combination makes it an ideal party wine because it's interesting enough for people who know wine but simple enough for those who just want a glass of red while they nibble on chicken wings.

A BARGAIN WHITE

Finding a $10 chardonnay that is well-made, enjoyable and readily available isn't impossible, but it often seems like it is. That's because too much grocery store–quality chardonnay is made to be a touch sweet or is doused with so much "fake oak" that it tastes like vanilla extract with an alcohol chaser.

This is where *Hess Select Chardonnay,* about $10, comes in. Hess is a longtime and respected California producer that is best known for its expensive wines, but the company gives just as much attention to its $10 wines—hence, more than $10 worth of quality.

The Hess neatly combines everything that should be in a grocery store chardonnay—a little toasty oak flavor, green apple and pear fruit, and a smidge of tropical fruit in the middle. In all, it is crisp enough to balance the oak, another rarity in wine of this price. And again, a wine that is party-friendly because it is balanced and approachable.

And how does a $10 wine get oak aging, which adds greatly to production costs? It doesn't, because that's reserved for wines that cost more than $25. Wines such as this use what the industry calls oak adjuncts—bags of oak chips or oak staves attached to steel tanks. This "fake oak," when used with restraint as it is in the Hess, gives oak quality without the time and expense of $1,000 oak barrels.

A WINTER-WORTHY ROSÉ WINE

I have long been suspicious of boxed wine—not because it comes in a box, but because it is made above all to hit price points and not necessarily for quality. That means a great boxed wine in one vintage can turn mediocre if the price of grapes goes up for the next vintage and cheaper grapes of lesser quality are used to make it.

So when you find a great boxed wine, such as the *Bota Box Rosé,* buy it and enjoy it. The Bota box costs about $20 for a three-liter box (equivalent to four bottles). That works out to less than $5 a bottle, an amazing value for a traditional dry rosé that isn't made to taste like a red wine that is pink in color or a less sweet version of white zinfandel. The wine is crisp and fresh, with watermelon and ripe strawberry fruit. Be sure to serve it chilled.

The Bota Box Rosé won't win awards, but this isn't damning with faint praise. It's not supposed to win any awards. What it will do is please party guests who want something refreshing to drink in between all of the rich and fatty food that often makes up the holiday-party circuit.

SPARKLING WINE TO TOAST WITH

Segura Viudas is one of Spain's biggest sparkling wine producers, which explains why its cava—the Spanish version of sparkling wine—can be so inexpensive, as little as $7 or $8 a bottle. That the *Segura Cava* has been one of the world's great wine values for years speaks volumes about how much Segura cares about the wine it makes.

Most sparkling wine is nonvintage—that is, it uses grapes harvested in different years. This allows producers to maintain quality even if the quality of the grapes varies. That's one secret to what Segura does, producing a sparkling wine that is consistently bone-dry, with tart green apple flavors balanced by a little tropical fruit, the yeastiness that you expect from more expensive Champagne-style wines and delightfully tight bubbles.

It's not as soft or as sweet as Prosecco, the Italian sparkling wine, so know that difference going in. But also know that it's the quintessential excellent party wine—inexpensive, well-made and fun to drink.

SWEET WINE

Good sweet wines have their place—they are the sort of thing that people enjoy with brownies or chocolate chip cookies. California's Quady Winery has made sweet wine for more than 40 years, but it didn't get all that much attention until the sweet red wine craze of the past several years. And that's when retailers discovered the winery's *Red Electra Moscato,* about $12. It is made with two little-known grapes, orange muscat and black muscat, and is several steps above the cheap, sweet moscatos that were popular a few years ago. In other words, it has more than sweetness—lots of ripe red cherries mixed with berries and peaches, plus a little fizziness and an orange-ish aroma that only muscat grapes can give a wine.

Serve the Red Electra well-chilled, and keep it around the desserts.

BEST GIFT WINES

Wine makes a great gift—and these choices are well-priced...

Hostess gift: Sparkling wine is always an appropriate and welcome way to say thank you, and *Valdo Prosecco Brut,* about $12, is a stellar example of the Italian style of Prosecco, especially for the price. It has more structure—that is, it's more than sweetish wine with bubbles—than similarly priced Proseccos, plus it has soft citrus fruit and an appealing character that says, "This is more than a cheap Prosecco."

Dinner party: Not sure what goes with what? Not sure that even if you knew, you would get it right? Then consider *Louis Latour Mâcon-Villages Chameroy,* about $13. This is chardonnay from the Mâcon in the French region of Burgundy, generally regarded as the best place in the world for chardonnay. Hence, its price is practically a steal. Look for floral and honey aromas, ripe pear fruit and that distinctive French minerality. That's a flavor profile that will pair with almost everything except red meat. If you know steak is on the menu, bring the Veni Vidi Vici Merlot (see above).

Wine geek: The key to making wine geeks happy is to find something just odd enough to appeal to them, and the *Little James Basket Press Blanc,* about $12, does that. It's from a part of southern France better known for red wine, and it combines two grapes that are rarely mixed—viognier and sauvignon blanc. But the softer viognier, with peach flavors, tones down the citrus in the sauvignon blanc, and the result is fresh and delightful.

Boss or client: Italian winemaker Riccardo Cotarella is famous for his high-scoring and expensive wines from his country's most famous regions. This makes the *Falesco Vitiano* red, white and rosé wines all that more appealing because you get the prestige and quality of Cotarella for around $10 a bottle. It's perfect if you are on a budget because you're getting $20 wine for $10 or $12, depending on where you buy it.

Wine with Hot Dogs? Yes! Burgers and Ribs, Too

Jeff Siegel, the Wine Curmudgeon, a wine writer, wine critic and wine judge who specializes in inexpensive wine. He is author of *The Wine Curmudgeon's Guide to Cheap Wine* and oversees the award-winning WineCurmudgeon.com website, which annually ranks among the most influential wine sites on the Internet. He also teaches wine, spirits and beer at El Centro College in Dallas.

Hot dogs on the grill—or even hamburgers, pork ribs or barbecued chicken—don't shout wine. But why not?

If you're inclined to enjoy a little alcohol with your summery, casual cookout foods, wine works just as well as—and often better than—beer or mixed drinks. But that's true only if you pick wines that feel right for summer and that go well with these foods.

Here are the wines to try at your next barbecue (or picnic!), all very affordable at $10 or so…

WINES FOR HOT DOGS, BRATWURST AND SAUSAGES

The Germans and Alsatians in eastern France have long enjoyed wine in the "wurst" way, usually with a dry riesling, native to both Germany and Alsace. The match works with most sausages because even dry rieslings can be slightly sweet, offsetting the spice and salt in the meat (and you can poach your sausage in the same wine instead of beer before you grill it). Good-quality German and Alsatian rieslings cost well over $10—starting around $18—but there is an Aussie wine, *Yalumba Y series Riesling,* about $10, that's a wonderful alternative. You'll taste some lemon and citrus fruit (but not especially tart), a stony sort of finish and a hint of sweetness.

What about the classic American hot dog? It's actually more of a *red* wine food! What you'll want, though, is a *light* style of red. One of my favorite pairings with hot dogs is *Bogle Petite Sirah,* about $10. Petite sirah, not to be confused with syrah or shiraz, is its own grape, and this wine shows the difference—*almost* dark and *almost* plummy but without much in the way of the tannins and their astringent character that you notice in the back of your mouth or the heaviness typical of many other red wines.

WINE FOR HAMBURGERS

Hamburgers also are red wine food—especially if piled high with cheese and bacon. But don't limit yourself to the usual grocery-store cabernet sauvignon and merlot. Try *Hedges C.M.S.*, about $12. It's a red blend from Washington State with black fruit flavors that is made with cabernet, merlot and syrah. As such, it has a little of each—tannins and acidity of the cabernet, merlot to smooth out the rough spots and syrah to add a little richness.

Or try a French malbec. Though malbec has become associated with Argentina, it actually is a French grape.

The Argentine style of wine is very fruity, while those from France, such as *Le Vassal de Mercuès*, about $12, are much darker and more interesting. This malbec is both earthy and almost rustic, something that doesn't happen much anymore. Look for a little spice as well, plus malbec's signature blueberry and black cherry fruit. It pairs perfectly with a burger.

WINE FOR BARBECUED CHICKEN

How do you like to make barbecued chicken? With a sweetish red sauce? Marinated in olive oil, lemon juice and garlic? Or with salt and pepper and a few other spices?

Regardless of method, dry rosé wine is the choice. This dry pink wine is so versatile and goes well with so many kinds of foods and preparations that it should be on a list such as this every time.

One excellent choice: The South African *Mulderbosch Rosé*, about $12. It's made with the cabernet grape, not common for a rosé, and so has a little more heft to it than many rosés. But it's still low in alcohol with a crisp, refreshing finish.

Vinho verde, the nonvintage Portuguese white wine with an almost greenish tint, doesn't get enough respect. Even though it usually costs very little (between $6 and $10), it comes with a welcome fizziness, a hint of sweetness and very low alcohol content. It's often lumped in with wine not worth drinking. That's not true—especially outside on a hot day! Next time you grill chicken, try *Broadbent Vinho Verde*, about $9—it's a step up from the $6 wines, with less fizziness and sweetness and more lemon-lime fruit. Regardless of brand, always serve vinho verde ice-cold. Otherwise, it can taste like warm beer.

WINE FOR GRILLED SHRIMP

This is white wine food, and the usual pairing is a citrusy New Zealand sauvignon blanc. But there are plenty of other options, including two types of wine that aren't as well-known as sauvignon blanc but can deliver more value.

The first is a white blend from the French region of Gascony made with grapes that have traditionally been used to make Armangac, the area's version of brandy. The grapes—ugni blanc and colombard, with a little sauvignon blanc sometimes thrown in—make a dry, lemony, crisp wine with an almost grapey overtone. It will complement shrimp's richness and fishiness (as well as almost anything you would use as a marinade or spice rub on shrimp). One widely available Gascon white blend is from *Domaine de Pouy*, about $10.

Pinot gris is the same grape as the pinot grigio that Italy exports in shiploads to the US. The difference is in style—pinot gris has more fruit and a richer mouthfeel. Oregon makes some of the best pinot gris wines in the world, and *A to Z Wineworks* does a nice job selling pinot gris for around $13. The lime and lime zest flavors practically jump around your mouth, while there is a bit of tropical fruit in the middle.

WINE FOR BARBECUED PORK RIBS

Again, how do you like your ribs? Carolina style, with the tangy mustard sauce? Or with a Memphis or Kansas City–style spice rub? Or with a sweet red sauce?

Again, go with rosé wine—but in this case, the Spanish *Marqués de Riscal* made with the tempranillo grape, about $10. I tasted this wine with $25 French and $16 California rosés, and it was the most impressive—clean, crisp, with some orangey fine aromas and fresh cherry fruit. It's easily one of the best rosés I've tasted this summer.

The other choice for barbecued ribs is a six-grape red blend from California called *Firehouse Red*, about $12, made by Leese-Fitch. Leese-Fitch is part of a larger company that includes Plungerhead and Hey, Mambo and that makes grocery store wine that is a step above most of the others. The Firehouse Red has a lot of red and black fruit, but it also has soft tannins and enough acidity to offset the fruit. All that fruit will pair with almost any sauce or spice rub you use on your ribs.

8 Big Gardening Mistakes to Avoid in the Spring

Teri Dunn Chace, author of *The Anxious Gardener's Book of Answers* and more than 35 other gardening titles. She has gardened in a variety of climate zones and soil types and was the winner of the prestigious American Horticultural Society Book Award in 2016 for her book *Seeing Seeds.* TeriChaceWriter.com

Late winter is hard on a gardener. Your green thumb is twitching, but the days still are short and the garden is far from ready for planting.

My advice: Get started! "Stage-setting" late winter/early spring tasks will make all the difference when it comes time to plant (and beyond). But it's important not to act too soon or improperly—you could damage your plants, the soil or your yard's good appearance…

FIRST TASK: SPRUCE UP YOUR TOOLS

Why it matters: Dirty blades, loose bolts and dull edges make garden tools less useful and make chores more difficult—even dangerous.

Mistake: If tools are dirty, don't force off or chip off caked-on crud. That can gouge a tool surface—and might strain your hand, wrist or arm in the process.

What to do instead: Wipe down each tool with a damp rag. Still dirty? Immerse it in a bucket of lukewarm water for an hour or more. This may reveal still-persistent crud or rust spots—sand these off or scrub with steel wool. Then wipe blades with a soft, oil-soaked rag. Some people swear by linseed oil, but vegetable oil from the kitchen will do just fine, honestly. Burnish wooden handles with the oily cloth, too. Check bolts on loppers and clippers, and tighten loose ones with a wrench.

Make sure all edges are sharp. A dull pruner, for example, will mash stems rather than slicing them. Not pretty or healthy. Clamp a dull tool in a vise so it won't wiggle while you work. Then use a 10-inch, single-cut file—the kind with a single set of parallel diagonal lines—to patiently, neatly restore the original factory bevel. Or ask at your local garden or hardware store about professional sharpening—usually about $10 a tool.

REPAIR WINTER-DAMAGED SHRUBS AND TREES

Why it matters: Snow and ice can snap off branches, and extreme cold can kill branches, too. To improve your garden's looks and health, prune branches with damaged or dead parts in early spring (once daytime temps are above freezing).

Tip: Cutting on a warmer, sunny day is more pleasant for you and better for the tree.

Mistake #1: **Cutting only at the point of damage.** That can leave the plant looking awkward. Also, stubs left behind eventually rot and may spread rot to the rest of the tree.

What to do instead: Clip or saw off a branch or stem all the way back to the trunk or a main stem. Make it flush.

Exception: If there is a substantial branch collar—that thick area where a branch attaches to the trunk—don't cut into it. It forms a protection zone, helping to keep infection out of the trunk. Also, removing the collar can cause unwanted sprouts to grow in the wound area.

Mistake #2: **Cutting too liberally.** For example, taking out an entire limb when only a branch or two coming off it is damaged. That can set a plant back years in looks and health.

Not sure a branch is dead? Leave it! A dormant limb can look dead but still have life in it. Check back in a few weeks to see if it is showing signs of life.

Tip: Truly dead branches will snap, not bend, and they feel lighter and hollower and may be shedding bark.

Mistake #3: **Cleaning up a shrub or tree too late.** If you wait until such plants leaf out, it's harder to get a good overview, and it's harder to see the shoots that sprout from the roots, which divert energy from the rest of the plant.

What to do instead: Get busy before the leaves emerge to take care of problems that are damaging the plant. Take out shoots at the base of the plant, and thin out branches that are rubbing or crossing one another so densely that healthful air can't easily circulate.

PRUNE (SOME) FLOWERING SHRUBS

Why it matters: Cutting back flowering shrubs improves looks and helps the plants focus energy on blooming.

Mistake: Doing major aesthetic pruning on stems that could have bloomed, diminishing a shrub's flower show.

What to do instead: Plants that bloom on "old wood"—last year's growth—should not be pruned for appearance until the year's flowering is over. But do it right after the blooms fade or drop their petals. *Some common plants to prune right after they bloom:* Beautybush, daphne, forsythia, honeysuckle, kerria, jasmine, lilac, mock orange, smoke tree, weigela. (*Note*: It's fine to cut back dead/damaged branches any time.)

If, however, a shrub blooms on "new wood"—the current season's growth—it's safe to cut it back in early spring while the plant is still dormant, before the buds show green. The surge of spring energy will lead to fresh, new branches ready to bloom. *Some common plants to prune early:* Abelia, beautyberry, broom, butterfly bush, caryopteris, crape myrtle, nandina, Pee Gee hydrangea, potentilla, rose-of-Sharon, roses and viburnum.

PREPARE YOUR FLOWER BEDS

Why it matters: Spring, not fall, is decidedly the best time to prep your garden perennials. Research has shown that it's better for hardiness if perennials aren't trimmed back until after winter.

Mistake: Jumping the gun on removing mulch from your flower beds. If you laid down compost, straw, chopped leaves or some other organic mulch last fall, don't remove this protective covering too early. Spring's temperature swings can cause harm to treasured plants.

What to do instead: Wait until the daytime temperatures are reliably above freezing. That's true even if the plants below have started to show growth. Better safe than sorry! When you do remove mulch, use your hands, a light rake or a leaf blower rather than a shovel, hoe or heavy-duty rake. Work rather gently so that you don't inadvertently break or uproot plants.

Once you remove the mulch, cut all dead perennial stalks right down to the ground or at least to the crown of the plant (the spot where the plant stems meet the roots). Fresh, new growth will soon follow.

PREPARE THE SOIL

Why it matters: Healthy, aerated, well-drained soil is the garden ideal, and fooling with it too early can compromise this.

***Mistake #1:* Inadvertently compacting your soil.** If you get to work outside too early in the year, when the ground is still semifrozen or muddy, your footsteps or the wheelbarrow can over compact the soil. (Semifrozen soil goes through freeze-thaw cycles and is easy to compact.) That denies the reawakening plants the oxygen in the soil that they need.

What to do instead: Hold off until the ground dries out a bit more, or try placing a plank where you walk or kneel to distribute your weight more evenly.

***Mistake #2:* Leaving open ground.** A cleared garden area (flower bed or vegetable garden patch) may look tidy, but not for long—it's an open invitation to weeds. And exposed ground is vulnerable to compaction or erosion when drenching spring rains pound your soil.

What to do instead: Sprinkle nourishing compost (homemade or store-bought) over the beds to a depth of one to three inches. Take care not to bury the crowns of emerging perennials or spring-flowering bulbs. Do this on a pleasant day when there is no rain or wind in the forecast. Unlike some mulches, compost is rich in organic matter, contributing nutrition and texture to soil. As it breaks down, it generates heat—a hedge against springtime's temperature swings.

SPRING LAWN DOs AND DON'Ts

Did you know that winter's cold toughens grass and strengthens its roots? That's the good news. But the freezing season can leave your lawn looking ragged. *Here's what to do—and what not to do—to get your lawn off to a good start this spring...*

Do: Thoroughly remove all debris (sticks, twigs, last year's leaves). Use a rake or even a good outdoor broom, which is gentler.

Don't: Be rough, lest you uproot shoots or dislodge chunks of sod.

Do: Patch bare spots. If you use seed, water frequently with a gentle spray until the grass is up and growing strongly. If you use sod, be sure to remove enough soil in the area so that it is level with surrounding grass.

Don't: Use sod in shade. It will struggle. And don't use a weighted roller over any freshly sown lawn areas—sod or not. Once standard practice, it's now discredited because it compacts soil.

Do: Spread ground limestone to nourish the emerging grass (follow label directions).

Don't: Fertilize yet. Instead, wait until spring is well under way and you've mowed a few times. At that point, a dose of lawn fertilizer will be beneficial (follow label directions).

For Healthier Plants...

To help plants thrive, determine your soil's composition...

• **Ribbon test**—moisten a handful of soil to a puttylike consistency. Squeeze it between your fingers to create a "ribbon." If the ribbon reaches a length of one to two inches, the soil has even proportions of sand, soil, silt and clay. If the soil is too gritty to hold the ribbon shape, it's sandy. If the ribbon reaches 2.5 inches or longer, it has the consistency of clay. Add compost if the soil is sandy or like clay.

• **Worm-count test**—dig a one-foot-square one-foot-deep hole. Place the soil on a tarp. If you count less than a dozen earthworms, add organic material. If that doesn't improve your soil, it may be polluted with chemicals—send a sample to a local university extension office for comprehensive testing.

• **Drain test**—fill the worm-count hole with water. If it takes longer than one hour for the water to drain, you could have a drainage problem, so plant elsewhere.

John Parsen, soil scientist, University of Wisconsin, Madison.

TAKE NOTE...

Plants That Repel Pests

Plants that humans enjoy but bugs really hate...

• **Marigolds** repel mosquitoes, squash bugs and tomato worms—they have a natural compound used in many insect repellents.

• **Lavender** is attractive to bees but not to other insects.

• **Lemongrass** repels mosquitoes—it contains citronella, used in many repellents.

• **Garlic** repels mosquitoes and other bugs.

• **Rosemary** drives away flies, mosquitoes and cabbage moths.

• **Basil** keeps mosquitoes and flies away.

• **Catnip** attracts cats but repels mosquitoes.

• **Petunias** have a licorice-like scent to repel aphids, tomato hornworms and squash bugs—although some types of pests, such as slugs and caterpillars, like it.

• **Mint** keeps ants and mice away.

Reported in *USA Today*.

Plants You *Don't* Want in Your Garden

For various reasons, avoid these plants in your garden...

• **Mint** tastes good and has a wonderful odor, but its roots are highly invasive—grow it in containers.

• **Aloe vera** has healing properties, but its juice is toxic to pets.

• **Belladonna** has lush green foliage and purple flowers but is extremely toxic and should be kept away from children and pets.

• **Mimosa** shrubs and trees have feathery leaves and showy pink flowers, but they are extremely invasive and very difficult to get rid of.

• **Japanese barberry** tolerates drought and shade and resists deer—but it is invasive, carries sharp barbs and harbors ticks that can cause Lyme disease.

BobVila.com

15

Car Care

Never Overpay for Car Repairs Again

When it comes to repair costs, many car owners are driving blind. Vehicles have become increasingly complex, making it increasingly hard to know how much repairs should cost...or to know about money-saving alternatives. *To make car-repair cost decisions...*

WHEN YOU TAKE YOUR CAR FOR REPAIR

These tips apply to independent garages and service departments at dealerships...

- **Some "aftermarket" replacement parts are as good as original parts**—but you should know which to accept. A garage might make its repair prices lower by always using "aftermarket" replacement parts—parts not made by the same companies that made the parts originally installed on the car—and might tell you that costlier "original equipment manufacturer" (OEM) parts never are worth the extra money. Meanwhile, a new-car dealership might always recommend OEM parts despite their high cost and tell you that aftermarket parts are inferior—even though the automakers themselves sometimes buy parts from these aftermarket companies.

The truth lies in between—it's fine to save money by buying certain aftermarket parts and from certain parts makers...but there are times when it's better to pay up for OEM.

What to do: Ask what company makes the aftermarket part. If it's ACDelco, Bosch, Denso or NTK, the part likely is every bit as reliable

Note: Prices, rates and offers throughout this chapter and book are subject to change.

Jill Trotta, ASE Certified Technician/Adviser with more than 25 years of experience. She has worked as a technician, service adviser, service manager, parts director and shop owner. She is director of the automotive group at RepairPal, which offers auto-repair information including repair-cost estimates and evaluations of more than 4,200 independent repair facilities nationwide. RepairPal.com

as the OEM part. These companies are highly respected in the industry—the automakers themselves often buy parts from them. If the aftermarket part is made by a different company, ask someone at your repair shop (or your dealership's parts department) if he/she would trust this part in his own car. You'll probably get a straight answer because the shop could easily sell you the OEM part instead.

Exception: If you need to replace a component that performs a significant amount of computer processing, pay extra for the OEM part if it is available. Opting for an aftermarket computer component is a false savings—it might cause problems with other systems in your car that could be very expensive for your mechanic to chase down.

• **High-end brake pads are one upgrade that truly is worth the price.** When you take your car for a brake job, you might be offered several brake pad options including "organic" brake pads for as little as $10 per set..."low metallic organic" pads for perhaps $20...or ceramic brake pads that could cost $80 to $120. Is a garage that advises high-end brake pads just trying to up-sell you for little benefit?

What to do: Ante up for ceramic brake pads—they likely will stop your vehicle faster than other pads and therefore keep you safer. They also last longer than organic pads and don't cause as much wear to brake rotors as metallic pads, so in the long run they won't add as much to your car-ownership costs as their up-front cost suggests.

• **Female drivers are more likely to be overcharged in major metro areas.** It's not news that female car owners sometimes get charged more than men for the same repairs—studies show that they pay around 8% more, on average. But while these overcharges are common in big cities, it turns out that they are much less likely in small cities and rural regions. Repair shops and service departments in small communities cannot risk ruining their reputations with the locals—if word got out that they were overcharging, everyone in the area would soon know it.

What to do: Anyone—woman or man—would be wise to use an online auto-repair price estimator, such as the "Get an Estimate" tool at my employer's site RepairPal.com, to judge whether an offered price is fair. And unfortunately, this is especially true for women who live in large cities or other densely populated areas.

• **Bills for "scheduled maintenance" might be inflated by fluid flushes that you don't need.** If a shop recommends replacing your car's coolant, brake fluid, power-steering fluid and/or transmission fluid when you take it in for scheduled maintenance, beware—the shop might be trying to sell you a service that your car does not need. These fluid changes once were routine, but they are needed far less often with modern cars.

What to do: Check the scheduled maintenance section of your vehicle's owner's manual—not a maintenance schedule created by the shop!—to see whether this fluid replacement is recommended at your current mileage. If it isn't, ask the shop to justify the fluid change. There *might* be a valid reason—perhaps the mechanic did a test that revealed the presence of excess water in your brake fluid, for example...or perhaps the fluid change is a potential solution to a problem that you have been experiencing with the car. If the shop's only explanation is some form of "It's better to do it more often than the owner's manual says," decline the service and, if the shop persists in pushing the service, find a different shop.

BEFORE YOU BUY YOUR NEXT CAR

• **High-end cars don't just cost more to maintain than economy cars, they cost a lot more.** Thinking about treating yourself to a $50,000 or $60,000 luxury car this year...or something even more expensive? Get ready to treat your mechanic as well. As a rule of thumb, a vehicle's cost of repairs will be roughly proportional to its original sticker price—for example, it costs about four times as much to keep an $80,000 luxury sedan on the road as a $20,000 economy car.

Expensive vehicles have more systems and features than economy cars, so there's more that can break. When their parts do break, they often are very expensive to replace—and less expensive aftermarket parts might not even be available. And the complexity and relative rarity of high-end cars means that mechanics may take longer to diagnose and fix problems or that the vehicle must be taken to a specialized mechanic who charges a high rate.

What to do: Don't stretch your budget to buy an expensive car unless there's also room in your budget for four-figure annual repair bills once the warranty ends. RepairPal's Cost Index Score can give you an idea about the repair bills you might be in for with a particular model (RepairPal.com/index_scores).

If you want a luxury car that won't inflate your maintenance and repair bills any more than necessary, buy from one of the Japanese luxury brands—Lexus, Infiniti or Acura. Lexus is a division of Toyota...Acura is a division of Honda...and Infiniti is a division of Nissan, so these generally can be worked on by mechanics familiar with mainstream Japanese cars. They even use some of the same parts as those brands. If you don't want to pay thousands per year, on average, in repair bills after warranty, avoid European luxury brands such as Audi, BMW, Mercedes and Porsche, which tend to be among the most expensive cars to maintain and repair.

- **One make of car known for reliability can be more expensive to repair than buyers expect—Subaru.** Subaru has a reputation as a reliable brand (although in the latest reliability rankings by *Consumer Reports* and JD Power, the brand didn't do as well as you'd expect). But while Subarus often are reliable, they can be surprisingly expensive to repair. In many ways, they are built a bit differently from other makes, so they can be tricky—and time-consuming—for mechanics who do not work on them regularly.

Example: Many Subarus have "boxer" engines mounted in an unusual position in the engine compartment and with pistons that move horizontally rather than up and down.

What to do: If your Subaru is out of warranty, take it to a dealership or independent mechanic specializing in Subarus even if that means traveling a bit farther. If there is no such shop in your area, that's a reason to lean toward a different make of car instead.

BEWARE...

Car Repair Rip-Offs and How to Avoid Them

If a mechanic recommends extra maintenance beyond that suggested in the owner's manual or makes every recommendation sound like an emergency, go elsewhere. *Other red flags...*

- **If parts prices seem high,** check other shops to find the going rate.
- **If the shop says that it thought a repair would fix a problem but it turned out to be something else,** insist on a refund for the first repair or a discount on the next one.
- **If a shop says that certain parts just wear out quickly in certain cars—**such as yours—go to another shop for a second opinion.
- **If a dealer insists that you return there for all service, do not pay attention—**you usually need a dealer only for warranty work, recalls and some high-tech repairs requiring special equipment.

ConsumerReports.org

- **One type of car is less expensive to maintain than car buyers fear—electric vehicles.** Despite car-buyer concerns about the high cost of replacing worn-out lithium ion batteries, electric cars (and some hybrids, such as the Toyota Prius) actually have proved very affordable to keep on the road. The current generation of batteries generally will last at least 150,000 miles if not longer. And overall, electric cars break far less often than gasoline or diesel cars because they have many fewer moving parts and because the parts they do have tend to be less stressed.

Example: An electric vehicle has no gas engine, so you never have to replace a timing belt or a head gasket—or even change the oil.

A recent study by AAA found that average annual maintenance and repair costs for electric cars were nearly 20% less than those for the average gas-powered vehicle. The savings can be even greater if you opt for an economy-oriented electric car, such as the Chevy Bolt or Volt, rather than a performance-oriented one such as a Tesla.

What to do: If you're looking for an economical car for short-to-medium trips—say, up to around 200 miles—strongly consider buying electric. Not only will you save money on fuel, you'll probably save on repairs and maintenance as well.

Easy Car Repairs Not to Ignore

Scheduled maintenance, such as regular oil changes, can be irritating to arrange but can catch multiple small problems before they become major ones...

- **Check engine light** could mean anything from a loose gas cap to a repair costing a few hundred dollars. But even at the high end, failing to address the problem will lead to much more expensive repairs later.
- **Small windshield cracks** may cost little to fix or nothing at all if your insurance covers them—but letting them go can lead to windshield replacement and a possible ticket for driving with a cracked windshield before you get a new one.
- **Puddles under the car** could mean leaking oil, transmission fluid, water or gas—fixing the problem will avoid bigger issues later.

MoneyTalksNews.com

Common Reasons for Breakdowns

Dead batteries and flat tires are increasingly common reasons for car breakdowns. Newer vehicles (those less than five years old) have more problems of these types than older vehicles did.

Reasons: Easy-to-damage, low-profile tires and electronic keyless ignition, which can tax the battery if the key fob is stored too close to the vehicle.

John Paul, senior manager of traffic safety, AAA Northeast.

If Your Car Doesn't Have a Spare Tire...

What to do if your car doesn't have a spare tire...

- **Upgrade to a run-flat tire.** Run-flats operate like standard tires but will survive a puncture for a short period at a reduced speed. Depending on your vehicle, the cost may range from $150 to more than $600 per tire.
- **Keep a tire-repair kit in your vehicle.** Repair kits can patch a small hole if your car does not have a spare tire. A can of sealant costs roughly $10, while a full kit with an air compressor may cost between $20 and $80.
- **Purchase roadside assistance.** Sign up for AAA if roadside assistance isn't already included with your car's warranty or insurance.

AARP: The Magazine.

US Cars Dominate Latest Safety Ratings

US-brand vehicles dominate safety ratings for 2017 models based on federal government test results (ratings for 2018 cars were unvailable at press time)...

Safest subcompact cars: Chevrolet Sonic, Honda Fit.

Safest compact cars: Buick Verano, Ford Focus.

Safest intermediate-sized cars: Acura TLX, Subaru Legacy.

Safest large cars: Cadillac XTS, Tesla Model S.

Safest small SUV: Acura RDX.

Safest midsize SUVs: Ford Edge, Subaru Outback.

Safest large SUVs: Ford Expedition, Lincoln Navigator.

Jack Gillis, director of public affairs for the Consumer Federation of America, Washington, DC. For 37 years, he has published *The Car Book.*

BEWARE...

Deadliest Days to Drive

The deadliest driving days are the 100 days from Memorial Day until the start of school. During that period, about 1,000 people in the US die in crashes with vehicles driven by teenagers ages 16 to 19—a 16% higher death rate per day than at other times of year.

Statistics from AAA, Heathrow, Florida, quoted in *USA Today*.

Apps That Help You Avoid Speeding Tickets

For iOS devices, the free *Speed Cameras & Traffic* app lets you see the speed limit for whatever road you are traveling on, plus alerts you to upcoming speed cameras and radar traps. For Android, try *CamSam Plus*, $0.99.

USA Today.

Wintertime Car-Safety Kit

Be sure to include the following in your car during winter...

- **Pack a car cell-phone charger** because areas with weak reception can kill a battery quickly.
- **First-aid kit.**
- **Warning light, hazard triangle or road flares.**
- **Water and foods with a long shelf life,** such as protein bars.
- **Tire jack and lug wrench, tire sealant and a portable compressor.**
- **Flashlight and extra set of batteries.**
- **Tubes of sand** to spread around tires if you get stuck and need extra traction.
- **Jumper cables** or portable battery booster.
- **Blanket.**
- **Winter boots and socks.**

Consumer Reports, CR.org.

Never Buy a Lemon: Tricks to Check Out Any Used Car

Corey Sandler, author and journalist who has written more than 200 books about consumer topics over the past 30 years including *Econoguide Buying or Leasing a Car.* His latest book is *Bottom Line's Secrets of the Savvy Consumer.*

Many thousands of vehicles were engulfed by floodwater during recent hurricanes. Some of these now-ruined cars and trucks—that can be shined up today but will rot, lose their electrical systems and fall apart over time—will be snuck onto the used-car market by disreputable sellers and go on to bedevil their owners. (For more on the signs of flood damage, see below.)

In general, buying a used vehicle can save you big bucks—but only if you manage to dodge basket-case cars and trucks that will require endless or expensive repairs.

You might know the standard advice to pay a mechanic you trust $100 to $200 to examine a used vehicle before you buy...and purchase a vehicle history report from a company such as Carfax (Carfax.com, $39.99 for a single report). That can be money well-spent—but you don't want to spend it more often than necessary.

You can be the first to spot trouble in a used vehicle offered by a dealer or an individual—even if you are in no way a car expert. Here are six savvy things anyone can do to weed out bad used vehicles *before* consulting a mechanic or buying a Carfax report, potentially saving hundreds of dollars in the process...

- **Look where there *shouldn't* be paint.** If the vehicle was in a significant accident, it probably was repainted by a body shop. If you know where to look, you might be able to find "overspray" from this second paint job—that is, paint where there is not supposed to be paint. This might include tiny spots of paint inside wheel wells...on the rubber trim around windows...or under the hood on stickers or on parts that would not have been present when the bare body panels were originally painted in the factory.

Next, step back from the vehicle and compare its body panels. If the paint on some panels seems subtly different from the paint on others, it might mean that certain panels were repainted following an accident. This will be much easier to spot on a bright, sunny day. (Make sure you're comparing metal parts. It's perfectly normal for the color of plastic body panels, such as bumpers, to not quite match the color of painted metal.)

• **Check the gaps between body panels.** If a gap is visibly wider than the same gap on the other side of the vehicle...or the same gap is wider at one end than the other...it might mean that the car was in a serious accident. If any of the doors appears slightly out of line with the rest of the vehicle when shut, that, too, could point to a major accident.

• **Look for areas under the hood** that appear much cleaner than the rest of the engine compartment. These areas might have been cleaned to hide the fact that the vehicle has been leaking fluids, or a particular component might be clean because it was only recently replaced. If you see an oddly clean area, ask the seller whether the vehicle has needed any work or experienced any problems lately. If he/she says that a part needed to be replaced, ask to see the paperwork from the mechanic and confirm that it was something straightforward, such as a new starter or alternator. If the seller denies that anything has gone wrong, ask why this one area looks so much cleaner. Walk away if he cannot offer a reasonable-sounding explanation.

• **Check the wear on the accelerator pedal,** the driver's seat upholstery and driver's seat springs. The pedal and upholstery typically should not show significant wear if there is less than 50,000 miles or so on the odometer, and the seat springs should not sound or feel old and squeaky. If any of these things are true, there might be more miles on the vehicle than its odometer suggests.

Also: If the brake pedal shows significant wear, the vehicle might have endured lots of tough stop-and-go driving.

• **Put your hand on the hood before starting the vehicle.** Certainly, you should take the vehicle for a test-drive to make sure that there are no obvious issues with how it handles or sounds and to make sure there are no liquids dripping from it afterward. But before this test-drive, feel the hood. If it feels warmer than other body panels, the seller might have started and run the vehicle just before you arrived. This might have been perfectly innocent—maybe he backed the car out of the garage for you—or it might have been to hide the fact that this vehicle does not start reliably when its engine is cold. Let the engine cool for perhaps 20 to 30 minutes before starting it up again for the test-drive. Use this time to examine it inside and out.

• **Do not be lulled by the existence of a warranty.** A warranty might guarantee that any problems with the car can be fixed without paying out of pocket—but not necessarily. Ask *who* is providing this warranty and who will do the repairs. If the protection is being offered by a dealership that sells this make of car and has its own service department, the warranty could well be reliable. If it is offered by an independent used-car lot, it could have little or no real value. Either way, ask for a printed copy of the terms of the warranty and read it before buying.

If you are assured that a used vehicle is covered by its original manufacturer warranty—the most reliable type of vehicle warranty—jot down the vehicle identification number (VIN) found on the driver's doorjamb or visible through the windshield on the driver's side above the dash. Contact the service department of a dealership that sells that make of car, give the VIN and ask about the vehicle's warranty status. In some cases, the full manufacturer's warranty does not carry over if the car is resold by the original owner.

Example: Hyundai and Kia vehicles come new with a 10-year/100,000-mile power train warranty that's reduced to a five-year/60,000-mile warranty for subsequent owners.

If you are told by a car's seller that the vehicle still is covered by an extended warranty purchased by an earlier owner, ask to see the warranty contract covering this specific vehicle and read this carefully to confirm that it will transfer to a subsequent owner. Also, look up reviews of the company providing this extended warranty to get a sense of whether it can be trusted.

• **Three additional things worth doing when buying a used car from an individual,** not a dealership or lot...

• *Ask, "Has it been garaged?"* If it has, ask to see its garage space and examine the floor. Stains where the car was parked could mean that the vehicle has had oil or other fluid leaks.

• *Ask to see the vehicle's maintenance records.* It's a bad sign if the owner cannot produce a well-organized file showing that maintenance has been handled on schedule.

• *If the vehicle has a trailer hitch and/or you see a travel trailer or boat in the driveway, ask, "Oh, is it powerful enough to tow?"* If the seller brags that it is, make polite conversation about what the owner has towed, where and how often. If you give the impression that you are impressed by the vehicle's towing capacity, you're likely to get honest answers. But in fact, towing is tough on many parts of a vehicle, including its engine and brakes. If the vehicle has done lots of towing, that could be a reason to walk away.

SPOT A FLOOD-DAMAGED CAR

Vehicles that have been in floods are prone to a wide range of problems, some of which might not appear until years later when corrosion has taken its toll. *To avoid these cars...*

• **See if a vehicle has a known history of flood damage.** You can search this for free through Carfax (Carfax.com/press/resources/flooded-cars). This database includes a vehicle only if its flood damage was reported to an insurance company, however. To be even safer, pay for the full Carfax Vehicle History Report ($39.99 for one report...$59.99 for three or $99.99 for six) and check where the vehicle previously was owned—if it was owned in Florida or in or near Houston, sites of recent hurricanes, stay away.

• **Examine the carpeting.** Look for mud on and under the vehicle's carpeting. Also be suspicious of any used car that has carpeting that looks brand-new and/or does not fit the floor of the car perfectly. This replacement carpeting might have been installed because original carpeting was ruined in a flood.

• **Look for mud under the hood.** Pay particular attention to the tight spots. These spots are tricky to clean, so they might still show signs of mud.

• **Take a good whiff.** Get inside the vehicle, shut its doors and windows and see whether your nose picks up a musty odor. The smell of mold and mildew can be harder to hide than the visual signs of flood damage.

GOOD TO KNOW...

Best Times to Buy a Car

• **Mondays,** when discounts average 8.1%, because few people take the time to test-drive and negotiate at the start of the workweek.

• **December,** when SUVs, including luxury models, get price drops as dealers try to earn year-end sales incentives and bonuses.

• **New Year's Eve,** when monthly, quarterly and annual sales goals all merge—December 29 and 30 are almost as good for buyers.

• **May,** if you are looking for a midsize SUV, since new models start coming out in June.

• **October** for big pickups—the biggest discounts are on October 30.

• **November** for compact and midsize sedans, with the biggest discounts on mainstream cars often used for commuting.

Analysis by TrueCar, reported at Cars.USNews.com.

Snazzy Car Features That Can Cost You Big Later

Some fancy optional car features could cost you a fortune down the road...

Some cars have headlights that swivel as the car turns to better illuminate around corners... multizone climate control that lets the front-seat passenger and even rear passengers set different temperatures than the driver...multifunction electronic displays that combine features such as a music system, navigation and backup camera into one unit...and side-view mirrors that include lights, heaters, motors and sensors that detect surrounding vehicles and send warning signals to the driver.

These all are very nice features, and all very expensive to replace. A high-end headlight assembly easily can cost $1,000 to $2,000...multizone climate-control repairs often cost more than $1,000...a multifunction electronic display unit can run $3,000 or much more...and even a side mirror can cost well over $500.

Jill Trotta, ASE Certified Technician/Adviser and director of the automotive group at RepairPal.com, a website offering auto-repair information.

Beware Car Ads

The most misleading numbers in car advertisements...

- **Very low lease payments**—these come with very low mileage limits and may exclude taxes and fees.
- **Hidden drive-off fees**—the drive-off fee is the amount paid up front to get a low payment, and it can be very high to get the advertised monthly lease price.
- **Prices that apply to a different car from the one advertised.** Dealers routinely show pictures of fully loaded, high-trim car models when advertising the price of the base model.
- **A price that is available only on a limited number of vehicles.** Dealers advertise a great price on a specific model but have only one or two cars equipped that way.

Roundup of experts on car advertising, reported at MarketWatch.com.

Car Dealer Trick

It's easier for a car dealer to trick you with an electronic contract. The dealer instructs the customer to use a finger to sign a computer screen rather than printing a copy for signing. Consumers are less likely to examine on-screen contracts, upping the odds that the dealer could sneak in extra costs.

Best: Insist on a printed contract, and review it before signing.

Rosemary Shahan, founder and president of Consumers for Auto Reliability and Safety, Sacramento, California. CarConsumers.org

5 Ways to Increase Your Car's Trade-In Value

For a higher trade-in value on your vehicle, follow this advice...

- **Keep some of your personal belongings inside the vehicle.** If your car is empty, the dealer may lowball you because he believes that you are in a rush to sell.
- **Focus on the tires.** If your tires are in good shape, don't worry about buying a new set. However, if they are not, purchase an inexpensive set. Heavily worn tires can decrease the trade-in value by more than the cost of cheap new tires.
- **Make minor repairs.** Fixing small problems such as a burned-out headlight or buffing out a scratch can increase the price you will get by more than the cost of the repair.
- **Present documentation.** Bring oil-change records and other maintenance-related paperwork to show that your car was well-kept.
- **Play one dealer against another.** Get purchase offers from multiple dealerships to maximize your bargaining leverage.

GoBankingRates.com

5 Colors That Boost Your Car's Resale Value

On average, cars depreciate 33.1% in the first three years of ownership. But yellow ones depreciate only 27%...orange, 30.6%...green, 30.9%...white, 32.6%...red, 32.7%. Yellow, orange and green are not common car colors—they make up only 1.2% of all three-year-old cars. This may increase the demand for them as used cars.

Car colors with lower-than-average resale value: Gold, which depreciates 37.1% over three years...purple, 36.7%...beige, 36.6%...silver, 34%...black, 33.6%...gray, 33.5%...brown, 33.5%.

Analysis by iSeeCars.com.

16

Family Time

4 Warning Signs Your Marriage Is in Trouble

Is your marriage in trouble? It might be. Research shows that couples in unhappy marriages wait an average of six years before seeking professional help. By then, problems often have become deeply entrenched, making it more challenging to break free from hurtful ways of interacting.

No matter how long you've been married, it makes much more sense to nip relationship problems in the bud before problems get out of hand.

But how can you tell early on when your marriage is headed for trouble? Here are four warning signs that it's time to be proactive about a less-than-satisfying relationship...

THE ABSENCE OF FIGHTING

Although most people know that constant fighting is a marital risk factor, the opposite also is true—the absence of fighting doesn't bode well for relationships.

The worrisome pattern goes like this: One spouse—let's say the wife—has serious misgivings about something her husband does. In the early years of marriage, she tells him about it, but he becomes defensive. They fight about their differences often. Over time, he fails to change his actions or be responsive to her needs.

Eventually, she stops complaining and temporarily resigns herself to the situation. Based on her silence, he assumes that she has finally accepted his idiosyncrasies and that she is no longer unhappy. But unfortunately, he's dead wrong. She is more unhappy than ever and is secretly planning her escape.

Michele Weiner-Davis, LCSW, founder of The Divorce Busting Center in Boulder, Colorado, which helps on-the-brink couples save their marriages. She is the best-selling author of eight books including *Healing from Infidelity*, *The Sex-Starved Marriage* and *Divorce Busting*, and is a TEDx speaker. DivorceBusting.com

As counterintuitive as it might seem, when your spouse is complaining, it often is a sign of caring and emotional involvement. "Nagging" or "criticizing" might feel off-putting, but the absence of these behaviors, coupled with emotional distance, might be indicative of an emotional shutdown that is hard to overcome.

To avoid creating insurmountable emotional obstacles, it's important to express feelings openly and honestly when something truly bothers you. Although it's not advisable to focus on every little relationship annoyance, pushing aside important feelings to avert immediate conflict will only create bigger problems.

Conversely, if your spouse sounds "like a broken record," it means that you're not listening to something important that is being said. You need to heed your partner's comments so that feelings of resentment don't fester. Showing that you care and that you are willing to change, even if it's not your first choice, is what good marriages are all about.

Exception: If you're in a marriage where you both have very easygoing, laid-back personalities and can happily give up on your individual preferences in many areas of your life—and therefore never fight—no worries. That can work, too.

LITTLE OR NO TOUCHING

Although the need to be physically close varies from person to person, touch is a tie that binds. Typically, couples can think back to times early in their relationships when just the sight of each other gave them butterflies in their stomachs. They have fond memories of walking hand-in-hand, exchanging back rubs, kissing passionately and engaging in extended foreplay and lovemaking, all of which felt incredibly good and defined the relationship as different from all others.

But then something happened. Touching seemed to disappear. They stopped sitting next to each other on the couch. No more hand-holding. Never a reassuring arm around a shoulder. The passionate kisses turned into occasional perfunctory pecks on the cheek. Physical affection, passion and eroticism vanished.

If you and your partner used to be physically affectionate and felt good about your sexual relationship but this is no longer the case, it's time to talk about it with each other. Although there may be extenuating circumstances—such as a medical condition or busy travel schedules—going for a long time physically disconnected is a red flag for a marriage. It can be a symptom of unexpressed unhappiness...and can be a powerful factor leading to infidelity or divorce.

When you have this important conversation with your spouse, describe in loving, positive and actionable terms what you've been missing and what you would like to do about it.

Example: "It seems to me that we haven't been physically affectionate lately. I miss cuddling in bed and giving foot rubs, massages and hugs. I also would like to make love more often. It would be great if we could have sex at least once or twice a week. Plus, I want to feel that you're into it. I'd love it if you would initiate sex more often and if you'd be willing to try new things."

Perhaps the two of you have been so busy that you simply have overlooked the importance of connecting sexually. If so, consider scheduling times to have sex. Then, once you have placed sex on your calendar, allow your creativity to make sex special.

NOT FOCUSING ON "US"

Healthy relationships consist of three parts —you, me and us. Yes, it's important to feel good about yourself and your life separate from your spouse. You must have interests and activities that feed your soul. But balance between individual pursuits and togetherness is essential if a relationship is to thrive.

One of the common reasons for a relationship breakdown is that the two partners have developed independent lives that rarely intersect. They have separate responsibilities. They

GOOD TO KNOW...

Tunes Improve Teamwork

But only when the music is upbeat. *New study:* Cooperative spirit was one-third higher in those who listened to "happy" music compared with less pleasant (think heavy-metal) tunes.

Journal of Organizational Behavior.

don't have hobbies in common. They don't take pleasure in each other's accomplishments, interests, hopes and dreams. They become little more than roommates. Although some people resign themselves to this separate lifestyle, they often are married to spouses who eventually tire of the loneliness and decide to strike out on their own to find new, more loving relationships.

If you and your partner have become increasingly independent and no longer share your lives in a meaningful way, it's time to make a change. Ask yourselves, *What enjoyable activities did we do together in the past that we can re-create now?* Maybe you used to cook meals together or go for evening walks or take exercise classes. Or what about new hobbies? You could take up birding or take a wine-tasting course or start a couples' book group.

For that matter, what about something as simple as going to the grocery store together? Time together, no matter what you choose to do, is the healing factor.

KIDS TAKING CENTER STAGE

Most parents agree that having children is one of life's greatest gifts. In our quest to give them the best in life, we often put more energy into their well-being than into the health of our marriages. We chauffeur them to after-school lessons and weekend sports. We overspend on their electronic gadgets and clothes. We forgo date nights so that they can have friends sleep over. And an uninterrupted adult conversation? What's that?

Here's the warning: If you've neglected your marriage because your kids are your top priority, you are playing with fire. When kids leave home, you won't have a real marital relationship. Many divorces occur after the youngest child leaves home.

To prevent that, no matter how busy you are raising your children, have a scheduled date night once every week or two. If your kids are young enough to need a babysitter, get one—and then leave the house. What you do together is less important than the fact that you're making time for each other. Additionally, you should try to spend 10 to 15 minutes every night "checking in," asking about your spouse's day. Unless the children are very young, see to it that they occupy themselves during this check-in time to give the two of you a chance to reconnect without interruption.

If you worry that prioritizing your marriage is "selfish," keep in mind that outwardly valuing your spouse is a gift for your kids. Children learn about intimate adult relationships by watching their parents interact. When kids observe their parents modeling loving relationships—being physically affectionate, calmly resolving conflict, demonstrating respect, appreciation and kindness, and being good friends—it paves the way for them to create healthy adult relationships in the future.

Love Hacks: Improve Your Relationship in 5 Minutes or Less

Eli J. Finkel, PhD, professor in the psychology department and the Kellogg School of Management at Northwestern University, Evanston, Illinois. He is director of Northwestern's Relationships and Motivation Lab and author of *The All-or-Nothing Marriage: How the Best Marriages Work*. EliFinkel.com

Sure, it takes time and effort to build a successful relationship, but there are some quick, easy, surprisingly effective ways to strengthen your bond with your partner. These simple, research-based strategies are not likely to salvage a deeply troubled relationship, but they can help keep a relatively happy one on solid ground until there's time for a grander gesture. *Six of the simplest ways you'll ever find to strengthen your relationship...*

- **Make a big deal about your partner's little victory.** Listen intently and respond enthusiastically when your partner tells you about something that went right for him/her that day. Do this even if he describes something very small, such as fixing a broken appliance or receiving positive feedback from a colleague. Caring partners know that they must provide support when their loved ones experience challenging times. But research published in *Journal of Personality and Social Psychology* found that reveling in partners' victories also is pivotal for relationships, increasing trust, intimacy and overall satisfaction.

Next step: After your partner shares the story of a small success, suggest something that commemorates the accomplishment, such as, "That's worth opening a bottle of wine." This turns an everyday moment into a relationship-building shared celebration.

- **When your partner makes a misstep, picture an external, temporary explanation for it.** Your partner arrives late to dinner, leaving you waiting. Do you think, *He doesn't care about my time*...or *He was probably stuck in bad traffic?* If you're like most people, it often is the former, negative conclusion. We tend to blame individuals and ignore potential external factors.

This tendency is very bad for relationships—blaming our partners for everyday missteps decreases our satisfaction with our relationships, makes our partners feel persecuted and gains us nothing. When you feel let down by your partner, instead take a moment to ask yourself, *What temporary, outside factor could be to blame for this?*

Do exactly the opposite when your partner gets something right—think up a permanent, internal explanation for this success.

Example: If your partner brings home your favorite ice cream, don't think, *Oh, he did that just because he wanted ice cream, too*—instead think, *He's such a thoughtful person.*

- **Reflect on what your partner has done recently for the sake of the relationship.** Find a few minutes every month or so to mentally list two or three things your partner has done lately for you or for your relationship and note to yourself that you are grateful for these actions. They can be small things—maybe she walked the dog even though it was your turn...or he called in the middle of a busy day just to say he loved you.

Several studies have found that focusing on gratitude for even a few minutes a month is an effective way to strengthen the emotional bonds between partners. One researcher even referred to gratitude as a "booster shot for romantic relationships." It's so powerful that it can lead to a virtuous cycle—your sense of gratitude might boost your positive feelings for your partner so much that your partner senses your positivity and starts feeling and acting more positively toward you, too, encouraging kind deeds and warm feelings on both sides.

- **Be your own neutral arbitrator after arguments.** Most of us get caught up in self-righteousness after we argue with our partners—we tell ourselves that our side of the disagreement was 100% correct and our partner's side was 100% wrong. Instead, try this trick soon after an argument—mentally revisit the exchange from the perspective of a neutral third party who wants the best for all involved. What would this person think about the disagreement? How might he find the good that could come from it?

A recent study of 120 married couples in the Chicago area found that doing this significantly improved marital satisfaction—even though the couples did it for only a few minutes every few months. These couples still argued as much as ever, but their arguments did not lead to the same degree of lingering displeasure.

Next step: Attempt to take this neutral perspective during arguments.

- **Learn to accept your partner's praise.** Some people struggle to accept compliments from their partners, often because they suffer from low self-esteem and/or consider themselves unlovable. Overcoming this tendency could do wonders for their relationships—receiving kind words from a partner makes people feel much closer.

A psychologist at Renison University College in Canada found a way for people who have trouble accepting their partners' compliments to greatly improve this ability. After receiving a compliment, take a moment to silently explain to yourself why your partner admired you...and to reflect on what this compliment means to you and its significance for your relationship. Doing this will encourage you to see the praise in abstract terms, rather than only in terms of the specific, isolated item or event that was complimented. It's easy to dismiss compliments for isolated things—*Sure, I got that one thing right, but it was just luck*—

but much more difficult to dismiss abstract praise.

• **Touch.** It won't surprise you to learn that happy couples tend to do more affectionate touching—such as holding hands, giving shoulder rubs, placing a hand on a partner's knee—than unhappy couples. What is surprising is that affectionate touching is very effective at *making* couples feel closer—so effective, in fact, that it's likely to work even if your partner knows that you're doing it only because it takes a lot less thought and effort than most other relationship-building strategies. In one study, psychologists at Carnegie Mellon University found that people felt more secure in their relationships and more trusting of their partners following physical contact, even when they knew that their partners were making physical contact only because the academic running the study had just instructed them to. If touch can make couples feel closer under those entirely unromantic circumstances, it's very likely to work in your life as well.

Surprising Things You Can Put in a Prenup

Robert J. Nachshin, Esq., founder of the Law Offices of Robert J. Nachshin, a family law firm based in Los Angeles, and coauthor of *I Do, You Do...But Just Sign Here: A Quick and Easy Guide to Cohabitation, Prenuptial and Postnuptial Agreements.* RJNPC.com

A prenuptial agreement can do more than just spell out which spouse retains certain assets in case of a divorce. It also can be a useful way to spell out guidelines and expectations for behavior *during* the marriage.

These so-called "lifestyle clauses" can sometimes raise eyebrows—for example, provisions that a spouse remain under a certain weight often are considered inappropriate and demeaning. But in many cases, lifestyle clauses can encourage couples to explore concerns about important issues—beyond money—that are likely to arise over the course of a marriage.

Important: Some lifestyle clauses have been challenged in court—for example, whether an infidelity clause is enforceable—and rulings have been mixed. The rules vary widely from state to state. Your prenup should include a "severability clause" stating that if one or more of its clauses is invalidated by a court, the rest of the agreement, such as directions on the division of assets, still stands.

Most prenups come into play after a divorce has been initiated, but there has been a growing trend toward including clauses that define acceptable behavior *within* the marriage...and that mandate penalties—often token fines of a few hundred dollars—for violations. These penalties may not hold up in a court of law, and they may be merely symbolic for couples who have merged their finances, but they can be helpful in defining the parameters of what's acceptable in the marriage.

Here are six ideas to consider for lifestyle clauses—and two to avoid—when drawing up your prenup...

CONSIDER THESE PRENUP CLAUSES

• **Avoiding intrusive in-laws.** Dealing with family members is often a point of contention for married couples, such as when one spouse's parents visit too often and/or stay too long. You can head off potential strain on your marriage by addressing the issue in your prenup. Your agreement may include a clause that limits in-law visits—for example, that in-laws can visit only once every six months and that the visits can last no more than two weeks. For in-laws living nearby, the clause may limit them to, say, two visits per week.

• **Incentivizing vacations.** Your prenup can specify how often vacations should take place—such as at least once a year—and even how much money will be spent on them. These clauses make sense when one spouse is a workaholic and might need extra incentive to take time off. Some couples include a provision that shared assets can be used to pay only for family vacations—not, say, to pay for a trip that only one spouse takes with friends or to visit his/her extended family.

• **Discouraging (and defining) cheating.** In many states, courts won't financially penalize an unfaithful spouse when dividing assets in a divorce. But an infidelity clause in your prenup can impose a financial penalty on the spouse who transgresses—for example, by requiring the cheating spouse to pay all divorce-related legal fees. And while including an infidelity clause may not keep your spouse from cheating, it can provide an opportunity to discuss your values and feelings about fidelity before you get married, which may benefit your relationship down the road. If you find that you and your spouse-to-be disagree substantively about these issues, it's better to know that now—even if that disagreement ends your relationship.

Caution: If you include an infidelity clause in your prenup, make sure that you define what "infidelity" (or "cheating") means in the context of your marriage. Does it include only sexual relationships? Does sexting (sending sexually charged text messages) or e-mailing sex-related messages count as cheating? These discussions can further help to clarify each spouse's stance on fidelity in a relationship.

• **Ensuring quality time.** A prenup can cap the amount of time that a husband or wife spends on hobbies or other activities that typically involve only one spouse.

Example: Your prenup may cap the amount of time one spouse spends playing golf or tennis or watching sports on TV to 10 hours per week.

An agreement also can specify that a couple spend a minimum amount of "quality time" together, defining "quality time" according to their shared interests and values.

Example: You could specify that the two of you will eat dinner together at least four times a week or partake of at least one shared cultural activity per month, such as going to the theater or visiting a museum. Such a mandate may seem controlling, but it's one way that a busy couple with diverse interests can encourage themselves to spend time together.

• **Navigating social-media pitfalls.** People live more and more of their lives online, which is one reason that social-media clauses are becoming an increasingly popular addition to prenuptial agreements—especially for people whose online reputations, either for professional or personal reasons, are very important to them. To retain control of how you are presented online, for example, you might specify in a prenup that your spouse needs your approval to post photos of you online…or that in the case of a divorce, your ex won't post anything disparaging about you online.

• **Encouraging marriage counseling.** While a marriage is meant to be a lifetime commitment, a prenup can strengthen that intent by also including a commitment to work on problems should they arise. To that end, you can include an agreement that you and your spouse will seek professional marriage counseling for at least a set period—say, three months or six sessions—before either of you initiates a divorce. This provision may help you avoid a split, and even if it doesn't, sessions with a counselor might help you end your relationship in a more amicable and open way.

TAKE NOTE...

Avoid These Prenup Clauses

• **Setting divorce terms involving children.** Courts regularly invalidate prenup clauses involving how children will be treated in the case of divorce—for example, agreements about the amount of child support a spouse must pay or guidelines for visitation rights in case of divorce. Don't bother including such clauses in your prenup, as they likely will be overruled. Some prenups do, however, include what attorneys call a "no diaper" clause—specifying that the couple will not have children.

• **Setting sky-high penalties.** Celebrity prenups have generated headlines for including million-dollar penalties for cheating, but that doesn't mean that yours should attempt a similarly dramatic payout. In fact, if the terms spelled out in your prenup seem unreasonable, a judge is more likely to invalidate those clauses. There is no hard-and-fast rule regarding the right amount to seek, but courts are likely to reject penalties that are more than 10% of the annual income of the cheating spouse.

Robert J. Nachshin, Esq., Los Angeles.

Mom or Dad Is Dating Again! How to Avoid a Family Rift

Carol Hughes, PhD, psychotherapist and divorce coach based in Laguna Hills, California. She has more than 30 years of experience working with divorcing couples and their children and is one of the founding members of Collaborative Divorce Solutions of Orange County. DrCarolHughes.com

Divorced or widowed parents might feel excitement or hope when they return to the dating world after decades away. But their adult children might feel anxiety about the parent's safety and financial security (and their own inheritance)...renewed grief over the loss of the family unit...or discomfort at seeing the parent behave in a nonparental way.

Here's what parent and child should do—and not do—to protect their relationship during these emotionally difficult times...

WHY GROWN KIDS AREN'T HAPPY WHEN MOM OR DAD DATES

Parents often cannot understand why their adult children have a negative emotional response to the news that they are dating or in a new relationship. In fact, the adult children might not completely understand their own reactions.

The parent's return to the dating world forces a role reversal. Traditionally, it is parents who are asked to be happy for their children's happiness and parents who watch and worry while their children endure the ups and downs of meeting new partners and taking chances on new romances. When a parent dates, these roles are flipped, forcing unfamiliar and difficult-to-navigate dynamics for all.

If the parent settles into a new long-term relationship, that might force the adult child to finally confront the difficult fact that the family unit of his/her youth is gone forever. Intellectually, this adult child, of course, understands that the family unit ended when the parent was widowed or divorced—but some adult children manage to avoid psychologically confronting this fact until the parent starts seeing someone new. (This is especially likely if the parent is divorced, not widowed. The adult child might have been telling himself that his parents would get back together eventually.)

In these cases, the adult child is looking backward and grieving the loss of the old relationship just as the parent is looking forward in excitement to a new one. That difference in perspective virtually ensures that they will struggle to see eye to eye.

WHAT PARENTS SHOULD DO

To reduce the odds that a new romantic relationship will damage your parent/child relationship...

- **Share the news that you are dating again—or that you are in a relationship—in a calm, private moment.** Present this news in a straightforward manner, such as, "I wanted you to know that I'm dating again." Or "I wanted you to know that I'm seeing someone." And then let the adult child process what you've said and ask questions. Do not phrase this in a way that demands happiness from the adult child, such as, "Isn't it wonderful—I'm dating!"
- **Do not find fault with your adult child's reaction to your return to dating or a new relationship** even if that reaction is negative. There is nothing immature or even unusual about an adult child's less-than-positive response to this news. This is an emotionally challenging situation, so be ready to take any reaction in stride. Telling your adult child to "grow up" or asking, "Don't you want me to be happy?" only increases the odds that the parent-child relationship will suffer.
- **If you find someone who you think could become a long-term partner,** ask your kids if they want to meet this person rather than trying to force a first meeting. Offer the option of waiting to see whether the relationship lasts a while longer before agreeing to meet. Parents often have unrealistic expectations that their new partners will instantly become part of a happy family unit. That almost certainly will take time (if it happens at all).

Also: Dissuade your new partner from pushing too hard to form close bonds with your adult children when they do meet. Your partner should be pleasant and polite but should let your adult children take the lead in these relationships.

• **Continue to find as much time as possible for your adult children and your grandchildren**—ideally without a date by your side. When parents of adult children start spending time dating, they often spend less time with their children and grandchildren. This gives the adult children an additional reason to find fault with the parent's return to romantic life.

• **Reassure your adult children that your money is safe.** Your initial reaction to their financial worries might be, "My money is my business"..."My new partner loves me, not my money"...or "It's selfish of you to put your inheritance ahead of my happiness." But it is perfectly reasonable for your kids to be concerned. Relatively savvy people sometimes do fall victim to dating scams, and when they do, their entire families can pay the price. So rather than dismiss your kids' money concerns, you could reassure them that you are not splurging on extravagant gifts for this new partner...and that if you do someday remarry, you will get a prenup. Or you could agree to work with an estate planner (or some other trusted financial adviser) to make sure that your money remains in your family.

• **Reminisce with your adult children about the old days when your original family was intact.** This subtly reinforces the sense that your search for a new relationship does not invalidate the family unit of their youth.

• **Do not discuss your sex life with your adult kids.** It is surprisingly common for parents to share details about their revitalized sex lives with their adult children when they return to the dating scene. Doing this only makes a difficult situation even less comfortable for the adult children.

• **Do not denigrate your ex-spouse.** Detailing everything that was wrong with your ex will not help your adult children understand why you need someone new. It will only make them angry that they are being pushed to see their other parent in a negative light.

• **If you are divorced, do not ask your kids not to tell your ex that you're dating.** That would put your kids in an uncomfortable position and make it harder for them to see your new partner in a positive light. One option is to contact your ex with the news around the same time you tell your kids, assuming that your lines of communication with your ex remain open.

WHAT ADULT CHILDREN SHOULD DO

To remain on good terms with your parent—and help protect your parent if necessary...

• **Stifle any negative initial reaction you may have.** This negative reaction likely is rooted in your deep-seated emotions surrounding your childhood family unit, not in your true opinion of your parent's decision to date or of the new partner. If you can't say anything positive, say something noncommittal such as, "Thanks for letting me know. That's big news."

• **Raise any concerns you may have about your parent's finances** in a way that does not imply that a new partner is a gold digger or scammer. Suggesting that a new partner might be after your parent's money will only make your parent rush to his defense. Instead, note that starting a romantic relationship can have financial consequences, and recommend that the parent meet with a financial adviser or estate planner.

If after getting to know a new partner, you still harbor fears that this person might be after your parent's money, discuss these concerns with one of your parent's trusted peers who has met the new partner. A trusted peer is more likely than an adult child to be able to successfully discuss this difficult topic with the parent. Alternatively, you could discuss your concerns with an attorney who specializes in elder abuse. (You can find one through the National Academy of Elder Law Attorneys at NAELA.org.)

• **Don't be surprised if your parent's rekindled romantic life makes you experience doubts about your own marriage**—and don't overreact to these doubts. It is not uncommon for adult children to leave their spouses when their parents start dating again. Our parents are our relationship role models—whether we like it or not. When we see a parent searching for (or finding) someone new, we might feel an itch to do the same even if our relationship previously was sound. Meet with a counselor, and talk through your feelings about your parent's return to dating and your feelings about your own marriage before taking any big relationship steps.

- **Reassure yourself that your feelings about your parent's new relationship are completely unrelated to your feelings** for your *other* parent. Some adult children express negative feelings about a parent's new relationship because at some level they fear that accepting this relationship would be disloyal to their other parent (or to the memory of the other parent, if deceased). Such feelings are normal, but they are not accurate and are not helpful to anyone.

If you cannot shake negative feelings about your parent's new relationship, discuss these feelings with a therapist or clergy member.

Help for Colic!

Acupuncture may help relieve colic. Babies who cried for more than three hours a day and who were treated with acupuncture for two weeks had a greater reduction in crying than babies not given acupuncture treatment.

Study by researchers at Lund University, Sweden, published in *Acupuncture in Medicine*.

A Pill That Stops Peanut Allergies?

For 18 months, children with a peanut allergy were given a daily probiotic that contained *lactobacillus rhamnosus* and a peanut protein. Four years after the treatment ended, almost 70% of the children could eat peanuts without an allergic reaction.

Study by researchers at Murdoch Children's Research Institute, Melbourne, Australia, published in *The Lancet Child & Adolescent Health*.

TAKE NOTE...

Best Chores for Kids of All Ages

Five and under: Pick up toys...brush teeth ...comb his/her hair.

Six to nine: Take care of pets...operate appliances, such as a vacuum cleaner or dishwasher...make his/her own bed.

10 to 12: Take out trash...make his/her lunch ...clean the bathroom.

13 to 15: Mow the lawn...wash windows... clean the garage.

16 to 18: Wash clothes...do grocery shopping...handle car maintenance, such as getting an oil change or emissions testing.

Roundup of experts on tasks that children can do, reported in *The Wall Street Journal*.

Fido Helps Fight Allergies and Obesity

Children who grow up in homes with dogs have more gut bacteria that protect against allergies and obesity than those in dog-free households.

University of Alberta, UAlberta.ca.

Early-Life Mild Brain Injuries Have Lasting Effects

In a recent finding, young people who had a mild traumatic brain injury (TBI) at the average age of 13 were 10% more likely to be diagnosed with a psychiatric disorder as adults...and 2% more likely to die prematurely.

Self-defense: Ban dangerous or reckless plays in sports...teach safer tackling techniques...keep children off the field when a head injury is suspected...increase parental supervision of toddlers and preschool children...involve mental-health professionals in the management of TBI.

Study comparing more than 100,000 Swedes who suffered a TBI before age 25 with their siblings by researchers at University of Oxford, UK, published in *PLOS Medicine.*

Twitter Provides ADHD Insights

Patients may reveal more in social media than they do with a doctor. Researchers analyzed tweets of people who reported having attention deficit hyperactivity disorder (ADHD) and identified frequent words such as "cry" and "disappointed" that indicated mood swings. This data can help doctors develop more effective treatments.

University of Pennsylvania, UPenn.edu.

Smartphone Addiction Changes the Brain

Teenagers considered to be addicted to their phones and the Internet—based on a test of their usage habits—had an imbalance of brain chemicals similar to that seen in people experiencing anxiety and depression. They tended to say that Internet and smartphone addiction interfered with their daily activities, productivity, sleep and social lives...and they had significantly higher scores on scales of depression, anxiety, insomnia and impulsivity than teens whose test scores did not indicate addiction.

The addicted teens had an overabundance of the neurotransmitter *gamma-aminobutyric acid* (GABA) in their brains' emotional control center. Addictive substances such as alcohol are already known to alter GABA levels.

Hyung Suk Seo, MD, professor of neuroradiology, Korea University, Seoul, and leader of a study presented at a recent meeting of the Radiological Society of North America.

Is Your New Grad Impossible?

Caroline Kitchener, author of *Post Grad: Five Women and Their First Year Out of College*, reported by Karen Larson, former editor, *Bottom Line Personal*, BottomLineInc.com.

Think parenting teenagers is tough? Just wait. My friend's relationship with her daughter reached its lowest point only after the daughter graduated from college. That's not uncommon—the first year following college is a tumultuous time for many parent/child relationships.

When writer Caroline Kitchener interviewed several classmates for her book *Post Grad: Five Women and Their First Year Out of College,* she discovered that all had experienced friction with their parents, even though none had moved back home. One likely reason—recent grads value their independence, but many also turn to their parents for emotional and financial support.

Kitchener's tips for parents...

• **Don't harp on your financial help.** The more the parent mentions the money or lectures about financial responsibility, the larger the problem this is likely to cause for the relationship.

• **Find something nice to say about the first apartment even if it's a dump.** It might be the first time your grad has had a home to truly call his/her own. That's a life milestone, and your approval is meaningful.

• **Find something nice to say about the boyfriend/girlfriend even if you think your child could do better.** If you don't make an honest effort to understand what your grad sees in this person, you reject your child's ability to make adult decisions. If after a few months of genuinely trying, you still see a serious problem, you then could think about saying something.

• **Share a bottle of wine or a few beers.** Drinking is something that adults do together. If you're not a drinker, taking an exercise class together works too, such as yoga or spin.

How to Stay Close to Your Grandchildren When You Live Far Away

Nancy Samalin, MS, founder and director of Parent Guidance Workshops, a New York City–based organization that has been working with parents and grandparents for more than three decades. She is author of four bestsellers, including *Loving Without Spoiling: And 100 Other Timeless Tips for Raising Terrific Kids.* Samalin.com

The bond between grandparents and grandchildren is unique. Ideally, grandparents enjoy the company of a grandchild free of the stresses and responsibilities of a parent, and the grandchild basks in the grandparents' undemanding attention and love.

If you live far away from your grandchildren, you may worry that this bond will be harder to maintain. When you don't spend time with grandchildren, will they grow up barely knowing you? You worry that they may feel closer to the "other" grandparents because they see them more often.

You can be an integral part of your grandchild's life even if you aren't geographically close. *Here's how...*

MAXIMIZE VIDEO CALLS

You don't have to be a technical wiz to use video-call services such as *FaceTime* (for iPhones), *Google Hangouts* (for both Android and Apple devices) or *Skype* (for computers, tablets and smartphones). Being able to see each other on a call creates a greater feeling of closeness and involvement. Video also lets you see how your grandchildren are changing over time so that you feel part of their development.

To get the most out of video calls...

- **Favor frequent, short calls over less frequent ones.** Grandparents often think that the key to a close relationship is long, in-depth conversations. Not true! Calls can be short, but they should be frequent. A video chat allows you to stay in touch without being intrusive. Schedule a recurring day and time so that the call is an expected routine that the child looks forward to.

Enlist the child's parents as allies. Tell your children—your grandchild's parents—that you want to build the most positive relationship possible for the grandchild's sake as well as yours, and find a regular time that is convenient for the family. Get the parents' input on the activities, projects and interests that are central to their kids' lives so that you can bring these up during chats.

- **When a new grandchild arrives, start your video chats soon after.** As the baby grows and begins to respond to your voice and face, you will be establishing a connection and a ritual that are special to the child.

- **Ask questions that are easy to answer.** Children—even teenagers—generally are not good at small talk. They tend to clam up at questions such as, "How are you? What did you do in school today? What's new?" Make your questions specific instead of open-ended—"What was something funny or weird that happened in school today? Do you like your teacher?"

Just as you do with your friends, ask your grandchild about the things he/she enjoys.

Example: If the child is interested in dinosaurs, you could ask, "What's the biggest dinosaur? The scariest? Wow, that's such a long name—can you show me a picture? What else can you tell me about Tyrannosaurus rex?"

Ask an older child about sports, crafts, shopping, movies, theater, video games or other interests.

- **Don't just talk.** Read the child a story or have him read to you. Based on your grandchild's interests, ask him to teach you the words to a song...share a favorite poem...play the piano for you...demonstrate a new toy. Ask an older child to show you a model car, craft project or scrapbook. Find out her favorite food, and offer to cook it together the next time you visit.

SEND SURPRISES BY MAIL

As people rely more heavily on electronic communication, receiving packages in the mailbox every few weeks is a very special treat. Don't make these gifts elaborate or expensive. Depending on what your grandchild enjoys, you might alternate among books, puzzles, craft kits, games the family can play together, notebooks, key chains, costume jewelry or homemade delights such as a cartoon or other picture you drew just for the child. Search the Internet for "inexpensive gifts for kids" or "inexpensive gifts for teens" for more ideas.

LEARN YOUR GRANDCHILD'S COMMUNICATION TOOLS

Find out what methods your grandchild uses to communicate with his friends, and try using one or two of those tools. Expect these methods to change as the child grows—and be sure to embrace those changes.

Example: Older children often prefer text messaging or Instagram to Facebook, e-mail or talking by phone.

Have fun exchanging jokes, funny videos, cute animal pictures and photos you take of interesting sights in your neighborhood. On smartphones, you can play games together, in real time, from a distance, such as Scrabble, Words with Friends or the trivia game Quiz Up.

MAKE THE MOST OF VISITS

Whether you visit the family on their turf or they visit you, arrange to spend at least some time alone with your grandchild or grandchildren without their parents. If possible, spend time with each sibling individually as well. You will interact differently with each other one-on-one. Children feel special when you spend time alone with them.

- **Consider a family vacation destination.** If budgets allow, a vacation for the whole family away from home—whether at a cabin or a family-friendly resort—can be a wonderful way for all generations to reconnect away from the tensions of school and work.

- **Make kid time convenient for the parents.** During a visit, offer to take the children for an excursion so that the parents can have some uninterrupted time together...or, if possible, watch them for the weekend so that the parents can have a child-free getaway.

- **Keep outings simple.** When spending time with your grandkids, don't get caught up in planning elaborate outings that put everyone under pressure to have a good time. Often, the most enjoyable and memorable excursions involve low-key activities that will be fun for all and that give you something to talk about together.

Examples: Miniature golf, a movie, the zoo, a library or children's bookstore or just a walk in nature searching for signs of the season.

- **At home, enter your grandchild's world.** When at your grandchild's home for a visit, do what the child loves to do. Draw pictures together...play dress-up or make-believe... read to each other...find nursery rhymes on YouTube and sing them together. Play a card game, and let the child make up the rules. Ask an older child to teach you the finer points of using your smartphone or play you a song or video he downloaded.

In addition to playing, take part in the activities of daily life. Help your grandchild wash up at bedtime...look after the family pet... make lunch for each other. Some of the closest feelings and fondest memories are created during relaxed, everyday time together.

WHEN OTHER GRANDPARENTS LIVE NEARBY

Living far from your grandchildren can be especially painful if other grandparents live close to them. You may feel left out or at a disadvantage.

This doesn't have to be the case! If you shift your thinking so that you do not view the situation as a competition, everyone will benefit. And if you don't, your anxiety and resentment may negatively affect how you act around your grandchildren—and around the other grandparents. Remember that the more people who

JUST FOR FUN...

Keep Kids Occupied

Check out the American Library Association directory of topnotch children's websites on animals, the arts, history, literature, math/computers, science and other topics. Includes descriptions of the sites, age-appropriateness and links. GWS.ala.org

love a child, the better, and children have a limitless capacity to receive affection.

Focus on enjoying your interactions with your grandchild, and you will be able to build a unique and rich relationship no matter where you live.

Get Your Elderly Mom (or Dad) to Move Closer

Barbara McVicker, author of three books on elder care including *Stuck in the Middle: Shared Stories and Tips on Caring for Mom and Dad*, which became a PBS special. McVicker was a caregiver for her parents for 10 years. BarbaraMcVicker.com

It's stressful when your aging parents are far away. Maybe they're doing just fine, but you see signs of frailty. Perhaps you've already made a middle-of-the-night trip for a medical emergency...and you foresee more. So you want your parent or parents to move closer.

Unfortunately, Mom or Dad is likely to disagree. Even if they are becoming more fragile, the idea of packing up is daunting, and so is leaving friends, doctors and...home. Recently widowed? Change is even harder. *Here's how to get them on board...*

LAYING THE GROUNDWORK

Talk to your parents about their future, and do it sooner rather than later. Ask them how they expect to manage when they can no longer drive or fully care for themselves. They may clam up, but continue to bring it up before a health crisis—the worst time to make decisions—forces everyone's hand. Next, educate yourself—and enlist your siblings. There are many options—living with you...downsizing to a condo...finding a retirement or assisted-living community. Identify a few options that make sense. *Then...*

- **Hold a family meeting.** Your mom and dad need to have a say, no matter how right you think you are. Present the options...but it's fine to nudge them toward the one that you think is best. If at all possible, make this meeting happen in person—facial expressions and body language convey as much meaning as do words. Plus, you can give hugs.
- **Play up the positives.** Emphasize benefits that you know your parent will appreciate, such as being closer to family, including grandkids. Mom (or Dad) hates cooking and cleaning? Mention that senior housing can include housekeeping.
- **Listen to their fears.** Ask them to share their biggest worries. Be sure to show respect for these worries and emphasize how you will work with them to ease the stress.
- **Let 'em see your pain.** Few parents want to make their kids unhappy at any age. Be honest about your stresses. "I want to be able to help you. But traveling and taking time off work are not things I can regularly handle." You may feel quite emotional, and that's OK... but don't lose control!
- **Have a fallback.** Your parents still may say no, and that's their right. Be prepared with another suggestion such as moving to an assisted-living facility in their current location or hiring a geriatric care manager to oversee home care. Not ideal...but likely safer than the status quo.

Dogs Really Do Understand People

When listening, dogs use brain regions analogous to those that humans use to understand what other people say. Dogs' brains show that they are truly happy only if the tone of voice associated with praise is matched by actual words of praise being spoken. As with humans, the right side of dogs' brains deals with emotion and the left side of the brain with processing meaning—and it is only when both sides agree that they are hearing praise that a dog shows true happiness.

Study of MRI scans of 13 dogs led by researchers at Eötvös Loránd University, Budapest, Hungary, published in *Science*.

Dogs Also Get Colds

Dogs have similar cold symptoms to humans including coughing, runny nose and watery eyes. Many of these symptoms could be the result of a dog cold virus, but they also could be symptoms of more serious medical conditions including kennel cough, canine flu or bronchitis. If your dog is exhibiting symptoms of a cold, call your veterinarian.

American Kennel Club, New York City, AKC.org.

Safely Carry a Dog or Cat

Joseph H. Kinnarney, DVM, immediate past president of the American Veterinary Medical Association. He is a practicing vet at the Reidsville Veterinary Hospital in Reidsville, North Carolina. ReidsvilleVet.com

Pet owners often lift their dogs and cats in ways that are uncomfortable or unsafe—for the pet and/or for the owner. *What to do instead...*

• **Lifting and carrying a small dog.** Kneel or stoop facing one side of the dog. Reach over the dog with the arm that is toward the dog's back end, and then arrange that hand and forearm so that they are parallel to the dog's body, on the opposite side of the dog from your body. Position that hand under the dog's chest between its front legs. The rear legs of the dog should still be between your arm and your body. While holding the dog's chest, gently move your elbow toward your body, scooping up and supporting the dog's rear legs on your arm. Position your other hand along the side of the dog that's away from your body to prevent it from falling or scrambling away and/or to provide additional support to the animal's front end if necessary. If you ever played football, picture how your coach taught you to carry the ball.

Important: Periodically confirm that the dog's rear legs still are supported by your arm, not dangling, which is bad for the dog's spine. (It's fine if the front legs dangle.)

• **Lifting and carrying a larger dog.** If your dog is too big to be comfortably supported on one forearm, instead position the dog on a dog bed, blanket or stretcher and have several people carry this. (Or put the dog in a wagon that you can pull.)

When you have no choice but to lift a large dog by yourself, kneel facing one side of the dog. Wrap one arm behind the dog's rear legs, and place that hand against the far side of the dog. Wrap your other arm around the dog's chest—right in front of the top of its front legs, not up by the throat. Scoop in and up so that the arm around the front end of the dog supports the chest as much as possible without forcing the front legs backward and the arm around the back end supports both the upper rear legs and hips. Some people instead lift the rear end of a large dog by placing one arm under the abdomen, in front of the rear legs. That's acceptable for quick lifts, but it's not preferred for extended carrying—it leaves the rear legs dangling, which places stress on the dog's spine.

• **Lifting and carrying a cat.** The small-dog directions are appropriate for cats as well. But when carrying a cat that's prone to scratching, also secure one of its front legs between the thumb and forefinger of your carrying hand and the other front leg between the forefinger and middle finger of your other hand so that the cat can't scratch you.

EASY TO DO...

Keep an Eye on Your Pets When You Aren't Home

The Furbo dog camera, $199 at Furbo.com, works with iPhones and Android phones to let you see and talk to dogs, get alerts when they are barking and dispense treats remotely.

The Dog Monitor app, $4.99 for iOS, $5.99 for Android, lets you use a spare phone or tablet to view live video of your pet, talk from your phone and play prerecorded messages.

The Whistle Tracker, $79.95 at Whistle.com, is a collar attachment that connects to an app for iPhone or Android and lets you see your pet's location at all times—you can designate allowed areas and get alerts whenever your pet leaves those areas.

Komando.com

17

House Proud

Make Your Home Look More Upscale...for Hundreds, Not Thousands

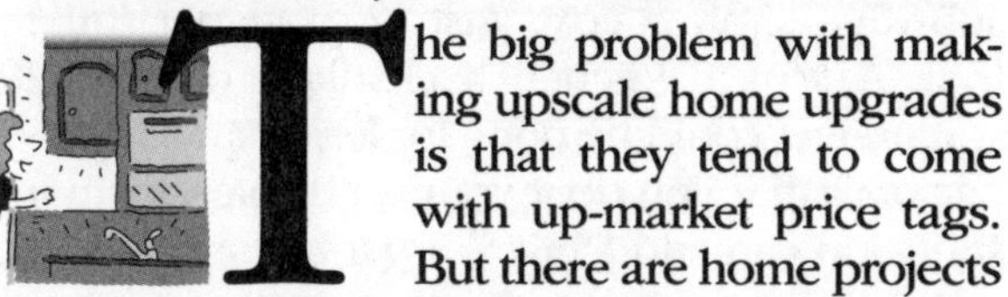

The big problem with making upscale home upgrades is that they tend to come with up-market price tags. But there are home projects that can bring a sense of class and distinction to a home for $1,000 or less—sometimes much less. These upgrades won't just impress your guests and make your house a more appealing place to live—they also could help attract buyers when you sell. We asked Hilary Farr, cohost of the popular HGTV show *Love It or List It*, for inexpensive ways to make a home appear more upscale inside. *Here are six of her favorite ways to get an expensive look for less...*

- **Install crown molding,** a decorative strip traditionally made from plaster or wood that runs along the tops of interior walls. This molding creates a visual transition between wall and ceiling and adds design detail, making a home feel more upscale. (It also hides drywall imperfections where walls and ceilings meet.)

Hiring a skilled plasterer to install a traditional plaster crown molding would be very costly...as would hiring a carpenter to put in an elaborate wood molding. There are less expensive, preformed moldings made from fiberboard, but those are very heavy and difficult to install well. Fortunately, there's a fourth option—install polystyrene foam moldings, which can be glued in place. Unlike wood moldings, polystyrene moldings do not expand and contract with changes in temperature, so cracks and gaps will not develop over time, and unlike fiberboard moldings, they are not very difficult to install. They are quite sturdy and can be lightly sanded and painted.

Note: Prices, rates and offers throughout this chapter and book are subject to change.

Hilary Farr, cohost of *Love It or List It*, which airs on HGTV Mondays at 9 pm ET/PT. She is president of Toronto-based interior design company Hilary Farr Design. HilaryFarr.com

Select a crown molding that is at least five inches in height—anything smaller will not make enough of an impression to be worth the trouble.

Cost estimate: Expect to pay about $2 per linear foot—that's less than $200 for a 20-foot-by-20-foot room. If you opt for professional installation, it might add up to $200 more per room to your bottom line, depending on the amount of molding and local labor rates.

Related project: Beef up your baseboards. Replace the insubstantial-looking molding found along the bottoms of most walls with baseboards that are five-and-a-half to six inches tall. These should match the room's crown molding in color and style, but they should be made of wood, which can take the beating that baseboards can get over time.

• **Expand the trim around interior window frames to make windows seem grander.** Windows are the single most important feature in the typical room—our eyes are drawn to them. The easiest, least expensive way to make windows appear more upscale and impressive from the inside is to expand the trim around them. Just add a "backband"—a three-quarter- to one-and-a-quarter-inch strip of wood that is nailed in place around the outer perimeter of the existing interior window trim and painted to match.

If you're willing to tackle a larger project, you could remove the existing window trim and replace it with something more substantial. This will look even better and save the effort of searching for a backband that will work with the existing trim. If you want to improve your home's curb appeal, upgrading the trim around the exterior of windows is worth considering, too.

Cost estimate: Backband molding made of paint-grade wood such as poplar for interior use or pine for exterior use typically costs just $1 to $2 per linear foot, so even factoring in the price of paint and finish nails, this project should cost no more than $30 to $50 per window.

Related project: Expand your window dressing. Purchase curtain rods that extend six to 18 inches beyond the edges of your windows on each side. Install these rods at least four inches above the tops of the windows and ideally all the way up near the ceiling or crown molding. Purchase curtains that extend all the way from this rod to the floor—they should just touch the floor, not stop a few inches above it. This also makes windows of modest size seem grand.

• **Install subway tile in your bathrooms and/or kitchen.** Home owners who want tile that seems upscale and special have three choices. They can pay up for expensive tile ...they can choose unusual colors or patterns that stand out but that might later go out of style or alienate future home buyers...or they can install subway tile.

Subway tile is rectangular—typically three inches by six inches—so it is more eye-catching than ordinary square household tile. It has been in use for well over 100 years but is timeless and has never gone out of style. White subway tile with black grout or black subway tile with white grout produces a particularly upscale result. A staggered "brick" tile pattern creates a traditional look...a straight-line tile-on-top-of-tile "stack" pattern creates a more modern look...while chevron and herringbone patterns, created by laying the tiles on a diagonal, are distinctive.

Cost estimate: Three-by-six-inch ceramic subway tile often costs just $2 to $3 per square foot. A typical kitchen backsplash of 15-to-20 square feet could be done for less than $200 per backsplash if you do it yourself. Professional installation can add $5 to $10 per square foot.

• **Upgrade interior doors.** High-end homes do not just look more upscale than other homes, they also feel more upscale. Their components are solid and substantial to the touch. One simple way to make a conventional home feel more solid and substantial is to replace its hollow-core wood interior doors with solid-core wood doors. This works because doors are among the parts of the home that are handled most frequently by home owners and guests.

When doors open with some weightiness and close with a subtle thunk, the whole house feels more upscale. Also, solid-core doors keep out noise better than hollow-core doors.

Cost estimate: Solid-core wood interior doors can be found for around $200 apiece. One way to control the cost of this project is to upgrade just the doors that you and your guests use most often, such as guest bathroom doors and/or master bedroom doors.

Related project: Upgrade doorknobs. Select new knobs based on their solid feel, not just their appealing looks. You can get a good-quality doorknob for $20 to $30.

• **Transform entryways from clutter receptacles into visual greetings.** In many homes, entryways are ad hoc storage areas. Shoes and umbrellas are lined up near the front door...keys, mail and other clutter rest on any available flat surface. Clutter is inelegant, especially as a first impression. Your home instantly will seem more upscale if you remove all clutter that can be seen from its entryway. If necessary, purchase closet organizing products to make it easier to stow entryway clutter in the hall closet...and/or an elegant, understated cabinet or a small table for the entryway featuring drawers to hide small clutter including keys and mail. Use the surface of this cabinet or table to place a beautiful element of welcome such as a vase containing one fresh flower.

• **Install laminate kitchen countertops that look like quartz, marble or granite.** Quartz, marble and granite countertops make homes look upscale because they are upscale—they typically cost $75 to $100 or more per square foot, installed. But these days, there are laminate countertops that do an excellent job of mimicking the look of those desirable, high-end materials for less than half the cost.

Examples: Wilsonart HD laminates (Wilsonart.com)...and Formica 180fx laminates (Formica.com).

Take a close look at the edge of laminate countertops in showrooms before buying. Some do a wonderful job mimicking high-end materials when you look only at the top but ruin the illusion by looking like laminates along the edge.

Cost estimate: $30 per square foot, installed, for laminate countertop.

GOOD TO KNOW...

Better Picture Hanging

If hanging multiple pictures, cut out cardboard or dark paper in the size and shape of frames and arrange the cutouts on the wall. This helps you visualize the best placement for the pictures in the space available. *Additional tips...*

• **To put a nail in the right spot,** place a bit of toothpaste on the part of the frame that will touch the nail, then hold the frame up and press it against the wall to mark the spot.

• **Before hammering a nail into the wall,** cover the spot with easily removable tape to prevent paint from chipping.

• **To avoid hitting your fingers,** hold a thick plastic comb flat against the wall and put a nail between two tines to hold it steady while you hammer it into place.

• **Hang lightweight art with dental floss instead of special picture wire.** It works just as well (and if this lightweight picture doesn't stay straight, wrap a piece of tape around the center of the floss to stop the picture from sliding).

• **To protect walls from scratches made by pictures,** slice two packing peanuts in half lengthwise before hanging a picture—glue half a peanut to each corner of the back of the frame.

QuickAndDirtyTips.com

Which Paint Colors Will Boost Your Home's Value?

Ron Reed, an interior designer based in Dallas who has served as program coordinator for interior design programs at Texas State University and University of North Texas and currently at El Centro College. He is author of *Color + Design: Transforming Interior Space.*

When the real estate website Zillow.com examined the effect that colors had on the closing prices of more than 32,000 homes that recently changed hands, it discovered something surprising—the color of paint used on the walls of a single room can add or subtract thousands of dollars of value.

In general, the Zillow analysis found that muted blues and grays add the most value ("muted" colors have some gray or black added, making them slightly darker and subdued)... while warm colors including reds, oranges and yellows *reduced* a home's value the most. But the financial impact of different colors varied in important ways from room to room—and for one particular room that every home has, the best paint color was completely different from other rooms.

We asked design expert Ron Reed to help our readers understand Zillow's room-by-room findings so that you can not only choose colors you like but also make your home worth more.

Caution: Although the Zillow study found that muted grays and blues are value-enhancing colors for almost every room individually, actually painting almost every room of a home blue or gray would make the home visually uninteresting. Instead, use these money-making colors mainly in rooms where they will make the biggest bottom-line difference to sale price based on this Zillow study...and/or in rooms that you hope to highlight to buyers...and/or in rooms where you just think the colors look good. In other rooms, avoid colors that Zillow says detract from value, and use a neutral color such as a warm white or creamy beige instead.

Note the room-by-room paint-color winners below...

• **Bathrooms.** Blue walls add $5,440 to the value of a home...white walls subtract $4,035.* The color of bathroom walls was found to have a bigger bottom-line effect on home selling prices than that of any other room—and even a bigger effect than the color of home exteriors. As any real estate agent can tell you, modern-seeming bathrooms are a big selling point for a home. Shades of blue that fare especially well for bathrooms include light powder blue and periwinkle (a lavender blue). Shades of white that fare especially poorly include off-whites such as eggshell.

Why these colors: Blue is the color of water. Our minds associate water with cleanliness, something home buyers particularly value in bathrooms. Besides, people just like blue—surveys inevitably find that it is the most popular color in general.

The surprise here is that white paint is a money loser in bathrooms—we tend to think of white as the safe, inoffensive wall color. Perhaps the problem is that white was the most common bathroom paint color for so long that it now seems old-fashioned and out of date—buyers like bathrooms that seem modern.

Or perhaps the problem is that the trendiest bathroom countertop right now is Carrara marble, which is mostly white with gray veins. Combining white countertops with white walls can result in a bathroom that lacks visual contrast. Painting bathroom walls white seems unlikely to detract much value if the bathroom's flooring, countertops and cabinets supply lots of color.

Note: The Zillow study implies that all the bathrooms in a home should be painted blue, but from a design perspective, it generally is better to use different wall colors in the home's various bathrooms to avoid making the home seem redundant and dull. Consider painting the master bathroom blue as recommended by Zillow—the master bath is the bath that tends to matter most to buyers—while selecting different colors for the home's other bathrooms. Green or blue-green can be good alternatives here.

• **Bedrooms.** Blue walls add $1,856 to the value of a home...pink walls subtract $208. Shades of blue that fare especially well include light cerulean (a sky blue) to cadet blue (a somewhat grayish blue). Pinks that fare especially poorly include light pink to antique rose (a slightly brownish light pink).

Why these colors: Home buyers' general preference for calm, cool, muted colors such as blue makes good sense in bedrooms—calm is conducive to sleep. Certain pinks and warmer colors in general tend to be stimulating rather than calming.

*All dollar figures cited in this article are averages. The actual effect the color of a room or the exterior has on a home's value will vary based on the overall value of the home, the locality and other factors.

Note: Here, too, the Zillow study implies that all the bedrooms should be painted the same color to make the house worth the most possible. In the real world, that would be too repetitive. Consider painting the master bedroom blue and the home's other bedrooms in soft whites or warm neutrals. If you do paint the master bedroom blue, use a "harmonious" shade of blue for the master bathroom. One option that often works is to select a slightly more "muted" version of the bathroom blue for the bedroom—that is, the same blue but with a bit more black added. Avoid using a shade of blue that has some green in one room and a shade of blue that has some purple in the next—that will not seem harmonious.

• **Living room.** Shades of light brown add $1,809 to the value of a home...blue or gray walls subtract $820. The living room is the one room that bucked the prevailing popularity of blue and gray—and in a big way, because blue and gray both *reduced* homes' values when used in living rooms. Shades of light brown that fare especially well in living rooms include light beige, pale taupe and oatmeal. Blues and grays that fare especially poorly include pastel gray, periwinkle and pale silver to light blue.

Why these colors: The living room is where we gather with family and friends to enjoy one another's company. It's where we sit together around fireplaces in the winter. So psychologically it does make some sense that this would be the place where home buyers might prefer certain warm colors rather than cool ones. And even here, the warm colors that home buyers favor are relatively calm shades of light brown, not bright, exciting reds and oranges.

• **Kitchen.** Blue walls add $1,809, on average, to the value of a home...yellow walls subtract $820. Shades of blue that fare especially well include light blue to soft gray-blue. Shades of yellow that fare especially poorly include straw yellow to marigold (yellow-orange).

Why these colors: As the world becomes increasingly hectic, people want their homes to serve as oases of calm. Blue is a cool, calming color. Perhaps blue kitchen walls help people feel calm for a few minutes in the morning before they rush out to tackle their daily responsibilities. That said, Zillow's blue kitchen recommendation will be controversial among interior designers. Many designers believe strongly that warm, welcoming colors are called for in kitchens because kitchens (like living rooms, described above) are spaces where people interact and entertain.

It is particularly surprising that yellow hurt the value of kitchens in the study. Historically, yellow has been a popular kitchen color, especially for kitchens that lack sufficient natural light—yellow walls mimic sunlight, helping people wake up in the morning as they sip their coffee. The specific shades of yellow cited in the Zillow study provide a possible explanation—straw and marigold are shades of yellow that range from golden (slightly orangey) yellow to orange. Orange is not a color we associate with morning sunlight—it's more of a sunset color. It's probably safe to paint a kitchen a soft or muted yellow as long as you don't select a pure yellow.

• **Dining room.** Blue walls add $1,926 to the value of a home...red walls subtract $2,031. Slate blue to pale gray-blue fare especially well, as does navy blue when combined with white "shiplap" (overlapping boards) that covers the lower sections of walls. Reds that fare poorly include brick red, terra-cotta and copper red.

Why these colors: This fits well with the general pro-blue trends described above. It is interesting that the anti-blue counter trend found in living rooms did not apply to dining rooms even though families gather here, too. Perhaps the reason is that warm colors—especially red—were popular choices for dining rooms back in the 1990s and early 2000s, so dining rooms that still have these colors now might seem dated. (And a bit dingy if they have not been repainted since the 1990s.)

• **Home exterior.** The exterior color called "greige"—a mixture of gray and beige that can be light, medium or dark in tone—adds $1,526 in value...while a brown exterior subtracts $1,970. Medium brown and stucco—a tan color—are among the shades of brown that fare especially poorly.

Why these colors: The popularity of greige is no surprise—as noted above, gray is in vogue these days…and adding a natural tone such as beige to that gray can help a home's exterior work more naturally with its surrounding landscape. Straight brown was a popular color for home exteriors around 15 years ago, so perhaps it now makes homes seem dated to home buyers.

Also: The Zillow study found that navy blue and dark gray are good choices for front doors, adding $1,514 in value. Home exteriors tend to be muted in color, so a significantly darker door provides an appealing contrast. (No front-door color was singled out by the study as a money loser.)

THE COLOR THAT DOESN'T GO OUT OF STYLE

What if you want to paint a room or the exterior of your home now in a color that will add to its value in the future? Odds are that the muted blues and grays that impress today's home buyers will not fall out of style very soon—blue has been the world's most popular color for decades, and gray is at worst seen as inoffensive.

How to Properly Dispose of Household Items

WiseBread.com

Small appliances: Use the website Search.Earth911.com to find local recycling centers for your unwanted coffeemakers and microwave ovens.

Worn-out linens: Donate old sheets to animal shelters to be used as bedding. Alternatively, you can give them to the Salvation Army or other local charities. They work with partners to recycle the used linens into rags or fiber for furniture or insulation.

Hangers: While Goodwill does not accept plastic hangers, other thrift or secondhand clothing stores are more than happy to take them. Wire hangers can be returned to the dry cleaner.

Worn-out athletic shoes: Nike Stores have a shoe-recycling program, called Reuse-a-Shoe, which will accept worn-out athletic shoes from all brands and recycle the components to create athletic and playground surfaces.

Expired medication: You may be tempted to flush your old medication down the toilet, but this can contaminate the water system. Instead, find an independent pharmacy authorized to take back your outdated medication using the website DisposeMyMeds.org.

Outdated cell phones: Best Buy accepts defunct cell phones for recycling, but if you have a working device, donate it to Cell Phones for Soldiers (CellPhonesForSoldiers.com).

The 8 Home Smells That Could Be Signs of Danger

Danny Lipford, host, *Today's Homeowner with Danny Lipford*, a nationally syndicated TV series. He has more than 30 years of experience as a remodeling contractor in Mobile, Alabama. TodaysHomeowner.com

You think you smell fish—even though you haven't cooked anything resembling salmon or swordfish in days. Or maybe it's the smell of your fireplace—even though you haven't set fire to a log in weeks. Or the odor resembles ammonia, rotten eggs or something else entirely.

Such household odors can serve as clues that there are hidden dangers in the home—problems that could be pricier to repair and potentially hazardous to your health if not found and fixed fast.

Here's what home owners need to know about eight home odors…

- **Fishy smell that's not fish.** Some people refer to this as a urine or burning rubber smell. This could be something electrical in the home overheating and melting its insulating plastic or rubber—which could lead to a fire.

The most likely culprit is an appliance, such as a dishwasher, washing machine or an air conditioner. Sniff near each of these while they are running to try to identify the source. When you think you have found the source, either call in a repair professional to investigate...or replace the appliance if it is approaching the end of its useful life.

Warning: If the odor seems to be emanating from a wall switch, outlet or some other part of your home's electrical wiring, not an appliance, switch off the circuit breaker and call an electrician.

• **Ammonia smell that's not ammonia.** Some people describe this as the smell of death, and they're right—a mouse or some other small animal likely has died inside your home. One solution is to find and remove the corpse, and that's often easier said than done—there's a good chance that it is in a hard-to-reach spot inside your walls, ceiling or floor.

Use your nose to find where the smell is strongest, and search everywhere you can in that area. Consider buying and using a small snaking digital inspection camera to peek into walls, behind cabinets and appliances and into other tight spots. Ridgid Hand-Held inspection cameras are a good choice, starting at less than $150.

Unfortunately, even with a snaking camera, you won't be able to see everywhere without drilling holes in walls, and that usually causes more problems than it solves. Of course, you could just wait for the smell to go away, which typically takes a few weeks.

Meanwhile, inspect the perimeter of your home for gaps where rodents can enter, and seal these to prevent further invasions. Also, deploy rodent traps—not rodent poison—in the home. If you use poison, additional rodents might die in their hard-to-reach nests inside your home, creating more bad smell.

• **Damp, musty smell.** This usually signals mold or mildew, which could become a big problem for both your home and your health if not quickly remedied. Use a digital hygrometer to check the relative humidity of each room in the house—you can find these for less than $10 online or at home-improvement stores. If you get readings above 50%, run a dehumidifier. Apply an antimicrobial spray to carpets, curtains and fabric-covered furniture in any room that has high humidity and/or a musty odor.

Meanwhile, search these rooms for water leaks. Look behind refrigerators and under sinks for wet spots. Visit the room during the next hard rain to look for visible leaks. Go down to the basement, crawl space or room directly beneath this musty room to look for evidence of water leaks there, too—those could point to leaks that are hard to spot in the room above.

• **Musty or smoky odor from a fireplace that's not in use.** First, make sure that the chimney dampers are closed. Chimney smells can be drawn into the house when these are left open.

If that's not the problem, vacuum and then scrub the "firebox"—the area that contains the fire at the base of the chimney. If the smell persists after the firebox has dried following this cleaning, call in a chimney sweep to clean and inspect your chimney. Mention that you suspect water might be getting in. The problem might be as simple as a dislodged chimney cap, or there might be cracks in the masonry.

Be sure the chimney sweep checks whether the damper is sealing sufficiently. You can purchase and use an inflatable damper, sometimes called a fireplace draft stopper. These are available for less than $100.

• **Dusty burning smell when you turn on your heat for the first time in months.** Burning smells understandably trigger home owner anxieties, but this one usually is not a problem—the dust that settled on the unit over the summer is simply burning away. This smell should disappear on its own within a few hours of turning on the heat. Do replace your HVAC system's filter if you haven't done so recently because it might be allowing excessive dust to collect on heating components.

Warning: Turn off your heating system, and call in an HVAC repair pro if you see smoke coming from vents and/or the burning smell occurs at any time other than the heating system's first few uses of the season.

• **Chemical smell from new furniture, carpet or paint.** A fresh coat of paint, a new piece of pressed-board furniture or a new carpet can off-gas volatile organic compounds (VOCs) that are not just unpleasant to smell but also unhealthy to breathe. When possible,

BEWARE...

Areas in Your Home That Can Make You Sick

• **Vacuum cleaners** can harbor bacteria that can cause breathing problems—clean the filter often, open windows when vacuuming and wear a mask while cleaning.

• **Refrigerator shelves and drawers** can harbor bacteria—clean the shelves and fruit and vegetable drawers regularly using warm water and baking soda, and wash fruits and vegetables before refrigerating them.

• **Bath mats** may contain mold, dust mites and bacteria—wash them several times a month.

• **Blenders** can collect microorganisms at the bottom—take a blender apart and wash it after each use, before putting it away.

DumbLittleMan.com, a self-improvement website.

remove new pressed-wood furniture and carpeting from its packaging and let it air out in your garage for at least an hour, and preferably overnight, before bringing it into your home. If that isn't feasible, open all the windows in the room and run fans to circulate the air for at least an hour and as long as a full day. That method also works when you are painting interior walls.

• **Sewage smell.** This sometimes is confused with the rotten-egg smell described below, but it's less "eggy" and more like the smell of an outhouse or a portable toilet. It probably is coming from a drain. Use your nose to determine which one—it could be the drain of a toilet, sink, tub or shower.

One possibility is that there isn't enough water in this drain's "P trap." The P trap is a curved piece of pipe below the drain that should be full of water—the water blocks offensive odors from your sewer line or septic tank from wafting back into the house. If this is the case, running the water for a few seconds (or flushing the toilet) should solve the problem. You also will have to air out the house to get rid of the odor that's already there. This is especially likely if the toilet, sink, tub or shower has gone unused for months—the water in the P trap might have evaporated.

If that does not solve the problem—or if you see that the water is not draining properly—the odor probably is coming from material clogged in the drain line. Put on rubber gloves, and use a flexible 16-to-18-inch drain-cleaning brush to clear out any gunk from the drain. Next, let the hot water run for a few minutes (or flush the toilet) to confirm that it is now draining properly. Then shut off the water and pour one cup of bleach into the drain. Let the bleach sit for 30 to 60 minutes, then run the hot water (or flush the toilet) again. If the odor persists, you may need to rent or purchase a plumber's auger or snake to dislodge the clog.

ROTTEN-EGG SMELL COULD BE TWO THINGS

A rotten-egg smell might be a potentially dangerous natural gas leak. Get everyone out of the house—leaving the door and windows open so that some gas can escape—and call your gas company immediately to report the problem and request further instructions. Natural gas itself is odorless, but a sulfurlike rotten-egg smell is added so that leaks will be detected.

If a faint rotten-egg smell occurs only when your hot water is running, however, it's probably not a gas leak at all but rather a small amount of odorous sulfur in the water. Sometimes you or a plumber can solve this problem by shutting off the water line leading to the water heater, using a hose to drain the tank and then refilling the tank.

Paint Strippers Can Kill You in Minutes

Katy Wolf, PhD, director of the Institute for Research and Technical Assistance, a nonprofit organization that identifies safer alternatives for industrial and consumer solvents and other products, Los Angeles. IRTA.us

A 21-year-old Tennessee man died in 2017 while refinishing a tub in an unventilated bathroom. Fumes from methylene chloride, a chemical in the paint stripper he was using, caused carbon monoxide to build up in his blood, and within minutes his heart stopped beating.

Most paint strippers sold in hardware stores and home centers contain methylene chloride, yet few people who use these products understand the danger. These products are known to be responsible for at least 56 accidental-exposure deaths in the US since 1980, and the true death toll is no doubt higher—some methylene chloride fatalities are likely recorded as heart attacks, with no one realizing that this chemical is to blame.

Methylene chloride also is known to cause cancer, though that's a risk mainly for people who have prolonged exposure to it because they use paint strippers in their professions, not for consumers who use them only occasionally.

What to do: Choose a benzyl alcohol–based paint stripper rather than one that contains methylene chloride. It's safer and does a good job stripping paint, though it does not work as quickly as methylene chloride.

If you do use a methylene chloride paint stripper, do so outdoors or in a large, well-ventilated area, never in a small and/or enclosed space. Do not use methylene chloride to strip the inside of bathtubs, storage tanks or similar objects even if they are not fully enclosed—its fumes are heavier than air, so they can quickly build up to lethal levels inside these, even outdoors.

Household Help with Common Products

- **Mayonnaise** restores water-stained wood finish—massage a bit onto fresh water damage, let it sit for a half-hour and wipe off.
- **A crayon or candle wax** can unstick a stuck zipper—rub up and down on both sides of the zipper.
- **Extend razor blade life by laying an old pair of jeans flat** and pushing the razor—clean and dry—several times along the pant legs. (Push the razor, don't pull it toward you, or you'll damage the pants.)
- **Use white toothpaste** to remove crayon marks from walls—just rub it onto the crayon and keep rubbing.
- **Put plain yogurt** on a painful sunburn, leave it on for 10 minutes, then wipe off the yogurt with a cold cloth—this should ease the pain.

Roundup of experts on fixes for household problems, reported at MoneyTalksNews.com.

---

9 Little-Known Uses for Baby Oil

MoneyTalksNews.com

Baby oil comes in handy for a variety of tasks. *See below...*

- **Drip a little onto a swollen finger** to make ring removal easier.
- **If a jewelry chain is knotted,** rub a drop of oil onto the tangle and then pick it apart with a straight pin.
- **Use to shine stainless steel or chrome,** and put a small amount on a cloth before dusting wood—the dust will stick to the cloth.
- **Lubricate a squeaky hinge with a drop or two.** Saturate a bandage and wait a bit—after absorption, the adhesive should lift off easily.
- **Baby oil lifts off price-sticker residue and can fix a stuck zipper**—use sparingly to avoid staining the garment.
- **Use on legs before shaving,** instead of gel or soap.
- **Dab some on a temporary tattoo** to take it off.
- **Saturate cuticle edges** with baby oil before polishing nails—afterward, use a cotton ball or tissue to remove the oil and any excess polish.
- **Use baby oil instead of massage oil** or cream.

Many Wood Floor Cleaners Are Bad for Wood Floors

Debbie Gartner, founder of TheFlooringGirl.com, which provides flooring and home décor advice. She previously owned a flooring store in the New York City area.

Many of the best-known, most heavily advertised wood cleaners, including Murphy Oil Soap, Mop & Glo and Orange Glo, actually are poor choices for your wood floors. They contain oils or waxes that can temporarily make floors look shinier... but that also build up a residue on the floor and degrade the polyurethane finish. Within weeks of using these products, floors often appear cloudy, dull and worse than ever. Home owners who use these floor cleaners often find themselves locked into an endless cycle of floor care—to keep their floors looking nice, they must reapply these products every few weeks to temporarily restore the shine that these cleaners promise but only very briefly provide.

What's more, once you have applied these cleaners to your wood floors even a single time, a flooring pro will not be able to restore your floors with a "screen and recoat"—a relatively simple buffing followed by reapplication of polyurethane—because of the waxy residue that's left behind (the polyurethane just won't adhere). Instead, if you hire a pro to restore your floors, they might have to be sanded to bare wood before a new finish can be applied. That could cost you an extra $1,000 for 1,000 square feet, compared with a simple screen and recoat. It also will be much more disruptive for you because the process will take longer and send far more dust into your home's air.

What to do: Never use any cleaner on your wood floors that promises to provide a "shine" or "sheen"—these words are a tip-off that the cleaner includes oils or waxes. Instead, select one that specifically says it is formulated for hardwood floors and leaves no residue. One good choice is Bona Hardwood Floor Cleaner. It's effective, widely available, inexpensive and easy to use (US.Bona.com).

Solve Problems with Petroleum Jelly

MoneyTalksNews.com

Got a household problem? *Put petroleum jelly to work...*

Remove candle wax: Apply petroleum jelly around the edges, let it sit for a minute and then wipe the wax and jelly away with a soft cloth.

Remove stuck stickers: Rub on a little petroleum jelly, and after a few hours, use the edge of a credit card to remove the sticker.

Deter squirrels: To keep squirrels away from your bird feeder, apply petroleum jelly to the pole. The squirrels will be unable to climb up the slippery surface.

Silence hinges: Apply it on hinges of cabinets or doors to eliminate squeaks.

Open a rusty padlock: Rub a thin coating of jelly on the key, and ease it into the opening to access a rusty padlock.

Unstick a zipper: Apply a small amount of petroleum jelly to the teeth to help loosen the zipper.

Prevent blisters: Put some jelly on your shoes where they are irritating your feet.

Keep lids loose: Cover the insides of the lids or the necks of bottles of glue and nail polish, and the caps will come off easier.

EASY TO DO...

Homemade Hand Cleaner

If your hands are grimy from working on a grill or a car, mix one tablespoon of sugar with enough water to make a paste. Scrub your hands with it, then wash as usual.

TheManual.com, a website offering lifestyle advice for men.

Make Your Mower, Blower and Other Outdoor Equipment Last

Danny Lipford, host, *Today's Homeowner with Danny Lipford*, a nationally syndicated TV series. He has more than 30 years of experience as a remodeling contractor in Mobile, Alabama. TodaysHomeowner.com

Wouldn't it be great if gas-powered lawn and home equipment had dashboard lights, like cars, to warn you of potential maintenance problems? That might help you avoid breakdowns and hundreds of dollars in repair bills for equipment ranging from lawn mowers and snowblowers to leaf blowers, trimmers and chain saws. *In the absence of such warning lights, here are some key steps to take to extend the life of your gas-powered equipment and avoid costly problems...*

- **Store equipment with a full fuel tank in the off-season.** Some people run all the fuel out of a tank and engine at the start of a period of nonuse because gasoline can degrade in just a few months, resulting in poor engine performance. But allowing fuel tanks and fuel lines to sit empty for an extended period increases the odds that rust will develop on metal engine and fuel-system components.

Better: Leave the tank full of fuel, but add a fuel stabilizer, such as STA-BIL, which can keep fuel fresh for up to 24 months.

- **Use ethanol-free fuel.** Unlike modern cars, which are designed to run effectively on gasoline containing 10% to 15% ethanol, small engines in most gas-powered equipment are likely to run better and last longer if given gas that does not include any biofuel. (The ethanol in gas is made from corn or other starch-based crops.) Pure-Gas.org can help you locate merchants in your area that sell ethanol-free fuel. It's more expensive than ethanol-containing fuel but worth it to extend the life of your equipment.

- **Tackle oil changes at the end of the equipment's usage season.** Old, used oil can damage engine components, and allowing used oil to sit in an engine for months lets any dirt and debris in that oil settle more deeply, which can be bad for the engine as well. When storing equipment for an extended period, make sure that it contains fresh oil.

- **Clean away dirt and grass clippings.** Caked-on dirt and grass can trap moisture and lead to device-destroying rust. Don't just hose away obvious dirt and grass—clean off the undersides of power equipment, too...and remove any covers and clean underneath them if there's a chance that dirt and debris could have worked their way inside. If rust already is forming, use a grinder or sander to remove it, then apply a primer followed by a rust-inhibiting spray paint.

- **Lubricate cables, pulleys and other moving parts.** Apply silicone spray lubricant to all moving metal parts at least once each year, and then work these parts back and forth a few times to spread the silicone.

Get Your Lawn Off Drugs

Paul Tukey, former director of the SafeLawns Foundation and current chief sustainability officer of Glenstone Museum, a Potomac, Maryland, museum that has maintained its 220-acre grounds without synthetic chemical pesticides or fertilizers since 2010. An HGTV producer, Tukey is author of *The Organic Lawn Care Manual: A Natural, Low-Maintenance System for a Beautiful, Safe Lawn.* PaulTukey.com

In keeping up with the Joneses—or for your own enjoyment—it's natural to want your lawn to look as good as a golf fairway. But did you know that the average home owner applies as much as 10 times more chemical products per acre of lawn than the average farmer?

"Weed & feed"...fertilizer...insecticides. The chemicals that we use to grow lush, green, uniform lawns are, in many cases, poisons that destroy the underlying soil and harm the surrounding ecosystem while leeching toxins into the ground and exposing them to the water, our families and our pets. On top of that, typical lawn products make your lawn *more* dependent on additional chemicals, creating a vicious cycle where your lawn is essentially addicted to them!

No matter how lush and green a lawn appears on the surface, it isn't truly healthy unless it's "drug-free." Addicts follow 12-step programs to get healthy. Your lawn, too, can get free of drugs—and still look great—with this 12-step detox program. It's a bit of work, but you'll emerge with a beautiful, healthy and safe organic lawn.

Even better, I have found that organic lawns are less expensive to maintain in the long run. Although more natural fertilizers are more expensive than their mass-produced counterparts, well-cared-for natural lawns are more resistant to drought, which means far less watering over time. About 50% less mowing (because natural lawns grow more slowly) costs you less in time and equipment wear-and-tear. With less watering and mowing, you could easily save hundreds of dollars over time. And because the organic fertilizers become part of the soil, the need to add fertilizer greatly diminishes over time. *Here's what to do...*

***STEP 1:* Understand that you have a problem.** The culture of chemical-based growing has made America's lawns (and gardens) dependent not on nature's own growing mechanisms but on the next application of chemicals. And these are not friendly chemicals.

Example: Check the label on a bag of weed & feed, a common treatment that combines weed killer and fertilizer. You'll most likely see all kinds of warnings about not letting the product run off into storm drains or streams or other water, not letting it come in contact with birds and frogs and other critters (including pets and children), not letting it touch bushes and other plants, not getting it on your skin, etc. It's nasty stuff.

***STEP 2:* Know the organic lawn concept.** If you want a lawn that's self-sustaining and free of toxins, your strategy should be to mimic and enhance nature instead of trying to override it with harmful chemicals.

Cornmeal...fish...alfalfa...and compost are the types of ingredients in organic fertilizers that nourish not just your lawn but also the earthworms and microorganisms that truly healthy lawns depend on, all of which are killed by many chemical treatments.

***STEP 3:* Decide what kind of lawn you want.** There are three types of organic lawns, each of which requires a different level of commitment. Do you want your yard to look like Fenway Park or Augusta National Golf Club? That control and uniformity are possible without chemicals, but it requires significant time and effort. The second option is a vibrant, healthy lawn made mostly of grass, even if that grass isn't as flawless and consistent as a professionally manicured baseball field. This takes less time than a perfect lawn, although more time than most home owners might want to put in.

The third option requires the least skill and exertion and gets your lawn off drugs right away—being happy to mow anything green that comes up from the ground as long as it's healthy and attractive. This could include significant clover, wild grass and other "unintentional" growth. Don't worry—it doesn't have to include weeds such as dandelions and crabgrass. It feels good under the feet. It's still a lawn. This is the path most novice home owners should start with, and you can always ramp up to the next level if you decide to.

***STEP 4:* Listen to the weeds.** Your lawn is trying to talk to you, so listen. Weeds are Mother Nature's messengers. Their presence indicates problems with the soil—your lawn's foundation. When you understand why weeds are growing, you can change the soil to make it more suitable for growing grass.

Dandelions, for example, are telling you that your soil doesn't have enough calcium—add calcium (see Step 6), and you will have fewer dandelions. One of the most common and dominant weeds, plantain, tells you that your soil might need to be loosened through aeration—bingo, less plantain. The presence of clover is your soil's way of asking you to treat it with cottonseed meal, corn gluten, alfalfa meal or some other nitrogen-rich byproduct and—you guessed it—if you do, you are likely to see less clover.

***STEP 5:* Test your soil.** Before treating your lawn with natural additives as described earlier, confirm what your weeds have told you by getting a soil test. Most state universities maintain soil labs that will conduct an analysis for around $12 to $25. Contact your university system, and ask how to get one. If your state university doesn't provide this service, check with your county's extension office for local sources.

***STEP 6:* Treat your soil with high-quality calcium.** Organic lawns grown in most of the country will benefit from an autumn dose of calcium, which will help eliminate the most common and obvious weed—dandelions—as well as many others. Applying lime (which many home owners already do) is one way, but make sure it's the right type. Dolomitic limestone, the most common type, is high in magnesium but fairly low in calcium. Instead use *calcitic* limestone, which has enough calcium—and use pellets rather than powder to keep potentially harmful dust to a minimum. One brand found in many hardware and garden stores is Soil Doctor.

If the soil test shows that your soil is alkaline—with a pH over 7—use gypsum instead of lime because gypsum won't affect the soil's pH. As with limestone, pellets are better for most lawns.

***STEP 7:* Mow high.** The best defense against weeds is tall grass. Many weed seeds need light to germinate, and they don't germinate well with tall grass towering over them. If they do germinate, tall, lush grass will crowd out their sprouts. Set your mower blade height to between three and four inches off the ground.

***STEP 8:* Sharpen your blade.** By sharpening your mower blade after every eight hours of mowing, the blade will cut the grass cleanly instead of tearing it. Torn blades of grass are more likely to turn brown, and they're more susceptible to harm from pests and disease. A good tutorial on how to safely sharpen mower blades is at THD.co/2oGw67u.

***STEP 9:* Don't over-rake.** Overzealous leaf-raking can destroy the soil composition and beneficial organisms while spreading weed seeds. *What to do:* Drag your rake across the lawn with just enough pressure to pull the leaves away.

***STEP 10:* Aerate high-traffic areas.** High-traffic areas—usually patches by the driveway and walkway near the road—are prone to common plantain weeds, which can be identified by their broad, oval leaves surrounding tall, thin flower stalks rising from the center. Plantain weeds thrive in compacted soil. Grass does not. Although the entire lawn can benefit from aeration, it is especially useful for these high-traffic areas. You can rent a "core aerator" (with hollow spikes that remove cores of soil rather than solid spikes that only poke holes) at a hardware store for about $35 to $90. Core aerators require more exertion to operate than lawn mowers—if you'd rather not tackle it, hire a lawn service to core-aerate for you.

***STEP 11:* Overseed in the fall.** October is an ideal lawn-care month in most of the country, although it will be a bit earlier in the coldest regions and a bit later in the warmest. This is the time for the calcium treatment mentioned earlier. It's also the perfect time to overseed, especially on thin or patchy areas. Overseeding will rejuvenate your lawn before the frost sets in, and grass seeds will outcompete weed seeds. This is the one time of year when an aggressive raking can help, just prior to overseeding. The raking helps loosen the soil to get better seed-to-soil contact. Be sure to water daily until the seed germinates.

***STEP 12:* Top-dress your lawn with compost.** This step can be costly, but top-dressing your lawn with compost in the fall is probably the single best thing you can do. Although it looks like black dirt, compost isn't soil. It is decomposed organic matter that serves several critical functions including adding nutrients. Order a bulk delivery from a nearby compost manufacturer (search online for "bulk compost delivery" and your zip code) or your municipality.

JUST FOR FUN...

Quick-and-Easy Tree Identification

Get a step-by-step guide to 250 common species. Go to ArborDay.org, and click on "Trees," then "Tree Identification."

The Smartest Things You Can Do to Protect Your Home from Winter

Richard Trethewey, an expert adviser on the popular home-improvement show *This Old House* since it debuted in 1979. Based in Boston, he is president of RST (Thermal) Inc., a manufacturer's representative company that provides training to the skilled trades, and also is on the editorial board of *This Old House* magazine. ThisOldHouse.com

In much of the country, winter is a home owner's worst enemy. Extreme cold and the cycle of thawing and freezing attack your home's critical systems and sap expensive heat and energy. Sure, turning down your thermostat helps, but only so much—and who wants to shiver? *Truly* preparing your house for winter can protect vital systems, greatly reduce energy bills and make you more comfortable. But what if time or money doesn't allow you to make every winter preparation? No problem. *Here's what to do for the best result and to get the most bang for your buck...*

• **Prioritize.** Every house is an ongoing progression of problems. When one problem is fixed, another eventually will appear—and usually there are multiple problems at once. In the weeks and months before winter, however, you should focus your attention on fortifying your home to keep warm air in...and to keep cold air and water out. Since heat rises and water and cold air fall, you must concentrate your finite time and resources on shoring up the roof and insulating the attic—in that order.

• **Invest in a roof inspection.** Hire a roofer to conduct an inspection before you spend a single dollar anywhere else. The reason? If you have even a trickle of water coming in through the roof, it can turn into a huge headache.

The tiniest leak may not be a big deal in the fall. But when that thin stream of water freezes and expands as ice in winter, your tiny leak will become a big leak, which will then freeze and expand even more. Water rots your home's wood frame, saturates and ruins insulation, creates a breeding ground for dangerous mold and generally causes havoc inside the home.

Keeping water out in winter should be your number-one priority—and water is most likely to enter through the roof, where even the most observant home owner might not be able to spot a small leak. Faulty roofs also enable the formation of ice dams, which are ridges of ice that prevent water and melting snow from properly draining off the roof. Ice dams, which form when uneven roof temperatures cause snow to melt and then refreeze in concentrated areas, can cause catastrophic damage to ceilings, walls, insulation and the roof itself.

The national average cost for a roof inspection is $217, according to HomeAdvisor.com, although it could be as low as $75 or as high as $700. If you have it, spend it. Hopefully, your inspector will tell you that your roof is in great shape, get in his/her truck and leave. If that's the case, it's time to move on to insulation. However, if the inspector finds some problems that need fixing, expect to spend $770 for the average roof repair, according to HomeAdvisor.com. (The typical range is $331 to $1,223.) You won't enjoy writing that check, but keep in mind that replacing damaged portions of the roof and dealing with water damage inside in the spring would come with a much less forgiving price tag.

• **Insulate your attic—big time.** Unless you have the means to cloak your home in a thermal barrier by hiring a crew to insulate your walls, garage, basement and rafters, you should plug the heat leaks in order of priority. The attic is your priority—that's where rising warm air tries to escape from inside and sinking cold air tries to enter from outside. If you wouldn't go outside in a blizzard without a warm hat, don't let winter arrive without a well-insulated attic.

Many attics are already insulated...poorly. Either insulation is where it should be but there's not enough of it...or some parts are insulated but others aren't. And some attics, even in cold regions, aren't insulated at all, sometimes because insulation was removed to perform work on the underlying structure and simply never replaced. Insulation should cover the attic floor, fill the gaps between joists, protect any open penetrations around piping and fill knee walls, which are walls with attic space immediately behind them.

The average cost to have a professional insulate an attic ranges from $1,357 for blown-in cellulose insulation to $1,574 for roll or batt fiberglass insulation—that's the familiar fluffy pink stuff—to $2,170 for spray-foam insulation. (Some builders find that the denser and more rigid rockwool, also called mineral wool, batt insulation performs better than fiberglass rolls, even if it can be more difficult to work with. Rockwool batts add about 25% to 50% to the cost of fiberglass, installed.)

Insulation in an attic can pay for itself fairly quickly through lower energy costs. The Department of Energy website, Energy.gov/energysaver/types-insulation, can help you sort out the pros and cons of different types, including how well they lend themselves to do-it-yourself (DIY) projects.

Because it's dusty work in a cramped environment, installing attic insulation generally is not considered a DIY project, but it can be done. It must, however, be done right. Even small gaps left behind can dramatically reduce R-value, which is a measurement of heat retention by which all insulation is classified. *This Old House* offers a primer on insulating your own attic, which is a good place to start. Go to ThisOldHouse.com and search "insulate attic."

- **Consider a home-energy audit.** Poorly insulated attics bleed more energy than any other part of the home, but your entire structure has vulnerabilities that are likely invisible to you. This is where a home-energy audit comes in. Home-energy auditors examine houses from top to bottom with equipment such as thermal imagers, special fans and prods to find leaks, drafts, weak spots, shoddy insulation, exposed pipes, inefficient appliances and other chinks in your home's energy armor.

Energy.gov and the federal Energy Star program (EnergyStar.gov) will help you learn what to expect from an audit. Contact your utility company, and ask whether it offers free or discounted home-energy audits, which many utilities do. If not, the average cost to hire a professional is about $394. While that's a hefty price tag for many people, it will be money well-spent if the audit unmasks your home's neediest points.

- **Things you can do for less...or for free.** Clean your gutters, or have them cleaned, before freezing weather comes. Clogged gutters encourage the formation of ice—which can push or pull your gutters loose, lead to destructive ice dams and even result in injuries from massive falling icicles.

Upgrading older, energy-inefficient windows is a worthwhile but expensive improvement. If that's not possible, consider buying transparent insulating film that adheres to the glass portion of your existing windows. It doesn't obstruct your view—in fact, you can leave it on year-round if you choose—but it can significantly reduce window-based energy bleed in both winter and summer.

Example: The Gila LEG361 Heat Control Residential Window Film, which says it cuts cooling costs by up to 30%, sells for about $30 and includes a roll that measures 36 inches by 15 feet.

If you're confident that you can safely do so, flush your water heater through its drain valve to clear out sediment and sludge, which can improve efficiency and reduce costs in the high-demand winter months. If this isn't something you want to do yourself, pay a plumber to do it (about $100)—it should take less than an hour and is worth it.

Heat escapes and cold air enters through gaps under exterior doors. A $10 draft guard can prevent most of that waste. Virtually all homes will benefit from weather-stripping tape applied to doors and windows. Each roll costs about $5 and can service two or three doors. If you have forced-air heating, replacing the filters for about $10 each can take enormous pressure off your heating system, reducing the cost of running it.

Finally, walk around the exterior of your house, and examine the siding for holes and gaps. When you find a gap, fill it with regular household caulk, which costs $5 to $10 per tube and can be applied with a $15 caulk gun.

Avocados Are Sending People to the Hospital

Sheel Sharma, MD, clinical associate professor in the Hansjörg Wyss Department of Plastic Surgery, NYU Langone Medical Center, New York City. NYULangone.org

Avocados have seen a surge in popularity—think avocado toast! But they can be dangerous. Anecdotal evidence suggests that emergency rooms have recently seen a surge in patients who sliced open their palms or fingers while cutting into these increasingly popular fruits. Actress Meryl Streep is perhaps the most prominent victim.

Unlike most fruits and vegetables, avocados have tough exterior skins but extremely soft flesh inside. People push down hard on knives to cut through that tough skin, only to have the knife slice very quickly through the fruit's soft flesh...and into the hand that's holding the avocado.

There are nerves, tendons and blood vessels very close to the skin of palms and fingers, so the damage can be extensive. Victims sometimes require delicate surgery followed by as much as three to six months of rehab before full use of the hand is restored.

Not long ago, bagels were the food most closely associated with these sorts of kitchen-knife injuries. (Like avocados, bagels tend to be tough on the outside but soft within.) Bagel injuries seem to be less common lately, perhaps because many bagel fans have purchased bagel slicers.

To safely slice an avocado without slicing yourself...

- **Place the avocado on a cutting board**—don't hold it in your palm.
- **Cut until you reach the pit**...then flip the avocado over to cut the other side down to the pit.
- **Twist the fruit open to reveal the pit inside.** And then twist the pit to remove it.

Be sure to use a knife that has a sharp blade—a dull blade could have trouble getting through the tough skin, meaning more pressure must be applied to cut it. More pressure means greater odds of the knife slipping—and an injury.

If you cannot be deterred from holding an avocado in your palm when cutting it open, at least hold it in a hand towel when doing so. The cloth of the towel may be sufficient to protect the hand should the knife slip. Here, too, cut down only to the pit, then flip the avocado over to cut the other side.

How to Ripen an Avocado

Put an avocado in a paper bag with a ripe banana—the ethylene emitted by the banana will speed the avocado's ripening.

TheKitchn.com

Get Pesticides Off Apples

To remove pesticide residue from conventionally grown apples, mix one teaspoon of baking soda in two cups of water, submerge the apples in a bowl with a cover for two minutes, then rinse.

Even better: Buy organic.

Study by researchers at University of Massachusetts and Massachusetts Pesticide Analysis Laboratory, both in Amherst, published in *Journal of Agriculture and Food Chemistry.*

How to Make the Best Grilled Chicken Ever!

Linda Gassenheimer, an award-winning author of numerous cookbooks, including *Delicious One-Pot Dishes* and *Fast and Flavorful: Great Diabetes Meals from Market to Table* and creator of the recipes for *Bottom Line's Beat Diabetes Now!* She writes the syndicated newspaper column "Dinner in Minutes." DinnerInMinutes.com

Why don't people get as excited about chicken on the grill as they do about steak? The truth is, chicken from the grill can be scrumptious—*when it is perfectly cooked.* That means it is browned and crisp but not black on the outside and juicy but not mushy (or pink!) on the inside. Most people don't know how to achieve that grilled chicken perfection—but you can. *Here's how to make perfect grilled chicken every time...*

TIPS FOR GREAT RESULTS

• **Make sure the grill grates are very clean.** Chicken grilled on grates that aren't clean will pick up the charred residue from previous grilling. This will spoil the flavor. One way to get your grates ready for perfect chicken is to heat the grill to a high temperature to burn away grease and other residue...then brush the grates with a piece of crumpled aluminum foil held with tongs. When the grates are clean, oil them with vegetable oil–soaked paper towels to help prevent sticking. This is best done using tongs to hold the paper towels.

• **Trim visible fat from chicken to minimize flare-ups.** Many people think that flames licking at chicken are a good thing—but that's not so. Flames easily can burn the food and destroy the flavor. If a flare-up occurs even though you've trimmed the fat, move the chicken to another section of the grill until the flare is out. You also can close the cover of the grill to reduce oxygen and starve the flame.

• **When using a barbecue sauce or glaze, don't put it on when the chicken is raw.** Instead, add it four to five minutes before the chicken is done cooking to keep the sugar in the sauce from burning. Or warm the sauce, and brush the chicken with it after it comes off the grill. (This precaution does not refer to most *marinades*, which tend to contain far less sugar than sauces and glazes.)

• **Chicken should be at room temperature before placing it on the grill.** If it has been marinating in the fridge, remove it about one hour before grilling.

• **Use an instant-read thermometer to know when the chicken is done.** For white meat (breasts) and the upper part of the wing where there is white meat, a thermometer should read 165°F. For dark meat (legs and thighs), a thermometer should read 170°F.

HOW TO PREP AND GRILL DIFFERENT CUTS OF CHICKEN

Grilling and turning times will vary according to your grill's heat, the size of your chicken pieces, how you've prepared the meat and other factors, but here are the essential instructions for grilling great chicken—try these out and adjust according to your results...

• **Boneless, skinless chicken breasts.** Your goal with skinless breasts is crisp on the exterior and juicy on the interior. But having no skin or visible fat can lead to dry, chewy results. *Here's how to grill the perfect boneless breast...*

Even out the meat. A boneless, skinless chicken breast is uneven with a thicker center and thinner end. Flatten the breast so that it has an almost-even thickness. The best way to do this is to put it in a sealable plastic bag and flatten it with a rolling pin or meat bat. The breast should end up about three-quarters-inch thick.

Marinate the flattened chicken or brine it for about 20 minutes in the refrigerator. A basic brine is one-quarter cup salt to four cups water. Or use a marinade of your choice (but not a sugary glaze). This helps keep the chicken moist. Pat the chicken dry with a paper towel before grilling.

Place the chicken on the grill over indirect heat. Cook for five minutes, turn, then cook three minutes more. Breasts without the bone cook quickly.

• **Boneless, skinless chicken thighs.** Open chicken thighs to form a flat surface. Since the bone has been removed, the thigh can easily be spread apart and opened flat. Remove visible fat. Spray both sides with olive oil. Place the thighs on the grill over direct heat. Cook for five minutes. Move them to indirect heat, and turn the chicken. Continue to cook for three to four minutes more. Without the bone, these will cook quickly.

• **Chicken breasts, legs and thighs with skin and bones.** The goal is to have a crisp skin with the meat cooked through but not overcooked. For chicken breasts, start by placing them, skin-side down, for 10 minutes over direct heat (400°F to 450°F). Then turn the chicken breasts over and move them to indirect heat (375°F to 400°F), for 10 to 15 minutes. Check the meat temperature after 10 minutes to see if it has reached 165°F. Continue to cook for the final five minutes if needed. For the chicken legs and thighs, start them over direct heat for five minutes. Turn them over, and continue to cook them over direct heat for five minutes more. Then move the meat to indirect heat for 10 to 15 minutes to finish cooking. Check the temperature of the meat after 10 minutes to see if it has reached 170°F. Continue to cook for five minutes, more if needed, to reach 170°F.

• **Chicken wings.** These have a lot of skin that drips fat that can create flare-ups. Watch the wings carefully, and move them to new spots when flare-ups happen. Place them over direct heat for four to five minutes, turning once during that time. Then move them over indirect heat, and grill 12 minutes more, turning them once.

DELICIOUSLY SIMPLE GRILLED CHICKEN RECIPES

Korean Grilled Chicken Breasts

4 Tablespoons low-sodium soy sauce
4 Tablespoons rice vinegar
4 crushed garlic cloves
4 teaspoons sesame oil
4 Tablespoons honey
3 teaspoons ground ginger
¾ pound boneless, skinless breasts

Mix the soy sauce, rice vinegar, garlic, sesame oil, honey and ginger in a bowl. Place the chicken in a sealable plastic bag, and flatten it with a rolling pin so that it is an even thickness. Add half the mixed sauce to the bag, and seal it. Refrigerate about 20 minutes, turning the bag over once during that time. Add the remaining marinade to a saucepan, and set aside. To get ready for cooking, remove the chicken from the refrigerator and set it out to bring it to room temperature, about one hour. Remove the chicken from the bag, and discard the bagged marinade. Pat the chicken dry with a paper towel. Grill as described above for boneless breasts.* While the chicken grills, bring the marinade in the saucepan to a simmer. Cook for two minutes to warm and thicken the sauce. Remove the chicken to two dinner plates, and spoon the reserved sauce on top. Serves two.

Barbecued Chicken Sliders

½ cup low-sugar barbecue sauce
2 medium crushed garlic cloves
½ teaspoon hot pepper sauce
¾ pound boneless, skinless thighs
Olive oil spray
6 slider rolls

Preheat the grill. Mix the barbecue sauce, garlic and hot pepper sauce in a bowl. Set aside. Grill as described above for boneless thighs, and after cooking for five minutes and moving the chicken to indirect heat, turn it and spoon a little of the sauce mixture over the cooked side.

While the chicken grills, open the slider rolls and put them on the grill, cut-side down, to toast, about two minutes.

Remove the chicken from the grill once it has finished cooking, and cut it into one-quarter-to-one-half-inch slices. Divide among the slider rolls. Spoon the remaining sauce over the chicken, and close the rolls. Serves two.

Sweet and Spicy Grilled Wings

½ cup balsamic vinegar
½ cup honey
3 crushed garlic cloves
Several drops hot pepper sauce
8 chicken wings
2 Tablespoons sesame seeds

Mix the balsamic vinegar, honey, garlic and hot pepper sauce in a bowl, and set aside. If the wings are in the refrigerator, remove about one hour before grilling so that they come to room temperature. Grill as described for wings, and brush their top sides with the sauce about three to four minutes before they are done.

Meanwhile, heat the remaining marinade in a saucepan until thick, about four to five minutes. When the wings are done grilling, divide them between two plates and spoon the sauce over the wings. Sprinkle on the sesame seeds. Serves two.

*Cooking time will depend on grills. Check for doneness with an instant-read thermometer.

Cook Meat Like a Master: 5 Myths Busted

Meathead Goldwyn, who shares the science of cooking meat at his popular website, AmazingRibs.com. Meathead's love of cooking began when he was 10 years old and his parents opened a restaurant. Known as the "Barbecue Whisperer," Meathead has judged barbecue and other foods and drinks at several competitions from Italy to California. Based in the Chicago area, he is author of *The New York Times* best-seller *Meathead: The Science of Great Barbecue and Grilling.*

The myths about the best way to prepare and cook meat are plentiful—and many cookbooks still promote this misinformation. On the website AmazingRibs.com, meat fanatic Meathead Goldwyn and his scientific advisers debunk myths about all kinds of cuts of meat with methodical testing.

Result: The truth about the tastiest ways to prepare meat.

Five myths you shouldn't believe...

***MYTH:* Let meat come to room temperature before cooking.**

Reality: Many recipes, especially those for thick steaks or large roasts, direct you to take the meat out of the refrigerator an hour or two before cooking to allow it "to come to room temperature."

Theory: Room-temperature meat will cook more quickly than cold meat.

That may be true, but when we tested this theory, a one-and-a-half-inch-thick steak took more than two hours for the center to come to room temperature. A three-and-a-half-inch-thick, four-and-a-half-pound pork roast took a whopping 10 hours! The meat's temperature had risen from 38°F (refrigerator temperature) to only 49°F after two hours. And after five hours, it began to smell funny.

Important: At room temperature, dangerous microbes can reproduce quickly.

Also, cold meat attracts more smoke than warm meat, a process called *thermophoresis.* It's the same phenomenon that causes your mirror to fog up after a shower. And a smoky flavor is something we like in our meat, right?

***MYTH:* Boil ribs to make them tender.**

Reality: Many people boil ribs before grilling them to save time and to achieve the desired "fall off the bone" results. This is a mistake. When you boil meat and bones, the flavor—and many nutrients—are pulled from the meat and left behind in the water. That's why the water is cloudy...and why soup is so tasty.

Ribs are most flavorful when roasted. If you need to speed up the cooking process, you are better off steaming or microwaving them and then finishing them on the grill or under the broiler.

Properly roasted ribs are tender but still have some chew to them, similar to a tender steak. The meat should not fall off the bone—if it does, chances are the ribs have been boiled and won't be as flavorful.

***MYTH:* Marinating meat makes it more tender.**

Reality: Marinades do not penetrate meats very far, rarely more than an eighth of an inch, even after many hours of soaking. Meat is about 75% water, and there is not much room for more liquid. Think of a kitchen sponge that is loaded after wiping up a spill—once full, it cannot absorb any more liquid. A marinade can soften the proteins in muscle fibers and connective tissues, but because the marinade does not penetrate very far, it does not tenderize much beyond the meat's surface.

Spices and herbs on the surface of meat can add a wonderful aroma, and a touch of sugar can help with browning and add flavor—but marinades can tenderize only very thin cuts of meat such as skirt steak.

***MYTH:* Chicken is done once the juices run clear, and pink meat means that it is undercooked.**

Reality: The meat and juices in chicken, turkey and pork are colored pink by the protein *myoglobin.* When cooked, myoglobin absorbs light differently and no longer appears pink. However, there is no fixed temperature at which myoglobin changes color.

In addition, red or purple bones, or pink meat next to bones, do not indicate that chicken is undercooked. Bones can be red because marrow is where the blood is made. As birds age, more calcium is deposited on the bones, so the marrow becomes less visible and less porous. Red or purple bones are more common now because chickens grow faster (they have been bred to grow faster, and they are fed foods that make them grow fast), so most are only seven to eight weeks old when they are butchered.

Purple bones can discolor adjacent meat, making it appear pink even when it's safely cooked. The pink color also can come from nitric oxide or carbon monoxide, by-products of smoke or combustion gases in gas ovens and grills and charcoal grills.

Bottom line: Chicken meat, including any that remains pink, is safe to eat when a food thermometer indicates that the meat is at 165°F.

***MYTH:* A pop-up turkey thermometer is fine to let you know when your bird is done.**

Reality: You cannot rely on the pop-up thermometer that comes with your turkey or pop-up thermometers that you buy yourself.

How they work: The thermometer tip melts at a specific temperature and releases a spring that pops the stem up. Although these thermometers can be accurate in some cases, they also can stick. And they read only one small part of the turkey. Plus, they often are set to pop up at 175°F or higher, which is too high—and which is why so many turkeys are overcooked and taste like cardboard.

What to do: Pop out the thermometer that comes in your turkey. Then, when you think the cooking might be done, check the temperature with a digital meat thermometer, which is more accurate and faster than a dial thermometer. A whole turkey is safe when cooked to a minimum of 165°F. Check the temperature in several places—especially the innermost part of the thigh and the thickest part of the breast—and make sure that all parts of the turkey have reached that level.

TAKE NOTE...

Apps for Better Grilling

Photo Cookbook—Barbecue Grilling, free for iOS, offers dozens of well-illustrated recipes and photos showing every step of the cooking process.

Grill-It!, $1 for iOS or Android, has helpful illustrations and a variety of recipes in multiple categories, with a search option to find dishes with a particular ingredient.

GrillTime, $2 for iOS, is a timing tool for steaks and other foods—you select the meat, thickness and how you like it cooked, and it creates a timer.

Steak Timer, $1 for iOS, is simpler to use but is only for timing the cooking of steaks.

BBQ Timer by Jerry M, free for Android, is another simple app—and can show its timer on your phone's lock screen so that you can check it at a glance.

Roundup of experts on grilling-related apps, reported in *The New York Times*.

Butternut Squash Fries

This healthy and flavorful version of regular fries is packed with vitamins and is virtually fat-free with a fraction of the calories of the real thing.

2 large butternut squash
Canola oil nonstick cooking spray
1 teaspoon salt

Directions: Preheat the oven to 425°F. Peel the squash with a vegetable peeler. Then cut off the ends of each squash and slice each in half. Remove the seeds and slice the squash into fries. Spray a large nonstick cookie sheet with canola oil. Arrange the fries on the sheet in a single layer, spray them with canola oil and sprinkle evenly with salt. Bake for 40 minutes, turning once. When done, the fries should be crispy and brown at the edges. Serve right out of the oven. Makes four servings.

Janet Bond Brill, PhD, RDN, FAND, a nationally recognized nutrition, health and fitness expert who specializes in cardiovascular disease prevention. She is based in Allentown, Pennsylvania. DrJanet.com

Rice Has Arsenic... How to Cook It Clean

Andy Meharg, PhD, professor and chair of plant and soil sciences, The Institute for Global Food Security, Queen's University Belfast, Northern Ireland. He tested methods of cooking rice for the BBC program *Trust Me, I'm a Doctor.*

Most of us eat rice, but most of us don't know that rice is the leading food source of arsenic, an element that occurs naturally in air, soil and water—and from contamination from industrial waste, pesticides and fertilizers.

The arsenic content of rice varies by where it is grown. For example, rice grown in California tends to have less arsenic than rice grown in Arkansas, Louisiana, Missouri and Texas. White rice tends to have less arsenic than brown rice.

Regular exposure to inorganic arsenic, the primary form of arsenic in rice grain, is linked to an increased risk for bladder, lung and skin cancers, heart disease and type 2 diabetes.

Good news: Cooking rice a certain way can eliminate most of the arsenic.

Recent study: Scientists from Queen's University Belfast tested three different methods of cooking rice to determine how they affected levels of arsenic.

METHOD #1. Researchers used a ratio of two parts water to one part rice, cooking the rice until all the water was either absorbed or steamed out.

Result: Most of the arsenic still was present in the rice after cooking.

METHOD #2. Rice was cooked with five parts water to one part rice. After cooking, excess water was drained off, and then the rice was rinsed under a running tap until the water ran clear.

Result: Arsenic was reduced by 50% compared with method #1.

METHOD #3. The rice was soaked in water overnight at room temperature. It then was rinsed under a running tap until the water ran clear, drained and transferred to a saucepan with a ratio of five parts water to one part rice. The rice was then cooked and drained.

Result: Arsenic was reduced by up to 82% compared with method #1.

Bottom line: Use method #3.

Cooking instructions: Bring rice and water to a rapid boil over high heat, uncovered—this takes seven to eight minutes. Turn the heat down to medium-high. Boil white rice 10 minutes more. Boil brown rice 20 minutes more. Drain.

Secrets to Incredibly Flavorful Desserts

Mark Henning, pastry sous-chef at The Modern, a two-Michelin-star restaurant located in the Museum of Modern Art in New York City. He is a graduate of the Culinary Institute of America. TheModernNYC.com

The Modern restaurant in New York City is acclaimed not just for its entrées but also for its mouthwatering desserts, which are known for being upscale yet playful and flavorful. In a city with literally tens of thousands of restaurants, The Modern is one of just 16 that earn two or more Michelin stars.

We asked Mark Henning, pastry sous-chef at The Modern, how he manages to deliver such impressive flavors time and time again. It turns out that the primary secret to creating memorably flavorful desserts lies not in advanced cooking techniques but in savvy ingredient selection—and you can use the same ingredients when you make desserts at home.

Here, Henning's tips on how to choose ingredients that will lift your desserts out of the ordinary...

- **Trust your nose—and your local farmers—when you select fruit.** People have their pet theories about how to tell when different kinds of fruit are ripe and therefore flavorful, but all you really need is your nose. If a fruit has a lot of scent, it almost certainly has a lot of flavor. If it has little scent, it's likely to have little flavor.

When possible, shop at farmer's markets and ask the farmers which fruits are doing especially well this year and which are not. Weather fluctuations dramatically affect the quality of fruit, and farmers know what's thriving and what's struggling.

Example: Last year, it was tough to find flavorful fresh figs, so at The Modern, we switched over to nuts instead for some of our desserts (see below).

• **Know which fruits you can trust during the cold months.** There are many different delicious fruits to choose among during the warm months, but you must be extremely selective when it's cold. That's because markets still might have a wide range of fruits on their shelves, but very few will be at their best.

Tip: The most flavorful cold-weather fruit options often include persimmons, Concord grapes, figs and citrus.

• **When you can't find a great fruit, use nuts or even a sweet vegetable.** Don't resort to subpar or past-its-prime fruit when you don't have great fruit. Instead, flavor your desserts with nuts (available at a high-quality level year-round). Nuts do not last forever, though—taste yours to make sure that they have no hint of rancidity before allowing them into your dessert! Nuts can be frozen, too. My favorite nuts for desserts include hazelnuts (hearty and heavy, ideal for winter desserts—at The Modern they are sometimes candied and served with ice cream)...and macadamias, an excellent choice if you're looking for a lighter flavor.

Or try sweet potato, a delicious fall vegetable that's sweet enough to substitute for fruit in desserts—anything from cakes to tarts to pies.

• **Change your flour, change your flavor.** Try different flours now and then. Graham flour is nutty and sweet like graham crackers, with a wonderful coarse texture, and works wonderfully in crusts...while nut flours (almond, pistachio, hazelnut) not only lend their nutty flavors but also have a high fat content that can make baked goods moister.

Changing the flour you use in a recipe can alter the result in unexpected ways, however, so look for recipes that specifically call for these alternate flours if you do not have the time or inclination to learn how to incorporate them into your current recipes through trial and error. If you do wish to replace the all-purpose flour in your favorite recipe with a different flour, one option is to first replace only a quarter of the flour and gradually increase this percentage in future attempts.

EASY TO DO...

No-Guilt Chocolate "Bark"

Microwave one cup of dark chocolate chips for 60 seconds...stir...microwave for 30 seconds or so to melt completely...stir. Mix in three cups of crispy whole-grain rice cereal, one cup of chopped dried apricots and one-half cup of chopped nuts. Spread on waxed paper on a cookie sheet. Refrigerate two hours or freeze 30 minutes. Break into pieces to enjoy.

Marjory Abrams, chief content officer, Bottom Line Inc., and author of the "Eat Like Margie" blog available at BottomLineInc.com.

18

Life Coach

The Single Most Important Secret to Happiness

The human brain has a negativity bias—it endlessly searches for the bad news but often overlooks the good. That negativity bias made sense for our ancient ancestors because focusing on what could go wrong is a smart survival strategy when you are in a world where lions and tigers pose real threats. But for modern humans, the tendency to fixate on potential problems can leave us feeling anxious and unhappy even when we are safe and life is good. To overcome this—and be happy—we sometimes must remind ourselves to "take in the good."

Taking in the good means taking certain steps that encourage the brain to appreciate the good things happening all around us so that we balance out all the problems and challenges that the brain naturally notices. Not only is this a path to a happier life—it also can help build the psychological resources needed to be a more calm, confident and capable person. *Here's how to do it...*

NOTICE SOMETHING POSITIVE WHEN YOU'RE FEELING NEGATIVE

There likely are lots of things you could feel good about even when life seems bleak. The challenge is that these feel-good things might be stuff that you take for granted because they seem ordinary and inconsequential.

Examples: You could feel good about the fact that you live in a safe community surrounded by trustworthy neighbors...that you have a roof over your head and enough food to eat...or that the building you are in is heated or cooled to a comfortable temperature.

Rick Hanson, PhD, psychologist and founder of the Wellspring Institute for Neuroscience and Contemplative Wisdom, San Rafael, California, and author of *Hardwiring Happiness: The New Brain Science of Contentment, Calm, and Confidence.* RickHanson.net

The fact that people have come to take these things for granted does not mean that they are not wonderful and worth appreciating. Throughout human history, people often have lacked these things. Stop taking them for granted for a moment, and you could start to turn around your bad day.

Once you identify something positive—either something important such as the love of your spouse or something smaller such as your favorite comfy chair—resist the temptation to immediately set it aside and focus on whatever problem currently is competing for your attention. Instead, spend 10 to 20 seconds with the positive thought. Explore it, and enjoy it. Picture yourself absorbing it, as if it were warmth spreading throughout your body. Consider what, specifically, you find rewarding about this positive thing.

Seeing the reward in something triggers the release of the neurotransmitters *dopamine* and *norepinephrine* in the brain. These neurotransmitters flag the experience for storage in your long-term memory. The more positive, rewarding experiences you add to your long-term memory, the more you will come to see your life in a positive light.

Examples: If you enjoy taking off your shoes after a long day, ask yourself, *Why does taking my shoes off feel so rewarding?* Maybe it's because your feet feel an instant surge of comfort. If you enjoy talking to your grown child on the phone, ask yourself, *Why are these conversations so rewarding?* Maybe they give you a sense of being loved.

DIVIDE EXPERIENCES INTO THEIR COMPONENTS

We generally take in an experience as if it were a single unit—we enjoyed our trip to our favorite vacation destination...or enjoyed reading a book by our favorite author. But any experience actually can be divided into a handful of components—our thoughts...our sensations...our emotions...our desires...and our actions. Focusing *separately* on these components creates additional opportunities to have positive feelings—and even when an overall experience is not pleasant, we can dial in to some component of it that is.

Example: Most books we read will not give us as much enjoyment as a book written by our favorite author, but we still can focus on the pleasurable sensation of relaxation we get when reading almost any book.

Here's how we can use these five components to take in the good—even when an overall experience is not good...

- **Thoughts.** Look for a good idea or positive insight that you derived from the less-than-great experience.

Example: A man who divorced his wife realized, *Neither of us was a bad person, we just got busy with our own lives and stopped putting enough time and effort into each other.* The breakup had been among the worst experiences of his life, but the above realization helped him see himself and his ex-wife in a more positive light and served as inspiration to do better in his current relationship.

- **Sensations.** Tasting a juicy piece of fruit ...seeing a beautiful dress...smelling freshly baked bread. A pleasant sensation can be a powerfully positive thing even during a difficult day. Pleasant sensations do not just make us feel momentarily satisfied, they also have an analgesic effect, literally reducing any pain we might be feeling.

Example: A man who is having a terrible morning at work finds himself staring out his office window, sipping a cup of coffee, lamenting how things went wrong. His day might suddenly seem brighter if he focuses on the sensation of seeing the peaceful view outside the window...or the sensation of smelling or tasting the coffee.

- **Emotions.** Emotions include both fleeting feelings and longer-lasting moods. What most people do not realize is that they can encourage their positive feelings to stick around and become good moods.

When something happens that gives you a positive feeling in a small way that ordinarily would soon pass, focus on this event and your feelings about it for 10 seconds or longer. There's a good chance your mood will improve.

Examples: Someone holds a door for you...someone says, "You look nice today"...

you have a warm memory about a family member or a beloved pet...or you hear an upbeat song. Do not waste these positive mini-experiences!

• **Desires.** Some things we desire are good for us...some are bad for us. But any desire can be used to take in the good. When you desire something positive—something that could make life better for you or others—simply spend a little time appreciating this desire. Surprisingly, reflecting on the fact that we desire to do something positive for ourselves (such as exercise) or for the world (such as volunteering with a charity) can make us feel positive even if we have not yet done these things.

When you desire something that isn't good for you or the world, focus not on the desire itself but on your ability to delay or stop yourself from acting on it.

Example: You desire a sugary dessert but are trying to cut back. Focus on the sense of satisfaction and self-worth you get from standing up to this desire even if you cannot always stand up to it.

• **Actions.** When you take a positive action —something that you would like to encourage yourself to do more often—in response to a negative incident, remain focused on your action for at least 10 seconds after you have completed it.

Example: A woman who considers herself overly passive stands up straight and tells a man what she thinks of him when he cuts in front of her in line at a coffee shop. She then spends 10 seconds thinking about her willingness to calmly and confidently stand up to this man (a positive)...rather than focusing on the man's unpleasant behavior (a negative). This significantly increases the odds that the entire event will be stored in her memory as a positive experience.

EASY TO DO...

Trick to Control Emotions

Talk to yourself in the third person to help control your emotions.

Example: If you are feeling upset, saying, *Why is John upset?* makes you less emotionally reactive than saying, *Why am I upset?* Doing this gives you a bit of distance from your feelings.

Study led by researchers at Michigan State University, East Lansing, and University of Michigan, Ann Arbor, published in *Scientific Reports*.

The Older You Are, the Happier You Can Be

David Mischoulon, MD, PhD, a psychiatrist and director of the Depression Clinical and Research Program at Massachusetts General Hospital and an associate professor of psychiatry at Harvard Medical School, both in Boston. He has authored or coauthored more than 200 articles and book chapters and has also coedited a textbook on natural medications for psychiatric disorders.

The image of a "grumpy old man" (or "grumpy old woman") is pervasive in movies, TV shows and other media. Perhaps it's because we assume that as we grow older, our lives will be filled with aches and pains, sickness and depression. But it turns out that this age-old stereotype isn't usually true.

Game-changing finding: In a 2016 study published in *Journal of Clinical Psychiatry*, researchers found that happiness *increases* with age. While those in their 50s, 60s and beyond reported more cognitive impairment and physical ailments, they were happier, more satisfied, less depressed and anxious and experienced lower levels of perceived stress than younger adults.

How could this be? While the study did not determine exactly why older people tend to be happier, greater experience and wisdom most likely contribute to one's superior mental health in later life. Plus, as we transition from building careers and raising families to having more personal time, we're under less daily pressure and have more time to engage in meaningful activities that make us happy.

Our brains help out as well. The *amygdala*, an almond-shaped section of the brain that controls our emotional responses to stress, has been shown in brain scans to be less active in older people than in younger individuals when both are presented with upsetting images. This could be another reason why seniors deal with negative events more calmly and positively.

COULD YOU BE HAPPIER?

It's worth noting that some people who have experienced tragedy and misfortunes may have less capacity for happiness than others. But for almost everyone, there are ways to improve the way you feel about yourself and your life—no matter what your age or circumstances.

Strategies to boost your mood, happiness and satisfaction with life...

Happiness booster #1: **Foster the right kind of connections.** More than fame, career success, money, IQ or genes, close connections are what promote happiness throughout life, according to a 75-year study from Harvard. In fact, study participants with the most satisfying relationships at age 50 were found to be the healthiest at age 80.

What to do: Make it a priority to spend time with friends, family and colleagues whose company you enjoy. And don't assume that just because you're married and/or have children you're automatically covered when it comes to close connections. You need to regularly assess whether your relationships are having a positive impact on your psychological well-being. If not, do something about it.

Also: If you are married or in some other type of romantic relationship, you need to make time for each other to fan the flames of love. Travel, have sex and/or take up a new hobby together. Remember birthdays and anniversaries. Don't take each other for granted!

Happiness booster #2: **Fake it 'til you make it.** Whether you feel like it or not, putting on a happy face can actually lift your spirits.

Evidence: In a 2012 study, researchers at University of Kansas found that those who smiled while performing stressful tasks had lower heart rates and self-reported lower stress levels afterward.

What to do: When you are in social situations, practice smiling...even when you don't feel like it. Flexing the facial muscles that form a smile tells the brain you are happy. And conveying a positive demeanor attracts others to you, which boosts your mood.

HAPPINESS QUIZ...

How Happy Are You?

No measures of happiness apply to everyone, but some basic questions can give you an idea. Using the 1-to-7 rating scale that follows, indicate how much you agree with each of the five statements below. Total the numbers for your results.

1. In most ways, my life is close to my ideal ____
2. The conditions of my life are excellent ____
3. I am satisfied with my life ____
4. So far, I have gotten the important things I want in life ____
5. If I could live my life over, I would change almost nothing ____

Rating scale:

7: Strongly agree
6: Agree
5: Slightly agree
4: Neither agree nor disagree
3: Slightly disagree
2: Disagree
1: Strongly disagree

The higher your score, the greater your life satisfaction:

31-35 = Extremely satisfied
26-30 = Satisfied
21-25 = Slightly satisfied
20 = Neutral
15-19 = Slightly dissatisfied
10-14 = Dissatisfied
5-9 = Extremely dissatisfied

Credit: The Satisfaction with Life Scale was created by Ed Diener, Robert A. Emmons, Randy J. Larsen and Sharon Griffin.

Happiness booster #3: **Show up on a regular basis.** This could be at your job...or if you are retired, some other activity or hobby that you enjoy and do regularly. The sense of accomplishment from a job well done improves mood and life satisfaction.

What to do: If you have a fulfilling job, activity or hobby, stick with it. If you are in a job that causes you anxiety—or creates a toxic environment—it may be too difficult to derive pleasure from it no matter how positive you try to be. If so, request a transfer to a different department, look for a new job or change your expectations so that you are less affected by the negativity.

If you are retired, cultivate an existing interest by joining a club or starting a hobby. For example, if you enjoy bird-watching, join a bird-watching group that meets regularly for outings.

Happiness booster #4: **Be grateful.** It may sound trite, but it's true—people who are grateful for what they have lead healthier and more contented lives.

What to do: Even if this strikes you as a little hokey, make a list of what you are grateful for. Doing this makes you appreciate what you have, instead of worrying about what you don't have. Then take a few minutes each day to review/update the list at the same time every day. Do it first thing in the morning...on your commute to work...while brushing your teeth...or before you turn out your light at night. After a few weeks, ask yourself if you're feeling any happier. Chances are, the answer will be yes!

Use Your Dreams to Help Solve Problems and Improve Skills

Denholm J. Aspy, PhD, visiting research fellow in the School of Psychology at The University of Adelaide in Australia. He is founder of the Lucid Dreaming Australia website and lead author of the academic paper "Reality Testing and the Mnemonic Induction of Lucid Dreams: Findings from the National Australian Lucid Dream Induction Study," published in *Dreaming*. His website is LucidDreamingAustralia.com.

When one is asleep, there is something in consciousness which tells us that what presents itself is but a dream.—Aristotle (384–322 BC)

Have you ever been aware that you are dreaming *while* you are dreaming? That sensation is called *lucid dreaming*. Once awareness has been achieved, dreamers often can take control of their dreams, opening the door to solving problems, improving skills and having adventures.

The ability to be conscious during dreams, and thus have some control over them, can help in...

- **Solving complex problems.** In the book *Exploring the World of Lucid Dreaming*, author Stephen LaBerge tells the story of an architect who developed the ability to do a "walk-through" in his dreams of buildings that he is designing—before they're built. He spots potential problems and makes changes to the blueprints to fix them.
- **Controlling chronic nightmares.** Several studies have found that people who suffer from chronic nightmares can use lucid dreaming to take control of their bad dreams and alter the nightmarish story lines. This can reduce the negative power of nightmares and even their frequency.
- **Mastering motor skills.** To get better at a physical skill—hitting a golf ball or parallel parking, for example—typically requires many hours of repetitious practice. Lucid dreaming might be a shortcut. In a German study, volunteers tried to toss coins into a cup during the day. They scored 3.7 out of 20, on average. They were taught to try lucid dreaming and practice the coin toss in their dreams. The next morning, those who had experienced lucid dreaming scored 5.3, on average—while participants who hadn't achieved lucid dreaming showed no improvement.
- **Having vivid and fun adventures.** Some lucid dreamers say they use the dreams to enjoy exhilarating adventures...to fly through the sky like Superman...to visit distant worlds...and to be the heroes of tales that they shape in their sleeping minds.

More than half of adults have experienced lucid dreaming at least once in their lives. Some find themselves dreaming lucidly as frequently as once a month or even several times a week. But recent research has found that by combining several known strategies, the majority of people can experience one or more lucid dreams within just one week of trying.

HOW TO ACHIEVE LUCID DREAMING

Below is a series of steps that can help you become a lucid dreamer. It's best to tackle these steps in order—when you can reliably accomplish one, move on to the next. Once you've practiced all the techniques described in these steps, you may find yourself going back to one or more of them—not necessarily all of them—the next time you want to induce a lucid dream. You can expect to become more proficient at inducing lucid dreaming over time.

***STEP 1:* Hone your dream-recall skills.** Before you try to have lucid dreams, practice remembering the dreams that you currently experience. After you wake up each morning, spend a minute or two reflecting on what you dreamed that night.

Helpful: Start a dream journal, and jot down as much as you can remember each morning. People tend to forget most of their dreams soon after they wake, but reflecting on dreams and writing them down can significantly improve dream recall. This is important because research strongly suggests that the better people are at recalling their dreams, the more likely they are to experience lucid dreams. Once you can recall at least one dream most mornings, move on to the next step—but keep on with your new habit of recalling your dreams as soon as you wake up.

***STEP 2:* Frequently ask yourself whether you are dreaming even when you are awake.** At least 10 times each day, silently ask yourself, *Am I dreaming?* and then very carefully consider whether you could be. This might feel silly—sometimes your first thought will be, *Of course I'm awake*—but it's important to take the possibility that you might be dreaming seriously each time. If you make this "reality testing" a habit during your waking life, you encourage your sleeping brain to start doing it when you are dreaming, which makes it much more likely that you will realize that you are dreaming.

Helpful: The sleeping brain is very good at explaining away evidence that it is dreaming, which can make the "reality testing" trickier than it might seem. (Flying cows? Sure, that happens.) One strategy that can increase its effectiveness is to close your lips and then attempt to inhale through your mouth as part of each reality test. If you are awake, inhaling this way will be impossible—you'll just feel suction behind your lips. But your sleeping brain does not inhibit your breathing even when you dream that you are clamping your lips shut, so if you do try this "inhalation test" in a dream, you are likely to experience a weird contradictory sensation of air moving through closed lips. This confirms to the dreamer that he/she is dreaming.

Try reality testing for a few days to a week, and then move on to the next step—but keep on doing early-morning dream recall and reality testing.

***STEP 3:* Set an alarm for five hours after you typically fall asleep.** If you normally fall asleep at around 11 pm, for example, set an alarm for 4 am. Don't worry—the plan is for you to be awake only briefly. Find an alarm that wakes you gently.

Helpful: Use a multialarm clock or smartphone set for two different times so that you also will wake up when you need to later in the morning.

Alternative: If you regularly wake up once a night to urinate, you can skip the alarm. Just use that natural awakening as a reminder to practice the step below.

During these waking moments, prompt yourself to have lucid dreams using the instructions below.

Reason: People do most of their dreaming in their final two to three hours of sleep each night, but they are most likely to experience lucid dreams if they prompt themselves to do so while awake very soon before dreaming. Briefly waking up five hours after falling asleep gives you a chance to do this.

***STEP 4:* Instruct yourself to notice that you are dreaming.** When your alarm wakes you in the middle of the night, turn it off and then immediately tell yourself (silently, in your mind), *The next time I'm dreaming, I will notice that I'm dreaming* (or words to this effect), while imagining yourself becoming aware of a dream. Repeat this phrase to yourself several times before allowing yourself to fall back to sleep. This strategy takes advantage of something called "prospective memory"—the human brain is pretty good at remembering to perform planned actions in the near future... even when it's asleep.

Note: Try to remain awake for at least 10 minutes when you do this. If you fall back asleep any faster than that, you might not be sufficiently alert for your instructions to yourself to take hold. If you find that you tend to fall back asleep too quickly when you do this step, turn on the lights and write your instruction to yourself several times. (Step into another room to do this if the light would bother your partner.)

Exception: It's best to leave the lights off if you have trouble falling back asleep after you wake up in the middle of the night.

Caution: If you have chronic trouble sleeping, you might not want to experiment with waking yourself up in the middle of the night. The good news is that in my research, there was no evidence of poorer sleep as people learned these techniques. But I recommend that people skip a day practicing these techniques if they're feeling sleep deprived.

Lucid dreaming is by no means an essential skill for a healthy and happy life. But people who train themselves in this way and then consistently experience lucid dreaming are wildly enthusiastic about how it enhances their lives. In my experience, nearly anyone can learn lucid dreaming. If you want to take control of your dreams, now you know how.

TAKE NOTE...

Daydreaming May Signal Intelligence

People who reported more frequent daydreaming earned higher scores on measures of intellectual and creative abilities.

Eric Schumacher, PhD, associate professor of psychology, Georgia Tech University, Atlanta, and coauthor of a study of more than 100 people's brain patterns, published in *Neuropsychologia*.

How Knowing Yourself Well Can Greatly Improve Your Relationships

Roger Flax, PhD, who has been a corporate communications trainer and leadership consultant for more than 45 years. He is owner of The Horizon Companies and creator of Horizon Talent Developer, a nationally known mentoring program for corporations, Summit, New Jersey. HorizonTalentDeveloper.com

A health-care professional believed she was doing a great job—but her coworkers considered her ineffective and uninspiring. A husband thought of himself as a great listener—but his family members thought he cared about no one's opinion other than his own. A doctor saw herself as unspectacular—but everyone around her believed she was wonderful.

The way people perceive themselves can differ dramatically from the way the world sees them. And this can hurt relationships and careers. *Here's how to see how the world sees you and what steps you need to take...*

WHOSE PROBLEM IS IT?

Perception gaps—where you're perceived differently from how you really are—often last a lifetime. When events force people to confront these perception gaps, they inevitably reason that it's everyone else who has got them wrong. "I'm misunderstood," they reassure themselves. "The world just doesn't know the real me."

The truth is that when people's perception of themselves differs from the world's perception of them, it is the "misperceived" people who have the problem. If they do not achieve greater self-awareness quickly, their relationships, careers and reputations can suffer.

Examples: An executive who misperceives his strengths and weaknesses continually sets himself up for failure by taking on projects that don't fit his actual skills. A father does not take steps to improve his relationships with his grown children because he does not acknowledge the areas where he needs improvement.

These people will spend their lives making the same mistakes time and again and wondering, *Why does this keep happening to me?* They lose credibility in the eyes of the people around them because they do not deliver the results they promise and fail to hold themselves accountable for shortcomings that seem obvious to everyone else.

Why are people so prone to misperception? It often dates back to childhood. When kids receive praise or criticism about certain aspects of themselves from their parents, teachers or peers, it can make such a deep impression that they continue to believe that these are their strengths and weaknesses for the rest of their lives, ignoring all evidence to the contrary.

HOW OTHER PEOPLE REALLY SEE YOU

If you ask people their opinions of you, they often will just tell you what they think you want to hear. They don't want to risk upsetting you or damaging their relationship with you. But you can structure your questions in a way that encourages honest responses. *Ask people whose opinion you value...*

- **"If you were to list three of my strengths and three of my weaknesses, what would they be?"** This question doesn't ask whether you have weaknesses...it assumes that you have them—everyone does—and asks what those weaknesses are.

Similar: "Give me five adjectives that describe me—and at least two of them cannot be positive."

- **"If you were my boss, what would you see as most likely to derail my career?"** Bosses are allowed to tell the truth, even when it hurts, in a way that most people are not. Encouraging people to picture themselves in this role thus increases the odds that they will tell the truth.

- **"If you were to recommend one thing for me to improve about myself this year, and I absolutely had to do it, what would it be?"** This question does not ask, "What's wrong with me?" It asks, "What should I improve about me?" That's a key distinction—it casts your area of weakness not as a shortcoming but as a temporary challenge that you soon will overcome. Overcoming challenges is a positive thing, not a negative, and people often are happy to help with positive things.

GOOD TO KNOW...

Why Some People Are More Social Than Others

Are you friendly and outgoing? If the answer is "yes," some of the credit goes to the genes that regulate *oxytocin*, a "social" hormone that influences empathy, trust and communication skills. This finding may help in the development of treatments for people with impaired social skills, such as those with autism.

Psychoneuroendocrinology.

DIFFERENT OPINIONS

Pose these questions to as many different categories of people as possible—friends, colleagues, relatives, underlings, bosses, clients and so forth. Don't be surprised if you receive vastly different answers. If you're like most people, you probably act differently when you are around your bosses than when you're around people who report to you or clients...and/or differently around friends than relatives.

Example: Colleagues and clients might say that you're a great listener, but your family members insist that you are a terrible listener. They all might be right—you might not listen as well at home as you do in the office.

If someone attempts to avoid saying anything negative—or mentions only inconsequential shortcomings—prod with, "Come on, be honest with me. It's for my own good."

Do not argue if someone says something negative about you that you do not agree with. The point of this process is to learn how the world sees you, not to argue with the world that it's wrong about you. Thank this person for his/her feedback, and remind yourself that in the long run, hearing criticism is less painful than living in denial and wondering why the world never treats you the way you think you deserve to be treated.

After you have received feedback from multiple people whose opinions you value, consider how you can use the information you gathered to improve yourself.

Example: The chief compliance executive of a major bank turned everybody off, in and out of the company. After learning that people negatively perceived her listening, problem-solving and communication skills versus how she perceived herself, she changed her style dramatically, became more empathetic, tactful and compassionate, and re-earned the respect and trust of people who previously avoided her. She earned a promotion within a year.

Follow up nine to 12 months later with the people who provided feedback. Ask, "Is there anything else I could be doing?" Or retake the feedback exercise with the same people to learn if you've made progress.

10 KEY WAYS PEOPLE MISPERCEIVE THEMSELVES

Individuals can misperceive almost anything about themselves, but in over 20 years of feedback survey findings by The Horizon Companies, we have found that certain misconceptions occur particularly frequently...

- **Decisiveness.** You believe that you act as soon as the facts are in, but other people might see you as indecisive and wishy-washy. Different people have different opinions about how much evidence is required before it is appropriate to act.

- **Listening skills.** You consider yourself a great listener—so great, in fact, that you often figure out what people are trying to say before they finish speaking. That encourages you to rush speakers along or lose focus on what they're saying, leading them to see you as a poor, inattentive listener.

- **Motivational skills.** You think that your speeches are inspiring and fire up your employees. But if your employees found your speeches unmotivating, would any of them let you know?

- **Persuasiveness.** You think you can convince anyone of anything. But unless you have spent decades working in sales or have the track record to back up this feeling, it might not be true.

- **Modesty.** You consider yourself modest and selfless, yet other people might see you as pompous and self-centered. Truly modest and selfless people often do not even mention these qualities on their lists of attributes.

- **Problem-solving.** You always seem to have found an answer before anyone else in the room, so naturally you see yourself as a gifted problem-solver. Maybe everyone else in the room sees your quick answers as evidence that you jump to conclusions prematurely.

- **Conflict resolution.** You value your ability to bring an end to disagreements and arguments. But do other people see you as a skilled conflict resolver...or a bully? It could be the latter if people think you are forcing them to adopt your preferred solution.

- **Bringing substance to debates.** You believe your opinions are rooted in solid evidence. But some people who are confident in this area are seen by others as relying too much on unsupported opinions. Perhaps things that seem like unassailable facts to you are less certain to others.

- **People skills.** You think you treat everyone around you with tact and courtesy—but they consider you curt and rude. Different people can have very different opinions about what it means to be polite.

- **Dealing with change.** You think you are flexible and open to change and new practices, yet others say that you are closed-minded, set in your own ways and won't let anything go.

Your Attention Span Is Shrinking: How to Get Your Focus Back

Cynthia Green, PhD, a clinical psychologist, author and one of America's foremost experts on brain health. She is founding director of The Memory Enhancement Program at Icahn School of Medicine at Mount Sinai, New York City, and president and CEO of Total Brain Health and TBH Brands, LLC, in Montclair, New Jersey. CynthiaGreenPhD.com

---

Admit it—you reach for your smartphone every time you're waiting in a line or even when you wake up at night. We won't even mention that bathroom thing.

When you're home, you're surfing the Internet...or you have the radio or TV on as a constant backdrop...or both. No wonder it's harder to concentrate for any length of time than it used to be. While it's great to connect with old friends on Facebook or be able to look up sports or movie trivia any time, the impact this has on our attention spans is not good...at all.

Why that matters: Cognitive decline is real and can begin as young as age 45 even if you are healthy. We're not talking about dementia, either—smaller problems, such as forgetting someone's name, can be a normal part of aging. Research has shown that continuing to learn is key to minimizing this decline—but to learn, you need to focus. To find out more, we interviewed brain health expert Cynthia Green, PhD.

HOW DISTRACTIONS AFFECT LEARNING

Say we just met. If I tell you my name at the same time that your phone starts vibrating in your pocket and you glance at the screen, you're not going to hear what I said. Later, you'll think you forgot my name, but you never learned it in the first place!

Constantly switching between activities and attempting to multitask (which no one is actually good at) is exhausting for the brain, draining it of the energy needed to focus.

Result: We make mistakes big and small and are less productive, more forgetful and just slower at everything.

So...it's time to *rebuild* your attention span and your ability to focus. Like any skill, it takes practice. The point isn't only to ward off future cognitive disease but also to improve your ability to accomplish more and feel less stress from perpetual distractions...now.

CONCENTRATION BUILDERS

You probably expect me to tell you to stop using technology so much. Sure, that will help. But few of us can resist its lure for long, and these days no one wants to miss that important e-mail or breaking news flash. Instead, you need to exercise better control over the disruptions, put technology to work for you and engage in activities that strengthen attention. *My recommendations...*

- **Stop being so available.** You don't have to answer every call, text or e-mail the minute you receive it—and the truth is, you don't even have to *know* about every call, text or e-mail the minute you receive it, either. When you're working on a must-do or should-do task, eliminate distractions. Turn off the TV, and quit e-mail, text notifications, Facebook, Twitter and news app notifications until you get your task done. If there are certain people who you feel *must* be able to reach you instantly, set your phone and other devices to "do not disturb" but program in exceptions for those people.

- **Build up your tolerance.** Digital withdrawal can be very difficult, so take a lesson from behavior-modification therapy and reward yourself for small successes. Set certain times of day when you'll check e-mail, etc., and don't look in between. Start by telling yourself, *I'll go for 15 minutes without checking my device*, and then when the time is up, give yourself five minutes to glance at e-mail, Facebook, etc. Next, extend your uninterrupted time to 30 minutes before checking, then 45 minutes, then an hour. And experiment with rewards that don't entail going online, such as having a cappuccino.

- **Find a meditative hobby.** I'm not going to tell you that you have to meditate to improve your attention span—although "mindful meditation," including special breathing and visualization exercises, does exactly that by increasing brain volume and density in areas that improve cognitive function such as the *hippocampus*. But if you're not into meditation, you can get similar benefits from the regular practice of other focused, meditative activities such as gardening...walking in nature...running...swimming laps...drawing or painting...knitting or crocheting...yoga or tai chi.

If you would like to try actual meditation, you don't have to go to a class. Online meditation training (yes, I see the irony of online training!) provides similar benefits to sitting in a meditation class, studies suggest. One app that I recommend is *Headspace*, which provides mini-meditations and mindfulness exercises (Apple and Android, $12.99 a month or $7.99 a month if you pay for the year).

• **Get moving.** Regular aerobic exercise also expands the size of the hippocampus. Activity that gets your heart pumping stimulates the release of chemicals that improve the health and survival of brain cells and promotes the growth of new blood vessels in the brain. *Result:* You'll think faster and more clearly. Yes, even brisk walking counts!

• **Be social offline.** Social media helps us keep in touch with friends and family and introduces us to new people we might not ever encounter otherwise. But we lose out on the many cognitive benefits of face-to-face social interaction. *Example:* Online, you can take time to frame your thoughts before you answer or comment, but you can't pause for five minutes when someone asks you in person, "What's the best mystery you ever read?" By putting yourself in more situations where you have to answer questions and make decisions immediately, you're exercising that ability to think on your feet. *What to do:* Get out there with people...and talk!

• **Play timed games.** There are all kinds of purported brain-training and memory-boosting activities, but to rebuild attention span, choose ones that make you beat the clock. Timed word games such as Boggle, in which you have three minutes to write down words you find, are ideal because you have to pay attention and think fast. Sports such as racquetball and tennis, and even dancing, also are great choices because you have to move and react within a certain time. *Tip:* Dance lessons, which require you to learn new steps, are especially effective because you're using your body and your brain and socializing all at once.

• **Drink up.** Mild dehydration interferes with the ability to concentrate, but here's the catch—your attention span suffers even if you aren't feeling thirsty yet. So drink water throughout the day whether you think you need it or not.

• **Break out the wiggy music.** Listening to symphonies moves the brain to pay attention as it tries to predict what's coming next in these complex pieces, research has found—and this may train the brain to sustain attention.

• **Use pen and paper.** The very act of writing in longhand engages your brain in ways that promote attention span and new learning. *Example:* When students take notes by hand, they listen better and learn more than when they use a laptop, studies show.

• **Say good night to your phone.** If you don't get enough sleep, you're going to be less focused and make more mistakes, no matter what else you do. Yet how many of us go to bed with a phone or a tablet on our nightstand? If you hear it ping or look at the blue light that the screen emits, that disrupts sleep. So turn off message notifications, and leave your devices far enough away that you're not tempted to pick them up as soon as you wake up. If you need an alarm, a traditional clock still can get the job done. Your brain will thank you!

Signs It's Time to Break Up with a Friend—and How to Do It Right

Mark Goulston, MD, founder and CEO of the Goulston Group, a consulting company that helps business owners think outside the box, Los Angeles. A psychiatrist and an FBI and police hostage-negotiation trainer, he has written numerous books including *Talking to Crazy: How to Deal with the Irrational and Impossible People in Your Life*. GoulstonGroup.com

Healthy friendships are based on mutual respect and generosity. Any friendship will go through periods when one person gives more than the other or when misunderstandings lead to hurt feelings. Good friends weather these times because of their shared desire to make each other's lives better. But a friendship that is frequently out of balance can be destructive.

How do you know whether a friendship has crossed that line and is hurting you...and what should you do about it?

RECOGNIZE THE SIGNS

A friendship may not be worth continuing if your friend...

• **Causes you more pain than pleasure.**

Examples: You get a knot in your stomach when you hear the person's name...you rarely look forward to the time you will spend together...you increasingly dread speaking to him/her.

• **Often criticizes you.** A basic expectation of friendship is that friends build each other up. Having a friend who is courageous enough to point out a blind spot in you can be valuable, but positive messages should dramatically outnumber negative ones.

Equally important is the way that negative feedback is delivered. Does your friend use a kindhearted tone and ask your permission first...or catch you off-guard and use harsh language?

Healthy feedback: "I've noticed something you are doing that might be hurting your chances of success. Is it OK if I point it out to you?"

Destructive feedback: "That was dumb."

Ask yourself: Do I feel motivated to improve because of this person's feedback? Or do I feel judged and resentful?

If your friend criticizes you to others behind your back, he/she is not acting as a true friend. The same is true if he makes remarks about others that he knows you will find hurtful. *Example:* He says something derogatory about someone who is overweight when he knows you are concerned about your own weight.

• **Takes without giving.** Good friends don't keep score—they take pleasure in enriching each other's lives. But if one person is doing nearly all the giving, that's a problem. If you always bring soup when your friend is sick...provide a ride to the airport...pick up the dinner check...but your friend doesn't offer to help when you are sick or need a ride, the balance is unhealthy.

Your friend may not be as quick as you to anticipate a need, so don't assume a lack of generosity just because he doesn't offer. But if he always has an excuse when you ask for help—or if he says yes to requests but does not follow through—your friendship is out of balance.

• **Manipulates.** Manipulative people seek control by being indirect. *Examples:* Gossiping about mutual friends so that you wind up in the middle of their dispute...giving you uncomfortably lavish gifts and accusing you of being unappreciative.

• **Acts moody, irritable or sullen.** We all have bad days and bad months. But someone who is consistently easy to upset and difficult to please—or who spends most of your time together complaining and venting—may be a source of stress you don't need.

There is a saying that you are the average of the five people you spend the most time with. What this means is that spending time with positive, emotionally healthy people improves your own character. Spending time with negative people tends to pull you down to their emotional level.

STEPS TO TAKE

If you suspect that a friendship has become unhealthy, don't just disappear from the person's life. *What to do...*

• **Tell him how you feel, and give him an opportunity to change.** Ask him why he does or says certain off-putting things, because when he does, you find yourself becoming defensive. This is a difficult conversation—confronting someone constructively is a challenge that many people prefer to avoid—but if you have not told the person what is bothering you, you bear some responsibility for the problem.

• **Try the "wince confrontation."** When you talk with your friend, be specific about what the troublesome behavior is, and keep your comments focused on behavior, not personality. Two techniques that can help you communicate clearly without putting the other person too much on the defensive...

The wince confrontation: Let the person know that confronting him is painful for you. (I call this the "wince confrontation" because you feel like wincing when you say it.)

Assertive humility: Present the problem as a request for help rather than a criticism.

You can combine these two communication techniques—for example, "I need your help with something (*assertive humility*). I'm wondering if we should take a break from each other, and I feel really sad saying this (*wince confrontation*). We've been friends for a long time, and the reason I'm at the end of my rope is that I have noticed a pattern where, when we are together, most of our time is spent with you talking about how terrible everything is. It's wearing me down. I want to be able to look forward to our time together instead of dreading it. To do that, I need us to spend more time talking about what is going right in our lives rather than dwelling on what is wrong."

If you do your best to communicate clearly and compassionately, you may feel shaken and sad, but you also will feel good about taking a stand on your own behalf.

• **Give your friend time.** No matter how carefully you phrase your request, your friend may be upset or may resist the message. Don't assume that this immediate response is his final response. Most people are not used to receiving straightforward feedback and may need time to process it.

• **If, after a few days or weeks, your friend still is not willing to change,** don't let things drift. State clearly that you need to take a break from—or possibly end—the relationship. *Example:* "I think it's better if we take a break from seeing each other for a while" or "I think it's best for us to part company."

• **If the person still will be in your life**—maybe you work together or go to the same school or house of worship—explain that, of course, you still will be civil but that the relationship will be no more than that.

• **If your friend changes his behavior but then reverts to his old ways,** talk to him again. *Example:* "I've noticed that you're doing (fill in the blank). Going forward, I would appreciate your not doing that because it probably will make it nearly impossible for us to have a relationship in the future."

• **If your friend bad-mouths you to others,** remind the person who told you about the bad-mouthing that he has a choice to not listen to the bad-mouthing.

7 Mistakes People Make When They Apologize

Harriet Lerner, PhD, a psychologist in private practice in Lawrence, Kansas, and award-winning author of 12 books including *The Dance of Anger* and *Why Won't You Apologize? Healing Big Betrayals and Everyday Hurts.* HarrietLerner.com

At some point, each of us is going to hurt another person with our words or actions. Giving an apology allows us to repair the damage—assuming that we do it right. But many of us don't do it right. And a poor apology—or no apology at all—can add insult to injury.

Here are common mistakes people make when apologizing and what to do instead...

***MISTAKE:* Avoiding making an apology.** We may feel embarrassed and uncomfortable about what happened and avoid the individual rather than have to face him/her.

Example: Sally borrowed a serving dish from her neighbor and forgot to return it. Three months later, when the neighbor left a voice message asking about it, Sally left the dish on the neighbor's front porch. Although she returned the dish, she couldn't bring herself to offer an apology.

Better: Sally returns the dish and says, either personally or in a note, "I'm sorry I kept your dish for such a long time. You were kind enough to lend it to me. I should have gotten it back to you the very next day."

***MISTAKE:* Adding a "but" in your apology.** This little word will undo the sincerity of any apology and almost always signals a rationalization, excuse or criticism.

Example: Mina corrected her husband's stories in front of other guests at a dinner party. Later, when faced with her husband's anger, Mina said, "I'm sorry I did that, but it's hard for me to sit there silently when you don't have your facts straight."

Better: "I'm sorry that I corrected your stories at the party. It was wrong. You've told me before that you don't want me to do that, and there is no excuse for forgetting. I want you to know that it won't happen again."

GOOD TO KNOW...

The Best Way to *Accept* an Apology

When you are the hurt party, it's best to open your heart and graciously accept a sincere apology. Healing gets stalled if we refuse to accept the olive branch or if we use the other person's apology as a springboard to bring up more criticisms or rehash old grievances.

Wrong way to accept an apology: "I'm glad you apologized, but maybe next time you'll think about how much you hurt me when you say things like that."

Better way: "Thank you for the apology." There may be more you need to say on the subject, but save it for a future conversation when it won't cancel out the apology and make the other person think, *What's the point?*

Harriet Lerner, PhD, psychologist, Lawrence, Kansas.

***MISTAKE:* Apologizing with words alone when a reparation is due.** Sometimes, to be sincere, the words "I'm sorry" have to be backed by a reparative action.

Example: Mark spilled red wine on his friend's carpet and was effusive in his apologies. His host said not to worry about it, so it didn't occur to Mark to offer to pay the cleaning bill.

Better: "I'm so sorry I spilled my wine. Please let me know what it costs to remove the stain. I insist on reimbursing you." If the friend refuses this offer, Mark still can do something special for her such as sending flowers or taking her out to lunch.

***MISTAKE:* Focusing on the other person's feelings and reactions rather than your own behavior.** A common way we ruin an apology is to say something along the lines of, "I'm sorry you feel that way."

Example: "I'm sorry that the joke I told at the meeting made you upset." The problem with that—there is no accountability. You're saying, in effect, "I'm sorry that you reacted the way you did to my perfectly reasonable behavior."

Better: "I'm sorry I told that sexist joke at the office party. It was wrong and out of line. I feel bad that I was so insensitive." A true apology focuses on your own behavior and not on the other person's response.

***MISTAKE:* Just expecting forgiveness.** It's only natural that we want our apology to lead to forgiveness, but pushing for forgiveness can make the hurt person feel wronged all over again.

Example: Ann was furious with her brother for arriving a half hour late to her wedding. He said that he was very sorry and that he had lost track of time—and then pressed her to forgive him. When Ann said that she didn't forgive him, Alan got mad at her as if she were at fault.

Better: "Ann, I'm so sorry that I came late to your wedding. I feel terrible that I wasn't on time for the most important day of your life. There is no excuse. I understand that what I did was serious and that you may stay angry for a long time."

***MISTAKE:* Apologizing as a quick way out.** Sometimes an apology requires a long-term effort rather than a simple "I'm sorry." To heal, the hurt party needs us to really "get it"—to validate and care about his/her feelings and to carry some of the pain we've caused. This requires us to put aside our defensiveness and listen with an open heart to the essence of what the other person is trying to tell us. Don't use the apology as a way to muzzle the other person or silence his anger.

Example: Rick said to his wife, Molly, "I told you a hundred times that I was sorry about my affair. It's time you stopped bringing it up."

Better: "Molly, I am so sorry for the pain I caused you with the affair. I am always here to listen whenever you need to talk. I want you to know that I often think about how I betrayed you and hurt our marriage." No apology has meaning if we haven't listened carefully to the hurt party's anger and carried some of the pain—even if it takes a long time.

***MISTAKE:* Overapologizing.** Offering "I'm sorrys" again and again can create distance, interrupt the normal flow of conversation and irritate those around us who have to stop and reassure us—"No, really, it's fine."

Better: If you're prone to voicing an endless stream of sorrys, tone it down. If you have inconvenienced your friend by misplacing your car keys and needing a ride home, don't apologize numerous times. One sincere apology usually is enough.

Exactly What to Say in Awkward Situations

Barbara Pachter, a business communication and etiquette consultant based in New Jersey. She is an instructor in the School of Business at Rutgers University and author of *The Communication Clinic: 99 Proven Cures for the Most Common Business Mistakes.* Pachter.com

A colleague criticizes you in front of your boss...an acquaintance asks you an overly personal question...a stranger cuts in front of you in line. The shock of unexpected and unpleasant situations such as these might make you say things that you later regret...or freeze up and say nothing at all, which can add to the awkwardness.

The best responses in these situations are both polite and powerful. Being polite reduces the odds that the already unpleasant situation will escalate, while being powerful shows that you stand up for yourself.

What to say in 10 common awkward situations...

- **Someone raises his/her voice while speaking with you.** Say, "I want to talk about this but not this way." Or "I want to help...but yelling won't help me help you. It will only make us both unproductive." Say this calmly but loudly enough to be heard. Opening with the phrase "I want to help" (or "I hear you" if that better fits the situation) often begins to calm yellers—it lets them know that you are listening and potentially even on their side. Refusing to proceed with the discussion until this person lowers his voice sends the message that you will not allow yourself to be intimidated.

- **Someone cuts in front of you in line.** Say, "Excuse me, I believe I was here first." This response calls attention to the transgression without criticizing the transgressor, who may have cut ahead accidentally.

- **Someone says something thoughtless but not intentionally offensive to you.** Say something lighthearted that pokes gentle fun at the thoughtless statement. It can be tricky to get this just right—if your response is too hostile, you could develop a reputation for being touchy.

Example: A coworker says you're good with computers "for someone your age." You don't want to bite this coworker's head off—he probably was trying to pay you a compliment, and it just didn't come out right—but letting his comment linger without response could reinforce the impression that you are too old to be truly tech-savvy. You could respond with a smile and say, "Thank you! That's quite a compliment from someone your age."

If a good line doesn't pop immediately to mind, you could always smile and calmly repeat back the offending portion of the statement followed by "huh?"—such as "for someone my age, huh?" Saying this buys you a few extra moments to think of an effective lighthearted line, such as, "Looks can be deceiving." If you still can't, just leave it there, or just say, "Thank you."

- **There's something you want from someone.** Making requests often makes people feel uncomfortable, so they phrase the request in ways that seem undemanding. They might convert their requests into questions, asking, "Could I have..." or "Can you..." which gives the decision-making power to the other person. Or they might ask people to "try" to do whatever it is they are requesting. This softer approach can be appropriate at times, especially if you are talking up the ladder. But using a sentence that begins in a direct assertive way such as, "I would like..." or "I want to..." makes it very clear what you want and is more likely to produce the desired results. Listen to the difference—"Boss, I would like to be assigned to the ABC project" versus "Boss, can you assign me to the ABC project?" Both are polite, but the first version leaves no doubt about what you want and makes you seem confident—people are more likely to do things for people who appear certain about what they are asking.

• **A know-it-all is running his mouth.** Say calmly, "How do you know that to be true?" and/or "What facts do you have to support your position?" If the know-it-all responds that he just feels it to be true or that "it's obvious," reply that "you are welcome to believe whatever you want, but if you expect me to believe it, you're going to need to produce facts to support what you say."

• **Someone asks about your income, your politics, your sex life or some other inappropriate subject.** Say, "I'm not comfortable discussing that," and then immediately take the conversation in a different direction before an awkward silence ensues. Saying, "I'm not comfortable..." is better than saying, "That's inappropriate," because it contains no accusation. Rather than taking someone to task for a social faux pas, you are merely saying that your personal preference is to keep this private.

• **Someone criticizes something about you or your work in front of a group.** Say, "Why are you saying that?" or "Help me to understand what you mean by inadequate/wrong/incomplete..." You are requesting details about what this person thinks you got wrong. When you do this, do your best to make your tone and body language inquisitive, not defensive—don't cross your arms or raise your voice. Maybe this person is right and the criticism is deserved—if so, hearing the details will help you improve. Or maybe this person is wrong and/or intentionally trying to make you look bad in front of a group or a boss—if so, asking for details often will make this obvious. Whether the criticism is valid or not, asking for details sends the message that you are not defensive and that you are confident about your work.

• **Someone interrupts you.** Say, "Hold that thought..." and then continue with what you were saying. This acknowledges the person who wants to speak but leaves no doubt that you are not done speaking and have no intention of yielding until you are. You might have to raise your volume slightly and speak over the interrupter for a few seconds until he realizes you're not yielding.

Helpful: If the same person interrupts you frequently, pick a private moment to say, "You have useful things to say, but when I get cut off, I lose my train of thought. I'd appreciate it if you would let me get through what I'm saying before jumping in."

• **Someone accuses you of treating him rudely or unfairly—and he has a point.** Say, "You know what, you're right. It won't happen again." It's natural to become defensive in these situations, but even if you come up with a way to justify your misstep or misstatement, doing so will only escalate the awkward situation and damage the relationship. Admitting an error almost always dials down the tension—and despite what many people think, admitting mistakes shows strength, not weakness.

• **Someone pays you a compliment.** Say, "Thank you," or "Thank you. I appreciate your comments." Receiving praise is an awkward situation for some people. They become embarrassed and feel an urge to downplay or deflect the positive things that are being said about them. Ignore this urge. Instead look the person in the eye, express sincere gratitude for the compliment and then stop talking before you spoil the moment.

EASY TO DO...

Gain People's Trust When You First Meet Them

When you first meet someone, have a happy expression and hold your hands relaxed at your sides. Avoid hunching over to look at your phone. Keep your elbow at your side when shaking hands—that draws the other person closer than arm's length. And stand erect with head and shoulders squared and weight evenly balanced. Smile in response to what other people say or do—don't simply maintain a plastered-on smile at all times.

Roundup of experts on behaviors that produce snap judgments, reported in *The Wall Street Journal*.

Hidden Harms of Long-Ago Trauma: It's Never Too Late to Get Help

Vincent J. Felitti, MD, clinical professor of medicine at University of California, San Diego, and an expert on how childhood trauma affects adults. He is coprincipal investigator of the Adverse Childhood Experiences (ACE) Study, one of the largest investigations of childhood abuse and neglect and later-life health and well-being.

If you have ever suffered physical, sexual or emotional abuse, you might think that psychological scars are the only long-lasting damage. But that couldn't be further from the truth.

A lingering threat: Volumes of scientific evidence show that these negative experiences also increase risk for chronic disease and early death...even when the incidents occurred several years earlier.

THE SHOCKING STATISTICS

The veil of secrecy regarding abuse has slowly lifted as more people have recently opened up about their past. With sexual abuse, in particular, recent allegations lodged against film producer Harvey Weinstein, actor and comedian Bill Cosby and others have prompted a renewed interest in the harmful effects of such experiences—whether the victim is a child or an adult.

Even though sexual abuse in adulthood has been linked to physical health problems, such as headaches, digestive disorders and other chronic ailments, the most extensive research has focused on the long-term effects when mistreatment occurs during childhood.

Landmark investigation: The Adverse Childhood Experiences (ACE) Study, a massive collaborative research project cosponsored by the Centers for Disease Control and Prevention, looked at the backgrounds of 17,000 adults, beginning in 1995 at Kaiser Permanente in San Diego. With more than 20 years of follow-up, the study offers crucial insights into the physical effects of abuse and mistreatment.

In the original research, two-thirds of the study's middle-class participants reported at least one incident of childhood trauma or neglect. More specifically, 28% reported physical abuse...and 21% said they were abused sexually. More than one in five people reported three or more categories of adverse childhood experiences, or ACEs. (To determine your own ACE score, see the next page.)

THE HEALTH RISKS ARE REAL

The ACE Study determined that the more of these experiences a person has suffered, the higher his/her risk is for a range of mental and physical health conditions.

For example, compared with participants who did not experience any abuses or mistreatment, those who reported four categories of adverse childhood experiences were twice as likely to be diagnosed with lung cancer and/or depression as adults. They also had a fourfold increase in chronic lung disease, such as chronic obstructive pulmonary disease (COPD), and a sevenfold increase in alcoholism. A person with six or more categories of ACEs had their life expectancy shortened by nearly 20 years.

WHY PHYSICAL HEALTH SUFFERS

It's easy to imagine how trauma would affect a person's mental health. But why would it also impact physical health? *Long-term research has identified such factors as...*

- **Coping mechanisms.** Trauma victims are more likely to use self-soothing habits, such as smoking, drinking, overeating and drug abuse, which are helpful in the short term but are known risk factors in the long term for many chronic health problems.
- **Complex brain-mediated effects.** Chronic stress due to ACEs can distort the function of brain networks, resulting in immune system suppression, which in turn can lead to a variety of diseases. In addition, it causes the release of pro-inflammatory chemicals that are responsible for additional diseases such as heart disease, pulmonary fibrosis, etc.

WHAT HELPS MOST

If you experienced trauma as a child, it is never too late to get help to reverse or at least moderate the negative physical and/or emotional effects of ACEs. The strategies below, which tend to yield positive results more quickly than psychotherapy and/or antidepressants, are likely to also be helpful for those who experienced trauma as an adult...

• **Tell a trusted person.** People who have experienced childhood trauma often carry the secret into adulthood. Victims of abuse feel shame and assume that they did something wrong to deserve the abuse. By simply telling someone, and having that person continue to accept you, the shame dissipates.

• **Try eye movement desensitization and reprocessing (EMDR).** The American Psychiatric Association recognizes this therapy as an effective treatment for trauma. Studies have found that trauma victims no longer had signs of post-traumatic stress disorder after as few as three, 90-minute EMDR sessions.

How it works: During EMDR, a clinician asks the patient to hold a traumatic memory in mind while the therapist moves one or two fingers from side to side, or diagonally, in front of the patient's eyes. This guides the eyes to move as they do during the rapid eye movement (REM) sleep phase, during which the most active dreaming occurs. Dreaming can help process trauma and move it to long-term memory, enabling the patient to feel as if it is now resolved and only in the past.

The therapist repeats the process multiple times as needed, until the distress related to the targeted memory is gone and a positive belief replaces it. For example, a rape victim shifts from feeling horror and self-disgust to feeling empowered—*I survived it and I am strong.*

To find an EMDR clinician near you, visit the website of the EMDR Institute at EMDR.com. Check with your health insurer to see if your policy covers the treatment.

• **Consider clinical hypnosis.** This method helps patients identify past events or experiences that are causing problems. With hypnotherapy, a trained practitioner uses imagery and presents ideas or suggestions during a state of concentrated attention that helps bring about desired changes in thinking.

To find a certified hypnosis professional in your area, visit the website of the American Society of Clinical Hypnosis at ASCH.net. Check with your health insurer to see if clinical hypnosis is covered.

HOW TRAUMATIC WAS YOUR CHILDHOOD?

For each of the following questions, give yourself one point for every "yes" answer. *During your first 18 years of life...*

1. Did a parent or other adult in the household often swear at you, insult you, put you down or humiliate you? Or act in a way that made you afraid that you might be physically hurt?

2. Did a parent or other adult in the household often push, grab, slap or throw something at you? Or ever hit you so hard that you had marks or were injured?

3. Did an adult or person at least five years older than you ever touch or fondle you or have you touch his/her body in a sexual way? Or try to or actually have oral, anal or vaginal sex with you?

4. Did you often feel that no one in your family loved you or thought you were important or special? Or that your family didn't look out for one another, feel close to one another or support one another?

5. Did you often feel that you didn't have enough to eat, had to wear dirty clothes and had no one to protect you? Or that your parents were too drunk or high to take care of you or take you to the doctor when needed?

6. Were your parents ever separated or divorced?

7. Was your mother or stepmother often pushed, grabbed or slapped? Or did she often have something thrown at her? Or was she sometimes or often kicked, bitten, hit with a fist or hit with something hard? Or ever repeatedly hit for at least a few minutes or threatened with a gun or knife?

8. Did you live with anyone who was a problem drinker or an alcoholic or who used street drugs?

9. Was a household member depressed or mentally ill, or did a household member attempt suicide?

10. Did a household member go to prison?

Takeaway: If you score a four or higher, tell your doctor about your history of abuse and follow the advice in the main article. If these steps don't help, consult a trained therapist.

19

On the Job

How to Disagree with Your Boss Without Getting Fired

Telling your boss that he/she made a poor decision doesn't have to be a stupid career move—but you do need to approach this conversation in a smart way. Get it wrong, and your boss could see you as an impediment or even an adversary, and that's a battle you're unlikely to win. But if you get it right, it actually could boost your career—smart employers value employees who say what needs to be said even when that's difficult. *The key is how you handle the disagreement...*

SCENARIO 1: DISAGREEING ABOUT A NEW PLAN

Say your boss lays out a plan or voices his opinion, and you immediately spot a potential problem.

Your inclination might be to hold your tongue for the moment—perhaps you're in a meeting and don't want to disagree with your boss in front of a group...or perhaps you hope something will change your boss's mind without your having to step in. But waiting usually is a mistake. If you say nothing now and disagree later, your boss might wonder why you didn't speak up sooner—before time was lost and resources were committed to the original idea. And psychologically, the longer he believes in an idea, the less open he is likely to be to alternatives.

Exceptions: It usually is a bad idea to disagree with a boss in front of a client, and it often is prudent not to disagree in front of your boss's boss either—unless you can do so in such a way that your boss does not lose face.

Note: Prices, rates and offers throughout this chapter and book are subject to change.

Steve Willis, vice president of professional services with VitalSmarts, a leadership-training company, Provo, Utah. His clients include Eli Lilly, J.P.Morgan, Johnson & Johnson and Intel. VitalSmarts.com

A three-step plan for minimizing the ruffled feathers when you disagree with a boss about a new idea...

1. Align your intentions with a greater good. If your boss views your disagreement as a me-versus-you confrontation and becomes defensive, it could harm your career. To greatly reduce this risk, frame what you are about to say as an attempt to help your boss or company achieve a greater goal. Ask yourself, *What is my boss under pressure to achieve, and how could the idea he just presented make it more difficult to achieve that?*

Example: Your boss says that he intends to switch to a supplier that charges lower prices but that you know to be unreliable. Before saying that you disagree with the decision, frame what you are about to say in terms of this cost-cutting goal. "The company has put an emphasis on cutting costs lately. When I hear that supplier's name, my concern is that when we've used it in the past, we ended up paying much more than we expected because of its mistakes and missed deadlines despite its low price quotes."

2. State the facts on which you are basing your disagreement before stating your conclusion. When people disagree, each may say what he thinks and then double back to explain how he came to that conclusion. But if you do that, your boss (and anyone else present who holds an opposing viewpoint) might feel in opposition to you as soon as he hears your position. Then, rather than objectively weigh your facts and reasoning, he might look for ways to shoot them down. Instead, state your conclusion after you present your evidence.

Example: In talking about an unreliable supplier, you might say, "We've ordered from that supplier twice. One time it sent the wrong parts, and one time it missed the delivery date. We had to place last-minute rush orders with other companies to get what we needed—and those rush orders were very expensive." Only then state your position that a different supplier would be a better choice...or that this supplier should be used only when there is no looming deadline.

3. Transform the disagreement into a dialog if other people are present. After you disagree with the idea your boss has presented, invite comment about the alternative that you just raised. Whether other people agree with you or not, this reduces the odds that your boss will see the situation as a me-versus-you challenge and increases the odds that it becomes a let's-hash-this-out-as-a-team cooperative situation.

Example: After presenting your position, you say, "I'm wondering whether others feel the same or differently."

SCENARIO #2: DISAGREEING ABOUT AN EXISTING DECISION

Say you didn't speak up the first time your boss said something that you disagreed with—perhaps you were not even present when the decision was presented—but the situation does not seem likely to improve on its own and you cannot stay silent any longer. *To disagree with your boss about a decision that he might think is no longer even in debate...*

1. Schedule time with your boss. If you plop your disagreement on your boss without any warning, he might justifiably wonder, *Why am I hearing this just now?* If you do so in front of a group, he even might suspect that he is being intentionally sandbagged. Asking for a one-on-one meeting to "raise a potential concern" can lead to a better result because it gives the boss a chance to mentally prepare for unwelcome news, so it doesn't feel out of left field (or threatening) when it arrives.

2. Before this meeting, consider why a reasonable person would have made the decision your boss made. The longer you allow a decision that you think is wrong to remain unchallenged, the greater the odds that you will start to imagine nefarious motives that might not really exist. *Why did the boss do this?* can transform into *How dare the boss do this to me!*

The odds of career-damaging conflict increase if you have this perceived negative motive in mind when you speak with your boss about the decision. So before your meeting, think through how a reasonable, well-meaning person could have reached the boss's decision.

Example: Your boss alters the department's bonus plan in a way that reduces the amount you are likely to receive. Could he have done this not with the intention of slashing your compensation but rather with the intention of rewarding different results?

3. Open the meeting by framing your purpose in a noncombative way. Say something such as, "There's a potential issue that I think should be considered." This is much more likely to lead to a productive conversation than opening with something negative such as, "I think you made a mistake." Quickly provide a key fact or two to support your position...and then propose a solution, ideally one that your boss can accept without having to admit that his original idea was completely wrong. Try to distill all of this down to just a few sentences, if possible.

4. Dial down potential anger by clarifying your intentions in a way that casts you as an ally. If your boss tends to react angrily when he feels challenged or you notice signs of anger as you present your position—hands balled into fists, for example—use don't/do statements about your intentions to stress that you actually are on your boss's side.

Example: "I certainly don't want to cause trouble for you—that's the last thing I would ever want to do—but I would like to get a handle on how this will work so that I can help you implement your decision successfully."

BETTER WAYS...

How to Handle Rudeness on the Job

Better ways to handle a rude colleague at work...

- **If you choose to respond, don't rush your responses.** This will help you stay calm and collected and helps to avoid giving pleasure to people who like to provoke reactions such as tears and apologies.
- **Reframe a toxic colleague's behavior by telling yourself you are not to blame...** the issue is being blown out of proportion... and you're learning valuable things despite the unpleasant atmosphere.
- **If possible, try turning the bully into a friend.** Offer flattery, smiles and other signs of appreciation even if they are not entirely sincere. Try to find something you agree with or admire and focus on that rather than on negative behavior.

Robert Sutton, PhD, professor of management science, Stanford University, California, and author of *The Asshole Survival Guide*, writing in *The Wall Street Journal*.

How to Make People Want to Agree with You

Robert Cialdini, PhD, behavioral scientist and former professor of psychology and marketing and president of Influence at Work, Tempe, Arizona, which offers speaking and training services about social influence. His most recent book is *Pre-Suasion: A Revolutionary Way to Influence and Persuade.* InfluenceAtWork.com

Whether you are trying to persuade someone to agree with your position on a topic or to get him/her to buy your used car, the power of your message isn't all that matters. A growing body of evidence suggests that what people see and hear *just before* you try to persuade them can have a dramatic effect on the outcome. There's no need to leave this to chance—there are "pre-suasion" tactics you can use before making your pitch that can set the stage for success.

These tactics are worth knowing even if you rarely need to persuade anyone of anything—knowing them will help you defend against them when other people try to use them on you.

Here's how to "pre-suade" people before you even try to persuade them...

- **Ask a question that alters how the answerer sees himself.** In one experiment, when people were approached by a stranger and asked to participate in an unpaid survey, only 29% said yes...but if they were asked, "Do you consider yourself a helpful person?" before being asked to participate, 77% said yes to participating in the survey.

When you ask people whether they think they have a particular quality, it encourages their minds to reflect on prior times when they exhibited that quality—and that greatly increases the odds that they will exhibit that quality in the moments that follow. Thus, asking about helpfulness encourages helpful behavior such as participating in a survey. Similarly, research shows that initially asking about a person's adventurousness encourages risk-taking.

• **Make someone believe that he already trusts you.** All the salespeople at a company that sold home fire alarms worked from the same sales script when they visited the homes of prospective customers, but one salesman added a twist—a twist that helped him record the company's highest sales totals every year. After starting his presentation, this salesman told clients that he had to retrieve something from his car and said, "Do you mind if I let myself out and back into your home?"

We typically let people enter our homes unescorted if we trust them, so when the customers agreed to this, at some level they convinced themselves, *I trust this man*. Once trust is established, it becomes much easier to move others in your direction.

• **Make a buyer think of a very large number...or make a seller think of a very small number.** Perhaps you've heard of the "anchoring" negotiation strategy. It works like this—a seller starts negotiations by quoting a very high asking price. He knows he won't get this price, but starting negotiations very high tends to "anchor" the ensuing back-and-forth near this high number, resulting in a higher final sales price than would have been reached if negotiations had started at a lower amount. Buyers can do the opposite and make a very low initial offer. But there's a drawback—opening with a very high (or low) number could offend the person with whom you are trying to negotiate, damaging the chance of making a deal.

Solution: It turns out that you can use anchoring without making an extreme and potentially anger-inducing opening offer. Simply make the other party think of a very high number (or very low number) related to what you are negotiating about just before you begin negotiations. After thinking of a very large number, even a high asking price doesn't seem so high. *Example:* You are selling your used car and are hoping to get $20,000 for it. You are about to begin bargaining with someone whom you suspect wants a much lower price than that. You could say first, "This car has only 50,000 miles on it."

• **Create an emotionally moving metaphor.** Ben Feldman was the greatest life insurance salesman of his era. In the 1970s and 1980s, he personally sold more insurance than many insurance *agencies*. When Feldman suffered a debilitating cerebral hemorrhage, his employer, New York Life, honored him by declaring it "Feldman February" and offering a prize to the agent who sold the most insurance that month. The prize was won by... Feldman himself. The 80-year-old closed $15 million in new policies from his hospital bed. Feldman's secret? Before he began his sales pitch, he would say, "When you walk out of life, your insurance will walk in." "Walking out of life" was a powerful metaphor for dying—it stirred listeners' emotions and created the image of death leaving a gap. If something we do leaves a gap in our family's protection, then we clearly have a moral responsibility to fill that gap—by buying insurance.

To craft an effective metaphor that will help you persuade people, find a way to equate whatever it is you are proposing with something that is widely considered desirable or correct...or to equate the alternative to what you are proposing with something widely considered frightening or incorrect. *Example:* If your goal is to encourage your listeners to accept a change, you might preface your remarks with novelist L. P. Hartley's famous line, "The past is a foreign country: they do things differently there." People often avoid change because it seems frightening. This metaphor instead makes the way things were done previously seem like the foreign and frightening option.

• **Ask for advice.** When we ask people for their advice, it encourages them to see themselves as members of our team, increasing the odds that they will support whatever cause we ask for advice about. But be sure to use the word "advice." When you ask people for their "opinions," it tends to have the opposite effect, encouraging them to see themselves as separate from you, decreasing the odds that they will support the cause you mention.

• **Play music.** There's an old adage in the advertising industry: *If you can't make your* *case to an audience with facts, sing it to them.* The advertisers are right—if you play music just before a group weighs a potentially divisive idea, that group will become more likely to unite behind the idea. Music gets everyone present into the same rhythm, inspiring them to act as one. *Helpful:* Choose songs that are familiar and inoffensive to the entire audience. Playing the latest hip-hop hit to a group of staid businessmen is unlikely to make them feel in step with your message.

• **Use an easy-to-pronounce name.** An analysis of 10 large law firms found that the more difficult an attorney's name was to pronounce, the lower that attorney tended to remain in the corporate hierarchy. (Don't blame ethnic bias for this—the finding held true even after researchers accounted for whether difficult names sounded foreign.)

Things that are difficult for people tend to be questioned, while things that are easy often escape deep scrutiny because they "just feel right." This applies even with something as basic as the name of the person presenting the idea.

If you are promoting a cause or product that has a long, challenging name, come up with a simpler name to use in conversation. If you have a hard-to-pronounce name, pick an easy-to-pronounce nickname and ask people to call you that. *Examples:* "Just call me Chuck"...or "Just call me Mr. Z."

How to Achieve More with Less—at Work and in Your Personal Life

Scott Sonenshein, PhD, the Henry Gardiner Symonds Professor of Management at Rice University in Houston. He is author of *Stretch: Unlock the Power of Less—and Achieve More Than You Ever Imagined.* ScottSonenshein.com

---

You may not want to hear this, or even believe it, but *less really is more* in a lot of important and useful ways. Researchers who have focused on management and psychology have proved it in ways that provide some surprising lessons. In both business and life, having access to more money, more stuff, more help and/or more time can reduce our odds of achieving our goals. We are particularly likely to hurt our chances of success when we focus on chasing more resources, rather than on squeezing as much as possible out of the resources we have.

Example: In the 1990s, many dot-com companies focused on expanding as quickly as possible, snatching up a lot more market share, adding many more employees and securing more and more venture capital dollars. After the dot-com stock market boom went bust, a University of Maryland professor discovered that most of the Internet companies that survived had bucked that conventional wisdom and had not prioritized getting big fast.

These survivors had figured out how to survive with less while their get-big-fast competitors knew how to solve various problems only by throwing money at them—a strategy that stopped working when the money dried up. Pets.com, which spent almost $12 million on advertisements to generate $619,000 in sales in its first year, ended up failing...while WrestlingGear.com, which targeted a niche market and made money on each transaction, is *still* around 20 years later.

The idea that you literally can do more with less can be very helpful in your private life, not only in business. Here are five ways to exploit the hidden advantages of having limited resources or tight deadlines...overcome the hidden challenges of abundance...and remind ourselves to get the most out of what we already have, rather than devote excessive time and effort to acquiring more...

• **Impose artificial limitations.** If your budget and time constraints for a vacation, a purchase or a project are the same as always, the options you eventually settle on likely will be the same as always, too. We feel constrained when we face limitations beyond what we normally face, but overcoming these limitations can lead to creative breakthroughs.

Example: In 1957, famed editor Bennett Cerf challenged an author to write a children's book using just 50 unique vocabulary words. The author was Theodor Geisel—who is better known as Dr. Seuss—and the book he wrote was *Green Eggs and Ham*, which would become one of the 20th century's best-selling children's books.

It wasn't great *despite* Cerf's word limitation—it was great *because* of the artificial restriction, which allowed Geisel to focus on using the words he did have available as creatively as possible, leading to a book that was unlike anything that came before it.

What to do: Experiment with imposing dauntingly low budgets, frighteningly close deadlines and other restrictions even when you do not need to. Challenge yourself to come up with creative ways to overcome these hurdles.

There will be times when the limitations do not lead to helpful results—when that happens, you can revert to your usual solution. But there also will be times when you uncover clever new solutions that you otherwise would have missed. As a bonus, you will improve your ability to cope when time and resources truly are limited, a skill that could prove to be vital at some future date.

• **Mentally deconstruct your resources into their component parts to uncover unconventional uses.** *Try this thought experiment:* Imagine that you must fasten two heavy steel rings together using only a candle and a match. How do you do it?

Most people presented with this challenge come up with the same strategy—light the candle and drip the hot wax onto the rings, sealing them together. But that doesn't work—candle wax is not strong enough to hold heavy steel rings together. A better solution reveals itself only if you stop thinking of the candle as just a candle and also see it for its component parts—wax and a wick. The wick is a piece of string that can be used to tie the rings together.

Most people fail to think up this solution because the human brain falls into a "functional fixedness" trap—it sees only the common use of resources.

What to do: A researcher at University of Massachusetts developed a simple way to overcome functional fixedness. When you struggle to find a solution to a problem given the resources available, reconsider each of your resources one by one in terms of component parts and ask yourself, *How can each of these separate parts be used to help solve the problem?*

• **When you need creative ideas and are short on time, do *mindless* work.** A deadline is approaching fast, and you have to come up with a great idea. What do you do? In fact, the best strategy might be to stop brainstorming and use some of your limited time to instead do a boring chore—even though this means adding a task to your to-do list when there already is little time to spare.

Here's why: Research has shown that people are significantly better at coming up with creative ideas under tight deadlines when they also perform tasks that are not mentally challenging. That's because the human mind is at its most creative when it is presented with a problem but then allowed to wander. When we need to come up with a creative idea fast, we tend to focus too much, inhibiting that wandering. Tackling a chore that does not require much brainpower can distract our focus just enough that the mind regains its freedom to wander.

This is similar to the familiar advice to "sleep on a problem," only faster and more effective—your sleeping brain might indeed come up with creative solutions, but it also might forget them before you wake.

What to do: Mow the lawn...fold the laundry...send out invoices. Pick a chore that you can almost but not quite perform on autopilot, and do this even though it seems like you don't have time for it right now.

• **Activate your "action mode."** When you have lots of time to get something done, it's easy to get stuck in a planning mode, thinking through each available option again and again. But there inevitably comes a point where additional planning does not lead to any greater odds of success...and sometimes there is so little useful information that even careful planning is mainly guesswork.

At these times, the best thing to do is to stop planning and start actually doing. But if you're a deliberate planner by nature, this can feel uncomfortable and irresponsible, and you might be tempted to continue planning instead.

What to do: Think back to times when you acted like a "doer," a person who takes action promptly. Then think back to times when you finished one project and did not wait long to start a new one...and then think back to times when you decided to do something and were so excited about it that you could not wait to get started. Research shows that reflecting on these three things often can shift people from "planning mode" to "action mode" in just minutes.

• **Identify dormant resources.** Most people (and organizations) have potentially valuable resources that currently seem to have no value because they are sitting dormant. There are attics, closets and warehouses full of unused supplies...résumés full of unused skills...and address books full of contacts that haven't been called in years. Unfortunately, once a resource becomes dormant, it tends to remain dormant because people turn their attention to acquiring new resources.

What to do: Start a list of the resources you have but have stopped using. Entries should include both physical supplies and tools...as well as unused skills, knowledge and connections. Ask friends and relatives to help you identify resources you have that you might have missed. For each entry on this list, brainstorm about ways the resource could be used to advance one of your current objectives. Dig out this list, and give it a fresh read whenever you think you do not have sufficient resources to achieve a goal.

Example: If you have a onetime acquaintance who held a position in local government, he/she could be contacted to help you sort out a problem that you are having with your town office.

Make Yourself More Valuable at Work

Some very smart ways to increase your value at work...

• **Develop more emotional intelligence through active listening**—pay close attention to coworkers and ask for clarification so that you really understand what they are saying. Show gratitude—thank people for their help and contributions.

• **Make more connections with peers**—acknowledge what you do not know, and ask peers for help.

• **If your company doesn't have a formal learning-and-development program,** create your own by attending conferences or classes.

• **Ask to get regular feedback from your manager.**

• **Set goals that are outside your comfort zone** but tied closely to corporate goals, and check in with your manager regularly as you move toward success.

• **Send better e-mails by getting right to the point** and making next steps clear.

Roundup of experts on workplace performance, reported at FastCompany.com.

Simple Ways to Boost Morale in the Office

Easy and inexpensive ways to keep your employees happy in a small business...

Birthdays off: Having a paid day off for an employee's birthday is a nice way to reward him/her for his work throughout the year. If his birthday falls on a weekend or busy time of the year, let him take his "birthday" on another day.

Employee of the Week: Giving an employee a token gift and a round of applause can go a long way in making someone feel wanted in the workplace.

Free food: When anything memorable happens, food is an easy way to celebrate the occasion.

Small gifts: People truly appreciate small gifts such as movie tickets and gift cards as an acknowledgment of their hard work.

Flexibility: Having the opportunity to come into work a little late or leave a little early—for example, to pick up children from school—builds employee loyalty and integrity.

Rhonda Abrams, small-business expert, writing in *USA Today.*

TAKE NOTE...

For Better Videoconferencing...

•**Do not type**—if you need to take notes, do it by hand. Typing creates distracting noise and can make it seem as if you are not paying attention or trying to work on something unrelated.

•**Look at your computer's camera** when you are introducing yourself or presenting—otherwise, look at the images of other people on the call.

•**Move the video-chat window so that it is near the camera,** making it easier to look at both.

•**Do not eat or have any food visible.**

•**To prevent interruptions,** put a note on the door if you are in a conference room or private office—use a prearranged signal if you are in a cubicle.

•**Stay focused,** and be sure to look at the screen throughout the call.

•**Keep your desk and the rest of your environment neat** or at least not distracting.

Roundup of experts on videoconferencing, reported at MarketWatch.com.

The Afternoon Slump Is Worse Than You Think

Daniel Pink, author of *When: The Scientific Secrets of Perfect Timing.* He also is author of *The New York Times* best-sellers *Drive: To Sell Is Human* and *A Whole New Mind.* He previously hosted the National Geographic Channel series *Crowd Control.* His TED Talk about the science of motivation is one of the 10 most watched since TED Talks began. DanPink.com

---

What should I do? is a question that receives a lot of attention. Frequently we overlook another important question—*When is the best time of day to do that?* But a growing body of research suggests that picking the wrong time of day to perform a challenging task can dramatically reduce your odds of success—and the wrong time of day to do certain things is not the same for everyone.

Here's how to use this knowledge to avoid problems and increase your success...

THE AFTERNOON PLUNGE

It's no secret that fatigue can sap our skills late at night, but it turns out that most people's batteries are nearly as drained in the mid-to-late afternoon—approximately 2 pm to 4 pm. This is more than just a little post-lunch sluggishness. Students who take standardized tests in the afternoon, rather than in the morning, experience score declines as severe as if they had missed about a half month of school. Medical professionals who examine colonoscopy scans in the afternoon spot only half as many polyps as in the morning. Fatigue-related traffic accidents peak twice each day—in the middle of the night...and between 2 pm and 4 pm.

Our moods follow a similar pattern—a study published in *Emotion* found that feelings of warmth toward others and overall happiness climb in the morning, then crash in early afternoon before recovering in late afternoon and evening.

What to do: Don't think of the mid-afternoon slump as a minor obstacle or a joke—it is no joking matter. Unless you are a night owl (more on that later), to the extent you can, avoid making important decisions or performing mentally challenging tasks between 2 pm and 4 pm. Tackle these tasks before or after that time window.

MORNING OR EVENING?

If you are going to move some of your more challenging life activities away from 2 pm to 4 pm, when should you do them? Morning typically is best for thought that requires vigilance and attention to detail, while late afternoon and early evening seem to be particularly good times to work on creative ideas. This might be because the mind is sharp enough to think clearly in the late afternoon/early evening, but it's still unfocused enough to drift, allowing it to form creative connections.

Consider these factors not only when scheduling what you do but also what's done for you. *Examples:* Schedule medical procedures and work by skilled professionals such as auto mechanics and plumbers for the morning. Otherwise, you might not get these pros when they are at their sharpest.

REDUCING THE PLUNGE

There is a wonderful way to minimize the mental drag of your afternoon plunge—take a nap. Numerous studies have found that napping improves problem-solving skills, information retention, alertness and reaction times. Yet most adults rarely or never nap—some because their work schedules do not allow it but others because they don't think they have time for naps...or because they tend to wake from naps feeling foggier than ever. But these people generally are napping wrong. The key to successful napping is to nap for only 10 to 20 minutes, no longer.

What to do: Just before a nap, drink a cup of coffee (or something else containing caffeine) and set an alarm to sound in 25 minutes. That gives you five to 15 minutes to fall asleep, followed by the appropriate 10 to 20 minutes of sleep. It takes caffeine 25 minutes to reach the bloodstream, so drinking coffee right before a short nap means that the caffeine kicks in just when you need a boost to shake off any grogginess from the nap. A Mayo Clinic study found that for most people, napping between 2 pm and 3 pm provides the biggest boost.

If napping is not an option, take a few minutes for a short, invigorating walk, ideally in nature...a brief social visit or phone call with someone whose company you enjoy...listening to a humorous podcast...or meditating.

THE NIGHT OWL EXCEPTION

Approximately one person in five is a "night owl" who is mentally sharpest in the late afternoon or early evening.

If you're not sure whether you're a night owl, note when you tend to fall asleep and when you tend to wake on nights when you have the freedom to go to sleep whenever you like because you have nothing on your schedule the following day. If the midpoint of these fall-asleep and wake-up times is 6 am or later, you're a night owl. *Example:* If you find yourself staying up until 2 am and waking up at 10 am during vacations, you're a night owl—6 am is the midpoint between 2 am and 10 am.

Also be aware that night-owlism can come and go during a lifetime. People are most likely to be night owls in their teens and early 20s...and least likely to be night owls before age 12 and after age 60. But anyone of any age can be a night owl.

The slump that hits most people in the early afternoon is more likely to affect a night owl later in the day, starting approximately six to seven hours after rising—but only if that night owl has the freedom to wake late and go to bed late. The daily ups and downs of a night owl who is forced by a job or other responsibilities to wake early are more difficult to predict.

What to do: There is no "cure" for being a night owl—but there is nothing inherently wrong with it, either. Still, night owls often struggle to fit themselves into a world that tends to be scheduled for early risers. Though there isn't much research on night owls and napping, if your schedule permits, you can try taking a nap (see instructions above) in the late afternoon or early evening. Finding a job that allows flexible working hours can work well for night owls. If that is not possible, night owls should at least try to avoid doing their most demanding work or making key decisions in the few hours starting about six or seven hours after they wake up.

TIMING LONG-TERM PROJECTS SO THEY SUCCEED

Besides their daily ebbs and flows of energy and focus, people also tend to have longer-term ebbs and flows in their ability to accomplish ongoing projects. *Here's how to avoid that phenomenon and have more success with your long-term projects...*

- **Begin big projects** (or implement major changes) on a "fresh start date." This includes the most obvious date—January 1—but also could be your birthday, the first day of a month or even just a Monday. It is psychologically easier to start new things on these days because your mind can imagine a new version of you beginning on this day, leaving behind the old, "flawed" version of you.

- **At the midpoint of a project,** it's common to experience a lull because the excitement of the start has passed and the end point still seems far away. It might help to rally yourself with *I really need to get going* self-talk (or rally your team in a group effort)—but even better is to say, "I/we really are in trouble." *Why:* Researchers have found that a midpoint slump can be converted into a midpoint jump by taking advantage of the "uh-oh" effect—that is, by scaring yourself with the fact that the halfway point has arrived and that there still is a lot left to do.

• **At the end of a project,** find a way to celebrate its conclusion. The end of an effort is what you and others are most likely to remember about it, so if you just let things drift to an end, you're wasting an opportunity. Instead, review what you achieved...and reward yourself (and/or your team) with a bonus or gift—a token gesture is fine. This greatly improves the odds that you will remember the effort fondly, which will make it easier to tackle other big projects in the future.

BEWARE...

Jobs That Can Turn Deadly

Adults with stressful jobs who have little control over setting daily priorities and deciding how to accomplish tasks were 15.4% more likely to die of any cause over a seven-year period than those who had more control over their workflow, a study of nearly 2,400 older workers found.

Stressed workers tend to eat unhealthy food and be overweight and are more likely to smoke and be sedentary—all of which can lead to cardiovascular disease.

Erik Gonzalez-Mulé, PhD, assistant professor of organizational behavior and human resources, Kelley School of Business, Indiana University, Bloomington.

Ask the Right Questions When You Leave a Job

Alan Sklover, Esq., an attorney specializing in employment law, executive compensation and severance agreement negotiation. He is the founding partner of Sklover & Company, LLC, New York City. The firm's website is SkloverWorkingWisdom.com.

Employers often conduct exit interviews with employees who are leaving. They ask the soon-to-be-former employees their opinions about the workplace, bosses and coworkers...why they are leaving...and other questions that could help the employer. Those employees should take advantage of this opportunity to ask some questions that will be useful to them, too. In fact, it's best to e-mail the questions below to whichever human resources employee will be interviewing you several days before the interview...

• **Am I owed money for unused vacation days or paid time off?** If so, how much? State law or company policy might dictate that employees get compensated if they have these remaining when they leave—but employers sometimes overlook this.

• **When do my health, life and disability insurance coverage end?** Employer-provided insurance benefits typically terminate at the end of the month in which the employee leaves the company, but this can vary.

• **I know I am covered by a confidentiality agreement, but are there any other continuing restrictions I should know about?** If you had access to your employer's trade secrets, you almost certainly were required to sign an agreement prohibiting you from sharing that information. But it's worth asking about additional restrictions. You might have signed a noncompete clause barring you from working for the employer's competitors for some amount of time...a nonsolicitation clause barring you from trying to hire away the company's employees or take its customers...a nonhire clause barring you from hiring the company's employees even if they come to you seeking work...and/or stock-trading restrictions that limit your right to buy or sell shares in the company soon after leaving. If there are restrictions, ask for copies of what you signed.

• **Can I get a copy of (or a look at) my human resources file?** In some states, employers are legally required to provide employees access to their files upon request, and employers sometimes provide access even when they are not required to. *Follow-up:* If you discover anything negative in your file that you do not believe is correct, question it and ask whether it can be removed.

• **When do you need my exit paperwork back? I'll have my lawyer look it over.** Outgoing employees inevitably are given documents to sign during their exit interviews. Take these home, and read them carefully before signing—you typically have 10 days to review them. If you're not certain of the implications of any of the documents or if you have an existing or a potential dispute with the employer, have an employment lawyer review them as well.

• **Who should I contact in the HR department if I have additional questions later?** Having a specific person to call and a direct phone number can make it a lot easier to get answers.

Questions *Not* to Ask at Job Interviews

Candidates often are asked by job interviewers whether *they* have any questions. You should ask ones that help you decide if the job and company are a good match for you.

But do not ask what the company does or how financially stable it is—you should know these things before walking in. Also, avoid asking about promotions, since your focus is supposed to be on the job you are seeking... or whether you can work different hours or part-time, since you are being interviewed for a specific position that has specific requirements.

It also is best not to ask directly if you can have the job—that may have been useful in the past, but now jobs rarely are offered on the spot, so the question likely will make the interviewer uncomfortable and could harm your chance of being hired.

USNews.com

Beware These LinkedIn Scams

Allison Wikoff, senior security researcher on the Counter Threat Unit (CTU) research team at Secureworks, an Atlanta-based cybersecurity company and a Dell Technologies company. She led the team that uncovered the Iranian cyberespionage organization. Secureworks.com

A sophisticated Iranian cyberespionage organization has been using the career-networking website LinkedIn to trick its victims, and it's not alone. *Here are LinkedIn scams used by this group and others...*

• **You might receive a message from a professional acquaintance asking to be added to your LinkedIn network.** But this LinkedIn request really is from a scammer using your acquaintance's name. Later on, this "acquaintance" might ask you to look over a file—but opening the file could load malware onto your computer.

• **You might receive a LinkedIn message from a job recruiter inviting you to apply for a position.** But if you fill out the job application, malware could be loaded onto your computer.

• **You might receive a LinkedIn request from a stranger expressing interest in your business or region.** The Iranian threat group created a LinkedIn profile for a fictional woman named "Mia Ash" to do this. Ms. Ash suc-

TAKE NOTE...

Good News for Older Workers!

More businesses are recruiting older workers. Big companies say older employees have strong communication and organization skills and can help younger workers deal with human interactions that they may not have faced before.

Among companies actively recruiting older workers are CVS...UnitedHealth Group...AT&T, which makes accommodations such as larger computer monitors for older employees...and insurance firm The Hartford.

AARP.org

cessfully built a rapport with many executives through LinkedIn and eventually asked them to take a look at a file, which loaded malware onto their computers.

This Iranian group previously used malware and similar techniques to steal trade secrets, but other scammers use similar strategies to steal victims' identities...loot bank or investment accounts...or install "ransomware" on their computers that encrypts files until money is paid.

What to do: Before accepting a LinkedIn request or offer, e-mail (or call or text) the person who seems to be sending this message and say, "I just received a LinkedIn request that appears to be from you. I wanted to confirm that it really is from you—I've read about LinkedIn scams." If you don't have contact info for this person outside what is provided via LinkedIn, use a search engine to find contact info for him or his employer.

If you do not have a LinkedIn account, periodically check LinkedIn to confirm that no one has started one under your name to scam your acquaintances. And if you own or manage a company, make sure that your employees are aware of these LinkedIn scams—your trade secrets could be at risk.

Negotiate a Better Starting Salary

Deborah Brown-Volkman, a professional certified career coach and president of Surpass Your Dreams, a career-coaching company based in Suffolk County, New York. SurpassYourDreams.com

Being offered a job is only part of the challenge for job hunters—negotiating a good starting salary is almost as important. *What to do...*

- **Don't indicate the salary you want until you're asked.** The deeper you get into the hiring process, the lower the odds that the employer will rule you out because your salary request is a bit high—by this point, the employer should understand the value you could bring to the organization.

- **When you are asked what salary you would require, respond with the typical salary range for the position...**and then turn the salary question back on the employer. You might say, "Based on my research, I see that these kinds of positions tend to pay $90,000 to $100,000. Is that what you're offering?" The websites Salary.com and Payscale.com can help you figure out this typical salary range. The difference between the figures generally should be $5,000 to $10,000, but potentially up to $25,000 for well-paid positions.

Another option is to respond to questions about the salary you would need by asking the employer how much it is paying, but in most cases the employer will not give a figure until you do. *Exception:* If you were initially contacted by a recruiter, this recruiter likely can tell you how much the employer is offering.

- **If the employer indicates that it can work with the salary range,** try to steer the conversation toward the monetary value *you can bring to the company*. Mention specific things you did to save or make money for other employers. The more you can establish your bottom-line value in these ways, the better the odds that the employer will be willing to stretch its budget a bit.

Alternative: If the employer indicates it cannot pay a salary in the range you cited, ask about nonsalary compensation. Is there a generous benefits package? Can the employer provide a company car? Might it be willing to pay a sizable annual bonus if certain goals are met?

- **When the employer makes you an offer,** counter with the figure you really want—perhaps the figure from the high end of the salary range you mentioned earlier. When an offer is made, that means the employer has concluded that you are the candidate it wants. Now you have a bit of leverage, and the employer may be willing to pay a few thousand above its initial offer—or even more than that for a high-paying position.

You are very likely to have leverage if finalizing your hire was put into the hands of a human resources employee. He/she probably was told to get you on board, and failing to do so could make him look bad.

If the employer won't budge on its salary offer, raise the topic of nonsalary compensation, as discussed earlier.

• **Don't let the employer base its salary offer on your current salary.** This is a common mistake among job hunters. If the employer knows that your current compensation is much less than the amount you want, make it clear that the former amount does not affect how much you would be worth in the new position. Explain that you accepted less from your past employer because that position provided something beyond financial compensation—for example, opportunity for on-the-job learning—but that your goal now is to receive appropriate financial compensation.

Franchises That Don't Cost a Lot

Eric Stites, CEO and managing director of Franchise Business Review, an independent market research firm that specializes in the franchise industry, Portsmouth, New Hampshire. FranchiseBusinessReview.com

---

A lot of great franchise opportunities are beyond the financial reach of most people. The initial investment to open a McDonald's franchise ranges from $1 million to $2.2 million...a UPS Store, $159,000 to $434,000...and a Planet Fitness gym, $700,000 to $3.8 million. But you still can find franchises that allow you to be your own boss and give you a good chance for financial success for a far smaller up-front cost. Many of these franchises can be managed from home, eliminating the need for office space and staff, and many don't require a strong business background.

Based on a survey of 13,000 franchise owners, here are 13 of the top-ranked franchises that many people can buy into for less than $20,000, starting with the lowest start-up investment (survey details are below). All are service businesses. Franchisors typically provide extensive training to operate the franchise, but depending on your state and locality, you may need additional certification or licensing.

• **CruiseOne/Dream Vacations.** Travel agents are making a comeback because the volume and variety of information on websites have overwhelmed many people planning vacations. CruiseOne franchises sell vacation packages to individuals, families and groups. The franchisor, World Travel Holdings, is one of the world's largest cruise-travel agencies. *Start-up investment:* $3,245 to $21,850. *Number of US franchises:* About 1,100. DreamVacationsFranchise.com

• **Baby Boot Camp.** Four million women a year give birth in the US. This business offers workout programs for new moms looking to balance their fitness needs and spending time with their young children. Classes take place in clients' homes or local parks. Many of the franchisees have expanded to include classes on nutrition and emotional support. *Start-up investment:* $3,690 to $9,699. *Number of US franchises:* About 85. BabyBootCamp.com

• **Proforma.** Franchisees handle printing and marketing for companies. Services range from designing business forms to overseeing production of promotional giveaways. *Start-up investment:* $4,730 to $39,695. *Number of US franchises:* About 682. OnlyProforma.com

• **Town Money Saver (TMS).** Small local businesses need affordable advertising to attract customers. TMS franchises produce direct-mail publications filled with coupons and offers from these businesses and collect revenue by selling ad space in the publications. More than 25 million of these publications are sent out monthly throughout the country. *Start-up investment:* $5,700 to $12,500. *Number of US franchises:* About 50. TMSFranchising.com

• **In Home Pet Services.** About 44% of US households have a dog and 35% have a cat. These franchises offer services such as dog walking, pet sitting and boarding for a variety of animals at each franchisee's home. *Start-up investment:* $9,200 to $31,100. *Number of US franchises:* About 15. InHomePetServices.com

• **Cruise Planners.** Franchisees, who have an alliance with American Express Travel, sell travel packages including all-inclusive resorts, Disney vacations and destination weddings. *Start-up investment:* $10,995. *Number of US franchises:* About 2,565. CruisePlanners Franchise.com

• **TSS Photography.** The franchise provides photography for schools and youth sporting leagues. Leads are generated through the franchisor's alliance with national organizations such as the YMCA and the Babe Ruth League. *Start-up investment:* $10,500 to $77,160. *Number of US franchises:* About 212. TSSFranchise Business.com

• **Auto Appraisal Network.** This franchise works for insurance companies, providing them with appraisals of the value of automobiles, especially classic and collectible cars. It is best for individuals with previous experience in the automotive field. *Start-up investment:* $12,000 to $20,000. *Number of US franchises:* About 25. AutoAppraisalNetwork.com

• **Executive Image Building Services.** Local businesses and organizations such as churches, schools and health-care facilities need basic maintenance services. This franchise offers cleaning, window-washing, carpet care and landscaping. *Start-up investment:* $8,500 to $73,000. *Number of US franchises:* About 30. ExecutiveImageCo.com

• **The Grout Doctor.** This franchise provides kitchen and bathroom tile and stone care, including regrouting, cleaning and repair, for home owners. *Start-up investment:* $14,405 to $37,415. *Number of US franchises:* About 70. GroutDoctorFranchise.com

• **TGA Premier Golf & Tennis.** This franchise provides tennis and golf enrichment programs that focus not just on skills but also on discipline and character development at elementary and middle schools and community centers. *Start-up investment:* $16,000 to $40,000. *Number of US franchises:* More than 100. PlayTGA.com/franchise

• **United Country Real Estate.** This franchise sells houses in rural America, as well as ranches, farms and vacation homes. *Start-up investment:* $13,790 to $35,350. *Number of US franchises:* More than 450. UnitedCountry.com

MONEYMAKER...

Earn $1,000 a Month or More as an Online Tutor

• **StudyPool** enables students to submit any questions they are struggling with, and then tutors "bid" on those questions by posting a price and delivery time. If a student chooses your offer, you answer the question to receive payment. StudyPool takes a 30% commission.

• **Wyzant** allows you to create your own schedule and set your own rates. The site takes a 20% to 40% commission based on how many hours you work. Some Wyzant tutors work full-time and earn more than $50,000 a year.

• **Chegg** starts at $20 an hour, and the best tutors can make $1,000 a month or more. Tutors in high-demand subjects such as computer science or engineering tend to do best with this service.

• **VIPKid** specializes in connecting Chinese students, ages four to 12, with English-language instructors. The rate is between $14 and $22 an hour.

WiseBread.com

• **Rhea Lana's.** Kids quickly outgrow new clothes. These franchises run children's clothing consignment sales and events in local communities. *Start-up investment:* $19,050 to $38,950. *Number of US franchises:* About 90. RheaLana.com

HOW THE FRANCHISES WERE CHOSEN

This franchise article is based on a study by the market research firm Franchise Business Review, which surveyed 13,000 franchise owners to come up with a list of the highest-rated franchises based on 33 benchmarks of satisfaction, as well as affordable start-up costs. Those costs typically include the initial fee to the franchisor (the company selling franchises), which can vary based on the size of the territory...plus costs such as equipment, marketing and working capital.

To check out the entire list, go to Franchise BusinessReview.com.

20

Safety Survey

How a Spy Prepares for the Worst—and How You Should, Too

It probably will never happen to you. You probably never will be kidnapped or car-jacked. You probably never will be targeted by a home invader or a mugger or caught in the middle of an "active-shooter" situation. But no doubt the people who find themselves in these terrible situations did not expect that these things would happen to them either. Sometimes the worst does happen. When it does, it's the people who are prepared with the right tools and techniques who have the best chance of surviving. *Here's what an experienced spy says you should know and do now...*

HOW TO SPOT DANGER

If you pay attention to your surroundings, you often can spot would-be muggers, rapists, terrorists and other dangerous people before they strike. Their faces and body language might betray out-of-place emotions—perhaps they look tense in a location where everyone else is calm and happy. Their movements might be unusual, too—if you are walking slowly and window-shopping, why hasn't this person passed you? *If you do spot a potential threat, these strategies can help you to assess and deter the danger...*

- **Pick a pointless path.** If you think someone might be following you, travel along a route that does not make much sense. Walk or drive through point C on your way from A to B. If this person takes the same route, the odds are high that you're being followed. In spycraft, this is known as a "surveillance-detection route." *Example:* A woman shopping

Jason Hanson, a former CIA officer who twice won the CIA's Exceptional Performance Award. He is founder of Spy Escape & Evasion, a Cedar City, Utah–based company that offers advanced safety training. He is author of *Spy Secrets That Can Save Your Life* and *Survive Like a Spy*. SpyEscapeAndEvasion.com

in a department store thought a man might be watching her. She walked from the shoe department across the store to the housewares department—where she spent a few minutes—and then back across the store to women's apparel. She saw the man lurking at each stop, so she pointed him out to a security guard. The man immediately ran away, and the guard walked the woman to her car.

Warning: A good surveillance-detection route does not take you through anywhere secluded, particularly if you are on foot. If someone does mean you harm, seclusion could give him/her an opportunity to strike.

• **Make extended eye contact...followed by verbal contact.** Your instinct when you feel the eyes of a predator upon you might be to avoid eye contact or scurry away. But that would only reinforce this predator's conclusion that you are a perfect passive victim—someone who won't fight back if attacked.

Instead, if you think a stranger is watching you, watch him back. Turn to face him and make strong, extended eye contact. This sends the message, *I know you're there, and I'm not intimidated.* That's enough to convince most bad guys that you're not a suitable target after all. If this person does not quickly break eye contact, make verbal contact as well. If you are confident that this person is up to no good, you could speak aggressively. If you are less certain, you could just speak in an ordinary fashion because that may be enough to fluster a predator who had expected to be in total control of the situation. *Example:* A man followed a married couple down a quiet street, switching sides of the road to get behind them. The husband turned, made steady eye contact and asked this potential mugger if he knew what time it was. The man appeared flustered, told him the time and then turned and walked the other way.

If someone whom you suspect has targeted you reverses his direction after you make eye contact and/or verbal contact, it is likely that he did have bad intentions.

• **Ask a lie-detector question.** *Scenario:* The man at your door offers a potentially legitimate reason for being there. Maybe he's selling vacuums, or he needs your signature for a delivery. Should you remove the door's security chain and open it? First, ask a question that should be easy for this person to answer, such as, "So, how many vacuums have you sold today?" or "Where did you park your delivery van? I don't see it." If this is a real salesman or delivery person, your question will sound like relatively normal conversation and he should answer without missing a beat. If this person is a criminal, there likely will be a pause as he tries to think up a plausible lie...and you might see a look of confusion or anxiety on his face.

TAKE NOTE...

To Find Hidden Spy Devices...

If you suspect hidden spy devices in a room...

• **Check the room while thinking like a spy,** actively looking for places where you might hide a bugging device.

• **Listen carefully—**many motion-sensitive cameras make soft clicks and buzzes when they are on.

• **Turn off all lights,** and look for small green or red LEDs.

• **Make a call on your cell phone,** and move around the room—if you notice interference or clicking in one area, a spy device may be operating there.

• **If you are especially concerned,** buy a professional RF signal detector, which looks for the frequencies that wireless cameras and voice recorders use.

Komando.com

BEST SELF-DEFENSE TOOLS

Guns are effective self-defense tools only if you know how to use them safely and it's legal to carry them where you live. Fixed-blade knives can be effective as well, but these, too, can attract odd looks. Below are two weapons—and one additional self-defense item—that you can bring almost everywhere without causing raised eyebrows...

• **Folding knife.** Knives can serve as weapons if you are attacked...or as cutting or prying tools if you become trapped. Folding knives can fit in a pocket or purse, but unfortunately, most of them are not made well enough to be reliable self-defense tools. Companies that make high-quality folding knives that won't let you down in an emergency include Spyderco (Spyderco.com, folding knife prices start at around $60 for a 5.8-inch knife with a 2.25-inch blade) and Benchmade (Benchmade.com, folding knife prices start at around $110 for a 6.8-inch knife with a 2.9-inch blade).

• **Tactical pen.** A tactical pen is an actual working pen, an item so harmless in appearance that you even can carry it onto an airplane. But it has a pointed end and is made of a strong material, typically steel, titanium or aircraft-grade aluminum. In an emergency, you can use it as a weapon—hold the pen in your fist and jab with it as you would an ice pick. *Example:* A Florida woman used her tactical pen to fight off two men who apparently meant to abduct her. Type "tactical pen" into Amazon.com to find numerous well-reviewed examples for less than $25.

Helpful: If you are grabbed by someone larger or stronger than you and you have no weapon or martial arts training, the easiest and most effective self-defense strategy is to gouge the attacker's eyes with your thumbs.

• **Bulletproof panel.** This is a lightweight sheet of Kevlar that slips into a laptop bag, briefcase or even a three-ring binder. In an active-shooter situation, hold the bag, briefcase or binder containing the panel in front of your chest to significantly reduce the odds that you will be hit by a fatal bullet. *Example:* BulletBlocker (BulletBlocker.com) offers a range of Kevlar panels, most for $100 to $220. They typically weigh 10 to 20 ounces.

HOW TO WARD OFF DANGER

Home invaders and burglars generally do not target houses randomly—they case neighborhoods and select properties that seem particularly vulnerable. You probably can guess what would make your home seem unappealing to bad guys—security cameras and an alarm system, a dog and exterior motion-detector lights. *What surprises many home owners is how easy and inexpensive it is to take advantage of these deterrents...*

• **If you don't want the dog, get dog toys.** Spread a few brightly colored dog toys around your yard, and put a dog bowl on your porch. Pick toys and a bowl meant for big dogs. That should be enough to convince a thief that there's a big dog waiting inside. Crooks avoid messing with big dogs even more than they avoid home-security systems—dogs don't take 10 minutes to respond to break-ins.

• **If you don't want the security system, get fake security cameras.** Type "fake cameras" into Amazon.com, and you'll find convincing examples that cost less than $20 apiece. Mount one on every side of your home. Criminals know that getting captured on video greatly increases their chances of getting captured in real life.

• **If you don't want to pay an electrician to wire motion-activated exterior lights, install solar-powered motion-activated lights.** Solar lights typically do not require any external electrical connections. They actually are a more reliable deterrent than wired lights, too, because they won't stop working during widespread power failures, a common time for break-ins. They are available for around $40 apiece in home stores and online.

Why We Are Vulnerable to a Pandemic

Miryam Z. Wahrman, PhD, a professor of biology at William Paterson University in Wayne, New Jersey, where she specializes in microbiology, hand hygiene and the interactions between bacteria and environmental surfaces. Dr. Wahrman is also author of *The Hand Book: Surviving in a Germ-Filled World.*

The 100th anniversary of the flu pandemic of 1918–1919—which killed approximately 50 million people, both young and old, over a period of about nine months—looms ominously over the world.

Even with all of the medical advances that have been made in the last century, it's possible that a similar deadly pandemic could occur again, according to many infectious disease experts. To learn more about the possible risks of a modern-day pandemic, we spoke with Miryam Z. Wahrman, PhD, a leading authority on communicable diseases.

•**What's the difference between the terms "epidemic" and "pandemic"?** An *epidemic* occurs when an infectious disease spreads rapidly to many people, exceeds what is expected based on recent experience and is typically concentrated in a particular geographic region. One example is the 2014–2016 outbreak of the Ebola virus, which was centered in West Africa and killed more than 11,000. A *pandemic* is an epidemic that spreads across a large region (potentially globally), is spread from person-to-person and affects a high proportion of the population. Besides the flu pandemic of 1918, another example is the 2009–2010 H1N1 influenza pandemic that killed an estimated 200,000 people worldwide.

•**Do you think a new pandemic is coming?** Based on the prevalence of infectious diseases in every corner of the globe, the history of past epidemics and the frequency of worldwide travel, there's a high likelihood that new (or old) pathogens will emerge in the near future.

There are constantly outbreaks of infectious diseases all over the world, including in developed countries. Some diseases originate in animals and are passed to humans, where they become serious threats to large populations. Other disease outbreaks occur as a result of a deliberate choice of people not to vaccinate or occur when viruses, bacteria or other microbes genetically change and evolve into new forms that evade our immune systems, or resist antibiotic treatments. It is critically important to track diseases all over the world in order to document outbreaks that could lead to epidemics or pandemics.

•**Can anyone predict which disease may cause a pandemic?** While it's impossible to definitively predict which viruses or bacteria will spread widely, many scientists believe that the flu strain H7N9, known as the avian flu, has the greatest potential to become an epidemic—and eventually spread globally into a pandemic. It has been followed worldwide by public health officials for six years now.

H7N9, a subtype of influenza A, has been circulating in poultry for years. In 2013, China reported the first known cases of a new strain of H7N9 in humans. The World Health Organization (WHO) reports that since 2013, 1,554 humans have been infected with H7N9 in China and roughly 40% of patients have died from the disease.

In the fifth wave of H7N9, October 2016 to July 2017, the highest number of cases, 766 infections, was reported, leading the WHO to declare that, "the virus is spreading, and...further intensive surveillance and control measures...are crucial." Fortunately, the sixth wave (2017 to 2018) showed a dramatic decrease in viral transfer to humans, possibly due to Chinese government health officials intervening when diseased birds were reported. So far it appears that the virus is mainly transmitted from poultry to humans and seldom from human to human, and there have been no reports of people acquiring H7N9 in the US. However, there is still concern that the transmission pattern could change, leading to the potential for an H7N9 epidemic/pandemic.

Of more immediate concern for Americans are influenza virus strains A and B, which contributed to the "high severity" flu season across all age groups in 2017-2018, with more

BETTER WAY...

Stockpiling for Emergencies

To be well-stocked for an emergency...

•**Store one gallon of water per day per person**—prioritize water over food.

•**Buy a large quantity of commercially prepared emergency supplies**—for example, an eight-day supply of Survival Tabs emergency food ration costs about $25.

•**Be sure to include long-lasting foods that taste good, need no cooking and are nutrient-dense.** *Good choices:* Peanut butter, nuts, trail mix, cereal, power bars and granola bars, dried fruit, canned meat and vegetables, powdered milk and vitamins.

•**Shop around and buy in bulk if possible**—Walmart, for example, sells bulk quantities of dehydrated stews.

Roundup of experts on stockpiling food for emergencies, reported at MoneyTalksNews.com.

than 277,000 laboratory-confirmed flu cases. Influenza vaccination is strongly advised, as serious complications, even death, from the virus can occur in all age groups.

•Why are we at risk for another pandemic? Our world population has more than doubled in the last 50 years, which means there are more people to infect—and to infect others. Also, more people than ever are traveling the globe. An infected person can travel to the other side of the world in as little as a day.

Global climate change is another concern. As parts of our environment become warmer, disease-carrying insects move to new areas and expose more people.

Also, while antibiotics have increased life expectancy, use and abuse of these medications lead to the development of antibiotic-resistant bacteria, or "superbugs," that are difficult or impossible to treat. Two such superbugs, found mainly in health-care facilities, are *Clostridium difficile* and *methicillin-resistant Staphylococcus aureus* (MRSA). They kill thousands in the US each year, although infections have declined due to improved medical procedures.

•Can pandemics be prevented? With the development of the Internet and advances in telecommunications and air travel, scientists are better able to collaborate and share data. By sharing resources and research between countries, diseases can be contained. Also, the development of vaccines and new antibiotics against contagious diseases is critical. Pharmaceutical companies are reluctant to spend resources developing and producing vaccines and antibiotics because it is not as profitable as selling drugs used for chronic diseases.

•What can we do to protect ourselves? Follow your doctor's advice on vaccinations. Additionally, one of the very best ways to keep germs at bay is to practice proper handwashing. Do not wait for a pandemic to comply.

My advice: Wash your hands with *plain liquid soap and warm water*, scrubbing for at least 20 seconds. Antibacterial soaps have become popular, but some studies have shown that they promote the development of drug-resistant bacteria. Also, studies show that using a single-use paper towel in public restrooms is more effective at ridding bacteria from the hands than warm-air dryers or jet dryers, which have been found to spew harmful microbes into the air. When soap and water are not available, hand sanitizers, such as Purell, are a good choice, but they do not get rid of superbugs such as *C. difficile*.

It's critical to wash your hands before touching your eyes, nose or mouth—the most common routes for germs to enter the body. Also, be sure to wash your hands before eating. And insist that health-care workers wash their hands before touching you or your loved ones.

•Are there any other precautions that people should be taking? Smartphones, keyboards and tablets have been shown to harbor harmful germs. It's a good idea to clean these devices by wiping the surface down, as needed, with a microfiber cloth or tissue lightly moistened with 70% rubbing alcohol.

The Swimming Danger No One Knows About

Donald S. Burke, PhD, director of advanced safety and engineering management in the Masters of Engineering Program at University of Alabama at Birmingham. UAB.edu

Numerous swimmers die each year after being subjected to electric current in the water from faulty wiring—but it isn't electrocution that kills them. It's drowning. This happens in swimming pools and hot tubs and also in water near marinas and docks.

What happens: Faulty pool wiring or faulty dockside or boat wiring or connectors allow electric current into the water. Even if this current is too weak to result in electrocution and death by itself, it still can cause a loss of muscle control, leading to drowning. Exactly how many people are killed by "electric shock drowning" (ESD) is not known—these deaths often are recorded as ordinary drownings with no one realizing that an electric current played a role.

New rules were added to the National Electrical Code (NEC) this year that require marinas to have ground-fault protection. Ground-fault circuit interrupters (GFCI) will immediately cut off the electric current when they detect an imbalance in the current flow. But these new rules apply only to docks constructed during or after 2017.

What to do: Do not swim in freshwater within 100 yards of a marina. The danger is greatest near marinas where there are dozens of boats and boat slips, any one of which could have a wiring problem. The risk for ESD is lower in salt water. (Salt water is more conductive than the human body, so any electric current is likely to go around swimmers, not through them.) *Also...*

• **If you have a dock, pool and/or hot tub installed,** hire a certified electrician to handle the wiring and to inspect it annually. If you own a boat, a certified electrician should annually inspect its wiring as well. Confirm that the electrician is certified to American Boat and Yacht Council standards.

• **If you swim in a community pool,** confirm that this pool is regularly inspected by a certified electrician.

• **If you experience a tingling sensation,** painful electric shock and/or diminished muscle control while swimming, get out of the water immediately if you can and warn other swimmers.

• **If you see someone struggling to swim near a marina or boat dock,** resist the urge to jump to the rescue. Instead, throw this person a flotation device and shut off the electricity nearby.

Unexpected Choking Danger: Soft Foods

Becky Turpin, director of home and community safety at the National Safety Council, a nonprofit organization based in Itasca, Illinois. She previously served as the adult injury prevention coordinator at University of Wisconsin Hospital and Clinics. www.NSC.org

Few people realize that soft foods such as pancakes and doughnuts pose a choking risk. But studies have found that soft baked goods are the second-most common cause of choking deaths, trailing only meat.

Because soft foods seem so harmless, people sometimes take dangerously large bites and/or neglect to chew sufficiently prior to swallowing.

And if people drink beverages while they still have soft baked foods in their mouths or throats, these items can absorb the fluid and expand, potentially blocking airways. White bread and other baked goods made with white flour are particularly prone to this.

Peanut butter is another soft food that poses a major choking hazard. It's so thick and sticky that it can become lodged in the throat.

Be very careful with soft foods if...

• **You are in your 70s or older.** People produce less saliva as they age, greatly increasing their risk of choking. That is a major reason why most people who choke to death are age 75 or older.

• **You are taking a medication that lists dry mouth among its side effects.** This is a side effect of many medications.

• **You are drinking alcohol and/or talking while eating.** Intoxication and conversation increase choking risks—especially when combined.

If someone starts choking: Perform the Heimlich maneuver on him/her. For instructions, go to www.NSC.org and search "Choking Prevention and Rescue Tips."

GOOD TO KNOW...

Know How to Get Help in Poison Emergencies

Free, confidential assistance is available 24/7 by calling 800-222-1222. Make sure that the poison hotline number is posted near all your home phones. Add it to smartphones by texting "poison" to 797979.

Index

D

E

F

M

N

O

P